BOOK SUMMARY

1. Real Number System

- Natural Numbers: $1, 2, 3, \ldots$

- Whole Numbers. $0, 1, 2, 3, \ldots$

- Integers: $\cdots -3, -2, -1, 0, 1, 2, 3 \cdots$

- Rational Numbers
  Ratio of two integers, denominator $\neq 0$.

- Irrational Numbers $\sqrt{2}, \sqrt{3}, \sqrt{7}, -\sqrt{5} \cdots$

Fractions

- $\dfrac{a}{d} + \dfrac{b}{d} = \dfrac{a+b}{d}$

- $\dfrac{a}{b} \cdot \dfrac{c}{d} = \dfrac{ac}{bd}$

- $\dfrac{a}{b} \div \dfrac{c}{d} = \dfrac{a}{b} \cdot \dfrac{d}{c} = \dfrac{ad}{bc}$

- $\dfrac{a}{c} + \dfrac{b}{d} = \dfrac{a \cdot d}{cd} + \dfrac{b \cdot c}{cd} = \dfrac{ad + bc}{cd}$

Properties of Real Numbers

- **Commutative:** $a + b = b + a; \quad ab = ba$

- **Associative:** $a + (b + c) = (a + b) + c; \ a(bc) = (ab)c$

- **Distributive:** $a(b + c) = ab + ac$

- **Identity:** $a + 0 = 0 + a = a; \quad 1 \cdot a = a \cdot 1 = a$

- **Inverse:** $a + (-a) = 0; \quad a\left(\dfrac{1}{a}\right) = 1$

2. Linear Equations/Inequalities in One Variable

- We can add or subtract same quantity on both sides of an **equation** or **inequality**.

- We can multiply or divide both sides of an **equation** and **inequality** by the same **positive** number.

- We must **reverse** the inequality symbol when we **multiply** or divide both sides of an **inequality** by a **negative** number.

- For *strict inequality* ($<$ or $>$), we do not include the end points of solution interval(s).

- For *non-strict* inequality ($\leq$ or $\geq$), we include the end points of the solution interval(s).

Absolute Value Equations and Inequalities

- $|x - a| = c \ (c > 0)$ has two solutions:
  $$\longrightarrow \quad x - a = c \ \text{ or } \ x - a = -c$$
  $$\longrightarrow \quad x = a + c \ \text{ or } \ x = a - c$$

- $|x - a| \leq b \ \ (b > 0)$
  $$\longrightarrow \quad x - a \leq b \ \text{ and } \ x - a \geq -b$$
  $$\longrightarrow \quad x \leq a + b \ \text{ and } \ x \geq a - b$$
  or: $(a - b) \leq x \leq a + b$

- $|x - a| \geq b$
  $$\longrightarrow \quad x - a \geq b \ \text{ or } \ x - a \leq b$$
  $$\longrightarrow \quad x \geq a + b \ \text{ or } \ x \leq a - b$$

3. Exponents and Polynomials

An expression of the type $5x^3 + 3x^2 - 2x + 9$ is a polynomial.

- It has **4 terms**: $5x^3, 3x^2, -2x, 9$

- Its **degree** is 3.

- Coefficients of its terms are $5, 3, -2, 9$

- **Like terms** in an algebraic expression are the terms that differ only in coefficients.

- Like terms in an expression can be combined to a single term by appending the common variable part to the sum of the coefficient.

- Polynomials can be added by combining their like terms.

Special Products

- $(a + b)^2 = a^2 + 2ab + b^2$
- $(a - b)^2 = a^2 - 2ab + b^2$
- $(a - b)(a + b) = \left(a^2 - b^2\right)$
- $(a + b)\left(a^2 - 2ab + b^2\right) = a^3 + b^3$
- $(a - b)\left(a^2 + ab + b^2\right) = a^3 - b^3$

Laws of Exponents

$$a^m \cdot a^n = a^{m+n}, \ \frac{a^m}{a^n} = a^{m-n}, \ a \neq 0,$$

$$\left(a^m\right)^n = a^{m \cdot n}, \ a^0 = 1, \ a^{-n} = \frac{1}{a^n}, \ a \neq 0$$

$$\left(\frac{a}{b}\right)^{-n} = \left(\frac{b}{a}\right)^n, \ a \neq 0, \ b \neq 0$$

$$(ab)^n = a^n \cdot b^n \ , \ \left(\frac{a}{b}\right)^n = \frac{a^n}{b^n} \ , \ b \neq 0$$

4. Factoring, Quadratic Equations and Inequalities

- Difference of squares

$$a^2 - b^2 = (a-b)(a+b)$$

- Trinomials of the type $x^2 + bx + c$

$$x^2 + bx + c = (x + \alpha)(x + \beta)$$

where $\alpha + \beta = b$, and $\alpha\beta = c$

- Trinomials of the type $ax^2 + bx + c$

$$ax^2 + bx + c = \frac{(ax + \alpha)(ax + \beta)}{a}$$

where $\alpha + \beta = b$, and $\alpha\beta = ac$

5. Rational Expressions

- We can evaluate a rational expression for a given value of the variable by substituting the variable by its value.

  If the **denominator is zero**, then the value of the expressions is **undefined**.

  If the **numerator and the denominator both are zero**, the value of the expression is **indeterminate**.

- We can simplify a rational expression by factoring the numerator and the denominator, and then canceling the common factors, if any.

- We can multiply and divide the rational expressions just as we perform these operations with numeric fractions.

- We can add the rational expressions just as we perform this operation with numeric fractions.

  $\Rightarrow$ Find LCD, change each rational expression to its equivalent form with LCD as the denominator, and then add the equivalent expression.

6. Linear Equations/Inequalities in Two Variables

- The graph of any equation of the type $ax + by + c = 0$ is a straight line.

- Slope of a line passing through two points (x_1, y_1) and (x_2, y_2) is

$$m = \frac{y_2 - y_1}{x_2 - x_1}$$

- Equation of a line with a given slope m and passing through a point (x_1, y_1) is

$$y - y_1 = m(x - x_1)$$

- Two lines are parallel if their slopes are equal.

- Two lines are perpendicular if the product of their slopes is -1.

- To graph linear inequality of the type $ax + by + c \leq 0$ or $ax + by + c \geq 0$, we first graph the line $ax + by + c = 0$ then we use a test point to find the region for the solution.

7. Systems of Linear Equations and Inequalities

1. We can solve a system of two equations in two variables by

   (a) Graphing the Two Equations.

   - If the lines intersect at a point then the coordinates of the point give the solution of the system.

   - If the lines are parallel then the system has no solution.

   - If the lines are coincident then every point on the line is a solution.

   (b) Using Substitution Method.

   - Find the value of one variable in terms of the second variable from one of two equations and substitute this in the second equation.

   - Solve the second equation for second variable.

   - Substitute the value of the second variable in the first equation and solve for the first variable.

   (c) Using Addition Method.

   - Multiply the two equations with appropriate numbers so that coefficients of at least one of the two variables are opposites.

- Add the two equations and solve the resultant equation for the variable.

- Substitute this value of the variable in any of the given two equations and solve for the second variable.

2. To solve a System of Linear inequalities we proceed as follows

- Find the solution region for each inequality as in Chapter 6.

- The region common to all the solution regions is the solution of the system.

8. Roots and Radicals

$$\sqrt[n]{a^n} = a \quad \text{if } n \text{ is odd}$$
$$= |a| \quad \text{if } n \text{ is even}$$

$$\sqrt[n]{a\,b} = \sqrt[n]{a}\,\sqrt[n]{b}, \quad \text{if } n \text{ is even then } a \geq 0, b \geq 0,$$

$$\sqrt[n]{\frac{a}{b}} = \frac{\sqrt[n]{a}}{\sqrt[n]{b}}, \quad \begin{array}{l}\text{if } n \text{ is even then } a \geq 0, b > 0 \\ \text{if } n \text{ is odd then } b \neq 0\end{array}$$

$$a^{m/n} = \sqrt[n]{a^m} \text{ or } \left(\sqrt[n]{a}\right)^m \quad a \geq 0, \text{if } n \text{ is even}$$

- Radical expressions having the same radicand and the same index are called **like radicals**.

- Like radical terms can be combined to a single term: $3\sqrt{5} + 4\sqrt{5} = 7\sqrt{5}$

- Conjugate of $a + \sqrt{b}$ is $a - \sqrt{b}$

- Rationalizing the denominator in a radical expression means converting the given expression to an equivalent expression with no radicals in the denominator. We can do that by

  multiplying and dividing the expression by the conjugate of the denominator, if the denominator is of the type $a + \sqrt{b}$.

  multiplying and dividing the expression with an appropriate term to clear the radical from the denominator.

$$\frac{5}{\sqrt[3]{a}} = \frac{5}{\sqrt[3]{a}} \cdot \frac{\sqrt[3]{a^2}}{\sqrt[3]{a^2}} = \frac{5\sqrt[3]{a^2}}{\sqrt[3]{a^3}}$$

$$= \frac{5\sqrt[3]{a^2}}{a}$$

- We solve equations involving radicals using the following procedure.

  ⇒ Transfer terms so that we have just one radical term on one side and all other terms on the other side.

  ⇒ Raise both sides to appropriate powers, to clear the radicals isolated on one side.

  ⇒ Simplify the equation and if there are still some radicals left in the equation then repeat the above process.

9. Quadratic Equations

We can solve quadratic equations by any of the following methods.

- Using Square Root Property
$$x^2 = k \longrightarrow x = \sqrt{k} \text{ or } x = -\sqrt{k}, k > 0$$

- Completing Squares
$$x^2 + 2x - 15 = 0$$
$$\longrightarrow (x+1)^2 - 1 - 15 = 0$$
$$\longrightarrow (x+1)^2 = 16$$
$$\longrightarrow x + 1 = 4 \text{ or } x + 1 = -4$$
$$\longrightarrow x = 3 \text{ or } x = -5$$

- Using quadratic formulas

If $ax^2 + bx + c = 0$ then
$$x = \frac{-b \pm \sqrt{b^2 - 4ac}}{2a}$$

- By graphing the function
$$f(x) = ax^2 + bx + c,$$

we can solve the equation
$$ax^2 + bx + c = 0.$$

The x-intercept(s) of the graph of $f(x)$ are the real solutions of equation
$$ax^2 + bx + c = 0.$$

PART

ALGEBRA
PART I

SUPPLEMENTED WITH:

- Multimedia Electronic Lecture Notes for Teachers
- Multimedia Electronic Tutors for Students
- Tools for Testing and Management

SECOND EDITION (REVISED)

Authors:

Man M. Sharma
Clark Atlanta University

Ravinder Kumar
Alcorn State University

Published by: EDUCO INTERNATIONAL, INC. (1-800-96-EDUCO)

Managing Editor

Man M. Sharma, Clark Atlanta University

Editors

Ray Treadway, Bennett College
Jatinder Singh, Clark Atlanta University

Production Supervisor

Man M. Sharma

Production Services

EDUCO International, Inc.

Desktop Publishing

Miriam R. Gaines, Clark Atlanta University

Graphics

Yun Gu Kim, Clark Atlanta University

Acknowledgments

The author express heartfelt thanks to the following persons for their suggestions, evaluations, and preparation of support materials, or for pilot testing the electronic lecture notes in their classrooms.

- Drs. Brewster and Rangi   (Central State University)
- Gary Hart   (California State University, Dominquez Hill)
- Connie Leggett   (Albany State College)
- Elaine Prince Lockley   (Mountain View Community College, TX)
- Rosa Marta   (InterAmerican University, PR)
- C. Pirvulescu   (ABM Academy, TX)
- Claire Sit   (LaGuardia Community College, NY)
- Peter Spier   (Prince Georgia Community College, MD)
- Angel Rivera   (University of Turabo, PR)
- Ray Treadway   (Bennett College, NC)
- Sayku Warity   (Barber Scotia College)

The production of this manuscript and other support materials would not have been possible without the support and encouragement from: Dr. Thomas W. Cole, (President, CAU); Dr. Kofi B. Bota (Vice President at CAU); and Dr. Argelia Velez Rodriquez (Program Officer, MSIP, U.S. Department of Education).

Additional Support

Partial support was provided by:

1. The U.S. Dept. of Education MSIP
2. The U.S. Army (Army Research Office)
   Grant #DAAL03-G-0380

ISBN: 1-888-469-18-8

Second reprint 1999

Printed at Replika Press Pvt Ltd, 100% EOU, Delhi 110 040, India

PREFACE

This textbook is written for college students whose school preparation did not include Algebra 2 or who graduated from school a long time ago.

The book is written with students in mind - simple language, highlights of key words, with different colors and character sizes.

Each section of a chapter is divided into logically arranged objectives. Each objective has:

- **discussion and illustrations** leading to rules and step by step procedure/ algorithm,

- **graded solved examples** showing step by step procedures,

- **margin exercises** similar to examples, presented in the margin to each example as warm ups,

Each **section ends** with a set of exercises arranged as per section objectives with adequate space for students to workout the exercises,

Each **chapter ends** with **Chapter Summary**, **Review Exercises,** and a **Self Test**. Chapter Summary provides definition of key words or phrases, rules and procedures, and a worked out example in the margin for each rule or procedure.

This book is supplemented with its electronic version that can be loaded on the file server of a local computer network to be used by the students either as electronic book or as a tutorial. The electronic version of the book is 100% compatible with this printed textbook and has the distinct advantage of dynamic graphics, pedagogically sound animations, visually appealing screen designs with attractive color combinations.

TECHNOLOGY SUPPORT

One of **the best and unique features** of this text is the technology support in the form of:

- Multimedia Electronic Lecture Notes for teachers. More details about MELN are given below, under a separate heading.

- Multimedia Electronic Tutor for students. These tutors are 100% compatible with the Lecture Notes.

- On-line Testing and Management. More details are given below.

- Free practice test diskettes for students.

- Appendix containing detailed illustrations for the use of calculator (TI-82).

Highlights of Contents:

The textbook contains nine chapters.

A. Electronic Lecture Notes

Special Features

- Electronic Lecture Notes are produced using Asymmetric Corporation's Multi-media "TOOLBOOK."

- The sequence of concepts and step by step algorithm are 100% compatible with the text.

- Vivid screen designs, dynamic graphics, and animation make the presentation of topics very clear as documented by students and teachers in several pilot studies.

- The MELN are designed to enhance interaction with students. This affords minimal writing and drawing on the board and more emphasis on class discussion.

- Teacher's electronic lecture notes can be loaded as tutorial on the network.

B. On-Line Testing and Management

Special Features

- A large question bank on disk with more than 3000 objective questions and 500 open ended questions with hints and solutions.

- Graphic editor to add new questions or modify existing questions/solutions.

- Test generator to print multiple versions of class tests or to produce on line testing from the question bank.

- On-line testing for: a) practice before the actual tests, b) actual graded tests, or c) make-up exams.

- Record Management System for on-line testing or practice testing.

- Enhanced electronic grade book with several unique features including; direct transfer of scores from on-line testing to the grade book, and **individualized progress report for students after every major test.**

- Separate practice test diskette, free to students for studying at home.

Man M. Sharma

TABLE OF CONTENTS

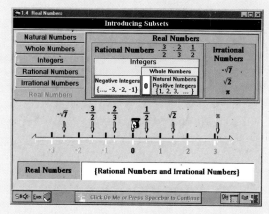

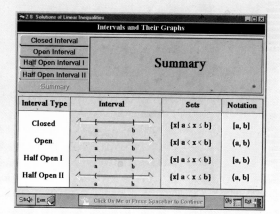

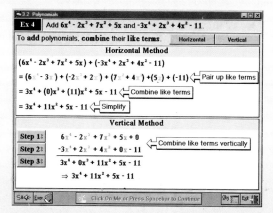

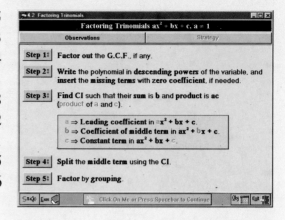

Chapter 5   Rational Expressions

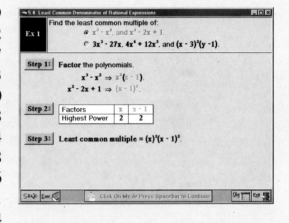

Chapter 6   Linear Equations/Inequalities in
Two Variables

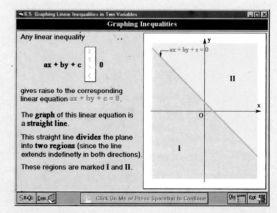

Sample Screens

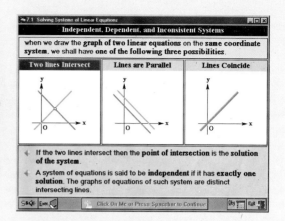

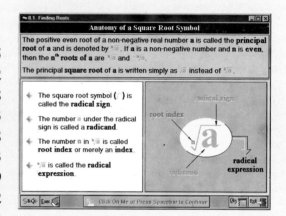

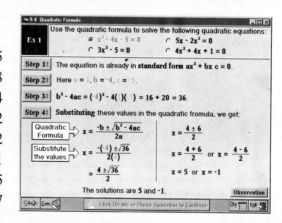

The equation is already in **standard form** $ax^2 + bx + c = 0$.

CHAPTER 1

REAL NUMBER SYSTEM

CHAPTER 1

REAL NUMBER SYSTEM

Introduction

In this chapter we will review and examine the properties of real numbers which will be used extensively throughout the discussion in this book.

This chapter is divided into the following sections.

1.1   FRACTIONS

Vocabulary

- **Natural Numbers:** The most commonly known and used numbers, namely 1, 2, 3, 4,... are called *natural numbers*. These numbers are used for counting. For this reason natural numbers are also called counting numbers.

- **Whole Numbers:** When the number *zero* is adjoined to the natural numbers, the resulting numbers 0, 1, 2, 3, 4, . . . are called *whole numbers*.

   Note: The natural numbers are contained in the whole numbers. The only whole number which is *not* a natural number is zero.

- **Fractions:** Numbers of the type $\frac{3}{5}$, $\frac{2}{7}$, $\frac{4}{6}$, . . . are called *fractions*. A fraction has three components.

   1.   A horizontal line called the *fraction bar*
   2.   A number above the fraction bar called the *numerator*
   3.   A number below the fraction bar called the *denominator*

$$\frac{3}{5} \quad \begin{array}{l} \to \text{Numerator} \\ \to \text{Fraction Bar} \\ \to \text{Denominator} \end{array}$$

The fraction is not defined if the denominator is zero.

1

Upon completion of this section we will be able to:

A. Define a factor of a number.
B. Write fractions in lowest terms.
C. Identify equivalent fractions.
D. Multiply and divide fractions.
E. Add and subtract fractions.
F. Perform operations on mixed numbers.
G. Use fractions to solve problems.

A. Define a factor of a number

We know that $12 = 2 \times 6$. The numbers 2 and 6 are called factors of the number 12. Similarly, $12 = 3 \times 4$. Thus 3 and 4 are also factors of 12.

If $n = mk$, then n is a multiple of k and k is a **factor** of n.

Notice that $12 = 12 \times 1$. Therefore, by the above definition, 1 and 12 are also factors of 12. In fact, *every number has at least two factors, namely, 1 and itself.* We see that 12 has factors other than 1 and 12. There are numbers which have no other factors except 1 and itself, for example 3 has no factors other than 1 and itself. Such numbers are called **prime numbers.**

A number is called **prime** if it is different from 1, and has no factors other than 1 and itself.

We list all prime numbers less than 50. They are:

$$2, 3, 5, 7, 11, 13, 17, 19, 23, 29, 31, 37, 41, 43, 47$$

A positive number different from 1 is called **composite** if it is not prime.

A number is said to be factored if it can be written as a product of two or more numbers. Thus, 12 can be factored in many ways, for example: 12×1, 2×6, 3×4, $2 \times 2 \times 3$. Each of these is called a **factorization** of 12. However, the factorization $2 \times 2 \times 3$ is of special interest as all the factors in this are prime. Such a factorization is called **prime factorization**.

Every number different from 0 and 1 has a prime factorization.

Warm Up

1. Which of 1, 3, 4, 5, 6 are factors of 15?

Example 1: Which of 1, 3, 4, 5, 7, 10, 20 are factors of 20?

Solution:

$20 = 20 \times 1$ shows that 1 and 20 are factors of 20.

$20 = 4 \times 5$ shows that 4 and 5 are factors of 20.

$20 = 10 \times 2$ shows that 10 is a factor of 20.

20 cannot be written as 3 times a number. Therefore, 3 is not a factor 20.

20 cannot be written as 7 times a number. Therefore, 7 is not a factor of 20.

We can check whether a number is a factor or not by using calculuator. See example 1, of section 1.1 in Appendix B.

Example 2: Which of the following are prime numbers?
13, 21, 26, 41

Solution:

13 is prime: The only factors of 13 are 1 and 13. Notice that 13 is not a multiple of any number between 2 and 12.

21 is not prime: 21 has factors other than 1 and 21. For example $21 = 3 \times 7$, which means that 3 is a factor of 21.

41 is prime: The only factors of 41 are 1 and 41. See if you can find factors of 41 different from 1 and 41.

26 is not prime: 26 has factors other than 1 and 26. For example $26 = 2 \times 13$, which mean 2 is a factor of 26.

21 and 26 are examples of **composite** numbers.

We can check whether a number is prime or not using calculator. See example 2, of section 1.1 in Appendix B

Example 3: Write prime factorizations of:

a) 32 **b)** 825.

Solutions:

a) One way to find the prime factorization is to start with the smallest prime and see which primes are factors of a given number.

$$32 = 2 \times 16$$
$$16 = 2 \times 8$$
$$8 = 2 \times 4$$
$$4 = 2 \times 2$$

Shaded Numbers are Prime Factors

Now if we multiply all the boxed factors, we get $2 \times 2 \times 2 \times 2 \times 2 = 32$. This gives us prime factorization of 32.

b) 825: Notice that the smallest prime number dividing 825 is 3.

$$825 = 3 \times 275$$
$$275 = 5 \times 55$$
$$55 = 5 \times 11$$
$$11 = 11 \times 1$$

Now if we multiply all the boxed factors of 825, we get $3 \times 5 \times 5 \times 11 = 825$. The shaded numbers are prime factors of 825.

Warm Up

2. Which of the following are prime numbers? 10, 13, 14, 17

Warm Up

3. Write prime factorizations of : 24 and 144.

Answers:
1. 1, 3, 5
2. 13, 17
3. $24 = 2 \cdot 2 \cdot 2 \cdot 3$,
$144 = 2 \cdot 2 \cdot 2 \cdot 2 \cdot 3 \cdot 3$

Notes: 1. It is advisable to check that the product of the factors, obtained in the above process, actually equals the number whose factorization is being worked out.

2. The order of factors in a prime factorization is not important.

3. Every natural number has a unique prime factorization.

B. Write fractions in lowest terms

Co-prime numbers: Two numbers are said to be co-prime if they do not have a common factor other than 1. **Coprimes** are also called **relatively prime**.

Examples:

a) $4 = 2 \times 2$, and $21 = 3 \times 7$ are co-prime numbers.

b) $6 = 2 \times 3$, and $15 = 3 \times 5$ are not co-prime, since 3 is a common factor.

The fraction $\dfrac{4}{21}$ is such that its numerator 4 and its denominator 21 are co-prime. Such fractions are said to be in **lowest terms**. The prime factorization of the numerator and denominator can be used to write a fraction in lowest terms.

Steps to write a fraction in lowest terms:

Step 1	Write the prime factorization of the numerator.
Step 2	Write the prime factorization of the denominator.
Step 3	Cancel common primes from the two factorizations. This amounts to dividing the numerator and denominator by the **greatest common factor**.

Warm Up

4. Write the following fractions in lowest terms $\dfrac{12}{52}, \dfrac{8}{36}$.

Example 4:   Write the following fractions in lowest terms.

a) $\dfrac{14}{21}$ b) $\dfrac{84}{90}$ c) $\dfrac{120}{135}$ d) $\dfrac{19}{35}$

Solutions:

a) $\dfrac{14}{21} = \dfrac{2 \cdot 7}{3 \cdot 7} = \dfrac{2 \cdot 7}{3 \cdot 7} = \dfrac{2}{3}$

b) $\dfrac{84}{90} = \dfrac{2 \cdot 2 \cdot 3 \cdot 7}{2 \cdot 3 \cdot 3 \cdot 5} = \dfrac{2 \cdot 7}{3 \cdot 5} = \dfrac{14}{15}$

c) $\dfrac{120}{135} = \dfrac{2 \cdot 2 \cdot 2 \cdot 3 \cdot 5}{3 \cdot 3 \cdot 3 \cdot 5} = \dfrac{2 \cdot 2 \cdot 2}{3 \cdot 3} = \dfrac{8}{9}$

d) $\dfrac{19}{35} = \dfrac{1 \cdot 19}{5 \cdot 7} = \dfrac{19}{35}$ (19 and 35 are co-prime.)

We can reduce fractions to lowest terms using calculator. See example 3, of section 1.1 in Appendix B.

C.   Identify equivalent fractions

Consider the fractions $\frac{4}{6}$ and $\frac{6}{9}$. Both these fractions reduce to $\frac{2}{3}$ in lowest terms since:

$$\frac{4}{6} = \frac{2 \cdot 2}{2 \cdot 3} = \frac{2}{3} \quad \text{and} \quad \frac{6}{9} = \frac{2 \cdot 3}{3 \cdot 3} = \frac{2}{3}.$$

Such fractions are said to be equivalent. We may establish the equivalence of two fractions by using the following rule.

Step 1	Find: (Numerator of first fraction) × (Denominator of second fraction)
Step 2	Find: (Denominator of first fraction) × (Numerator of second fraction)
Step 3	If the numbers in Steps 1 and 2 are equal, the fractions are equivalent, otherwise not.

Example 5: Which of the following fractions are equivalent?

a) $\frac{6}{8}$ and $\frac{16}{18}$ b) $\frac{15}{20}$ and $\frac{12}{16}$

Solutions:

Method 1: *(Use of Definition)*

In this method we reduce the fractions to lowest terms and recall that two fractions are equivalent if they reduce to the same lowest terms.

a) $\frac{6}{8} = \frac{2 \cdot 3}{2 \cdot 2 \cdot 2} = \frac{3}{4}$ and

$\frac{16}{18} = \frac{2 \cdot 2 \cdot 2 \cdot 2}{2 \cdot 3 \cdot 3} = \frac{8}{9}$

Since the fractions $\frac{6}{8}$ and $\frac{16}{18}$ reduce to different fractions in lowest terms, they are not equivalent.

b) $\frac{15}{20} = \frac{3 \cdot 5}{2 \cdot 2 \cdot 5} = \frac{3 \cdot 5}{2 \cdot 2 \cdot 5} = \frac{3}{4}$ and

$\frac{12}{16} = \frac{2 \cdot 2 \cdot 3}{2 \cdot 2 \cdot 2 \cdot 2} = \frac{3}{4}$

Since $\frac{15}{20}$ and $\frac{12}{16}$ reduce to the same fractions in lowest terms, they are equivalent.

Warm Up

5. Which of the following fractions are equivalent?

$\frac{2}{12}$ and $\frac{3}{18}$

$\frac{3}{14}$ and $\frac{10}{30}$

Answers:

4. $\frac{3}{13}, \frac{2}{9}$

5. $\frac{2}{12}$ and $\frac{3}{18}$

5

Method 2: *(Use of Rule)*

a) $\dfrac{6}{8}\times\dfrac{6}{18}$

$6\times 18 = 108$
$8\times 16 = 128$

Therefore, by the rule $\dfrac{6}{8}$ and $\dfrac{16}{18}$ are **not equivalent**.

b) $\dfrac{15}{20}\times\dfrac{12}{16}$

$15\times 16 = 240$
$20\times 12 = 240$

Therefore, by the rule $\dfrac{15}{20}$ and $\dfrac{12}{16}$ are **equivalent**.

D. Multiply and divide fractions

To multiply two fractions: $\dfrac{a}{b}\cdot\dfrac{c}{d}$

Step 1   Multiply the numerators of the two fractions, and write the result as the numerator of the product of the two fractions.

Step 2   Multiply the denominators of the two fractions, and write the result as the denominator of the product of the two fractions.

In other words, $\dfrac{a}{b}\cdot\dfrac{c}{d} = \dfrac{a\cdot c}{b\cdot d}$ (b and d are non zero. Therefore, $b\cdot d$ is non-zero also.)

Warm Up

6. Write the products in lowest terms $\dfrac{4}{15}\cdot\dfrac{10}{16}$

Example 6:   Find $\dfrac{3}{4}\cdot\dfrac{5}{6}$ and write the product in lowest terms.

Solution:

$$\frac{3}{4}\cdot\frac{5}{6} = \frac{3\cdot 5}{4\cdot 6} = \frac{15}{24}$$

$$= \frac{\mathbf{3\cdot 5}}{\mathbf{2\cdot 2\cdot 2\cdot 3}} = \frac{5}{8}$$

We can multiply fractions using calculator. See example 4, of section 1.1 in Appendix B.

Reciprocals

Two fractions are said to be reciprocals of each other if their product is 1.

For example: $\dfrac{2}{3}$ and $\dfrac{3}{2}$ are reciprocals of each other. Since, $\dfrac{2}{3}\cdot\dfrac{3}{2} = \dfrac{6}{6} = \dfrac{1}{1} = 1$.

To find the reciprocal of a fraction, simply interchange the numerator and the denominator.

To divide two fractions: $\dfrac{a}{b} \div \dfrac{c}{d}$

Step 1 Find the reciprocal of the second fraction (the divisor).

Step 2 Multiply the first fraction and the reciprocal of the second.

In other words $\dfrac{a}{b} \div \dfrac{c}{d} = \dfrac{a}{b} \cdot \dfrac{d}{c} = \dfrac{a \cdot d}{b \cdot c}$

$\downarrow \qquad\qquad \downarrow$

Divide   Multiply

Example 7: Find $\dfrac{3}{8} \div \dfrac{6}{15}$ and write the result in lowest terms.

Solution:

The reciprocal of $\dfrac{6}{15}$ is $\dfrac{15}{6}$.

Therefore, $\dfrac{3}{8} \div \dfrac{6}{15} = \dfrac{3}{8} \cdot \dfrac{15}{6} = \dfrac{3 \cdot 15}{8 \cdot 6} = \dfrac{45}{48}$. Now we reduce the fraction.

$\dfrac{45}{48} = \dfrac{3 \cdot 3 \cdot 5}{2 \cdot 2 \cdot 2 \cdot 2 \cdot 3} = \dfrac{3 \cdot 3 \cdot 5}{2 \cdot 2 \cdot 2 \cdot 2 \cdot 3} = \dfrac{15}{16}$

Note: $\dfrac{15}{16}$, which is the result of $\dfrac{3}{8} \div \dfrac{6}{15}$ is also called the **quotient of** $\dfrac{3}{8}$ and $\dfrac{6}{15}$.

Notice that the order of fractions, first $\dfrac{3}{8}$ and then $\dfrac{6}{15}$, is important.

Warm Up

7. $\dfrac{15}{18} \div \dfrac{25}{27}$

Answers:

6. $\dfrac{1}{6}$ 7. $\dfrac{9}{10}$

E.   Add and subtract fractions

To add fractions with like denominators : $\dfrac{a}{b} + \dfrac{c}{b}$

Step 1 To obtain the numerator of the sum of two fractions, add the numerators of the two fractions.

Step 2 The denominator of the sum is the same as the denominator of either fraction.

In other words, $\dfrac{a}{b} + \dfrac{c}{b} = \dfrac{a+c}{b}$

Warm Up

8. (a) $\dfrac{7}{8} + \dfrac{5}{8} =$

 (b) $\dfrac{9}{10} + \dfrac{3}{10} =$

Example 8: Add fractions and write the result in lowest terms.

 a) $\dfrac{3}{5} + \dfrac{4}{5}$ b) $\dfrac{3}{8} + \dfrac{7}{8}$

Solutions:

a) $\dfrac{3}{5} + \dfrac{4}{5} = \dfrac{3+4}{5} = \dfrac{7}{5}$

The result is already in lowest terms.

b) $\dfrac{3}{8} + \dfrac{7}{8} = \dfrac{3+7}{8} = \dfrac{10}{8} = \dfrac{2 \cdot 5}{2 \cdot 2 \cdot 2} = \dfrac{5}{4}$

To add fractions with different denominators we need first to rewrite the fractions in terms of equivalent fractions with the same denominator. The next example illustrates the procedure for converting a given fraction to an equivalent fraction with a new denominator.

9. Write $\dfrac{5}{7}$ as a fraction with 35 as the new denominator.

Example 9: Write $\dfrac{4}{7}$ as a fraction with 21 as the new denominator.

Solution: 7 is a factor of 21. Also, $21 = 7 \times 3$. So we multiply and divide the fraction by 3. We may observe that $3 = \dfrac{21}{7} = \dfrac{\text{new denominator}}{\text{given denominator}}$

$\dfrac{4}{7} = \dfrac{4}{7} \cdot \dfrac{3}{3}$ $\left[\dfrac{3}{3}=1.\ \text{Multiplication by 1 does not change the fraction.}\right]$

$= \dfrac{4 \cdot 3}{7 \cdot 3} = \dfrac{12}{21}$

We shall need the concept of the **least common denominator** of fractions for adding fractions with different denominators. The **least common denominator** is the same as **least common multiple** of the denominators. The **least common multiple (l.c.m)** of two numbers is the smallest positive number which has both numbers as its factors.

10. Find the l.c.m. of 15 and 20.

Example 10: Find the l.c.m of 12 and 18.

Solution: **l.c.m of 12 and 18**

| Multiples of 12: | 12 | 24 | **36** | 48 | 60 | 72 |
| Multiples of 18: | 18 | **36** | 54 | 72 | | |

Thus 36 is the least common multiple of 12 and 18.

8

Example 11:   Find least common multiple of 24, 18, and 16.

Solution:

Method 1 *(by writing multiples)*

l.c.m. of 24, 18, and 16

Multiples of 24:	24	48	72	96	120	**144** . . .
Multiples of 18:	18	36	54	72	90	108	126	**144** . . .
Multiples of 16:	16	32	48	64	80	96	112	128	**144** . . .

The smallest number which has 24, 18, and 16 as factors is 144. Therefore, the least common multiple of 24, 18, and 16 is 144.

Method 2 *(by using prime factorization)*

Write down the prime factorization of each number:

$$24 = 2 \times 2 \times 2 \times 3$$
$$18 = 2 \times 3 \times 3$$
$$16 = 2 \times 2 \times 2 \times 2$$

The different prime numbers found in the above factorizations are 2 and 3. The number 2 occurs a maximum of four times in 16, and 3 occurs a maximum of two times in 18.

Therefore
l.c.m. $= \underset{\text{four times}}{(2 \times 2 \times 2 \times 2)} \times \underset{\text{two times}}{(3 \times 3)} = 144$

Example 12:   Find the least common denominator of:

a) $\dfrac{3}{4}$ and $\dfrac{4}{5}$ b) $\dfrac{5}{6}$, $\dfrac{7}{8}$, and $\dfrac{4}{15}$.

Solutions:

a)   l.c.d. of $\dfrac{3}{4}$ and $\dfrac{4}{5}$ is the l.c.m. of 4 and 5.

Method 1 To find the l.c.m. of 4 and 5 write down multiples of 4 and 5.

l.c.m of 4 and 5

Multiples of 4: 4	8	12	16	**20**	24 . . .
Multiples of 5: 5	10	15	**20**	25 . . .

Therefore, the **l.c.d.** of $\dfrac{3}{4}$ and $\dfrac{4}{5}$ is 20.

Warm Up

11.   Find the least common multiple of 15, 20, and 28.

12.   Find the l.c.d of:
  (a) $\dfrac{4}{7}$ and $\dfrac{5}{3}$.

9

(b) $\frac{3}{8}, \frac{7}{10}, \frac{11}{15}$

Method 2 *(by using the prime factorization)*

Now $4 = 2 \times 2$, $5 = 5 \times 1$.

Therefore, the l.c.m. of 4 and 5 $= 2 \times 2 \times 5 = 20$

Hence, the l.c.d. of $\frac{3}{4}$ and $\frac{4}{5}$ is 20.

b)   The l.c.d. of $\frac{5}{6}, \frac{7}{8}$, and $\frac{4}{15}$ is the l.c.m. of 6, 8, and 15.

Method 1 To find the l.c.m. of 6, 8, 15

l.c.m of 6, 8, and 15

Multiples of 6:	6	12	18	24	30	36 . . . **120**
Multiples of 8:	8	16	24	32	40 . . . **120**	
Multiples of 15:	15	30	45	60 . . . **120**		

Therefore, the **l.c.d.** of $\frac{5}{6}, \frac{7}{8}$, and $\frac{4}{15}$ is **120**

Method 2 The l.c.d. of $\frac{5}{6}, \frac{7}{8}$, and $\frac{4}{15}$ is the l.c.m. of 6, 8, and 15.

Now $6 = 2 \times 3$, $8 = 2 \times 2 \times 2$, and $15 = 3 \times 5$.

The different prime factors are 2, 3, and 5. The number 2 occurs a maximum of 3 times, and the other two numbers occur only once.

Thus, the l.c.m. of 6, 8, and $15 = \underbrace{(2 \times 2 \times 2)}_{\text{Three times}} \times (3) \times (5) = 120$

Hence, the l.c.d. of $\frac{5}{6}, \frac{7}{8}$, and $\frac{4}{15}$ is 120.

To add two fractions with unlike (different) denominators:

Step 1	Find the l.c.d. of the two fractions.
Step 2	Change the two fractions to equivalent fractions with the l.c.d found in Step 1, as the common denominator.
Step 3	Add the new fractions by the rule for adding fractions with the same denominator.
Step 4	Reduce the resultant fraction.

Example 13:   Add: **a)** $\dfrac{3}{4} + \dfrac{5}{6}$ **b)** $\dfrac{2}{15} + \dfrac{7}{24}$

13. Add

Solutions:

a) $\dfrac{3}{4} + \dfrac{5}{6}$:   These fractions have different denominators.

(a) $\dfrac{4}{7} + \dfrac{5}{9}$

Step 1   Find the l.c.d. of $\dfrac{3}{4}$ and $\dfrac{5}{6}$.

The l.c.d. of $\dfrac{3}{4}$ and $\dfrac{5}{6}$ = l.c.m. of 4 and 6 = **12**.

$$\begin{bmatrix} 4 = 2 \times 2 \\ 6 = 2 \times 3 \\ \text{l.c.m.} = 2 \times 2 \times 3 \end{bmatrix}$$

Step 2   Rewrite the fractions with l.c.d. as the common denominator.

$$\frac{3}{4} = \frac{3}{4} \cdot \frac{\mathbf{3}}{\mathbf{3}} = \frac{9}{12}$$
$$\frac{5}{6} = \frac{5}{6} \cdot \frac{\mathbf{2}}{\mathbf{2}} = \frac{10}{12}$$

Step 3   Add the new fractions. (Notice that the new fractions have the same denominators.)

$$\frac{3}{4} + \frac{5}{6} = \frac{\mathbf{9}}{\mathbf{12}} + \frac{\mathbf{10}}{\mathbf{12}} = \frac{9+10}{12} = \frac{\mathbf{19}}{\mathbf{12}}$$

Step 4   Not needed since 19 and 12 are coprime.

b) $\dfrac{2}{\mathbf{15}} + \dfrac{7}{\mathbf{24}}$: These fractions have different denominators.

(b) $\dfrac{4}{21} + \dfrac{5}{12}$

Step 1   Find the l.c.d. of $\dfrac{2}{15}$ and $\dfrac{7}{24}$.

The l.c.d. = l.c.m. of 15 and 24 = 120

Step 2   Rewrite the fractions with the l.c.d. as the common denominator.

$$\frac{2}{15} = \frac{2}{15} \cdot \frac{\mathbf{8}}{\mathbf{8}} = \frac{16}{120} \qquad \frac{7}{24} = \frac{7}{24} \cdot \frac{\mathbf{5}}{\mathbf{5}} = \frac{35}{120}$$

Step 3   Add the new fractions. (Notice that the new fractions have the same denominators.)

$$\frac{2}{15} + \frac{7}{24} = \frac{16}{120} + \frac{35}{120} = \frac{16+35}{120} = \frac{\mathbf{51}}{\mathbf{120}}$$

Step 4 $\dfrac{51}{120} = \dfrac{\mathbf{3} \cdot 17}{\mathbf{3} \cdot 40} = \dfrac{\mathbf{17}}{\mathbf{40}}$

Note: The essential idea of using the l.c.d. while adding fractions with different denominators, is to get equivalent fractions with the same denominators. It can be done in another way.

For example, to find: $\dfrac{3}{4}+\dfrac{5}{6}$

Choose the product $4 \times 6 = 24$ as the common denominator.

Now, $\dfrac{3}{4}=\dfrac{3}{4}\cdot\dfrac{6}{6}=\dfrac{18}{24},\quad \dfrac{5}{6}=\dfrac{5}{6}\cdot\dfrac{4}{4}=\dfrac{20}{24}$

$$\dfrac{3}{4}+\dfrac{5}{6}=\dfrac{18}{24}+\dfrac{20}{24}=\dfrac{38}{24}=\dfrac{\cancel{2}\cdot 19}{\cancel{2}\cdot 2\cdot 2\cdot 3}=\dfrac{19}{12}$$

In general, the l.c.d. is preferred. It gives a number which is the smallest of the common multiples, and therefore makes it easier to manage computations.

To subtract fractions we follow the same rules for addition. Instead of adding the numerators, we subtract them.

Warm Up

14. Compute

(a) $\dfrac{8}{11}-\dfrac{3}{11}=$

(b) $\dfrac{7}{15}-\dfrac{5}{12}=$

Answers:

8. (a) $\frac{3}{2}$ (b) $\frac{6}{5}$ 9. $\frac{25}{35}$ 10. 60

11. 420   12. (a) 21 (b) 120

13. (a) $\frac{71}{63}$ (b) $\frac{17}{28}$

14. (a) $\frac{5}{11}$ (b) $\frac{1}{20}$

Example 14: Compute: **a)** $\dfrac{3}{5}-\dfrac{2}{5}$ **b)** $\dfrac{3}{8}-\dfrac{5}{18}$.

Solutions:

a) $\dfrac{3}{5}-\dfrac{2}{5}=\dfrac{3-2}{5}=\dfrac{1}{5}$

b) Find $\dfrac{3}{8}-\dfrac{5}{18}$. The denominators are different.

Step 1 Find the l.c.d. of $\dfrac{3}{8}$ and $\dfrac{5}{18}$

$8 = 2 \times 2 \times 2$
$18 = 2 \times 3 \times 3$
$\text{l.c.m} = 2 \times 2 \times 2 \times 3 \times 3 = 72$

The l.c.d. of $\dfrac{3}{8}$ and $\dfrac{5}{18}$ = l.c.m. of 8 and 18 = **72**

Step 2 Rewrite the fractions with 72 as the denominator.

$$\dfrac{3}{8}=\dfrac{3\cdot \mathbf{9}}{8\cdot \mathbf{9}}=\dfrac{27}{72}$$

$$\dfrac{5}{18}=\dfrac{5\cdot \mathbf{4}}{18\cdot \mathbf{4}}=\dfrac{20}{72}$$

Step 3 $\dfrac{3}{8}-\dfrac{5}{18}=\dfrac{\mathbf{27}}{\mathbf{72}}-\dfrac{\mathbf{20}}{\mathbf{72}}=\dfrac{27-20}{72}=\dfrac{\mathbf{7}}{\mathbf{72}}$

Step 4 Not needed since 7 and 72 are coprime.

F.   Perform operations on mixed numbers

In this section we will consider the following two types of fractions:

Proper Fractions: where the numerator is less than the denominator, such as

$\dfrac{2}{3},\dfrac{4}{5},\cdots$

Improper Fraction: where the numerator is greater than or equal to the denominator, such as $\frac{8}{5}, \frac{9}{4}, \ldots$. An improper fraction can be written as a sum of a whole number and a proper fraction as illustrated below.

$$\frac{8}{5} = \frac{5+3}{5} = \frac{5}{5} + \frac{3}{5} = 1 + \frac{3}{5}$$

| Improper Fraction | Whole Number | Proper Fraction |

The sum of a whole number and a proper fraction is usually written in a special way:

$$1 + \frac{3}{5} = 1\frac{3}{5} \qquad\qquad 4 + \frac{5}{9} = 4\frac{5}{9}$$

The numbers like $\left(1\frac{3}{5}\right)$ and $\left(4\frac{5}{9}\right)$ are called **Mixed Numbers**. All improper fractions can be written as mixed numbers.

Example 15: Convert $\frac{29}{11}$ to a mixed number.

Solution:

Method 1:

Divide 29 (numerator) by 11 (denominator).

$$\text{Divisor} \leftarrow 11\overline{)29} \begin{array}{l} 2 \rightarrow \text{Quotient} \\ \rightarrow \text{Divident} \end{array}$$
$$\underline{22}$$
$$7 \rightarrow \text{Remainder}$$

$$\frac{29}{11} = \text{Quotient} + \frac{\text{Remainder}}{\text{Divisor}} = 2 + \frac{7}{11} = 2\frac{7}{11}$$

Method 2:

$$\frac{29}{11} = \frac{11+11+7}{11} = \frac{11}{11} + \frac{11}{11} + \frac{7}{11} = 1 + 1 + \frac{7}{11} = 2 + \frac{7}{11} = \mathbf{2\frac{7}{11}}$$

Warm Up

15. Convert $\frac{35}{9}$ to mixed numbers.

Warm Up

16. Convert to improper

fraction: $8\frac{3}{7}$

Example 16: Convert $3\frac{2}{5}$ to an improper fraction.

Solution:

$$3\frac{2}{5} = \frac{3}{1}+\frac{2}{5} = \frac{3}{1}\cdot\frac{5}{5}+\frac{2}{5} = \quad \text{or}$$

$$\frac{3\cdot 5+2}{5} = \frac{17}{5}$$

$$\frac{15}{5}+\frac{2}{5} = \frac{17}{5}$$

Operations on mixed numbers are carried out by first converting mixed numbers to improper fractions and then following the rules for operations on fractions. It is advisable to convert the result into a mixed number if the final result is an improper fraction.

Warm Up

17. Compute

(a) $\left(3\frac{1}{5}\right)\cdot\frac{13}{16}$

(b) $\left(3\frac{1}{5}\right)\div\left(2\frac{2}{5}\right)$

(c) $4\frac{2}{3}+\frac{5}{7}$

Example 17: Compute the following.

a) $\left(2\frac{3}{5}\right)\cdot\frac{4}{9}$ b) $\left(2\frac{3}{5}\right)\div\left(1\frac{4}{9}\right)$

c) $\left(2\frac{3}{5}\right)+\frac{4}{9}$ d) $\left(2\frac{3}{5}\right)-\left(1\frac{4}{9}\right)$

Solutions:

Let us first convert the mixed numbers to fractions.

$$2\frac{3}{5} = \frac{2}{1}+\frac{3}{5} = \frac{10}{5}+\frac{3}{5} = \frac{13}{5} \qquad \text{Notice } 2\frac{3}{5}=\frac{2\cdot 5+3}{5}$$

$$1\frac{4}{9} = \frac{1}{1}+\frac{4}{9} = \frac{9}{9}+\frac{4}{9} = \frac{13}{9} \qquad \text{Notice } 1\frac{4}{9}=\frac{1\cdot 9+4}{9}$$

a) $\left(2\frac{3}{5}\right)\cdot\frac{4}{9} = \frac{13}{5}\cdot\frac{4}{9} = \frac{13\cdot 4}{5\cdot 9} = \frac{52}{45} = 1\frac{7}{45}$ $\quad \frac{52}{45}=\frac{45+7}{45}=1+\frac{7}{45}$

b) $\left(2\frac{3}{5}\right)\div\left(1\frac{4}{9}\right) = \frac{13}{5}\div\frac{13}{9} = \frac{13}{5}\cdot\frac{9}{13}$

$$= \frac{13\cdot 9}{5\cdot 13}$$

$$= \frac{9}{5} = 1\frac{4}{5}$$

c) $\left(2\frac{3}{5}\right)+\frac{4}{9} = \frac{13}{5}+\frac{4}{9} = \frac{13}{5}\cdot\frac{9}{9}+\frac{4}{9}\cdot\frac{5}{5}$

$$= \frac{117}{45}+\frac{20}{45}$$

$$= \frac{137}{45} = 3\frac{2}{45}$$

$\quad \frac{137}{45}=\frac{45+45+45+2}{45}$

14

d) $\left(2\dfrac{3}{5}\right) - \left(1\dfrac{4}{9}\right) = \dfrac{13}{5} - \dfrac{13}{9} = \dfrac{13}{5} \cdot \dfrac{9}{9} - \dfrac{13}{9} \cdot \dfrac{5}{5}$

$$= \dfrac{117}{45} - \dfrac{65}{45}$$

$$= \dfrac{52}{45} = 1\dfrac{7}{45}$$

Warm Up

17. (d) $3\dfrac{4}{5} - 2\dfrac{3}{7}$

Miscellaneous Examples

Example 18: Perform the indicated operations.

    a) $\dfrac{2}{9} + \dfrac{5}{12} + 1\dfrac{5}{8}$ **b)** $3\dfrac{2}{9} - \dfrac{5}{12} + 1\dfrac{5}{8}$

Solutions:

18. Perform indicated operations.

    a) Convert mixed numbers to fractions.

$$\left(1\dfrac{5}{8}\right) = \dfrac{1}{1} + \dfrac{5}{8} = \dfrac{8}{8} + \dfrac{5}{8} = \dfrac{13}{8}$$

(a) $\dfrac{4}{5} + \dfrac{3}{15} + 2\dfrac{3}{4}$

Therefore, $\dfrac{2}{9} + \dfrac{5}{12} + 1\dfrac{5}{8} = \dfrac{2}{9} + \dfrac{5}{12} + \dfrac{13}{8}$

l.c.m. of 9, 12, and 8 is 72.

$$= \dfrac{2}{9} \cdot \dfrac{8}{8} + \dfrac{5}{12} \cdot \dfrac{6}{6} + \dfrac{13}{8} \cdot \dfrac{9}{9}$$

$$= \dfrac{16}{72} + \dfrac{30}{72} + \dfrac{117}{72}$$

$$= \dfrac{16 + 30 + 117}{72} = \dfrac{163}{72} = 2\dfrac{19}{72}$$

    b) Convert mixed numbers to fractions.

$$3\dfrac{2}{9} = \dfrac{3}{1} + \dfrac{2}{9} = \dfrac{27}{9} + \dfrac{2}{9} = \dfrac{29}{9}$$

$$1\dfrac{5}{8} = \dfrac{1}{1} + \dfrac{5}{8} = \dfrac{8}{8} + \dfrac{5}{8} = \dfrac{13}{8}$$

(b) $3\dfrac{4}{5} - \dfrac{7}{15} + 1\dfrac{7}{10}$

Therefore, $\left(3\dfrac{2}{9}\right) - \dfrac{5}{12} + \left(1\dfrac{5}{8}\right) = \dfrac{29}{9} - \dfrac{5}{12} + \dfrac{13}{8}$

The l.c.d = l.c.m of 9, 12, and 8 = **72**

$$\dfrac{29}{9} - \dfrac{5}{12} + \dfrac{13}{8} = \dfrac{29}{9} \cdot \dfrac{8}{8} - \dfrac{5}{12} \cdot \dfrac{6}{6} + \dfrac{13}{8} \cdot \dfrac{9}{9}$$

$$= \dfrac{232}{72} - \dfrac{30}{72} + \dfrac{117}{72}$$

$$= \dfrac{232 - 30 + 117}{72} = \dfrac{319}{72} = 4\dfrac{31}{72}$$

Note: For a fraction it does not matter whether you first convert the answer to mixed number and then reduce to lowest terms or first reduce to lowest terms and then convert to mixed number.

Warm Up

19. Perform the indicated operations.

   (a) $\dfrac{4}{5} \cdot \dfrac{7}{10} \cdot \dfrac{15}{14}$

   (b) $\left(2\dfrac{1}{2}\right) \cdot \dfrac{4}{15}$

20. Compute: $\dfrac{4}{5} \cdot \dfrac{15}{16} \div \dfrac{4}{3}$

Answers:

15. $3\dfrac{8}{9}$ 16. $\dfrac{59}{7}$

17. (a) $\dfrac{13}{5}$ (b) $\dfrac{4}{3}$ (c) $\dfrac{113}{21}$ (d) $\dfrac{48}{35}$

18. (a) $\dfrac{15}{4}$ (b) $\dfrac{151}{30}$

19. (a) $\dfrac{3}{5}$ (b) $\dfrac{2}{3}$ 20. $\dfrac{9}{16}$

Example 19:   Perform the indicated operations.

a) $\dfrac{3}{4} \cdot \dfrac{5}{7} \cdot \dfrac{2}{6}$ b) $1\dfrac{3}{4} \cdot \dfrac{3}{7} \cdot 2\dfrac{5}{6} \cdot \dfrac{4}{9}$

Solutions:

a) $\dfrac{3}{4} \cdot \dfrac{5}{7} \cdot \dfrac{2}{6} = \dfrac{3 \cdot 5 \cdot 2}{4 \cdot 7 \cdot 6} = \dfrac{\mathbf{2} \cdot \mathbf{3} \cdot 5}{\mathbf{2} \cdot 2 \cdot \mathbf{2} \cdot \mathbf{3} \cdot 7} = \dfrac{5}{28}$

b) First convert mixed numbers to fractions. $1\dfrac{3}{4} = \dfrac{7}{4}, 2\dfrac{5}{6} = \dfrac{17}{6}$

$$\left(1\dfrac{3}{4}\right) \cdot \dfrac{3}{7} \cdot \left(2\dfrac{5}{6}\right) \cdot \dfrac{4}{9} = \dfrac{7}{4} \cdot \dfrac{3}{7} \cdot \dfrac{17}{6} \cdot \dfrac{4}{9}$$

$$= \dfrac{7 \cdot 3 \cdot 17 \cdot 4}{4 \cdot 7 \cdot 6 \cdot 9}$$

$$= \dfrac{\mathbf{7} \cdot \mathbf{3} \cdot 17 \cdot \mathbf{4}}{\mathbf{4} \cdot \mathbf{7} \cdot 2 \cdot \mathbf{3} \cdot 9} = \dfrac{17}{18}$$

Example 20:   Compute: $\dfrac{3}{4} \cdot \dfrac{5}{9} \div \dfrac{4}{3}$.

Solution:

$$\dfrac{3}{4} \cdot \dfrac{5}{9} \div \dfrac{\mathbf{4}}{\mathbf{3}} = \dfrac{3}{4} \cdot \dfrac{5}{9} \cdot \dfrac{\mathbf{3}}{\mathbf{4}}$$

$$= \dfrac{3}{4} \cdot \dfrac{5}{3 \cdot 3} \cdot \dfrac{3}{4} = \dfrac{5}{16}$$

G.   Use fractions to solve problems

Warm Up

21. Mr. Smith travels from one place to another with four stops in between. Distances covered before each stop are: $3\dfrac{1}{2}$ km, $12\dfrac{1}{2}$ km, $11\dfrac{2}{5}$ km and $9\dfrac{2}{5}$ km. Find the total distance travelled.

Example 21:   An irregular piece of park is shown in the figure below. How many yards does a person jog along the boundary of the park, when he goes around the park only once?

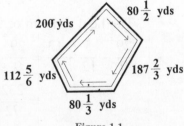

$80\dfrac{1}{2}$ yds

200 yds

$187\dfrac{2}{3}$ yds

$112\dfrac{5}{6}$ yds

$80\dfrac{1}{3}$ yds

Figure 1.1

Solution:

We must add the distances.

$$200 + \left(80\frac{1}{2}\right) + \left(187\frac{2}{3}\right) + \left(80\frac{1}{3}\right) + \left(112\frac{5}{6}\right)$$

Since some of the numbers are mixed numbers, we reduce them to improper fractions.

$$80\frac{1}{3} = \frac{241}{3}, \ 187\frac{2}{3} = \frac{563}{3}, \ 80\frac{1}{2} = \frac{161}{2}, \text{ and } 112\frac{5}{6} = \frac{677}{6}$$

Now, $200 + \left(80\frac{1}{3}\right) + \left(187\frac{2}{3}\right) + \left(80\frac{1}{2}\right) + \left(112\frac{5}{6}\right)$

$$= \frac{200}{1} + \frac{241}{3} + \frac{563}{3} + \frac{161}{2} + \frac{677}{6} \qquad \text{[the l.c.m. of 2, 3, and 6 is 6]}$$

$$= \frac{200}{1} \cdot \frac{6}{6} + \frac{241}{3} \cdot \frac{2}{2} + \frac{563}{3} \cdot \frac{2}{2} + \frac{161}{2} \cdot \frac{3}{3} + \frac{677}{6}$$

$$= \frac{1200}{6} + \frac{482}{6} + \frac{1126}{6} + \frac{483}{6} + \frac{677}{6}$$

$$= \frac{1200 + 482 + 1126 + 483 + 677}{6}$$

$$= \frac{3968}{6} = 661\frac{2}{6} = 661\frac{1}{3} \text{ yards}$$

Example 22: There are two square boxes with sides $9\frac{3}{4}$ inches and $5\frac{5}{6}$ inches. What is the difference between their sides?

Solution:

We must find: $9\frac{3}{4} - 5\frac{5}{6}$. Now, $9\frac{3}{4} = \frac{39}{4}$ and $5\frac{5}{6} = \frac{35}{6}$

Thus, $9\frac{3}{4} - 5\frac{5}{6} = \frac{39}{4} - \frac{35}{6} = \frac{39}{4} \cdot \frac{3}{3} - \frac{35}{6} \cdot \frac{2}{2}$ l.c.m. of 4 and 6 is 12

$$= \frac{117}{12} - \frac{70}{12}$$

$$= \frac{47}{12} = 3\frac{11}{12} \text{ inches}$$

Warm Up

22. A rectangular box is $4\frac{3}{4}$ inches long and $2\frac{2}{5}$ inches wide. Find the difference between its length and width.

Warm Up

Warm Up

23. Solve the same problem as Example 23 if ;

(i) the initial loading $= 15\frac{2}{5}$ cu ft.

(ii) first stop delivery $= 3\frac{1}{4}$ cu ft.

(iii) second stop delivery $= 5\frac{3}{4}$ cu ft.

(iv) third stop pick up $= 2\frac{1}{2}$ cu ft.

Example 23:

A concrete truck is loaded with $11\frac{5}{8}$ cubic feet of concrete. The driver delivers $2\frac{1}{2}$ cubic feet of concrete at the first stop and $3\frac{3}{4}$ cubic feet at the second stop. At the third stop the driver picks up $\left(1\frac{1}{4}\right)$ cubic feet of concrete not wanted by the customer. How much concrete is on the truck after the third stop?

Solution:

We must find:

$$11\frac{5}{8} - 2\frac{1}{2} - 3\frac{3}{4} + 1\frac{1}{4}$$

Already on the truck   Taken off the truck   Put on the truck

Now, $11\frac{5}{8} = \frac{93}{8}$, $2\frac{1}{2} = \frac{5}{2}$, $3\frac{3}{4} = \frac{15}{4}$, $1\frac{1}{4} = \frac{5}{4}$

Therefore,

$$\left(11\frac{5}{8}\right) - \left(2\frac{1}{2}\right) - \left(3\frac{3}{4}\right) + \left(1\frac{1}{4}\right) = \frac{93}{8} - \frac{5}{2} - \frac{15}{4} + \frac{5}{4} \quad \text{l.c.m. of 2, 4, and 8 is 8}$$

$$= \frac{93}{8} - \frac{5}{2} \cdot \frac{4}{4} - \frac{15}{4} \cdot \frac{2}{2} + \frac{5}{4} \cdot \frac{2}{2}$$

$$= \frac{93}{8} - \frac{20}{8} - \frac{30}{8} + \frac{10}{8}$$

$$= \frac{93 - 20 - 30 + 10}{8} = \frac{53}{8} = 6\frac{5}{8}$$

$6\frac{5}{8}$ cubic feet of concrete is still on the truck after the third stop.

Answers:

21. $36\frac{4}{5}$ 22. $2\frac{7}{20}$ inches

23. $8\frac{9}{10}$ cu ft.

EXERCISE 1.1

Answers:

1. _____

2. _____

3. _____

4. _____

In exercises 1-4, write each number as a product of prime factors.

1. 2   **2.** 6   **3.** 24   **4.** 27

Write all prime numbers between

5. 20 and 50.   **6.** 70 and 90.

Write prime factorizations of the numbers in exercises 7-11.

7. 18   **8.** 24   **9.** 88   **10.** 100   **11.** 135

In exercises 12-16, write each fraction in lowest terms.

12. $\frac{6}{9}$ **13.** $\frac{14}{18}$ **14.** $\frac{24}{36}$ **15.** $\frac{15}{21}$ **16.** $\frac{45}{75}$

In exercises 17-20, identify pairs of equivalent fractions.

17. $\frac{6}{9}$ and $\frac{8}{12}$ **18.** $\frac{12}{16}$ and $\frac{24}{36}$

19. $\frac{15}{18}$ and $\frac{75}{90}$ **20.** $\frac{18}{24}$ and $\frac{63}{84}$

In exercises 21-25, find the products and write your answer in lowest terms.

21. $\frac{5}{6} \cdot \frac{1}{3}$ **22.** $\frac{4}{9} \cdot \frac{3}{5}$ **23.** $\frac{5}{7} \cdot \frac{14}{11}$ **24.** $\frac{3}{8} \cdot \frac{4}{15}$ **25.** $\frac{15}{20} \cdot \frac{34}{56}$

In exercises 26-29, find the quotients and write your answer in lowest terms.

26. $\frac{7}{8} \div \frac{3}{4}$ **27.** $\frac{5}{9} \div \frac{15}{12}$ **28.** $\frac{12}{17} \div \frac{5}{7}$ **29.** $\frac{12}{19} \div \frac{21}{38}$

In exercises 30-31, find the products and write your answer in lowest terms.

30. $\frac{2}{7} \cdot \frac{7}{9} \cdot \frac{9}{2}$ **31.** $\frac{15}{26} \cdot \frac{4}{5} \cdot \frac{39}{40}$ 0.45

5.	_____
6.	_____
7.	_____
8.	_____
9.	_____
10.	_____
11.	_____
12.	_____
13.	_____
14.	_____
15.	_____
16.	_____
17.	_____
18.	_____
19.	_____
20.	_____
21.	_____
22.	_____
23.	_____
24.	_____
25.	_____
26.	_____
27.	_____
28.	_____
29.	_____
30.	_____
31.	_____

32. _____

33. _____

34. _____

35. _____

36. _____

37. _____

38. _____

39. _____

40. _____

41. _____

42. _____

43. _____

44. _____

45. _____

46. _____

47. _____

48. _____

49. _____

50. _____

51. _____

52. _____

53. _____

54. _____

In exercises 32-34, find the sums, and write your answer in lowest terms.

32. $\dfrac{3}{5} + \dfrac{4}{5}$ **33.** $\dfrac{7}{3} + \dfrac{5}{3}$ **34.** $\dfrac{11}{15} + \dfrac{7}{15}$

In exercises 35-39, determine the l.c.d. (least common denominator) of the fractions.

35. $\dfrac{3}{15}, \dfrac{2}{21}$ **36.** $\dfrac{4}{9}, \dfrac{5}{18}$ **37.** $\dfrac{5}{12}, \dfrac{13}{10}$

38. $\dfrac{7}{18}, \dfrac{5}{15}, \dfrac{11}{14}$ **39.** $\dfrac{4}{15}, \dfrac{2}{9}, \dfrac{37}{25}$

In exercises 40-42, write the fractions with numbers in parentheses as new denominators.

40. $\dfrac{5}{9}$, (27)   **41.** $\dfrac{11}{16}$, (96)   **42.** $\dfrac{19}{10}$, (40)

In exercises 43-46, find the sums, and write your answer in lowest terms.

43. $\dfrac{3}{5} + \dfrac{4}{7}$ **44.** $\dfrac{4}{15} + \dfrac{7}{24}$ **45.** $\dfrac{6}{9} + \dfrac{4}{15}$ **46.** $\dfrac{8}{21} + \dfrac{6}{35}$

In exercises 47-52, find the differences, and write your answer in lowest terms.

47. $\dfrac{4}{3} - \dfrac{2}{3}$ **48.** $\dfrac{7}{15} - \dfrac{2}{15}$ **49.** $\dfrac{10}{15} - \dfrac{2}{5}$

50. $\dfrac{7}{24} - \dfrac{3}{16}$ **51.** $\dfrac{8}{9} - \dfrac{7}{12}$ **52.** $\dfrac{14}{15} - \dfrac{5}{12}$

In exercises 53-54, simplify the expressions, and write your answer in lowest terms.

53. $\dfrac{3}{5} + \dfrac{4}{9} + \dfrac{5}{12}$ **54.** $4\dfrac{5}{7} - 2\dfrac{1}{7} + \dfrac{5}{14}$

1.2   ORDER OF OPERATIONS

After studying this section you will be able to:

A. Write products as exponents.

B. Use the order of operations and grouping symbols.

C. Understand the meaning of various inequality and equality (relational) symbols such as $=$, $\neq$, $<$, $>$, $\leq$, and $\geq$.

D. Translate word statements into relational symbols.

A.   Write products as exponents

Consider the prime factorization of 24.

$$24 = 2 \times 2 \times 2 \times 3.$$

- The factor 2 is repeated three times. The product of repeated factors $2 \times 2 \times 2$ is also written in the *exponent form* as 2^3, where the number 2 is the base and 3 is the exponent or the power.

$$\text{base} \leftharpoondown 2^3 \rightharpoondown \text{power}$$

- 2^3 is often read as "**two cubed**" or "2 to the power 3 " or "2 to the third power."

- The meaning of 2^3 is 2 multiplied by itself 3 times.

- Similarly, 2^2 is read as "**two squared**" or "2 to the power 2" or "2 to the second power."

A natural number exponent gives the number of times the base is used as a factor.

Note: A number raised to first power is the number itself. $2^1 = 2$, $4^1 = 4$

Example 1:	Evaluate the following

a) 3^4 b) 6^1 c) $\left(\dfrac{1}{2}\right)^2$

d) $\left(\dfrac{4}{7}\right)^3$ e) $\left(1\dfrac{2}{3}\right)^5$

Warm Up

1. Evaluate:

Solutions:

a) $3^4 = 3 \times 3 \times 3 \times 3 = 81$
The base 3 repeated four times, since the exponent is 4.

b) $6^1 = 6$ The exponent is 1

c) $\left(\dfrac{1}{2}\right)^2 = \dfrac{1}{2} \cdot \dfrac{1}{2} = \dfrac{1}{4}$ The base is $\dfrac{1}{2}$, exponent is 2

(a) $2^5 =$

(b) $7^1 =$

(c) $\left(\dfrac{1}{3}\right)^3 =$

21

Warm Up

1. (d) $\left(\dfrac{3}{5}\right)^3 =$

(e) $\left(1\dfrac{1}{4}\right)^3 =$

Answers:

1. (a) 32   (b) 7   (c) $\dfrac{1}{27}$ (d) $\dfrac{27}{125}$

(e) $\dfrac{125}{64}$

d) $\left(\dfrac{4}{7}\right)^3 = \dfrac{4}{7} \cdot \dfrac{4}{7} \cdot \dfrac{4}{7} = \dfrac{4 \times 4 \times 4}{7 \times 7 \times 7} = \dfrac{64}{343}$

The base is $\dfrac{4}{7}$, exponent is 3

e) $\left(1\dfrac{2}{3}\right)^5 = \left(\dfrac{5}{3}\right)^5$ Convert the mixed number to a mixed fraction

$= \dfrac{5}{3} \cdot \dfrac{5}{3} \cdot \dfrac{5}{3} \cdot \dfrac{5}{3} \cdot \dfrac{5}{3}$ The base is $\dfrac{5}{3}$, exponent is 5

$= \dfrac{5 \times 5 \times 5 \times 5 \times 5}{3 \times 3 \times 3 \times 3 \times 3}$

$= \dfrac{3125}{243}$ Convert the improper fraction to a mixed number

$= 12\dfrac{209}{243}$

B.   Use the order of operations and grouping symbols

If more than one operations are involved then different order of operation can lead to different results.

For example,

$$3 + 4 \cdot 5 = 3 + 20 = 23 \qquad \text{If addition is performed \textbf{after} multiplication}$$

and $\qquad 3 + 4 \cdot 5 = 7 \cdot 5 = 35 \qquad$ If addition is performed **before** multiplication

As we can see, we get different answers for computing the same expression if we follow different rules. Therefore, it is important, for the sake of consistency, to follow rules uniformly. The rules described below are accepted universally and also by all scientific calculators.

If no grouping symbols are present then follow the steps given below in this order:

Step 1	Evaluate all exponents.
Step 2	Perform all multiplications and divisions from left to right in the order in which they occur.
Step 3	Perform all additions and subtractions from left to right in the order in which they occur.

Warm Up

2. Evaluate

(a) $2^2 + 3^2 - 11 =$

Example 2:   Evaluate   **a)** $3^2 + 5^2 - 7$ **b)** $3 + 4 \times 6$

c) $3 + 5^2 - 7 \times 4$ **d)** $4 + 6 + 7 \times 6 \div 3$

e) $2 \times 8 - 4 \times 3$

Solutions:

a)   *Step 1* $3^2 + 5^2 - 7 = 9 + 25 - 7$ *Step 2*   is not needed

Step 3 $= 34 - 7 = 27$

b) *Step 2* $3+4\times6 = 3+24$ Step 1 is not needed

Step 3 $= 27$

2.

     (b) $4+5\times7 =$

c) *Step 1* $3+5^2-7\times4 = 3+25-7\times4$

Step 2 $= 3+25-28$

Step 3 $= 28-28 = 0$

     (c) $4+3^2-5\times2 =$

d) *Step 2* $4+6+7\times6\div3 = 4+6+42\div3$ Step 1 is not needed

Step 3 $= 4+6+14$

         $= 10+14 = 24$

     (d) $7+4+3\times9\div9 =$

     (e) $3\times7-9\times2 =$

e) *Step 2* $2\times8-4\times3 = 16-4\times3$ Step 1 is not needed

Step 3 $= 16-12 = 4$

In complex situations grouping symbols are used to indicate the order of simplification. The type of grouping symbols used are parentheses ( ), braces { }, brackets [ ], and fraction bar ——.

Some examples of the use of grouping symbols are:

$$2+(3+5\cdot4), \qquad 3^2+5+[4+(7-9\div2)], \quad \text{and} \quad (7+9)[6+\{5+4\div(3\cdot5-13)\}]$$

For each left grouping symbol [, {, or (there must be a corresponding a right grouping symbol], }, or) placed in a nest. Notice the nest formed in [6 + {5 + 4÷ (3·5 − 13)}] if the numbers and operations are not listed: [{ ( )}].

We use the following order of operations if grouping symbols are present.

> *Step 1*   Simplify within each grouping symbol starting from the innermost grouping symbol.
>
> *Step 2*   If fraction bars are present then simplify separately the numerator and the denominator of the fraction.

Observations:

1. While simplifying as described above, you may get terms like: 2(3), (2) 3 or (2) (3). All these mean multiplication. Thus, $2(3) = (2)3 = (2)(3) = 2\times3 = 6$

2. Sometimes may be *a dot* used for multiplication instead of a cross.

       Thus, $2\cdot3 = 2\times3 = 6$

This dot is not aligned at the bottom like 2.3, but it appears in the center like $2\cdot3$.

Warm Up

3 . Evaluate:

(a) $5(7+9) =$

(b) $3(9+8-11) =$

(c) $7(5+2\cdot6) =$

(d) $4^2 + 2 \div 7 =$

(e) $5+\left[3^2+(6-2)\div4\right] =$

(f) $7+\left[5+3\cdot\{2+4\div(6-2)\}\right] =$

(g) $7+\dfrac{3+4}{2\times5-3} =$

(h) $\left(2^2+5\cdot3\right)\left(9-6\div3\right) =$

Answers:
2. (a) 2   (b) 39   (c) 3   (d) 14
   (e) 3
3. (a) 80   (b) 18   (c) 119
   (d) $16\frac{2}{7}$ (e) 15   (f) 21
   (g) 8   (h) 133

Example 3:   Evaluate.

a) $3(5+11)$ **b)** $4(5+7-9)$ **c)** $3(8+5\cdot7)$

d) $6^2+3\div5$ **e)** $2+\left[5^2+(8-2)\div3\right]$

f) $4+\left[10+2\cdot\{1+6\div(1+1)\}\right]$

g) $4+\left(3+\dfrac{5+9}{2\times3+1}\right)$ **h)** $(4^2+3\cdot5)(7-4\div2)$

Solutions:

a) $3(\mathbf{5+11}) = 3(\mathbf{16}) = 48$

b) $4(\mathbf{5+7}-9) = 4(\mathbf{12}-\mathbf{9}) = 4(3) = 12$

c) $3(8+\mathbf{5\cdot7}) = 3(\mathbf{8+35}) = 3(43) = 129$

d) $6^2+3\div5 = 36+\mathbf{3}\div\mathbf{5} = 36+\dfrac{3}{5} = 36\dfrac{3}{5}$

e) $2+\left[5^2+(\mathbf{8-2})\div3\right] = 2+\left[\mathbf{5^2}+6\div3\right] = 2+[25+\mathbf{6\div3}]$
   $= 2+[\mathbf{25+2}] = 2+[27] = 29$

f) $4+\left[10+2\cdot\{1+6\div(\mathbf{1+1})\}\right] = 4+\left[10+2\cdot\{1+\mathbf{6\div2}\}\right]$
   $= 4+[10+2\cdot\{\mathbf{1+3}\}]$
   $= 4+[10+\mathbf{2\cdot4}]$
   $= 4+[\mathbf{10+8}] = 4+[18] = 22$

g) $4+\left(3+\dfrac{5+9}{2\cdot3+1}\right) = 4+\left(3+\dfrac{\mathbf{14}}{7}\right) = 4+(\mathbf{3+2}) = 4+(5) = 9$

h) $\left(4^2+3\cdot5\right)(7-4\div2)$

If two grouping symbols are not nested then, simplify the expressions within each grouping symbol separately.

$4^2+3\cdot5 = 16+3\cdot5 = 16+15 = 31, \qquad 7-\mathbf{4\div2} = 7-2 = 5$

Therefore, $(\mathbf{4^2}+3\cdot\mathbf{5})(7-4\div\mathbf{2}) = (31)(5) = 155$

We can compute these numeric expressions using calculator. See example 1, section 1.2 in Appendix B.

C.   Understand inequality and equality symbols

In order to be able to set up a bridge between word statements and mathematical expressions, we need some of the symbols explained in the following table.

SYMBOL	MEANING	EXAMPLE	VERBAL STATEMENT
$=$	equal to	$\dfrac{1}{2}+\dfrac{1}{2}=1$	$\dfrac{1}{2}$ plus $\dfrac{1}{2}$ equals 1
$\neq$	not equal to	$5 \neq 7$	5 **is not equal** to 7.
$<$	is less than	$4 < 9$	4 **is less than** 9.
$>$	is greater than	$8 > 3$	8 **is greater than** 3.
$\leq$	is less than or equal to	$5 \leq 5$ $5 \leq 7$	5 **is less than or equal** to 5. 5 **is less than or equal** to 7.
$\geq$	is greater than or equal to	$5 \geq 5$ $6 \geq 4$	5 **is greater than or equal** to 5 [since in this case equal to is true] 6 **is greater than or equal** to 4.

Example 4:   Which of the following statements are true or false?

a) $4 \neq 4$ b) $5 \neq 3$ c) $(4+2) > 7$

d) $(3+5) \leq (10-2)$ e) $(10 \div 2) > 5$

f) $(12 \div 2) > 5$ g) $(5 \cdot 4) \geq 8$

Solutions:

a) $4 \neq 4$ is **false**, since 4 equals itself.

b) $5 \neq 3$ is **true**, since 5 and 3 are not equal.

c) $(4+2) > 7$ is **false**, since 6 is less than 7.

d) $(3+5) \leq (10-2)$ is **true**, since 8 = 8. Notice 8 is equal to itself. Therefore, we can also say 8 is less than or equal to 8.

e) $(10 \div 2) > 5$ is **false**, since 5 is equal to 5 and not greater than 5.

f) $(12 \div 2) > 5$ is **true**, since 6 is greater than 5.

g) $(5 \cdot 4) \geq 8$ is **true**, since 20 is greater than 8, and therefore, we can also say that 20 is greater than or equal to 8.

Warm Up

4. Which of the following statements are True or False?

(a) $7 = 4$

(b) $5 \neq 5$

(c) $(9+2) < 13$

(d) $(7+9) < (15-3)$

(e) $(0 \div 5) < 4$

(f) $(15 \div 3) > 3$

(g) $(9 \cdot 4) > 25$

We can find the truth of these types of statements using calculator. See example 2 (section 1.2) in Appendix B.

The statements '3 is less than 5' and '5 is greater than 3' convey the same meaning. Thus $3 < 5$ can also be written as $5 > 3$. It follows that $<$ changes to $>$ if the expressions on two sides are swapped. A similar conclusion holds for $\leq$ and $\geq$.

Rule :   To change < into > or vice versa, swap the expressions on the two sides of the inequality.

To change ≤ into ≥ or vice versa, swap the expressions on the two sides of the inequality.

Warm Up

5 . (a) Express 5 < 9 by using >.

(b) Express 9 ≥ 5 by using ≤.

(c) Express 25 > 21 by using <.

Answers:
4. (a) F (b) F (c) T (d) F
(e) T (f) T (g) T
5. (a) 9 > 5 (b) 5 ≤ 9 (c) 21 < 25

Example 5:

a)   Express 3 < 5 by using >.

b)   Express 7 ≥ 5 by using ≤.

c)   Express 11 > 10 by using <.

Solutions:

a) 3 < 5 means *"3 is less than 5"* which is the same as *"5 is greater than 3."* Therefore, 3 < 5 → 5 > 3.

b) 7 ≥ 5 means *"7 is greater than or equal to 5'"* which is the same as *"5 is less than or equal to 7".*
Therefore, 7 ≥ 5 → 5 ≤ 7.

c) 11 > 10 means *"11 is greater than 10".* This is the same as *"10 is less than 11".* Thus, 11 > 10 → 10 < 11

D. Translate word statements into relational symbols

In order to apply mathematics to solve problems we should be able to translate the words (and sentences) in the problem in terms of mathematical expressions. We shall see how relational symbols are useful. Words such as *plus, increased by,* and sum indicate **addition;** words such as *minus, decreased by, less than* indicate **subtraction**; words such as *times, product, and of* indicate **multiplication**; and words such as *quotient, and divided by* indicate **division**. Consider the following example:

WORD STATEMENT	TRANSLATION INTO SYMBOLS	
Seven is *less than* eleven	7 < 11	Less Than
Five *plus* seven	5 + 7	Plus
Twenty *minus* nine	20 − 9	Minus
Four is *not equal* to three	4 ≠ 3	Not Equal To
Thirteen is *greater than or equal* to twelve	13 ≥ 12	Greater than or Equal to
Twelve is *less than or equal to* thirteen	12 ≤ 13	Less than or Equal to
Fifteen is *greater than* five	15 > 5	Greater than

26

Example 6:   Translate the following statements into symbols

Solution:

a) Fourteen decreased by three equals eleven.

14 decreased by 3 = 11

      ↓

14   –   3 = 11

b) Two times five increased by seven equals seventeen.

2 times 5 increased by 7 = 17

 ↓   ↓

2   ·   5   +   7 = 17

c) Six divided by two equals three

6 divided by 2 = 3

     ↓

6   ÷   2 = 3

d) The product of seven and three is greater than twenty.

7 multiplied by 3 > 20

     ↓

7   ·   3 > 20

e) Five is greater than the quotient of eight and four.

5 > 8 divided by 4

      ↓

5 > 8   ÷   4

Warm Up

6.

a) thirteen increased by four equals seventeen

b) four times nine decreased by sixteen equals twenty.

c) eighteen divided by three is less than seven.

d) six multiplied by four equals twenty four.

e) nine is greater than or equal to the quotient of twenty one and three.

Answers:

6. a) $13 + 4 = 17$
b) $4 \cdot 9 - 16 = 20$ **c)** $18 \div 3 < 7$
d) $6 \times 4 = 24$ **e)** $9 \geq (21 \div 3)$

EXERCISE 1.2

Evaluate the expressions in exercises 1-7.

1. 5^3 **2.** 7^2 **3.** $\left(\dfrac{2}{3}\right)^3$ **4.** 9^1

5. $\left(\dfrac{4}{3}\right)^5$ **6.** 8^3 **7.** $\left(2\dfrac{3}{4}\right)^3$

8. In the expression $3 + 5 \cdot 7 - 4^2$, describe the order in which you will perform the operations.

Answers:

1. _____
2. _____
3. _____
4. _____
5. _____
6. _____
7. _____
8. _____

In exercises 9-24, simplify the numeric expressions.

9. $3+5-7$ **10.** $4\cdot5+6\cdot2$ **11.** $5^2+7\cdot5$

12. $6^2-3^2+4^3\cdot5$ **13.** $5+7\cdot8$ **14.** $25-8\div4$

15. $10\cdot4\div2$ **16.** $10\div4\cdot2$ **17.** $2^5-6\cdot2+4\div4$

18. $3(5\cdot2-7)$ **19.** $2+\left[4+2(4-1)\right]$

20. $\dfrac{4(3-1)-1}{5^2+7}$ **21.** $(5-3)(9+2\cdot4)$

22. $4+2\left[17-2(5+8\div4)\right]$

23. $(3+5\cdot6)\div\left[12-\dfrac{6-2\cdot2}{3^2-7}\right]$ **24.** $(5+2\cdot2)^2\div\left(2^2-3\right)$

STATEMENTS

25. Which of the symbols $=$, $\neq$, $<$, $\leq$, $>$, and $\geq$ make the statements true?

a) $3\ldots\ldots\ldots\ldots4$
b) $5\ldots\ldots\ldots\ldots2$
c) $4\ldots\ldots\ldots\ldots4$

In exercises 26-29, rewrite the statements in a different way by changing the relational symbols.

26. $5<11$ **27.** $13\geq8$ **28.** $8>6$ **29.** $4\leq7$

In exercises 30-34, identify the true statements.

30. $3+5\cdot2>15$ **31.** $4^2+5=21$ **32.** $7^2+8\div2\neq49$

33. $(6-3)(4+2)\leq15$ **34.** $1+\dfrac{2}{3}+4\dfrac{1}{3}=6$

28

In exercises 35-44, translate the word statements into symbols.

35. Eight plus five is greater than ten.

35. _____

36. Twenty divided by four equals five.

36. _____

37. Quotient of thirty and five is less than nine.

37. _____

38. Product of five and six is not equal to 21.

38. _____

39. Three times five added to four makes (equals) nineteen.

39. _____

40. Nine decreased by five is less than or equal to four.

40. _____

41. Seventeen minus two times five is greater than three.

41. _____

42. Twenty two divided by two is less than three plus twelve.

42. _____

43. Nine raised to the power of four is not the same as (is not equal to) four raised to the power of nine.

43. _____

44. Three to the power of five plus seven is greater than two hundred.

44. _____

1.3   EXPRESSIONS AND EQUATIONS

In this section we will introduce the concept of a variable. We will use a variable to show how algebraic expressions and equations are constructed. Upon completion of this section we will be able to:

   A.   Find the value of an algebraic expression.
   B.   Translate phrases into algebraic expressions.
   C.   Distinguish an expression from an equation.

A.   Find the value of an algebraic expression

Variables are the building blocks for algebraic expressions. A **variable** is a symbol which is used to represent an unknown number. It is denoted by a letter such as: x, y, z, p, q, etc. Operations on variables are performed in the same way as operations on numbers.

For example,

a) $x \cdot x$ is written as x^2.

b) $2 \cdot x$, which is written as $2x$, denotes product of 2 and x.

c) $x^2 + x$ means the sum of x^2 and x.

d) $x - 2$ means 2 subtracted from x.

Algebraic expressions are created by using variables, numbers, operations, and grouping symbols. For example:

$$3x^2 + 5, \qquad x(x+2), \qquad 6x + 5yz - 7, \qquad \text{and} \qquad 5x^2 + (x-1)^2 y + 4$$

are some examples of algebraic expressions. An algebraic expression can be evaluated by replacing variables (unknown numbers) in the expression by the values which they may take. If an algebraic expression involves only one variable, say x, we say that it is an algebraic expression in one variable or specifically, an algebraic expression in x. If there are two variables, x and y, in an algebraic expression, we say that it is an algebraic expression in two variables or an algebraic expression in x and y.

Warm Up

1. Find the numerical values of

(a) $4x^2 + 7$ when $x = -1$

(b) $\dfrac{3x^2 - x + 2}{2(x+2)}$ when $x = 2$

(c) $(5x+1)^2 + 3$ when $x = 1$

(d) $15x$ when $x = -2$

Example 1: Find the numerical values of:

a) $3x$ when $x = 2$.

b) $4y^2 + 5$ when $y = 3$.

c) $(3x-2)^2 + 1$ when $x = 4$.

d) $\dfrac{4m^2 + 7m - 2}{2(m-1)}$ when $m = 2$.

Solutions:

a) $3x = 3 \cdot 2 = 6$ \qquad (Replace x with 2.)

b) $4y^2 + 5 = 4 \cdot 3^2 + 5 = 4 \cdot 9 + 5 = 36 + 5$ \quad (Replace y with 3.)
$$= 41$$

c) $(3x - 2)^2 + 1 = (3 \cdot 4 - 2)^2 + 1 = (12 - 2)^2 + 1$
(Replace x with 4.) $\qquad = 10^2 + 1 = 100 + 1 = 101$

d) $\dfrac{4m^2 + 7m - 2}{2(m-1)} = \dfrac{4 \cdot 2^2 + 7 \cdot 2 - 2}{2(2-1)} = \dfrac{4 \cdot 4 + 14 - 2}{2(1)}$

(Replace m with 2.) $\qquad\qquad = \dfrac{16 + 14 - 2}{2} = \dfrac{28}{2} = 14$

See example 1 and 2 or section 1.3, in Appendix B for evaluating expressions with calculator.

Example 2:

Evaluate the following expressions for the given values of the variables.

a) $3x - 5y$;
$x = 4,\ y = 2$

b) $5x^2 - 2yz + 8$;
$x = 3,\ y = 2,\ z = 4$

c) $(x^2 + 3y)(3y + 7)$;
$x = 1,\ y = 1$

d) $\dfrac{x^2 - 3y^2}{5y + x}$;
$x = 4,\ y = 2$

Solutions:

a) $3x - 5y = 3 \cdot 4 - 5 \cdot 2$
$= 12 - 10 = 2$

b) $5x^2 - 2yz + 8 = 5 \cdot 3^2 - 2 \cdot 2 \cdot 4 + 8$
$= 5 \cdot 9 - 16 + 8$
$= 45 - 16 + 8 = 37$

c) $\left(x^2 + 3y\right)(3y + 7) = \left(1^2 + 3 \cdot 1\right)(3 \cdot 1 + 7)$
$= (1 + 3)(3 + 7)$
$= (4)(10) = 40$

d) $\dfrac{x^2 - 3y^2}{5y + x} = \dfrac{4^2 - 3 \cdot 2^2}{5 \cdot 2 + 4} = \dfrac{16 - 3 \cdot 4}{10 + 4}$
$= \dfrac{16 - 12}{14} = \dfrac{4}{14} = \dfrac{2}{7}$

See example 1 and 2 of section 1.3, in Appendix B for evaluating expressions with calculator.

Warm Up

2. Evaluate the following expressions for the given values of the variables.

(a) $2x + 3y$; for $x = 2$, $y = 1$

(b) $2x^2 - yz + 4$; for $x = 1,\ y = 0,\ z = 1$

(c) $\left(x^2 + 6y\right)\left(x^2 + 6y\right)$ for $x = -2$, $y = -2$

(d) $\dfrac{11x^2 - 7y^2}{3x + 5}$ for $x = 3,\ y = 2$

Answers:

1. (a) 11 (b) $\frac{3}{2}$ (c) 39 (d) -30

2. (a) 7 (b) 6 (c) 64 (d) $\frac{71}{14}$

B. Translate phrases into algebraic expressions

In section 1.2 we examined how words are translated into symbols. In this section we examine how phrases may be changed to algebraic expressions.

Example 3:

a) **The sum** of *a number* and 11

b) 3 **subtracted** from *a number*

c) **The product** of 11 and *a number*

d) **The quotient** of *a number* and 4

e) **The quotient** of 4 and *a number*

f) 5 **times** *a number* plus **4**

g) **The difference** between **twice** *a number* and 7

Warm Up

3.

(a) The **difference** between three times a number and 4.

(b) The **quotient** of 7 and twice a number.

Answers:

3 (a) $3x - 4$ (b) $\frac{7}{2x}$

Note: When we say *a number* without specification, it means that we are talking about an unknown number. *An unspecified* number may be translated as x, y, z (any variable).

Solutions:

a) "The **sum** of a number and 11' translates to $x + 11$

number	plus	11
↓	↓	↓
x	$+$	11

b) "3 **subtracted** from a number" translates to $x - 3$

number	decreased by	3
↓	↓	↓
x	$-$	3

c) "The product of 11 and a number" translates to $11x$

11	times	a number
↓	↓	↓
11	$\cdot$	x

Recall $11 \cdot x$ and $11x$ mean the same thing, and we write it as $11x$ and not as $11 \cdot x$

d) "The quotient of a number and 4" translates to $\dfrac{x}{4}$.

a number	divided by	4
↓	↓	↓
x	$\div$	4

e) "The quotient of 4 and a number" translates to $\dfrac{4}{x}$.

4	divided by	a number
4	$\div$	x

f) "5 times a number plus 4" translates to $5x + 4$.

5	times	a number	plus	4
↓	↓	↓	↓	↓
5	$\cdot$	x	$+$	4

g) "The difference between twice a number and seven" translates to $2x - 7$

2	times	a number	minus	7
↓	↓	↓	↓	↓
2	$\cdot$	x	$-$	7

C. Distinguish an expression from an equation

An **equation** is a statement that expresses the equality of two algebraic expressions. Let us examine some word statements which translate into equations.

1. The sum of four times a number and 7 is 91.
This means

four	times	a number	plus	seven	equals	ninety - one
↓	↓	↓	↓	↓	↓	↓
4	$\cdot$	x	$+$	7	$=$	91

Thus, the given word statement translates to the equation, $4x + 7 = 91$

2. 'Twice the difference of a number and 7 equals the sum of the number and 20' translates to the equation: $2(x - 7) = x + 20$.

The difference between an expression and equation is that an equation contains an '=' sign. An expression does not contain an '=' sign.

Example 4:	Decide whether the following is an equation or an expression.

a) $4x^2 - 5y$ **b)** $4x^2 - 5y = 0$

c) $4x^2 = 5y$ **d)** $(3x + y)x - 2y$

Solutions:

a) $4x^2 - 5y$ is an *expression*

b) $4x^2 - 5y = 0$ is an *equation*

c) $4x^2 = 5y$ is an *equation*

d) $(3x + y)x - 2y$ is an *expression*

Warm Up

4. Decide whether the following is an equation or an expression.

(a) $4x^3 - 2x^2 + 3y + 2$

(b) $4y = 0$

Example 5:	Translate each of the following into mathematical symbols and decide whether the result is an expression or an equation.

a) Seven times a number decreased by two.

b) Seven times a number decreased by two equals five.

c) Five added to a number.

d) Five added to a number is seventeen.

Solutions:

a) **"Seven times a number decreased by two"** translates to $7x - 2$ (expression).

b) **"Seven times a number decreased by two equals five"** translates to $7x - 2 = 5$ *(equation)*.

c) **"Five added to a number"** translates to $x + 5$. (expression)

d) **"Five added to a number is seventeen"** translates to $x + 5 = 17$. (equation)

5. Translate into mathematical symbols and determine whether the result if an expression or an equation.

(a) Three times a number added to 5 is 16.

(b) Two times a number square added to 15 times that number.

We notice that an expression corresponds to a *phrase* and an *equation* corresponds to a sentence.

The solution of equation

An equation in a single variable is called linear if it does not contain powers of the variable which are greater than one. An algebraic expression in a single variable is also called linear if it does not contain powers of the variable which are greater than one. Some examples of linear equations are:

$$3x - 20 = 0 \qquad 4x = 7(x - 20) \qquad 3x = 5.$$

A number is called the **solution** of an equation (in one variable) if the equation results in a true statement when the variable is replaced by this number.

To find out if a number is a solution of an equation we use the following steps:

Step 1	Substitute the given number for the variable in the equation,
Step 2	Simplify the expressions on both sides of the equation

If the simplification results in a true statement, the number is a solution, otherwise it is not a solution.

Warm Up

6. Determine whether the given number is a solution of the equation given

   (a) $5x + 1 = 63; 12$

   (b) $7x + 5 = 54; 7$

Example 6: Given below an equation and a number, find whether the given number is a solution of the equation.

   a) $4x + 7 = 91; 21$ **b)** $2(y - 7) = y + 20; 25$

Solutions:

a) Substitute 21 for x in $4x + 7 = 91$.

$$4 \cdot 21 + 7 = 91 \longrightarrow 84 + 7 = 91$$
$$\longrightarrow 91 = 91 \qquad \textbf{True!}$$

Therefore, 21 is a solution of the equation $4x + 7 = 91$.

b) Substitute 25 for y in: $\quad 2(y - 7) = y + 20$

$$2(25 - 7) = 25 + 20 \longrightarrow 2 \cdot 18 = 45$$
$$\longrightarrow 36 = 45 \quad \textbf{False!}$$

Therefore, 25 is not a solution of the equation $2(y - 7) = y + 20$

Identify solutions from a set of numbers

A **set** is a well defined collection of objects. The objects belonging to the set are its **elements** or **members**. The set whose members are 1, 2, 3, 4 is written as {1, 2, 3, 4}.

To find the solution of an equation from a given finite set of numbers, we verify for each number in the set, one by one, whether or not it is a solution of the equation.

Example 7: Identify the solution from a given set:
   a) $2x + 9 = 5x; \quad \{0, 2, 3\}$.
   b) $3x - 2 = 0; \quad \{1, 4, 7\}$.

Solutions:

Warm Up

7. Identify the solution from a given set.
  a) $3x + 2 = 2x$;
     $\{0, 1, -2\}$

a) $x = 0$: Substitute 0 for x in $2x + 9 = 5x$ $2 \cdot 0 + 9 = 5 \cdot 0$

    0 is not a solution. $0 + 9 = 0$ **False**

    $x = 2$: Substitute 2 for x $2 \cdot 2 + 9 = 5 \cdot 2$

    2 is not a solution. $13 = 10$ **False**

    $x = 3$: Substitute 3 for x $2 \cdot 3 + 9 = 5 \cdot 3$

    3 is a solution $15 = 15$ **True**

Therefore, 3 is the solution of $2x + 9 = 5x$ in the set {0,2,3}.

b) $x = 1$:   Substitute 1 for x in $3x - 2 = 0$ $3 \cdot 1 - 2 = 0$
         1 is not a solution. $1 = 0$ **False**

      $x = 4$:   Substitute 4 for x $3 \cdot 4 - 2 = 0$
         4 is not a solution. $10 = 0$ **False**

      $x = 7$:   Substitute 7 for x $3 \cdot 7 - 2 = 0$
         7 is not a solution. $19 = 0$ **False**

Warm Up

b) $4x - 12 = x$;
  $\{-1, 3, 4\}$

Therefore, $3x - 2 = 0$ does not have a solution in {1, 4, 7}.

Note: An equation may have a solution outside a given set. For example $\frac{2}{3}$ is a solution of $3x-2=0$ since $3\left(\frac{2}{3}\right)-2=0$. However, $\frac{2}{3}$ is not in the set {1, 4, 7}.

Example 8:   The quotient of eighteen and three times a number is three. Does this problem have a solution in the set {1, 2, 3, 4}?

Warm Up

8.

(a) The product of 5 times a number is 30. Does this problem has a solution in the set {1, 3, 5 , 6}.

(b) The quotient of three times a number and 5 is 6. Does this problem have a solution in the set { 1, 4, 5, 7}?

Solution:

Step 1   Translate the given statement into mathematical symbols. The given statement is the same as:

  eighteen divided by, three times a number is (equals) three
    18   ÷   (3 x)   =   3

  which is the same as: $\dfrac{18}{3x} = 3$

Step 2   Take each number from the set {1, 2, 3, 4} and examine whether it satisfies the equation (i.e., whether it is a solution of the equation.)

  The equation is $\dfrac{18}{3x} = 3$

Test $x = 1$: $\dfrac{18}{3 \cdot 1} = 3 \longrightarrow \dfrac{18}{3} = 3 \longrightarrow 6 = 3$ **False!**

Test $x = 2$: $\dfrac{18}{3 \cdot 2} = 3 \longrightarrow \dfrac{18}{6} = 3 \longrightarrow 3 = 3$ **True!**

Test $x = 3$: $\dfrac{18}{3 \cdot 3} = 3 \longrightarrow \dfrac{18}{9} = 3 \longrightarrow 2 = 3$ **False!**

Test $x = 4$: $\dfrac{18}{3 \cdot 4} = 3 \longrightarrow \dfrac{18}{12} = 3 \longrightarrow \dfrac{3}{2} = 3$ **False!**

Step 3   *Conclusion*

  Hence we find that there is a solution of the problem in the set {1, 2, 3, 4}. This solution is 2.

9. Translate statement into mathematical symbols.

   (a) Thirteen subtracted from two times a number is 2 more than 5 times that number.

   (b) Does this problem have a solution in the set $\{-5, -3, 0, 1\}$? What is the solution?

Answers:

4. (a) expression   (b) equation

5. (a) $3x + 5 = 16$; equation

   (b) $2x^2 + 15x$; expression

6. (a) FALSE   (b) TRUE

7. (a) -2 (b) 4

8. (a) YES ; 6   (b) NO

9. (a) $2x - 13 = 2 + 5x$ (b) YES; -5

Example 9:   Twelve added to a number is three less than four times the number. Does this problem have a solution in $\{1, 2, 3, 4\}$?

Solution:

Step 1   Translate the statement into mathematical symbols. The given statement means:

Twelve	added to	a number	is (equals)	four times	the number	minus	three
12	+	x	=	$4 \cdot$	x	−	3

which is the same as $12 + x = 4x - 3$.

Step 2   Take each number from $\{1, 2, 3, 4\}$ one by one and examine whether it satisfies the equation (i.e. whether it is a solution.)
The equation is $12 + x = 4x - 3$

1) Test $x = 1$: $12 + 1 = 4 \cdot 1 - 3$
   $13 = 4 - 3 \longrightarrow 13 = 1$ False!

2) Test $x = 2$: $12 + 2 = 4 \cdot 2 - 3$
   $14 = 8 - 3 \longrightarrow 14 = 5$ False!

3) Test $x = 3$: $12 + 3 = 4 \cdot 3 - 3$
   $15 = 12 - 3 \longrightarrow 15 = 9$ False!

4) Test $x = 4$: $12 + 4 = 4 \cdot 4 - 3$
   $16 = 16 - 3 \longrightarrow 16 = 13$ False!

Step 3   *Conclusion:* There is no solution in the given set.

EXERCISE   1.3

Answers:

1. _____

2. _____

3. _____

4. _____

In exercises 1-4, evaluate the expressions for $x = 2$ and $x = 9$.

1. $2x + 3$

2. $3x - 5$

3. $\dfrac{x^2 + 1}{5}$

4. $25 - 2x$

In exercises 5-10, evaluate the expressions for the indicated value of the variable.

5. $3m - 4m^2 + 1$; $m = \dfrac{1}{2}$

6. $(4p + 7)\left\{5p^2 + 6p + \dfrac{4}{p}\right\}$; $p = 4$

7. $3x + 7y^2$; $x = 1, y = 2$

8. $5x^2 + \dfrac{3y}{5y - z}$; $x = 2, y = 3, z = 6$

9. $4p - 7q + 2pq$; $p = 5, q = 2$

10. $\dfrac{4m^2 + 7n^2}{3m - 4n}$; $m = 5, n = 3$

In exercises 11-18, change the phrases to algebraic expressions. Use x to represent the unknown variable.

11. Four times seven

12. A number increased by nine

13. Seven decreased by twice a number

14. Nine added to a number

15. Quotient of eleven and a number

16. Twenty minus quotient of seven and a number

17. Five added to the product of a number and two

18. Four added to three-fifths of a number

5. _____

6. _____

7. _____

8. _____

9. _____

10. _____

11. _____

12. _____

13. _____

14. _____

15. _____

16. _____

17. _____

18. _____

37

In exercises 19-22, identify as an equation or an expression.

19. _____

20. _____

21. _____

22. _____

23. _____

24. _____

25. _____

26. _____

27. _____

28. _____

29. _____

30. _____

31. _____

32. _____

33. _____

34. _____

35. _____

19. $3x^3 - 57x + y$

20. $4x^2 - 7x = \dfrac{8}{x+1}$

21. $5 + \dfrac{x}{3x-1} = 0$

22. $\dfrac{x^3 + 7x}{3x^2 + 5}$

In exercises 23-27, find the solutions, if any, of the equations in the set {2, 3, 5, 7, 10}.

23. $3x + 2 = 23$

24. $x^2 + 3x - 10 = 0$

25. $(3y + 4)(10 - y) = 0$

26. $\dfrac{z+6}{z-1} = 8$

27. $6m + 2(m + 3) = 14$

In exercises 28-34, change the word statements to equations. In each case, find the solution of the equation in the set {0, 1, 2, 4, 5}.

28. Sum of three times a number and four is nineteen

29. Difference of three times a number and ten equals twenty-one.

30. Quotient of sixteen and twice a number is four less than the number.

31. Five times a number exceeds three times the number by four.

32. Nine and three times a number adds up to twenty-one.

33. Two times a number equals five times the number.

34. Quotient of a number and eight is the quotient of two and the number.

35. Explain the difference between an algebraic expression and an equation.

1.4   REAL NUMBERS

After completing this section you will be able to:

- A. Set up number lines.
- B. Identify different kinds of numbers.
- C. Compare real numbers.
- D. Find the additive inverse or negative of a real number.
- E. Determine the absolute value of a real number.

A.   Set up number lines

Recall that 1, 2, 3, 4, . . . are called *natural numbers* or counting numbers, and **0**, 1, 2, 3, 4, . . . are called *whole numbers*. We now introduce negative whole numbers. The set of numbers ..., − 3, − 2, − 1, 0, 1, 2, 3... are called *integers*. The numbers ...−1, − 2, − 3, are called *negative integers* and 1, 2, 3,... are called *positive integers*.

We use the concept of **number line** to further explain the relationship between positive and negative integers. Take a point O on the line.

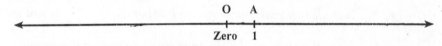

Figure 1.2

The point O will be used to represent the number 0 (zero). Choose any other point A on the right of O and let *OA* = 1 unit. The point A will represent the number 1. Now continue to mark points on the right of the number 1 at a distance equal to the *above* unit length from each other. This gives a representation of whole numbers on the **number line.**

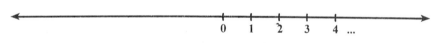

Figure 1.3

Now, starting with 0, mark points at a distance of unit length on the left of 0. This results in the representation of all integers on the number line.

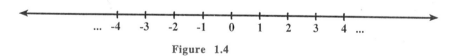

Figure 1.4

A point on the number line representing a number is called the **graph** of the number.

Notes: The number line extends *indefinitely* on both sides.

A number and its negative are equidistant from 0.

39

B. Identify different kinds of numbers

Not all quantities can be measured in terms of integers. For example, when we divide two apples equally among four person, each person gets one-half, i.e. $\frac{1}{2}$ an apple. The graph of $\frac{1}{2}$ is midway between the graphs of 0 and 1 on the number line. The number $\frac{1}{2}$ is an example of a rational number.

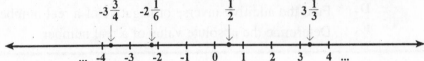

Figure 1.5

*In general numbers of the type $\frac{p}{q}$, where p and q are integers and $q \neq 0$ are called **rational numbers**.*

Observations:

(1) All integers are rational numbers: $\qquad 5 = \frac{5}{1}, \quad 9 = \frac{9}{1}, \quad -4 = \frac{-4}{1}\ldots$

(2) Not all rational numbers are integers: $\qquad \frac{1}{2}$ is not an integer.

(3) Not all points on the number line are rational numbers.

The numbers that are not rational numbers are called **irrational numbers**;

Consider for example;

1. The length of a hypotenuse of a right triangle with its base and height equal to 1 unit is not a rational number.

$$AB^2 = AC^2 + CB^2$$
$$= 1 + 1 = 2$$

Therefore, AB is a number whose square is 2.

The symbol for such a number is $\sqrt{2}$. It can be proved that $\sqrt{2}$ can not be expressed as a ratio of two integers. Therefore $\sqrt{2}$ is not a rational number. We call such numbers as irrational numbers. We shall discuss such numbers in more details in later chapters.

2. The ratio of a circumference of a circle to its diameter, for different circles, is the same number. This number is called pi (π). This number is an irrational number and its approximate value is 3.1416.

When all these numbers, i.e. integers, rational, and irrational, are graphed on the number line, the number line is completely filled up. This means that each point on the line represents a number, and each number can be represented by a point on the line. All these numbers put together are called **real numbers**, and the number line on which all these numbers are graphed is called the **real line**.

Introducing Subsets

Recall that

1) Set of Natural Numbers = $\{1, 2, 3, ...\}$

2) Set of Whole Numbers = $\{0, 1, 2, 3, ...\}$

3) Set of Integers = $\{..., -3, -2, -1, 0, 1, 2, 3, ...\}$

4) Set of Rational Numbers = $\left\{ \text{All integers} + \text{Numbers or the type } \frac{1}{2}, \frac{2}{3}, -\frac{4}{5}, ... \right\}$

5) Set of irrational numbers = $\left\{ \text{Numbers of the type } \sqrt{2}, \sqrt{3}, \sqrt{7} ... \right\}$

6) Set of real numbers = set of rational numbers + set of irrational numbers.

We may observe that natural numbers are contained in the whole numbers, whole numbers are contained in integers, the integers are contained in the rational numbers, and the real numbers contain rational numbers and irrational numbers. Following figure describes this hierarchy.

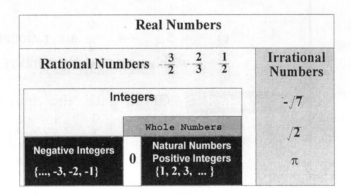

Figure 1.6

Example 1: In the set $\left\{ -4, 0, 1, \frac{9}{2}, -5\frac{1}{2}, \sqrt{3} \right\}$,

Identify the numbers which can be classified as:

a) natural numbers.   b) whole numbers.
c) integers.   d) rational numbers.
e) irrational numbers. f) real numbers.

Solutions:

a) 1 is the only **natural number** in the set.

b) 0, 1 are the only **whole numbers** in the set.

c) −4, 0, 1 are the only **integers** in the set.

d) $-5\frac{1}{2}, -4, 1, 0, \frac{9}{2}$ are the only **rational numbers** in the set.

Warm Up

1. In the set
$\left\{ 0, -5, \sqrt{6}, 3.8, \frac{2}{5} \right\}$,
Identify numbers which can be classified as :
a) natural numbers
b) whole numbers
c) integers
d) rational numbers
e) irrational numbers

41

e) $\sqrt{3}$ is the only **irrational number.**

f) All members of the set are **real numbers.**

We can find whether the number is rational or not by using calculator. See example 1, (section 1.4) in Appendix B.

2. In the set $\left\{0, -5, \sqrt{6}, 3.8, \frac{2}{5}\right\}$ indentify those numbers which are:
a) integers, but not natural
b) rational numbers but not integers c) rational numbers, but not whole numbers

Example 2: In the set $\left\{-4, 0, 1, \frac{9}{2}, -5\frac{1}{2}, \sqrt{3}\right\}$ identify those numbers which are:

a) integers, but not natural numbers.

b) rational numbers, but not integers.

c) rational numbers, but not whole numbers.

Solutions:

a) $-4, 0$ are integers in the set which are not natural numbers.

b) $-5\frac{1}{2}, \frac{9}{2}$ are rational numbers in the set which are not integers.

c) $-5\frac{1}{2}, -4, \frac{9}{2}$ are rational numbers in the set which are not whole numbers.

3. Graph all the numbers in the set $\left\{0, -5, \sqrt{6}, 3.8, \frac{2}{5}\right\}$ on the number line.

Example 3: Graph all the numbers in the set $\left\{-4, 0, 1, \frac{9}{2}, -5\frac{1}{2}, \sqrt{3}\right\}$, on the number line.

Solution:

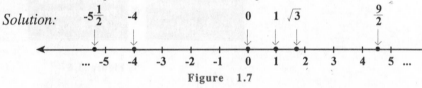

Figure 1.7

Graphing of $-4, 0,$ and 1 is simple.

Graphing of $\frac{9}{2}$: $\frac{9}{2}$ lies midway between 4 and 5.

Graphing of $-5\frac{1}{2}$: $-5\frac{1}{2}$ lies midway between -6 and -5.

Graphing of $\sqrt{3}$: Check with calculator $\sqrt{3} \approx 1.7$, a number between 1 and 2 and close to 2.

Answers:

1. a) no natural number b) 0 c) 0, −5
d) 3.8, $\frac{2}{5}$, 0, −5 e) $\sqrt{6}$

2. a) 0, −5 b) 3.8, $\frac{2}{5}$ c) 3.8, $\frac{2}{5}$, −5

3.

We can find whether the number is rational or not by using calculator. See example 1, (section 1.4) in Appendix B.

C.   Compare real numbers

For any two real numbers a and b, we say that a is **less than** b, if on the number line a is to the *left* of b.

>   "a is **less than** b" is written as $a < b$ in mathematical symbols.

>   "x is **greater than** y" is written as $x > y$ in mathematical symbols.

Notes: **1.** Since all positive numbers are graphed to the right of 0 on the number line, we have a > 0 for all positive real numbers a.

2. Since all negative numbers are graphed to the left of 0 on the number line, we have a < 0 for all negative real numbers a.

To determine if $a < b$ or $b < a$, locate the two numbers on the number line. The number on the left is smaller than the number on the right.

Example 4:	Which of the following are true?

>   **a)** $-5 < -7$ **b)** $5 < 7$ **c)** $-6 < -4$ **d)** $6 < 4$

Solutions:

>   Locate all the numbers on the number line.

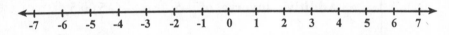

Figure 1.8

a) -7 is *to the left* of -5. Therefore, $-7 < -5$. Hence, $-5 < -7$ is **false**.

b) $5 < 7$ is **true**, since 5 is *to the left* of 7.

c) $-6 < -4$ is **true**, since -6 is *to the left* of -4.

d) $6 < 4$ is **false**, since 6 is *not to the left* of 4.

Observation:

>   *A quick look at the number line shows that if $m > n$ then $-m < -n$, for any two positive numbers m and n.*

Warm Up

4. Which of the following are true?
   a) $-5 > -8$
   b) $7 < 3$
   c) $4 > -5$

Answers:
4. a) True
   b) False
   c) True

D.   Find the additive inverse or negative of a real number

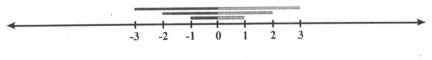

Figure 1.9

Examine the number line. The numbers **1** and **−1** are located at the same distance from 0 on its opposite sides. The same is true of **2** and **−2**; and also for **3** and **−3** . We say that 1 and −1 are additive inverses or opposite of each other. Similarly, 2 and −2 are additive inverses or opposites of each other; also 3 and −3 are opposites of each other. The additive inverse of 0 is 0 itself.

For each real number x, there is exactly one other real number which is at the same distance from 0 as x but on the opposite side of zero. These numbers are called **additive inverses** or **opposites** of each other. The additive inverse of a number x is written as $-x$.

Observe that the additive inverse of 2 is -2 and the additive inverse of -2 is 2. But additive inverse of -2 is written as $-(-2)$. Therefore, $-(-2) = 2$.

In general, for any real number x, $-(-x) = x$.

Warm Up

5. Write down the additive inverses of the following numbers.

$6, 3, -4, 5.2, \sqrt{3}$

Answers:

5. $-6, -3, 4, -5.2, -\sqrt{3}$

| **Example 5:** | Write down the additive inverses of the following numbers. |

$$0, \ 3, \ -5, \ \frac{7}{3}, \ \frac{-8}{9}, \ -\sqrt{2}$$

Solution:

Recall the notation that **additive inverse** of a real number x is written as $-x$.

Additive inverse of 0   is $-(0) = 0$,

Additive inverse of 3   is $-(3) = -3$,

Additive inverse of -5 is $-(-5) = 5$,

Additive inverse of $\dfrac{7}{3}$ is $-\left(\dfrac{7}{3}\right) = -\dfrac{7}{3}$

Additive inverse of $\dfrac{8}{9}$ is $-\left(\dfrac{-8}{9}\right) = \dfrac{8}{9}$

Additive inverse of $-\sqrt{2}$ is $-\left(-\sqrt{2}\right) = \sqrt{2}$

E.   Determine the absolute value of a real number

Figure 1.10

Recall that 2 and -2 are at the same distance from 0, but on opposite sides of 0. Suppose we are interested only in the distance from 0, regardless of the direction. Then we find that the distance of both 2 and -2 from 0 is 2. This distance is called the **absolute value.** Hence, the absolute value of 2 is 2 and the absolute value of -2 is also 2.

We write $\ \left|\, 2\,\right| = 2$, and $\left|-2\,\right| = 2$

Thus, the absolute value of a number is its magnitude, regardless of the direction or sign. Hence the absolute value of a number is always a positive quantity or zero.

$|5| = 5$ In general if $x > 0$ then $|x| = x$, or the absolute value of **a number** is the same as **the number.**

$|-5| = 5 = -(-5)$

In general if $x < 0$ then $|x| = -x$, or the absolute value of negative number is the opposite of that negative number.

Thus for any real number x; $|x| = \begin{cases} x & \text{if} \quad x \geq 0 \\ -x & \text{if} \quad x < 0 \end{cases}$

Example 6:   Express the following without absolute value notation.

a) $|4|$ b) $|-3|$ c) $-|3|$

d) $\left|\dfrac{-5}{7}\right|$ e) $|\sqrt{2}|$ f) $|-|5||$

g) $|0|$

Solutions:

a) $|4| = 4$ b) $|-3| = -(-3) = 3$

c) $-|3| = -(3) = -3$ d) $\left|\dfrac{-5}{7}\right| = -\left(\dfrac{-5}{7}\right) = \dfrac{5}{7}$

e) $|\sqrt{2}| = \sqrt{2}$ f) $|-|5|| = |-5| = 5$

g) $|0| = 0$

Example 7:   Simplify   a) $|10-5|$ b) $|12-3^2|$

c) $|18-4 \cdot 3|$ d) $\left|\dfrac{4-2}{5+3^2}\right|$

Solutions:

a) $|10-5| = |5| = 5$

b) $|12-3^2| = |12-9| = |3| = 3$

c) $|18-4 \cdot 3| = |18-12| = |6| = 6$

d) $\left|\dfrac{4-2}{5+3^2}\right| = \left|\dfrac{2}{5+9}\right| = \left|\dfrac{2}{14}\right| = \left|\dfrac{1}{7}\right| = \dfrac{1}{7}$

Warm Up

6.   Express the absolute value:

a) $\left|-\dfrac{4}{9}\right|$ b) $|\sqrt{5}|$

c) $\left|-|3|\right|$

7.   Simplify:

a) $|13-7|$ b) $|9-3^2|$

c) $|3+4 \cdot 5|$

Answers:

6. a) $\dfrac{4}{9}$ b) $\sqrt{5}$ c) 3

7. a) 6   b) 0   c) 23

EXERCISE 1.4

Answers:

1. _____
2. _____
3. _____
4. _____
5. _____
6. _____
7. _____
8. _____
9. _____
10. _____
11. _____
12. _____
13. _____
14. _____
15. _____
16. _____
17. _____
18. _____
19. _____
20. _____
21. _____
22. _____
23. _____
24. _____

In exercises 1-2, identify numbers which are
a) Natural numbers b) Integers c) Rational numbers
d) Irrational numbers

1. $\left\{-\sqrt{2}, 0, \frac{3}{7}, -\frac{2}{3}, 4, \sqrt{5}, -8\right\}$ 2. $\left\{\frac{5}{4}, \frac{9}{7}, \sqrt{6}, -2, -1\right\}$

In exercises 3-4, identify numbers which are:
a) integers b) rational numbers c) irrational numbers

3. $\left\{-1, 2, 0, 4, \frac{5}{7}, \frac{3}{5}, -1\frac{2}{3}, \sqrt{3}, -\sqrt{5}\right\}$

4. $\left\{4, -3, \frac{2}{3}, 1\frac{7}{11}, -\frac{4}{9}, \sqrt{7}, -\sqrt{11}\right\}$

5. Graph the numbers on the number line
$\left\{0, 2, \frac{3}{2}, -5, -\frac{4}{3}, -3, -2\frac{1}{4}, 6\right\}$

6. Graph $\sqrt{2}$ and $-\sqrt{2}$ on the number line.

7. Graph $-\sqrt{5}$ on the number line.

In exercises 8-15, identify true statements.

8. $5 \geq 4$ 9. $-4 \leq -7$ 10. $0 < 9$ 11. $-9 \leq 3$

12. $3 \geq 5$ 13. $4 \geq -5$ 14. $-3 > 2$ 15. $-5 > -1$

In exercises 16-21, find the additive inverse.

16. 6 17. -7 18. $-\sqrt{2}$ 19. 0

20. $-\frac{2}{3}$ 21. $2\frac{1}{4}$

In exercises 22-28, express without absolute value notation.

22. $|-8|$ 23. $\left|\frac{4}{3}\right|$ 24. $|3^2 - 11|$

25. $|(4-2)(2-5)|$ **26.** $||7-10|-8|$

    25. _____

    26. _____

27. $|6-7\cdot3|$ **28.** $\left|\dfrac{2^2-13}{4\cdot5+7}\right|$

    27. _____

    28. _____

1.5   ADDITION OF REAL NUMBERS

So far we have been using basic operations $(+,-,\times,\div)$ on positive real numbers. Here we will discuss how to add real numbers in general, positive or negative.

Upon completion of this section, we will be able to:

     A. Add two real numbers with the same sign.
     B. Add positive and negative real numbers.
     C. Add real numbers using the number line.
     D. Use the order of operations for real numbers.
     E. Do some more application problems.

Add two real numbers with the same sign

Rule: To add two real numbers; both positive or both negative we proceed as follows:

Step 1	Find the absolute values of the two numbers.
Step 2	Add the absolute values.
Step 3	If both the numbers are negative then assign negative sign to the number in step 2.

Example 1:   Compute: $7+3$.

Solution:

    Step 1 $|7|=7$ $|3|=3$

    Step 2 $|7|+|3|=7+3=10$

    Step 3   The sum is 10, since the numbers are positive.

Warm Up

1. Compute $12+9$

Warm Up

2. Find

   a) $(-8) + (-3)$

   b) $(-10) + 6$

   c) $(-9) + (-5)$

Answers:

1. 21   2. a) -11 b) -4 c) -14

Example 2:   Find: a) $(-10) + (-6)$
                        b) $-4 + (-7)$

Solutions:

a)   *Step 1* $|-10| = 10$ $|-6| = 6$

    Step 2 $|-10| + |-6| = 10 + 6 = 16$

    Step 3   The sum is -16, since both numbers are negative.

b)   *Step 1* $|-4| = 4,$ $|-7| = 7$

    Step 2 $|-4| + |-7| = 4 + 7 = 11$

    Step 3   The sum is -11, since both numbers are negative.

B.   Add positive and negative real numbers

To add a positive and a negative real number we proceed as follows:

Step 1	Find absolute values of the two numbers.
Step 2	Find the difference of the absolute values.
Step 3	Write the difference in step 2 with the sign of the number which has a larger absolute value.

Warm Up

3. Simplify

   a) $5 + (-12) =$

   b) $\frac{3}{2} + \left(-\frac{1}{2}\right) =$

   c) $-18 + 10 =$

Example 3:   Simplify:

   a) $-3 + 5$ b) $10 + (-7)$

   c) $-15 + 9$ d) $4 + (-11)$ e) $\frac{5}{2} + \left(-3\frac{1}{4}\right)$

Solutions:

a) $-3 + 5$:

    Step 1 $|-3| = 3,$ $|5| = 5$

    Step 2   To find the difference, subtract the smaller from the larger: $5 - 3 = 2$

    Step 3   Since 5 is positive and has the larger absolute value: answer = 2.

b) $10 + (-7) = 3$ Follow the same three steps.

c) *Step 1* $|-15| = 15,$ $|9| = 9$

    Step 2 Difference $= 15 - 9 = 6$

    Step 3 Answer $= -6$, since -15 has larger absolute value.

d) $4 + (-11) = -7$ Follow the same three steps.

e) $\dfrac{5}{2} + \left(-3\dfrac{1}{4}\right) = \dfrac{5}{2} + \left(-\dfrac{13}{4}\right) = \dfrac{10}{4} + \left(-\dfrac{13}{4}\right)$

    Step 1 $\left|\dfrac{10}{4}\right| = \dfrac{10}{4},$ $\left|-\dfrac{13}{4}\right| = \dfrac{13}{4}$

    Step 2 Difference $= \dfrac{13}{4} - \dfrac{10}{4} = \dfrac{3}{4}$

    Step 3 Answer $= -\dfrac{3}{4}$,   since the number with the larger absolute value is negative.

Warm Up

d) $|-12| + |-5| =$

e) $\left|-|-3|\right| - |2| =$

Answers:

3. a) -7 b) 1 c) -8

    d) 17 e) 1

C. Add real numbers using the number line

To add two numbers using the number line, we proceed as follows:

Step 1	Graph the first number on the number line
Step 2	If the second number is positive, move to the right as many units as the absolute value of the number.
	If the second number is negative, move to the left as many units as the absolute value of the number.
Step 3	The number representing the graph of the second number is the sum of the two numbers.

Example 4:   Simplify:

    a) $4 + (-7)$ **b)** $7 + (-4)$

    c) $-3 + (-5)$ **d)** $-8 + 5$

Solutions:

    a) $4 + (-7)$:   Starting from zero on the number line move 4 units to the right. Mark 4 on the number line. Starting with the graph of 4 count 7 units in the negative direction *[to the left of 4]* since -7 is negative.

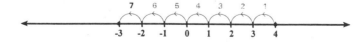

Figure 1.11

The final position is the graph of -3. Therefore, $4 - 7 = -3$.

Warm Up

4. Simplify, using the number line

    a) $7 + (-9)$

Warm Up

b) $6 + (-5)$

c) $-8 + 7$

d) $|-5| + 2$

e) $3 + (-7)$

Answers:

4. a) -2 b) 1 c) -1
    d) 7 e) -4

b) $\mathbf{7 + (-4)}$: Start at 0 and move 7 units to the right. Mark 7 on the number line. Starting with the graph of 7, count 4 units in the negative direction *[to the left of 7]*.

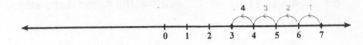

Figure 1.12

The final position is the graph of 3.
Therefore, $7 + (-4) = 3$.

c) $\mathbf{-3 + (-5)}$: Starting from 0, move 3 units to the left. Mark -3 on the number line. Starting with the graph of -3, count 5 units in the negative direction, since -5 is negative.

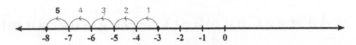

Figure 1.13

The final position is the graph of -8.
Therefore, $-3 + (-5) = -8$.

d) $\mathbf{-8 + 5}$: Starting from 0 move 8 units to the left. Mark -8 on the number line. Starting with the graph of -8, count 5 units in the positive direction (*to the right of -8*) since 5 is positive.

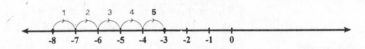

Figure 1.14

The final position is the graph of -3.
Therefore, $-8 + 5 = -3$.

D. Use the order of operations for real numbers

When real numbers are added using grouping symbols, we follow the same order of operations as discussed under fractions. Simplify starting with the innermost grouping symbol.

Example 5:   Simplify:

      a) $4 + [-5 + (-2)]$

      b) $-6 + [8 + \{4 + (-6)\}]$

      c) $\dfrac{3}{5} + \left[-1\dfrac{1}{2} + \left\{ 4\dfrac{1}{4} + \left(-3\dfrac{1}{2} \right) \right\} \right]$

Solutions:

a) $4 + [\mathbf{-5} + (\mathbf{-2})] = 4 + [-7] = -3$

b) $-6 + [8 + \{\mathbf{4} + (\mathbf{-6})\}] = -6 + [8 + (-2)] = -6 + [6] = 0$

c) $\dfrac{3}{5} + \left[-1\dfrac{1}{2} + \left\{ 4\dfrac{1}{4} + \left(-3\dfrac{1}{2} \right) \right\} \right] = \dfrac{3}{5} + \left[-\dfrac{3}{2} + \left\{ \dfrac{17}{4} + \left(-\dfrac{7}{2} \right) \right\} \right]$

$$= \dfrac{3}{5} + \left[-\dfrac{3}{2} + \left\{ \dfrac{17}{4} + \left(-\dfrac{14}{4} \right) \right\} \right]$$

$$= \dfrac{3}{5} + \left[-\dfrac{3}{2} + \left(\dfrac{3}{4} \right) \right]$$

$$= \dfrac{3}{5} + \left[-\dfrac{6}{4} + \dfrac{3}{4} \right] = \dfrac{3}{5} + \left(-\dfrac{3}{4} \right)$$

l.c.d = 20

$$= \dfrac{12}{20} + \left(-\dfrac{15}{20} \right) = -\dfrac{3}{20}$$

Warm Up

5. Simplify

   a) $5 - [3 + (-5) + 4]$

   b) $6 + [7 - \{5 + 3\}]$

   c) $\frac{4}{5} + \left[1 + \left\{ \frac{2}{5} + \left(-\frac{1}{5} \right) \right\} \right]$

Answers:
5.   a) 3   b) 5   c) 2

E.   Application problems

As seen earlier, for applications of mathematical concepts to problem solving, it is important to be able to translate words into symbols in order to form mathematical models. Some of the phrases like added to, plus, increased by, sum of, more than, etc. all translate to the mathematical symbol '+' (or the mathematical operation of addition). Recall that gain is always represented by a positive number, and loss by a negative number.

Example 6:   A new business had a profit of $ 400 in the first month, a loss of $1,300 in the second month, and a profit of $800 in the third month. What is the net profit or net loss over the first three months?

Solution: Profit is represented by positive numbers and loss by negative numbers.

Total profit $= 400 + (-1300) + 800 = [400 + (-1300)] + 800$

$$= -900 + 800 = -100$$

Therefore, the business had a net loss of $100 over the first three months.

Warm Up

6. A car dealer has a loss of $1000 in the first month, a profit of $2500 in the second month and a profit of $3500 in the third month. What is the net profit or loss over the three months?

Warm Up

7. In the National League Championship, the Braves Scored 10 points in the first two innings, 5 in the third, and the opposing team scored 6 in all three. How many points should the opposing team score to be tied with the Braves?

8. A car accelerated to a speed of 50 mi/hr and later slowed down by 25 mi/hr. What speed was the car moving then?

Answers:
6. Profit $5000   **7.** 7
8. 25 mi/hr

Example 7: In a football game, on three consecutive passes, Joe Montana of the 49'ers passed for a gain of 8 yards, again a gain of 24 yards, and was then sacked for a loss of 10 yards. What was his net gain or loss for the plays?

Solution: The net gain

$$= 8 + 24 + (-10) = [8 + 24] + (-10)$$
$$= 32 + (-10) = 22 \text{yds}$$

Therefore, 22 yards were gained.

Example 8: An airplane was flying at an altitude of 25,700 feet. Later, it dropped by 2900 feet. At what altitude was the plane then flying?

Solution: The altitude of the airplane is
$25700 + (-2900) = 22800$ feet.

EXERCISE 1.5

Answers:

1. _____

2. _____

3. _____

4. _____

5. _____

6. _____

7. _____

8. _____

9. _____

10. _____

Simplify the numerical expressions in exercises 1-16.

1. $4 + 3$

2. $-4 + 7$

3. $-3 + 5$

4. $6 + (-9)$

5. $3 + (-10)$

6. $-2 + (-9)$

7. $-6 + (-3)$

8. $-4 + (-10)$

9. $\frac{7}{5} + \left(-\frac{5}{4}\right)$

10. $7 + \left(-\frac{7}{6}\right)$

11. $3\frac{1}{2} + \left(-4\frac{1}{3}\right)$

12. $-\frac{7}{3} + 1\frac{1}{9}$

13. $-3 + [2 + (-5)]$ **14.** $6 + [4 + (-7) + 8]$ **15.** $[-2 + (-3)]$

16. $[2 + (-2 + 3) + 4] + [5 + (-9)] + [3 + (-4)]$

In exercises 17-21, write a numerical expression for each phrase, and simplify:

17. Sum of 4, -6, and 7

18. 3 added to the sum of 4 and -9

19. 4 increased by the sum of -12 and 8

20. Sum of 3 and -7 increased by 10

21. Sum of 5 and -2 added to -4

22. A pilot announces that the current altitude of their plane is 31,000 feet. He is forced to descend 2,700 feet. What is the new altitude?

23. The lowest temperature ever recorded in Little Rock, Arkansas, is $-5°$ F. The highest temperature ever recorded is $117°$ F more than the lowest temperature ever recorded. What is the highest temperature ever recorded?

11. _____

12. _____

13. _____

14. _____

15. _____

16. _____

17. _____

18. _____

19. _____

20. _____

21. _____

22. _____

23. _____

1.6   SUBTRACTION OF REAL NUMBERS

The presence of negative numbers allows us to subtract a larger number from a smaller number.

Upon completion of this section, you will be able to:

   A.   Subtract signed numbers.
   B.   Do subtraction problems that involve grouping symbols.
   C.   Do application problems involving subtraction.

A.   Subtract signed numbers

To subtract b from a $[a - b]$, we proceed as follows:

Step 1	Change the sign of the number to be subtracted $[b \rightarrow -b]$ (i.e. find the additive inverse of b.)
Step 2	Add a and $-b$.

In other words, **to subtract b** from a **we add opposite of** b to a.

Warm Up

1. Perform the indicated operation

   a) $7 - 4$

   b) $2 - 5$

   c) $-3 - (-9)$

   d) $-11 - (-6)$

Answers:

a) 3   b) –3   c) 6   d) –5

Example 1:   Perform the indicated operations:

   a) $8 - 3$ b) $3 - 8$
   c) $-5 - (-6)$ d) $-10 - (-7)$
   e) $\dfrac{-3}{7} - \left(\dfrac{-4}{3}\right)$

Solutions:

a)   **$8 - 3$:**   To subtract 3 from 8, we add opposite of 3 to 8.

$8 - 3 = 8 + (-3) = \mathbf{5}$ Add 8 and –3

b)   **$3 - 8$:**   To subtract 8 from 3, we add -8 to 3.

$3 - 8 = 3 + (-8) = \mathbf{-5}$ Add -8 and 3

c)   **$-5 - (-6)$:**   To subtract –6 from –5, we add opposite of –6 to –5

$-5 - (-6) = -5 + 6 = \mathbf{1}$

d) $\mathbf{-10 - (-7)} = -10 + 7 = \mathbf{-3}$

e) $\dfrac{-3}{7} - \left(\dfrac{-4}{3}\right) = \dfrac{-3}{7} + \dfrac{4}{3} = \dfrac{-9}{21} + \dfrac{28}{21} = \dfrac{-9 + 28}{21} = \dfrac{\mathbf{19}}{\mathbf{21}}$

54

Observations:

The symbol "–" has been used for different purposes:

- To represent negative numbers, such as: . . .–3, – 2, – 1 .
- To represent the additive inverse of a number, for example: –3, – (–3), etc.
- To represent subtraction, for example: 4 – 7, 8 – 4, etc.

B. Subtraction problems that involve grouping symbols

As explained earlier, addition and subtraction are performed from left to right. All rules for simplifications discussed earlier apply in this case as well.

Example 2:   Perform the indicated operations and simplify

a) $2 - (3 - 8)$

b) $(2 - 3) - 8$

c) $-5 - [(-3 + 1) - (5 - 8)]$

d) $\dfrac{-3}{5} - \left[\dfrac{4}{9} - \left(-1\dfrac{2}{3}\right)\right]$

e) $\dfrac{2}{3} - \left[\left(\dfrac{3}{2} - 5\right) + \left(\dfrac{-7}{4}\right)\right]$

Warm Up

2. Perform the indicated operation and simplify.

a) $\dfrac{3}{5} - \left[\left(\dfrac{7}{10} - 1\right) + \left(-\dfrac{5}{2}\right)\right]$

b) $-\dfrac{7}{5} - \left[\dfrac{1}{6} - \left(-2\dfrac{2}{3}\right)\right]$

c) $-8 - \left[-5 - (-7) + (-2)\right]$

Solutions:

a) $2 - (3 - 8) = 2 - (-5) = 2 + 5 = 7$

b) $(2 - 3) - 8 = -1 - 8 = -1 + (-8) = -9$

c) $-5 - [(-3 + 1) - (5 - 8)] = -5 - [-2 - (-3)]$

$$= -5 - [-2 + 3] = -5 - (1) = -6$$

d) $\dfrac{-3}{5} - \left[\dfrac{4}{9} - \left(-1\dfrac{2}{3}\right)\right] = \dfrac{-3}{5} - \left[\dfrac{4}{9} - \left(-\dfrac{5}{3}\right)\right] = \dfrac{-3}{5} - \left[\dfrac{4}{9} + \dfrac{5}{3}\right]$

$$= \dfrac{-3}{5} - \left[\dfrac{4}{9} + \dfrac{15}{9}\right] = \dfrac{-3}{5} - \dfrac{19}{9}$$

$$= \dfrac{-3}{5} + \left(-\dfrac{19}{9}\right) \quad \text{l.c.d.} = 45$$

$$= \dfrac{-27}{45} + \left(-\dfrac{95}{45}\right) = \dfrac{-122}{45} = -2\dfrac{32}{45}$$

Warm Up

2. d) $-8 - (-12)$

e) $\dfrac{2}{3} - \left[\left(\dfrac{3}{2} - 5\right) + \left(\dfrac{-7}{4}\right)\right] = \dfrac{2}{3} - \left[\left(\dfrac{3}{2} - \dfrac{10}{2}\right) + \left(\dfrac{-7}{4}\right)\right]$

$= \dfrac{2}{3} - \left[-\dfrac{7}{2} + \left(\dfrac{-7}{4}\right)\right]$

$= \dfrac{2}{3} - \left[-\dfrac{14}{4} + \left(\dfrac{-7}{4}\right)\right]$

$= \dfrac{2}{3} - \left(\dfrac{-21}{4}\right)$

$= \dfrac{2}{3} + \dfrac{21}{4}$ l.c.d. $= 12$

$= \dfrac{8}{12} + \dfrac{63}{12} = \dfrac{71}{12} = 5\dfrac{11}{12}$

Answers:

2. a) $\dfrac{17}{5}$ **b)** $-\dfrac{127}{30}$

 c) -8 **d)** 4

C. Application problems

As seen earlier, it is important to be able to translate words into symbols for solving problems. We have already encountered some of the phrases like subtract from, minus, difference between, less than, decreased by, etc. all of which translate to mathematical symbol '–' (subtraction). You should be careful to read *what is to be subtracted from what*.

Warm Up

3. In one month, the maximum rainfall was 12 inches. In the next month, it dropped by two inches. What was the max rainfall in the second month?

4. The top of the White House has an altitude of 34 feet and the underground facilities are 4 feet deep below sea level. Using zero as sea level, determine the difference between the two elevations.

Answers:

3. 10 inches **4.** 38 feet

Example 3: On a particular day the maximum temperature was 83°F. The next day the maximum temperature dropped by 4°F. What was the maximum temperature the second day?

Solution: 'dropped by' means 'decreased by' which indicates subtraction.

maximum temperature on second day $= 83 - 4 = 79°$F.

Example 4: The top of Mount Whitney, visible from Death Valley, has an altitude of 14,494 feet above sea level. The bottom of Death Valley is 282 ft below sea level. Using zero as sea level, determine the difference between these two elevations.

Solution: 14,494 represents the elevation of the top of Mount Whitney. The altitude above sea level is represented by positive numbers and the altitude below sea level is represented by negative numbers. The altitude of the bottom of Death Valley is represented by -282.

The difference between the two elevations:
$= 14494 - (-282) = 14494 + 282 = 14776$

EXERCISE 1.6

Answers:

Perform indicated operations in exercises 1-10.

1. $4 - 2$ **2.** $2 - 5$ **3.** $-4 - 7$

4. $5 - (-8)$ **5.** $9 - (-3)$ **6.** $-7 - (-8)$

7. $\dfrac{2}{3} - \left(-\dfrac{5}{9}\right)$ **8.** $-\dfrac{4}{15} - \left(-\dfrac{17}{12}\right)$

9. $2\dfrac{5}{9} - 1\dfrac{4}{15}$ **10.** $-2\dfrac{7}{15} - \left(-1\dfrac{4}{5}\right)$

Simplify the expressions in exercises 11-16.

11. $-13 - (-7 + 4) - (-5 + 6)$ **12.** $-4 - [5 - (7 - 12)]$

13. $(7 - 9) - 14 - (3 - 1)$

14. $-5 + [(-11 - 3) - (2 - (-5))]$ **15.** $\dfrac{3}{5} - \left[\left(\dfrac{4}{3} - 2\right) + \left(\dfrac{-6}{5}\right)\right]$

16. $-\dfrac{7}{3} - \left[\left(1 - 2\dfrac{1}{3}\right) - \left(-\dfrac{4}{9}\right)\right]$

In exercises 17-21, write a numerical expression for the phrases and simplify.

17. The difference between 4 and –5

18. – 8 decreased by 3

19. The difference between 3 and sum of –7 and 4

20. Fifteen subtracted from the sum of 9 and –5

21. 7 less than the difference between –5 and 8

1. _____
2. _____
3. _____
4. _____
5. _____
6. _____
7. _____
8. _____
9. _____
10. _____
11. _____
12. _____
13. _____
14. _____
15. _____
16. _____
17. _____
18. _____
19. _____
20. _____
21. _____

Solve the following word problems

22. _____

22. Felicia lives in a city where the altitude is 1023 feet. Her sister lives in a city where the altitude is 125 feet below the sea level. Find the difference between the altitudes of the two cities.

23. _____

23. On the first down Charlie passed to Bernard for a gain of 10 yards. On the second down Leslie was sacked for a loss of 19 yards. What was the net gain or loss for the two downs?

24. _____

24. After the first round of Jeopardy Dareth's score was -150, and Hannah's score was 2,300. How many more points does Hannah have than Dareth?

25. _____

25. On a cold winter day, the minimum temperature in Rosemont was $-2°$F. On the following day, the minimum temperature increased by $6°$F. What was the minimum temperature on the following day?

26. _____

26. On the morning of a winter day the temperature at a particular place was $10°$F below zero. By noon the temperature was $18°$F above zero. By how much did the temperature rise? (Graph -10 and 18, and find the distance between these two graphs).

1.7 MULTIPLICATION OF REAL NUMBERS

We know how to multiply two positive real numbers. Upon completion of this section we will be able to:

A. Multiply two negative numbers.
B. Multiply a positive and negative real number.
C. Order of operations.
D. Evaluate expressions involving variables.

A.   Multiplication of two negative real numbers

Before we define multiplication of arbitrary real numbers, we define the following.

Multiplication by zero	$0 \cdot a = a \cdot 0 = 0$ for any real number a .

The product of two negative real numbers is always positive.

To multiply two negative real numbers, a, b, we multiply their absolute value. The product of two negative numbers is always positive.

Example 1:   Find the following products.

a) $(-3)(-5)$ b) $(-9)(-8)$

c) $(-14)(-11)$ d) $(0)(-9)$

e) $\left(-\dfrac{5}{12}\right)\left(-\dfrac{4}{15}\right)$

Solutions:

a) $|-3| = 3, \ |-5| = 5$

     Therefore, $(-3)(-5) = |-3| \cdot |-5| = (3)(5) = 15$

b) $|-9| = 9, \ |-8| = 8$

     Therefore, $(-9)(-8) = (9)(8) = 72$

c) $|-14| = 14, \ |-11| = 11$

     Therefore, $(-14)(-11) = (14)(11) = 154$

d) $(0)(-9) = 0$ $0 \cdot a = a \cdot 0 = 0$, for all real numbers a

e) $\left(-\dfrac{5}{12}\right)\left(\dfrac{-4}{15}\right) = \dfrac{20}{180} = \dfrac{1}{9}$

Warm Up

1. Find the following products.

a) $(-6)(-3)$

b) $\left(-\dfrac{3}{5}\right)\left(-\dfrac{2}{6}\right)$

c) $(-17)(-11)$

d) $(-2)\left(-\dfrac{1}{2}\right)$

Answers:
1. a) 18   b) $\frac{1}{5}$ c) 187   d) 1

B.   **Multiplication of a positive and a negative real number**

If a and b are any two numbers and $a > 0$ and $b < 0$ then $(a)(b) = -(|a| \cdot |b|)$.
If the two numbers have different signs their product is always negative.

Example 2:   Find the products.

a) $3(-9)$ b) $4(-7)$

c) $(-9)(3)$ d) $(-8)(5)$

Solutions:

a) $|3| = 3, \ |-9| = 9$

     Therefore, $(3)(-9) = -(3 \times 9) = -27$

Warm Up

2. Find the products.

a) $6(-9)$

b) $3(-5)$

Warm Up

c) $(-8)(8)$

d) $(3)(-7)$

3. Find the products

a) $\sqrt{5} \cdot 2$

b) $\left(-\dfrac{4}{3}\right)\left(\dfrac{6}{5}\right)$

c) $\left(\dfrac{5}{9}\right)\left(-\dfrac{3}{10}\right)$

d) $\left(-\dfrac{3}{5}\right)\left(-\dfrac{3}{5}\right)$

Answers:

2. a) -54 b) -15 c) -64
   d) -21

3. a) $2\sqrt{5}$ b) $-\dfrac{8}{5}$ c) $-\dfrac{1}{6}$
   d) $\dfrac{9}{25}$

b) $|4| = 4, |-7| = 7$
   Therefore, $(4)(-7) = -(4 \times 7) = -28$

c) $|-9| = 9, |3| = 3$
   Therefore, $(-9)(3) = -(9 \times 3) = -27$

d) $|-8| = 8, |5| = 5$
   Therefore, $(-8)(5) = -(8 \times 5) = -40$

Example 3: Find the products.

a) $\sqrt{2} \cdot 0$ b) $\left(-\dfrac{3}{5}\right)\left(\dfrac{7}{6}\right)$

c) $\left(\dfrac{4}{9}\right)\left(-\dfrac{3}{2}\right)$ d) $\left(-\dfrac{4}{5}\right)\left(-\dfrac{2}{3}\right)$

Solutions:

a) $\sqrt{2} \cdot 0 = 0$

b) $\left(-\dfrac{3}{5}\right)\left(\dfrac{7}{6}\right) = -\left(\dfrac{3}{5} \cdot \dfrac{7}{6}\right)$

$$= -\left(\dfrac{21}{30}\right) = -\dfrac{3 \cdot 7}{3 \cdot 10} = -\dfrac{7}{10}$$

c) $\left(\dfrac{4}{9}\right)\left(-\dfrac{3}{2}\right) = -\left(\dfrac{4}{9} \cdot \dfrac{3}{2}\right) = -\left(\dfrac{12}{18}\right) = -\dfrac{2}{3}$

d) $\left(-\dfrac{4}{5}\right)\left(-\dfrac{2}{3}\right)$:

In this case both numbers are negative, therefore the product is a positive number, which is the product of their absolute values.

$$\left(-\dfrac{4}{5}\right)\left(-\dfrac{2}{3}\right) = \left(\dfrac{4}{5} \cdot \dfrac{2}{3}\right) = \dfrac{8}{15}$$

C.   Order of operations

Recall the order of operations discussed in Section 1.2.

Step 1   Evaluate all the exponents expressions, if any.

Step 2   Perform all multiplications and divisions from left to right in the order of occurrence.

Step 3   Perform all addition and subtraction from left to right.

If grouping symbols are involved then simplify within each grouping symbol starting first with the innermost grouping symbol.

Example 4: Simplify **a)** $-4(3)+5[7-6(-4)]$

b) $14(-5)+[(-7)(-5)-3(-5+4)]$

Solutions:

a) $-4(3)+5[7-6(-4)]$

$= -4(3)+5[7-(-24)]$ Simplify inside [ ]

$= -4(3)+5[7+24]$

$= -4(3)+5[31]$ Perform multiplication from left to right

$= -12+155 = 143$ Perform Addition

b) $14(-5)+[(-7)(-5)-3(-5+4)]$

$= 14(-5)+[(-7)(-5)-3(-1)]$ Simplify inside [ ]

$= 14(-5)+[(-7)(-5)-(-3)]$ Perform multiplication inside [ ]

$= 14(-5)+[35+3]$ Add inside [ ]

$= 14(-5)+38$ Perform multiplication

$= -70+38 = -32$ Perform Addition

Warm Up

4. Simplify

a) $4(3)+3[8-3(-4)]$

b) $-2[7-3(5+2)-3(-5)]$

Answers:

4. a) 72   **b)** –2

D. Evaluating expressions involving variables

Recall that in the earlier sections we evaluated algebraic expressions for positive rational values. We will now evaluate expressions for **any** real number, positive or negative.

Example 5: Evaluate

a) $2a(3x-5y)$ for $a=-3$, $x=-2$, $y=-1$

b) $(4x^2-3y)(2x-y)$ for $x=4$, $y=-10$

c) $(x-5y^2)(-3z)$ for $x=-2$, $y=2$, $z=-4$

Warm Up

5. Evaluate

a) $4a(2x-7y)$ for
$a=1$; $x=3$; $y=-1$

Solutions:

Substitute the given values of the variables in the respective expressions.

a) $2a(3x-5y)$: Here $a=-3$, $x=-2$, $y=-1$.

$2a(3x-5y) = 2(-3)[3(-2)-5(-1)]$ [Substitute the values]

$= 2(-3)[-6-(-5)]$ [Simplify inside brackets]

$= 2(-3)[-6+5]$

$= 2(-3)(-1)$

$= (-6)(-1) = 6$ [Multiply]

Warm Up

b) $\left(2x^2y - 3y\right)\left(3x^2y - y\right)$
   for $x = 2$; $y = 3$

b) $(4x^2 - 3y)(2x - y)$: Here $x = 4$, $y = -10$.

$$\left(4x^2 - 3y\right)\left(2x - y\right) = \left[4(4)^2 - 3(-10)\right]\left[2(4) - (-10)\right]$$

[Substitute the values]

$$= [4(16) - (-30)][8 - (-10)]$$
$$= [64 - (-30)][8 - (-10)]$$
$$= (64 + 30)(8 + 10)\quad[-(-a) = a]$$
$$= (94)(18) = \mathbf{1692}$$

c) $\left(x - 3z\right)\left(x - 3y^2\right)$ for
   $x = -3$; $y = 2$; $z = 1$

c) $(x - 5y^2)(-3z)$: Here $x = -2$, $y = 2$ $z = -4$

$$\left(x - 5y^2\right)\left(-3z\right) = \left[-2 - 5(2)^2\right]\left(-3(-4)\right)$$

[Simplify inside the grouping symbols ( );

$$= [-2 - 5(4)][12]$$
$$= (-2 - 20)(12)$$
$$= (-22 \cdot 12) = -\mathbf{264}$$

Answers:

5. a) 52   b) 495   c) 90

EXERCISE 1.7

Answers:

1. _____

2. _____

3. _____

4. _____

5. _____

6. _____

7. _____

8. _____

9. _____

10. _____

11. _____

12. _____

13. _____

14. _____

Find the products in exercises 1-11.

1. $(-2)(-4)$ 2. $(-7)\left(-\dfrac{5}{14}\right)$ 3. $\left(-\dfrac{6}{5}\right)\left(-\dfrac{10}{21}\right)$

4. $0 \cdot \left(-\dfrac{9}{13}\right)$ 5. $(5)(-7)$ 6. $(-9)(4)$

7. $\left(\dfrac{4}{5}\right)\left(-\dfrac{5}{14}\right)$ 8. $\left(-\dfrac{8}{15}\right) \cdot \left(-\dfrac{25}{24}\right)$ 9. $\left(1\dfrac{3}{4}\right)\left(-3\dfrac{3}{5}\right)$

10. $\left(-2\dfrac{2}{5}\right)\left(1\dfrac{2}{3}\right)$ 11. $-\sqrt{5} \cdot 0$

Find all the integer factors for the numbers in exercises 12-14.

12. -26 13. 18   14. -1

Simplify the numeric expressions in exercises 15-18.

15. $3[5(-2)-36]$

16. $-13(-8+4)$

17. $14\left(-\dfrac{2}{7}\right)-\left[\left(-\dfrac{5}{4}\right)\left(\dfrac{3}{10}\right)-3(2+(-7))\right]$

18. $-5(3^2-4)+7[-6\{2+(-5)\}+2]$

Evaluate the following expressions for $x=4$, $y=-1$, $z=-2$.

19. $3x^2+y$

20. $4x-7y-3z$

21. $(3x-5y)(4z)$

22. $(3x+1)^2(2y-z)$

23. $(5x+3y)^2-2z+7$

24. $-6x^2-y^2+8$

15. _____

16. _____

17. _____

18. _____

19. _____

20. _____

21. _____

22. _____

23. _____

24. _____

1.8 DIVISION OF REAL NUMBERS

Division can be converted into multiplication using reciprocal of the divisor.

Upon completion of this section we will be able to:

    A. Find quotient of real numbers
    B. Solve problems that involve grouping symbols
    C. Solve application problems involving division

A. Find the quotient of real numbers

In order to divide a number by another number, we need the definition of **reciprocal** or **multiplicative inverse** of a number.

Two numbers whose product is 1 are called **reciprocal** or **multiplicative inverse** of each other.

Note: Since $a \cdot 0 = 0$ for all real numbers a, 0 cannot have a multiplicative inverse.

63

Warm Up

1. Find the multiplicative inverse:

   a)   5

   b) $-\dfrac{3}{8}$

   c) -4

   d) $\dfrac{15}{13}$

Example 1:   Find the multiplicative inverse:

a) 3   b) -7 c) $-\dfrac{3}{4}$ d) $\dfrac{14}{5}$

Solutions:

a)   The multiplicative inverse of **3** is $\dfrac{1}{3}$

because $3\left(\dfrac{1}{3}\right) = 1$

b)   The multiplicative inverse of **–7** is $-\dfrac{1}{7}$

because $-7\left(-\dfrac{1}{7}\right) = 1$

c)   The multiplicative inverse of $-\dfrac{3}{4}$ is $-\dfrac{4}{3}$

because $\left(-\dfrac{3}{4}\right)\left(-\dfrac{4}{3}\right) = 1$

d)   The multiplication inverse of $\dfrac{14}{5}$ is $\dfrac{5}{14}$

because $\dfrac{14}{5} \cdot \dfrac{5}{14} = 1$

$$a \div b = a \cdot \dfrac{1}{b} \longrightarrow a \text{ multiplied by the reciprocal of } b.$$

2. Perform division:

   a) $48 \div 4$

   b) $-36 \div 9$

Example 2:   Perform division.

a) $35 \div 7$ b) $-24 \div 3$ c) $-(12 \div 6)$

d) $7 \div (-21)$ e) $0 \div 5$

Solutions:

Step 1: **Find the reciprocal**   *Step 2:*   **Multiply**

a)   **35 ÷ 7:**   The reciprocal of 7 is $\dfrac{1}{7}$

$35 \div 7 = 35\left(\dfrac{1}{7}\right) = 5$

b)   **– 24 ÷ 3:**   The reciprocal of 3 is $\dfrac{1}{3}$

$-24 \div 3 = (-24)\left(\dfrac{1}{3}\right) = -8$

c) $\quad -(12 \div 6):$ $\qquad$ The reciprocal of 6 is $\dfrac{1}{6}$

$$-(12 \div 6) = -(12)\left(\dfrac{1}{6}\right) = -2$$

d) $\quad 7 \div (-21):$ $\qquad$ The reciprocal of -21 is $\dfrac{1}{-21}$

$$7 \div (-21) = 7\left(\dfrac{1}{-21}\right) = -\dfrac{1}{3}$$

e) $\quad 0 \div 5:$ $\qquad$ The reciprocal of 5 is $\dfrac{1}{5}$

$$0 \div 5 = 0\left(\dfrac{1}{5}\right) = 0$$

Example 3: $\qquad$ Find the quotients:

$$\text{a)} \quad \dfrac{3}{4} \div \dfrac{7}{8} \qquad \text{b)} \quad \dfrac{5}{6} \div \left(-\dfrac{4}{5}\right) \qquad \text{c)} \quad \left(-\dfrac{12}{35}\right) \div \left(-\dfrac{9}{14}\right)$$

Solutions:

Step 1: $\qquad\qquad\qquad$ *Step 2:*

a) Reciprocal of $\dfrac{7}{8}$ is $\dfrac{8}{7}$ $\qquad$ $\dfrac{3}{4} \div \dfrac{7}{8} = \dfrac{3}{4} \cdot \dfrac{8}{7} = \dfrac{24}{28} = \dfrac{6}{7}$ Lowest Terms

b) Reciprocal of $-\dfrac{4}{5}$ is $-\dfrac{5}{4}$ $\qquad$ $\dfrac{5}{6} \div \left(-\dfrac{4}{5}\right) = \dfrac{5}{6} \cdot \left(-\dfrac{5}{4}\right) = -\dfrac{25}{24} = -1\dfrac{1}{24}$

c) Reciprocal of $-\dfrac{9}{14}$ is $-\dfrac{14}{9}$ $\qquad$ $\left(-\dfrac{12}{35}\right) \div \left(-\dfrac{9}{14}\right) = \left(-\dfrac{12}{35}\right) \cdot \left(-\dfrac{14}{9}\right)$

$$= \dfrac{168}{315} = \dfrac{8}{15} \quad \text{Lowest Terms}$$

Notes: **1.** If x and y are positive real numbers, and $y \neq 0$, then $\dfrac{-x}{y} = \dfrac{x}{-y} = -\dfrac{x}{y}$. The quotient of two non-zero numbers is negative if exactly one of the two numbers is negative.

2. If x and y are positive real numbers, and $y \neq 0$, then $\dfrac{-x}{-y} = \dfrac{x}{y}$. The quotient of two negative numbers is positive.

3. The quotient of 0 and any non-zero number is 0: $\dfrac{0}{x} = 0.$ $(x \neq 0)$

B. Solve problems that involve grouping symbols

We have discussed addition, subtraction, multiplication, and division of real numbers. The rules for simplification with the standard order of operations have already been discussed in earlier sections. We use the same rules in the following examples.

4. Simplify

a) $\dfrac{2(-4)-(-3)(-3)}{2^2(5-2)}$

b) $\dfrac{6}{8} \div \left[\dfrac{2}{3}\left(14+(-5)\right)-3\right]$

Answers:

4. a) $-\dfrac{17}{12}$ b) $\dfrac{1}{4}$

Example 4:   Simplify.

a) $\dfrac{3(-5)-(-6)(-2)}{3^2(4-2)}$ b) $\dfrac{4}{5} \div \left[\dfrac{3}{4}\left(12-(-4)\right)-2\right]$

Solutions:

a) Simplify the numerator and the denominator separately, and then divide.

Numerator: $3(-5)-(-6)(-2) = -15-12 = -27$

Denominator: $3^2(4-2) = \mathbf{3^2} \cdot 2$
$= 9 \cdot 2 = \mathbf{18}$

Therefore, $\dfrac{3(-5)-(-6)(-2)}{3^2(4-2)} = \dfrac{-27}{18} = -\dfrac{3}{2}$

b) $\dfrac{4}{5} \div \left[\dfrac{3}{4}\left(\mathbf{12}-(-\mathbf{4})\right)-2\right] = \dfrac{4}{5} \div \left[\dfrac{3}{4}(\mathbf{16})-2\right]$

Simplify inside ( ) and multiply

$= \dfrac{4}{5} \div [\mathbf{12-2}]$

Simplify inside [ ] and subtract

$= \dfrac{4}{5} \div \mathbf{10}$ Perform division

$= \dfrac{4}{5} \cdot \dfrac{\mathbf{1}}{\mathbf{10}} = \dfrac{4}{50} = \dfrac{2}{25}$ Lowest terms

---

C.   Simple applications

We shall use all that we have discussed so far in this chapter to translate simple word problems into equations.

5. January gives 5 balls to Roland and is left with 10. How many balls did he have?

Example 5:   Tony gives three candies to Jim, and is left with five candies. How many candies did Tony have?

Solution:

Name the unknown: Number of candies Tony had $= x$

Given condition: When Tony gives **3** candies to Jim, he is left with **5**.

Therefore the problem is: x decreased by **3** equals **5**. What is x?

In symbols: $x-3=5$. Think of a number which when decreased by 3 gives us 5: $\mathbf{8-3=5}$

Therefore, Tony had 8 candies.

Example 6: When 3 is added to a number it becomes 17. What is the number?

Solution:

Name the unknown: A number = x

Given condition: When **3** is added to x the result is **17**.

In symbols: $x + 3 = 17$

Think of a number which when increased by 3 gives us 17: **14** $+ 3 = 17$. Therefore $x = 14$.

Example 7: Newtie spends one-third of his daily pocket money on comics. If he spends two dollars on comics, how much pocket money does he get?

Solution:

Name the unknown: Newtie's pocket money = x

Given condition: **one-third** of Newtie's pocket money equals **2**.

In symbols: $\frac{1}{3}(x) = 2$ *i.e.* $\frac{x}{3} = 2$

Since $\dfrac{6}{3} = 2$ is a true statement, it follows that $x = 6$.
Therefore Newtie's daily pocket money is 6 dollars.

Example 8: Three times a number is -27. What is the number?

Solution:

Name the unknown: A number $= x$

Given condition: Three times x equals **–27**.

In symbols: $3x = -27$

Think of a number which when multiplied by 3 gives us –27:
$$3(-9) = -27.$$

Therefore, $x = -9$.

Warm Up

6. When 7 is subtracted from a number it becomes 7.

7. Jimmy eats two-fifths of an apple pie weighing 5 lbs. How many pounds of apple pie did he eat?

8. Two times a number is -48. What is the number?

Answers:
5. 15 6. 14 7. 2 8. –24

EXERCISE 1.8

Answers:

1. _____

2. _____

3. _____

4. _____

5. _____

6. _____

7. _____

8. _____

9. _____

10. _____

11. _____

12. _____

13. _____

14. _____

15. _____

16. _____

17. _____

18. _____

19. _____

20. _____

21. _____

22. _____

23. _____

24. _____

Find the multiplicative inverse of the numbers in exercises 1-5.

1. -3 **2.** 4 **3.** $\dfrac{1}{5}$ **4.** $\dfrac{-3}{7}$ **5.** $2\dfrac{1}{9}$

Find the quotients in exercises 6-15.

6. $36 \div 9$ **7.** $(-3) \div 24$ **8.** $(-12) \div 15$

9. $0 \div (-7)$ **10.** $\dfrac{4}{3} \div \dfrac{8}{5}$ **11.** $\left(-3\dfrac{5}{7}\right) \div 2\dfrac{11}{14}$

12. $12 \div (2 - 5)$ **13.** $(32 - 7) \div \dfrac{5}{8}$

14. $(-100) \div \left[-8 - (-3)\right]$ **15.** $(-72) \div (6 - 6)$

Simplify the numeric expressions in exercises 16-21.

16. $\dfrac{6(-3) - 2(-5)}{-2 - 6}$ **17.** $\dfrac{-3(5 - 2)}{3(-5) - 7(2 - 4)}$

18. $\dfrac{26 - 7(-2)}{3(6 - 3) - 1}$ **19.** $\dfrac{-22(-3 - 1)}{6(-3) + (-8 - 2)(-4 + 1)}$

20. $\dfrac{3^2(5 - 7)}{2^2(-4) + 3^2(8)}$ **21.** $\left(\dfrac{3}{4} + \dfrac{5}{8}\right) \div \left[\dfrac{3}{16}[11 - (-7)] - 4\right]$

In exercises 22-24 write the phrases in symbols and simplify, if possible:

22. The quotient of 15 and the difference of 7 and -3

23. The square of -8 divided by 12

24. 6 times a number divided by -36.

In exercises 25-28, the unknown number is an integer between −10 and 10. Write the statements in symbols and find the solution.

25. Five times a number is − 35.

26. Quotient of a number and − 3 is − 3

27. The quotient of 4 and one more than a number is $\frac{1}{2}$.

28. When the square of a number is divided by three, the result is 27.

For exercises 29-34, solve the following word problems. The solutions lie between 0 and 15.

29. On her birthday Janet kept 5 pencils to herself and distributed the rest equally among her four friends. Her friends got two pencils each. How many pencils were there?

30. A student gets 3 bonus points for each correct answer during a classroom discussion. Janice got 15 bonus points. How many questions did she answer correctly?

31. Raquel has six dollars more than Tawn. If Tawn has five dollars, how much money does Raquel have?

32. Twice the sum of a number and 5 is 10. What is the number?

33. When 7 is added to a number the result is 16. What is the number?

34. When a number is decreased by 6 the answer is −2. Find the number.

25. _____

26. _____

27. _____

28. _____

29. _____

30. _____

31. _____

32. _____

33. _____

34. _____

1.9   PROPERTIES OF ADDITION AND MULTIPLICATION

Operations of addition and multiplication have some properties which we use sometimes without notice. For example, we may add 8, 10, and 15 by any of the combinations.

$$8 + 10 + 15 = 18 + 15 = 33 \qquad \text{or} \qquad 10 + 15 + 8 = 25 + 8 = 33$$
$$10 + 8 + 15 = 18 + 15 = 33 \qquad \text{or} \qquad 8 + 15 + 10 = 23 + 10 = 33$$

We notice that by **adding** 8, 10, and 15 in different orders we get the same result 33. However, we cannot move around numbers like this while performing subtraction or division.

For example $\qquad 5 - 3 \neq 3 - 5$
and $6 \div 2 \neq 2 \div 6$.

In this section we will study different rules and properties for basic operations $(+, -, x, \div)$ that will allow us to move around numbers between different operations.

Upon completion of this section we will be able to:

- **A.** Identify and use the commutative properties of addition and multiplication.
- **B.** Identify and use the associative properties of addition and multiplication.
- **C.** Identify and use the identity properties of addition and multiplication.
- **D.** Identify and use the inverse properties of addition and multiplication.
- **E.** Identify and use the distributive properties of multiplication over addition.

A.   Commutative Properties

For any two real numbers a and b

$a + b = b + a$	Commutative property of addition
$ab = ba$	Commutative property of multiplication

Warm Up

1. Complete the statements.

a) $9 + 7 = 7 +$ ___

b) $3 \cdot 5 =$ ___ $\cdot 3$

Answers:

1. a) 9   b) 5

Example 1:   Complete the following statements:

a) $4 + 7 = 7 +$ ___   b) $-6 + 5 =$ ___ $+ (-6)$

c) $3 \cdot 7 =$ ___ $\cdot 3$ d) $(-4)(-2) = (-2)(\text{___})$

Solutions:

a)   The missing number is 4, since
     $4 + 7 = 7 + \mathbf{4}$ Commutative property of addition

b)   The missing number is 5, since
     $-6 + 5 = \mathbf{5} + (-6)$ Commutative property of addition

c)   The missing number is 7, since
     $3 \cdot 7 = \mathbf{7} \cdot 3$ Commutative property of multiplication

d)   The missing number is -4, since $(-4)(-2) = (-2)(\mathbf{-4})$
     Commutative property of multiplication

Subtraction and division are not commutative.

For example:
$$6 - 2 \neq 2 - 6 \text{ and } 6 \div 2 \neq 2 \div 6$$

B. Associative Properties

We know that addition and multiplication is performed on two numbers at a time. If we are to add or multiply three numbers, then which two of these are added or multiplied first is immaterial. This is usually described as a property known as "The Associative Property."

Associative Properties

For any three real numbers a, b, and c

$a + b + c = (a + b) + c = a + (b + c)$ Associative property of addition

$a \cdot b \cdot c = (ab)c = a(bc)$ Associative property of multiplication

Example 2:   Complete the following statements:

a) $3 + [5 + 7] = (3 + \underline{}) + 7$

b) $4[5(-6)] = (4 \cdot 5) \cdot \underline{}$

c) $3[(-4) \cdot 2] = [\underline{}(-4)] \cdot 2$

Solutions:

a)   The missing number is 5, since $3 + [5 + 7] = (3 + 5) + 7$
Associative property

b)   The missing number is -6, since $4[5(-6)] = (4 \cdot 5) \cdot (-6)$
Associative property

c)   The missing number is 3, since $3[(-4) \cdot 2] = [3 \cdot (-4)] \cdot 2$
Associative property

Example 3:   Given below are two statements. Provide justification for their truth using the associative and commutative properties.

a) $3 + [4 + (-7)] = (-7 + 3) + 4$
b) $(3 \cdot 4)(-5) = [4 \cdot (-5)] \cdot 3$

Solutions:

a) $3 + [4 + (-7)] = 3 + [-7 + 4]$ Commutative property of addition

$= [3 + (-7)] + 4$ Associative property of addition

$= (-7 + 3) + 4$ Commutative property of addition

Warm Up

2. Complete the following statements.

a) $5 + [3 + 2] = (5 + \underline{}) + 2$

b) $5(6(-7)) = (5 \cdot 6) \cdot \underline{}$

c) $2[(-3) \cdot 5] = [\underline{} \cdot (-3)] \cdot 5$

3. Justify the truth of the following statements.

a) $5 + [3 + (-7)] = (-7 + 5) + 3$

b) $(5 \cdot 6)(-7) = [6 \cdot (-7)] \cdot 5$

71

4. Simplify

a) $6+8+23+5$

b) $2 \cdot 5 \cdot 3 \cdot 4$

b) $(3 \cdot 4)(-5) = 3 \cdot [4 \cdot (-5)]$ Associative property of multiplication

$= [4 \cdot (-5)] \cdot 3$ Commutative property of multiplication

Example 4:   Simplify: **a)** $24+7+26+18+5$
b) $4 \cdot 8 \cdot 10 \cdot 5$

Solutions:

We compute each one of the above expressions from left to right [recall the order of operations].

a) $24+7+26+18+5 = 24+26+7+18+5$
$= (24+26)+(7+18)+5$
$= 50+25+5 = 50+30 = 80$

We have used commutative and associative properties of addition.

b)   In the simplification shown below, we have used commutative and associative properties. Identify which property is used in each step,

$4 \cdot 8 \cdot 10 \cdot 5 = 4 \cdot 10 \cdot 8 \cdot 5 = (4 \cdot 10) \cdot (8 \cdot 5) = 40 \cdot 40 = 1600$
  commutative   *associative*

C.   Identity Properties

For any real number a

$a+0 = a$ and $0+a = a$ Identity property of addition
$a \cdot 1 = a$ and $1 \cdot a = a$ Identity property of multiplication

The number 0 is called **additive identity** or **identity element for addition**. The number 1 is called **multiplicative identity** or i**dentity element for multiplication**.

5. Complete the following statements.

a) $3 + \underline{\ \ } = 3$

b) $0 + (\ \ ) = -8$

c) $1 \cdot \underline{\ \ } = -4$

d) $8 \cdot \underline{\ \ } = 8$

Example 5:   Complete the following statement

a) $4 + \underline{\ \ } = 4$ **b)** $0 + (\underline{\ \ }) = -5$
c) $1 \cdot \underline{\ \ } = -7$ **d)** $6 \cdot \underline{\ \ } = 6$

Solutions:

a)   Missing number is 0, since $4+0 = 4$
Identity property of addition

b)   Missing number is -5, since $0+(-5) = -5$
Identity property of addition

c)   Missing number is -7, since $1 \cdot (-7) = -7$
Identity property of multiplication

d)   Missing number is 1, since $6 \cdot 1 = 6$
Identity property of multiplication

D. Inverse properties

Inverse Properties

1. For each real number a, its **opposite** $-a$ is a number satisfying $a + (-a) = 0$ and $(-a) + a = 0$.

a and $-a$ are called **additive inverses** of each other.

2. For each real number $a(\neq 0)$, its **reciprocal** is $\dfrac{1}{a}$ such that $a \cdot \dfrac{1}{a} = 1$ and $\dfrac{1}{a} \cdot a = 1$

a and $\dfrac{1}{a}$ are called **multiplicative inverses** of each other.

Example 6: Complete the following statements:

a) $-3 + \underline{} = 0$ b) $-\dfrac{3}{5} \cdot \underline{} = 1$

Solutions:

a) Missing number is 3, since $-3 + \mathbf{3} = 0$
Additive inverse property

b) Missing number is $-\dfrac{5}{3}$, since $\left(-\dfrac{3}{5}\right)\left(-\dfrac{5}{3}\right) = 1$
Multiplicative inverse property

Warm Up

6. Complete the following statements.

a) $-6 + \underline{} = 0$

b) $-\dfrac{4}{9} \cdot \underline{} = 1$

Answers:

5. a) 0   b) -8 c) -4 d) 1
6. a) 6   b) $-\dfrac{9}{4}$

E. Distributive Properties

For any three real numbers a, b, and c

$a(b + c) = ab + ac$ and $(b + c)a = ba + ca$

Using the above distributive properties we can easily establish that for all real numbers

$a, b, c:$ $a(b - c) = ab - ac$ and $(b - c)a = ba - ca$

Example 7: Complete the following in two ways using (i) the rules for operations with grouping symbols, and (ii) the distributive property.

a) $4(3 + 7)$ b) $8(5 - 9)$ c) $-3(7 - 2)$

Solutions:

a) (i) $4(\mathbf{3 + 7}) = 4 \cdot \mathbf{10} = 40$

(ii) $4(3 + 7) = 4 \cdot 3 + 4 \cdot 7$ [Distributive property]
$= 12 + 28 = 40$

Warm Up

7. Simplify in two ways as in Example 7.

a) $3(2 + 5)$

b) $4(7 - 4)$

c) $-2(2 - 7)$

73

Warm Up

d) $2(3-5)$

b)   (i) $8(5-9) = 8(-4) = -32$

     (ii) $8(5-9) = \mathbf{8} \cdot 5 - \mathbf{8} \cdot 9$ [Distributive property]
$$= 40 - 72 = -32$$

c)   (i) $-3(7-2) = -3 \cdot 5 = -15$

     (ii) $-\mathbf{3}(7-2) = (-\mathbf{3}) \cdot 7 - (-\mathbf{3}) \cdot 2$ [Distributive property]
$$= -21 - (-6)$$
$$= -21 + 6 = -15$$

Distributive properties can be extended to more than three numbers.

   (i) $a(b + c + d) = ab + ac + ad,$
$$a(b + c + d + e) = ab + ac + ad + ae$$

   (ii) $(b + c + d)a = ba + ca + da,$
$$(b + c + d + e)a = ba + ca + da + ea$$

8. Compute
$(3 + 8 + 2 + 6) \cdot 8$

Example 8:   Compute: $(4 + 5 + 9 + 20 + 6) \cdot \mathbf{5}$.

Solution:

$$= 4 \cdot \mathbf{5} + 5 \cdot \mathbf{5} + 9 \cdot \mathbf{5} + 20 \cdot \mathbf{5} + 6 \cdot \mathbf{5} \quad \text{[Distributive property]}$$

$$= 20 + 25 + 45 + 100 + 30 \quad \text{[Multiply]}$$

$$= 100 + (20 + 30) + (25 + 45) \quad \text{[Associative \& Commutative properties]}$$

$$= 100 + 50 + 70 = 150 + 70 = \mathbf{220}$$

9. Write as a product using parentheses

a) $3x - 6y$

b) $4x - 4y$

Example 9:   Write the following as a product using parenthesis.

    a) $5x - 5y$ b) $5x + 10y$

Solutions:

a) $5x - 5y = \mathbf{5}(x - y)$ [Distributive property]

b) $5x + 10y = \mathbf{5}x + \mathbf{5}(2y)$ [Distributive property]
$$= \mathbf{5}(x + 2y)$$

10. Write without parentheses

a) $4(3x - 2)$

b) $2(2 - 3y)$

c) $-5(3y + 3z)$

Example 10:   Write the following without parentheses.
    a) $3(5y - z)$ b) $-(4x - t)$ c) $-5(3y + 2z - 6)$

Solutions:

a) $3(5y - z) = \mathbf{3}(5y) - \mathbf{3}z$ [Distributive property]

$$= (3 \cdot 5)y - 3z \quad \text{[Associative property]}$$

$$= 15y - 3z$$

b) $\quad -(4x-t)=-1(4x-t)$

$$=(-1)(4x)-(-1)t \qquad \text{[Distributive property]}$$

$$=(-1\cdot 4)x-(-t) \qquad \text{[Associative property]}$$

$$=-4x+t$$

c) We use the extended distributive property.

$-5(3y+2z-6)$

Answers:

$$=(-5)(3y)+(-5)(2z)-(-5)\cdot 6 \qquad \text{[Distributive property]}$$

$$=(-5\cdot 3)y+(-5\cdot 2)z-(-30) \qquad \text{[Associative property]}$$

$$=-15y-10z+30$$

7. a) 21 **b)** 12 **c)** 10 **d)** -4

8. 152

9. a) $3(x-2y)$ **b)** $4(x-y)$

10. a) $12x-8$ **b)** $4-6y$
c) $-15y-15z$

EXERCISE 1.9

Complete the statements in exercises 1-5. Explain which of the properties of real numbers are used.

Answers:

1. $\quad 3+(-7)=-7+\underline{\quad}$

2. $\quad -5+4=\underline{\quad}+(-5)$

1. _____

2. _____

3. _____

3. $\quad -6+(-8)=-8+\underline{\quad}$

4. $\quad (-3)(-7)=(-7)(\underline{\quad})$

4. _____

5. $\quad 5\cdot(-6)=(\underline{\quad})\cdot 5$

5. _____

Complete the statements in exercises 6-10. Explain which of the properties of real numbers are used.

6. _____

6. $\quad 4+[6+(-2)]=(4+\underline{\quad})+(-2)$

7. _____

7. $\quad -6+[4+(-5)]=(-6+4)+\underline{\quad}$

8. _____

9. _____

8. $\quad (3\cdot 4)5=\underline{\quad}(4\cdot 5)$

9. $\quad -7\cdot[4(-9)]=(-7\cdot 4)\underline{\quad}$

10. _____

10. $\quad (-11\cdot 2)\cdot 8=-11(\underline{\quad}\cdot 8)$

11. _____

12. _____

13. _____

14. _____

15. _____

16. _____

17. _____

18. _____

19. _____

20. _____

21. _____

22. _____

23. _____

24. _____

25. _____

26. _____

27. _____

In exercises 11-13 fill in the blanks so that the resulting statement is an example of associative property.

11. $\underline{\quad}(5 \cdot 7) = \left(6\underline{\quad}\right) \cdot 7$

12. $3 + \left[(-5) + \underline{\quad}\right] = \left(3 + \underline{\quad}\right) + 9$

13. $\underline{\quad} + \left[\ \underline{\quad}\ + 4\right] = \left[-9 + (-8)\right] + \underline{\quad}$

In exercises 14-17 use the commutative and associative properties to convert the left hand side to the right hand side.

14. $2 + (-3 + 5) = (-3 + 2) + 5$

15. $(5 + 7) + (-4) = (-4 + 7) + 5$

16. $(-5 \cdot 4) \cdot 9 = 9[4 \cdot (-5)]$ 17. $[3 \cdot (-6)] \cdot 7 = [7 \cdot (-6)] \cdot 3$

Complete the statements in exercises 18-21.

18. $-6 \cdot \underline{\quad} = -6$ 19. $(-19) \cdot \underline{\quad} = -19$

20. $\underline{\quad} + (-8) = -8$ 21. $\underline{\quad} \cdot (3) = 3$

In exercises 22-25 identify the property demonstrated in the statement.

22. $3 + (-3) = 0$ 23. $4 \cdot \dfrac{1}{4} = 1$

24. $-7 + 7 = 0$ 25. $\left(-\dfrac{2}{3}\right)\left(-\dfrac{3}{2}\right) = 1$

In exercises 26-34 use the indicated properties to rewrite the expression, and simplify if possible.

26. $3x + y$; Commutative property of addition

27. $xy + z$; Commutative property of addition

76

28. $xy + z$; Commutative property of multiplication

29. $(x + 4) + t$; Associative property

30. $(x \cdot 4)t$; Associative property

31. $3(x - y + z)$; Distributive property

32. $4(2a - 3p)$; Distributive property

33. $-9x - 18y$; Distributive property

34. $-(p - 7)$; Distributive property

In exercises 35-40 use $a = -2$, $b = 3$, $c = 4$ and verify each of the statements.

35. $(a - 2b)c = ac - 2bc$ **36.** $(-3a)(4b \cdot c) = [(-3a) \cdot 4b] \cdot c$

37. $c \cdot (-2a + 3b) = -2(ca) + 3(cb)$

38. $(3a - 4b)c - 3ac + 4bc = 0$

39. $-(-a) = a$ **40.** $\dfrac{1}{\frac{1}{a}} = a$

41. Compute $4 - (7 - 5)$ and $(4 - 7) - 5$, and verify that subtraction is not associative.

42. Compute $4 - 7$ and $7 - 4$, and verify that subtraction is not commutative.

43. Compute $45 \div (5 \div 3)$ and $(45 \div 5) \div 3$, and verify that division is not associative.

44. Evaluate $45 \div 5$ and $5 \div 45$, and verify that division is not commutative.

45. Evaluate $4 \div [36 + 8]$ and $4 \div 36 + 4 \div 8$, and verify that division does not distribute over addition.

28. _____

29. _____

30. _____

31. _____

32. _____

33. _____

34. _____

35. _____

36. _____

37. _____

38. _____

39. _____

40. _____

41. _____

42. _____

43. _____

44. _____

45. _____

1.10   CHAPTER SUMMARY

Examples

Fractions

1.   Reducing fractions to lowest terms

Step 1   Write the prime factorization of the numerator.

Step 2   Write the prime factorization of the denominator.

Step 3   Divide the numerator and denominator by common prime factors.

2.   Two fractions are **equivalent** if their reduced forms are identical.

1. Reduce $\dfrac{60}{126}$ to lowest terms.

$$60 = 2 \cdot 2 \cdot 3 \cdot 5$$

$$126 = 2 \cdot 3 \cdot 3 \cdot 7$$

$$\frac{2 \cdot 2 \cdot 3 \cdot 5}{2 \cdot 3 \cdot 3 \cdot 7} = \frac{10}{21}$$

2. $\dfrac{6}{9}$ is equivalent to $\dfrac{8}{12}$

Since $\dfrac{6}{9} = \dfrac{2}{3}$ and $\dfrac{8}{12} = \dfrac{2}{3}$

Operations with fractions

3.   Addition of fractions with like denominators.

A.   Add the numerators, place the result over the common denominator, and simplify.

4.   Addition of fractions with unlike denominators.

Step 1   find the l.c.d

Step 2   Change the fractions to equivalent fractions each with the l.c.d. as the denominator.

Step 3   Add the equivalent fractions.

Step 4   Reduce the resultant fraction.

5.   Subtraction of Fractions

Change subtraction to addition and proceed as in 4.

3. $\dfrac{4}{5} + \dfrac{7}{5}$

$$\frac{4 + 7}{5} = \frac{11}{5}$$

4. $\dfrac{4}{5} + \dfrac{7}{9}$

l.c.d = l.c.m of 5 and 9

$$= 45$$

$$\frac{4}{5} = \frac{4 \cdot 9}{5 \cdot 9} = \frac{36}{45}$$

$$\frac{7}{9} = \frac{7}{9} \cdot \frac{5}{5} = \frac{35}{45}$$

$$\frac{4}{5} + \frac{7}{9} = \frac{36}{45} + \frac{35}{45}$$

$$= \frac{71}{45}$$

71 and 45 are co-prime

5. $\dfrac{4}{5} - \dfrac{7}{9} = \dfrac{4}{5} + \dfrac{-7}{9}$

$$\frac{4}{5} + \frac{-7}{9} = \frac{36}{45} + \frac{-35}{45}$$

$$= \frac{36 - 35}{45} = \frac{1}{45}$$

6. **Multiplication of fractions**

Multiply the numerators and multiply the denominators.

6. $\dfrac{5}{7} \cdot \dfrac{4}{5} = \dfrac{5 \cdot 4}{7 \cdot 5} = \dfrac{4}{7}$

7. **Division of fractions**

- Multiply the first fraction and reciprocal of the second frection.

- Simplify, if necessary.

7. $\dfrac{4}{15} \div \dfrac{12}{25} = \dfrac{4}{15} \cdot \dfrac{25}{12} = \dfrac{4 \cdot 25}{15 \cdot 12}$

$= \dfrac{2 \cdot 2 \cdot 5 \cdot 5}{3 \cdot 5 \cdot 3 \cdot 2 \cdot 2} = \dfrac{5}{9}$

$= \dfrac{2 \cdot 2 \cdot 5 \cdot 5}{3 \cdot 5 \cdot 3 \cdot 2 \cdot 2} = \dfrac{5}{9}$

8. **Exponents**

a^n denotes the product of a with itself n times.

8. $4^5 = \underbrace{4 \cdot 4 \cdot 4 \cdot 4 \cdot 4}_{5 \text{ times}} = 1024$

9. In a^n, a is called the base and n is called the exponent.

9. 4^5 : 4 is the base
   : 5 is the exponent

10. **Order of Operations**

A. If no grouping symbols are present then;

10. $5 - 3^2 \cdot 4 + 7$

Step 1 Evaluate all exponent expressions.

$= 5 - 9 \cdot 4 + 7$

Step 2 Perform all multiplications and divisions from left to right in the order in which they occur.

$= 5 - 36 + 7$

Step 3 Perform all additions and subtractions from left to right in the order in which they occur.

$= -31 + 7 = -24$

B. If grouping symbols are present then within each grouping symbol starting from the innermost (grouping symbol) follow the usual order of operations described above.

$4 - 3[5 - 2(4 - 3)]$
$= 4 - 3[5 - 2 \cdot 1]$
$= 4 - 3(3) = 4 - 9 = -5$

Variables, expressions and equations

11. To evaluate an algebraic expression substitute the values for the variables and simplify.

12. The solution(s) of an equation are the values of the variable(s) which make the equation true.

Number line

13. All real numbers can be graphed on an open-ended line

For any two real numbers a and b, a is less than b ($a < b$) if a is to the left of b on the number line.

14. Additive inverse, or opposite, of a number a is $-a$.

15. The absolute value $|a|$ of a is the distance of a from 0 on the number line.

16. $|a| = \begin{cases} -a & \text{if } a < 0 \\ a & \text{if } a \geq 0 \end{cases}$

Addition of Real Numbers

17. Addition of two positive or two negative numbers

Step 1 Add the absolute value of two numbers.

Step 2 Assign the common sign to the sum.

Examples

11. Evaluate $3x^2 - 4xy$
for $x = 2$, $y = -2$
$3x^2 - 4xy$
$= 3(\mathbf{2})^2 - 4(\mathbf{2})(\mathbf{-2})$
$= 3 \cdot 4 - 4(2)(-2)$
$= 12 + 16 = 28$

12. $3x - 4 = x + 2$: $\{2, 3, -1\}$
$x = 2$: $\quad 3(\mathbf{2}) - 4 = \mathbf{2} + 2$
$\rightarrow \quad 6 - 4 = 2 + 2 \quad$ **Not true**
$x = 3$: $\quad 3(\mathbf{3}) - 4 = \mathbf{3} + 2$
$\rightarrow \quad 9 - 4 = 3 + 2 \quad$ **True**
$x = \text{-}1$: $3(\mathbf{-1}) - 4 = \mathbf{-1} + 2$
$\rightarrow \quad -3 - 4 = -1 + 2 \,$ **Not true**

13.

$-2 < 3$, since -2 lies to the left of 3 on the number line.

14. Additive inverse of -7 is
$-(-7) = 7$

15. The absolute value of -3
$=$ the distance of -3 to 0.
$= 3$.

16. $|-5| = -(-5) = 5$
$|5| = 5$

17. $5 + 7 = |5| + |7| = 5 + 7 = 12$
$(-5) + (-7) = -(|-5| + |-7|)$
$= -(5 + 7)$
$= -12$

18. Addition of two numbers with different signs.

Step 1   Find absolute values $|a|$ and $|b|$.

Step 2   Find the difference of $|a|$ and $|b|$.

Step 3   To the difference attach the sign of the number with the larger absolute value.

18. $5 + (-7)$

$|5| = 5$, $|-7| = 7$

$7 - 5 = 2$

Since $|-7| > |5|$ and the sign of -7 is negative

$\therefore 5 + (-7) = -2$

19. To subtract b from a, add the opposite of b to a and simplify:

19. $5 - 7 = 5 + (-7)$

$= -(|-7| - |5|)$

$= -2$

20. The product of any number with 0 is 0.

20. $5 \cdot 0 = 0$

21. The product of two numbers with the same sign is the product of their absolute values.

21. $(-5)(-7)$

$= |-5| \cdot |-7| = 5 \cdot 7$

$= 35$

22. The product of two numbers with the opposite signs is the negative of the product of their absolute values.

22. $7(-5)$

$= -(|7| \cdot |-5|)$

$= -(7 \cdot 5) = -35$

Division of Real Numbers

23. Division by zero is not defined.

23. $\dfrac{7}{0}$ is not defined

24. Two numbers are called **multiplicative inverses** or **reciprocals** of each other if their product is 1.

24. 9 and $\dfrac{1}{9}$ are reciprocals of

each other since:

$9 \cdot \dfrac{1}{9} = \dfrac{1}{9} \cdot 9 = 1$

25. To divide a by b $(b \neq 0)$

We multiply a with the reciprocal of b.

25. $7 \div 5$

$= 7 \cdot \dfrac{1}{5} = \dfrac{7}{1} \cdot \dfrac{1}{5} = \dfrac{7 \cdot 1}{1 \cdot 5} = \dfrac{7}{5}$

Properties of Addition and Multiplication

26. Commutative properties for addition:
$a + b = b + a$

26. $5 + 4 = 4 + 5$

27. Commutative properties for multiplication:
$ab = ba$

27. $7 \cdot 3 = 3 \cdot 7$

Examples

28. Associative properties for addition:
$(a+b)+c = a+(b+c)$

28. $(3+4)+7 = 3+(4+7)$
$\rightarrow \quad 7+7 = 3+11 \quad$ **True**

29. Associative properties for Multiplication:
$(ab)c = a(bc)$

29. $(4 \cdot 5) \cdot 2 = 4 \cdot (5 \cdot 2)$
$\rightarrow \quad 20 \cdot 2 = 4 \cdot 10$
$\rightarrow \quad \quad 40 = 40 \quad$ **True**

30. The number 0 is the additive identity:
$a + 0 = 0 + a = a$

30. $5 + 0 = 0 + 5 = 5$

31. The number 1 is the multiplication identity:
$a \cdot 1 = 1 \cdot a = a$

31. $6 \cdot 1 = 1 \cdot 6 = 6$

32. The opposite of a is also called the additive inverse of a: $\quad a + (-a) = (-a) + a = 0$

32. Additive inverse of 5 is -5
$5 + (-5) = (-5) + 5 = 0$

33. The reciprocal of a is also called the multiplicative inverse of a
$a \cdot \dfrac{1}{a} = \dfrac{1}{a} \cdot a = 1 \quad (a \neq 0)$

33. Reciprocal or multiplicative inverse of 5 is $\dfrac{1}{5}$
$5\left(\dfrac{1}{5}\right) = \dfrac{1}{5}(5) = 1$

34. Distributive properties:
$a(b+c) = ab+ac, \quad (b+c)a = ba+ca$
$(b+c)a = ba+ca$
$a(b-c) = ab-ac, a(b+c+d) = ab+ac+ad$

34. $5(4+7) = 5 \cdot 4 + 5 \cdot 7$
$5(11) = 20 + 35$
$\quad 55 = 55 \quad$ **True**

1.11   REVIEW EXERCISE

Write prime factors of numbers in exercises 1-2.

1. 108

2. 90

In exercises 3-4, identify pairs of fractions that are equivalent.

3. $\dfrac{15}{25}, \dfrac{21}{35}$

4. $\dfrac{36}{64}, \dfrac{27}{44}$

In exercises 5-15, perform the indicated operations. Write your answer in lowest terms.

5. $\dfrac{4}{15} \cdot \dfrac{21}{22}$

6. $\dfrac{8}{25} \div \dfrac{32}{15}$

7. $\dfrac{3}{4} \cdot \dfrac{7}{10} \cdot \dfrac{4}{9}$

8. $\dfrac{4}{9} + \dfrac{3}{9}$

9. $\dfrac{10}{7} - \dfrac{3}{7}$

10. $\dfrac{4}{9}+\dfrac{2}{7}$ **11.** $\dfrac{7}{18}+\dfrac{5}{12}$ **12.** $\dfrac{9}{16}-\dfrac{5}{24}$ **13.** $\dfrac{4}{5}+\dfrac{7}{10}-\dfrac{2}{3}$

14. 5^4 **15.** $\left(3\dfrac{1}{3}\right)^3$

In exercises 16-19, perform the indicated operations and simplify.

16. $5+7(2\cdot 2-3)$ **17.** $(12-7)\big[3+(9-5)(6-8\div 4)\big]$

18. $\left(3^2+4\div 2\right)^2 \div \big[5^2-7(5-3)\big]$ **19.** $(3-4\cdot 5+32\div 2)\div(3-6)$

In exercises 20-22, simplify each side of the inequality symbol and identify whether the statement is true or false.

20. $4+5\cdot 3 \geq 30-2\cdot 5$ **21.** $4^2+5(3-1) = 2\cdot 3+4\cdot 5$

22. $4^2+15\div 3 \neq 7\cdot 2+4$

In exercises 23-25, translate the word statements into symbols.

23. Four times five subtracted from thirty one equals eleven.

24. Quotient of twenty and four is less than or equal to five.

25. Eight multiplied by three does not equal quotient of eight and three.

In exercises 26-30, evaluate the expression for the given value of the variable.

26. $4x^2-7;\quad x=3$ **27.** $\dfrac{x-1}{x^2+2};\quad x=2$

28. $(3a-5)\left\{4a^2+3a-10\right\};\quad a=3$ **29.** $4p^2+q^3;\ p=1,\quad q=3$

30. $\dfrac{x^3+y^3}{2x-y};\quad x=3,\ y=4$

In exercises 31-33, change the phrases into algebraic expressions. Use x to represent the variable.

31. Two-sevenths of a number diminished by seven.

32. Product of a number and five, added to the quotient of three and the number.

33. Product of four and a number subtracted from the sum of four and the number.

In exercises 34-36, change the word statements to equations. Use x for the variable. Find the solutions of the equations in the set $\{0,1,2,3,4,5,6\}$.

34. The sum of two times a number and five is eleven.

35. Three times a number exceeds the sum of four and the number by six.

36. The quotient of fifty and a number equals product of the number and two.

37. Given the set of numbers $\left\{-3, 0, \dfrac{4}{5}, \sqrt{5}, -\dfrac{2}{7}, 1, 5\right\}$, identify which of these

numbers are:
a) Natural numbers   b) Integers
c) Rational numbers which are not integers   d) Irrational numbers
e) Real numbers which are not natural numbers

38. Graph the following numbers on the number line. $-3, 5, \dfrac{3}{4}, -\dfrac{5}{3}$

Simplify the expressions in exercises 39-41.

39. $\left|-\dfrac{5}{7}\right|$ **40.** $\left|4^2 - 2\cdot 3\right|$ **41.** $\left||3-7|-9\right|$

Complete the statements in exercises 42-44, and explain the properties of the real numbers used in each case.

42. $3 + [4 + (-7)] = (3+4) + (\ldots)$ **43.** $2[3+5] = 2(\ldots) + (\ldots)5$

44. $(5\cdot 7)4 = 5(\ldots 4) = 5(4\ldots) = (5\ldots)7$

In exercises 45-47, verify the statements for $a = 2,\quad b = 4,\quad c = -3$.

45. $(4a - 3b)c = 4ac - 3bc$ **45.** $-(-a) + 1\cdot b = a + b$

47. $[(2a+b)(3b-c)](a+2c) = (2a+b)[(3b-c)(a+2c)]$

1.12   SELF TEST

1. Write the prime factors of 234.

In exercises 2-3, decide which pair of fractions are equivalent.

2. $\dfrac{72}{48}, \dfrac{15}{10}$ **3.** $\dfrac{9}{33}, \dfrac{13}{55}$

Perform the indicated operations in exercises 4-10. Write your answers in lowest terms.

4. $\dfrac{15}{28}\cdot\dfrac{21}{10}$ **5.** $\dfrac{4}{15}\div\dfrac{6}{25}$ **6.** $\dfrac{4}{5}\cdot\dfrac{3}{8}\div\dfrac{9}{10}$ **7.** $\dfrac{3}{5}+\dfrac{11}{5}$

8. $\dfrac{5}{7}+\dfrac{3}{14}$ **9.** $\dfrac{5}{12}+\dfrac{7}{15}$ **10.** $1\dfrac{3}{5}+4\dfrac{2}{3}-3\dfrac{6}{7}$

Simplify the expressions in exercises 11-13.

11. $40 \div (10 \div (5-3))$

12. $-2[-6 + (-3)(-2)] \div 15$

13. $\left[\dfrac{1}{2}[15 - (-7)] + \dfrac{1}{2} \cdot 10\right] \div \left[\dfrac{5}{3}(-7 + 4)\right]$

14. Decide if the statement is true? $\quad 3^2 + 5(2 - 3) \geq |4 - 9|$

15. **Translate into symbols:** Three times the quotient of 5 and the sum of -3 and 7.

In exercises 16-17, decide if the indicated number is a solution of the equation.

16. $3x + 4x + 10 = 25;\ x = 3$

17. $5y - 2 = 4 + 3y;\ y = 3$

In exercises 18-19, evaluate the expressions for the indicated value of the variable.

18. $3x^2 + 5x - 2\ ;\ x = -3$

19. $\dfrac{|3a - b|}{4a^2 + b - 7}\ ;\ a = -2,\ b = 1$

In exercises 20-21, change the phrases or word statements into algebraic expressions or equations. Use x for the unknown.

20. Seven more than the sum of two consecutive numbers.

21. A rectangle with length 3 more than the width has a perimeter of 48.

In exercises 22-23, change the word statements to equations. Use x for the unknown. Determine if the equation has a solution in the set $\{0, 1, 2, 3, 4, 5\}$.

22. The sum of three times a number and 4 is nineteen.

23. The absolute value of a number subtracted from 3 is 2.

24. Given the set of real numbers $\left\{-5, -3, 0, 1, \sqrt{2}, 4, \dfrac{5}{7}, \dfrac{3}{4}\right\}$, identify the numbers which are;

a) Integers

b) Rational numbers that are not natural numbers

25. **Match the property in Column 1 with the statement in Column 2.**

Column 1		Column 2	
a.	Associative	A.	$3 + 5 = 5 + 3$
b.	Identity	B.	$3 \cdot (5 \cdot 4) = (3 \cdot 5) \cdot 4$
c.	Commutative	C.	$x + 0 = 0 + x = x$
d.	Distributive	D.	$a(3 + b) = 3a + ab$

CHAPTER 2

LINEAR EQUATIONS/INEQUALITIES

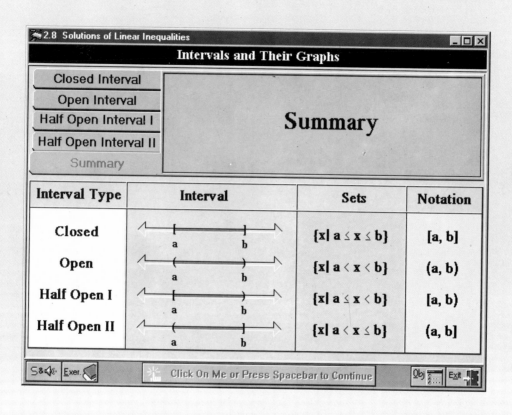

CHAPTER 2

LINEAR EQUATIONS / INEQUALITIES IN ONE VARIABLE

Introduction

In Chapter 1 we learned about algebraic expressions and equations. In this chapter we shall learn the techniques to solve some simple types of equations called linear equations and inequalities. Upon completion of this chapter we will be able to do problems dealing with:

2.1 SIMPLIFYING EXPRESSIONS

In this section we will examine how to simplify expressions. Simplification of algebraic expression is the first step in solving an equation.

Upon completion of this section we will be able to:

- A. Simplify expressions.
- B. Identify terms and numerical coefficients.
- C. Identify and combine like terms.
- D. Build expressions from word phrases.

A. Simplify Expressions

To simplify expressions we use the properties of addition and multiplication of real numbers discussed in Section 1.9.

Example 1: Simplify

a) $3x - 5 + 7$

b) $2(6y - 3z)$

c) $7(-5k + 2) + 4$

d) $4a - 3(b - 5)$

e) $3 \cdot 5 - 3(2m - 4)$

Solutions:

a) $3x - 5 + 7 = 3x + 2$

$-5 + 7 = 2$

Warm Up

1. Simplify

a) $2x - 7 + 4$

87

Warm Up

b) $5(3a - 4b)$

c) $5(-3k - 2) - 5$

d) $7x - 2(3 - y)$

b) $2(6y - 3z) = 2(6y) - 2(3z) = 12y - 6z$ Distributive Property

c) $7(-5k + 2) + 4 = 7(-5k) + 7 \cdot 2 + 4$
$= [7(-5)]k + 14 + 4 = -35k + 18$

d) $4a - 3(b - 5) = 4a - 3b - 3(-5)$
$= 4a - 3b + 15$

e) $3 \cdot 5 - 3(2m - 4) = 3 \cdot 5 - 3(2m) - 3(-4)$
$= 3 \cdot 5 - (3 \cdot 2)m - 3(-4)$
$= 15 - 6m + 12$
$= 15 + 12 - 6m$
$= 27 - 6m$

Answers:

1. **a)** $2x - 3$ **b)** $15a - 20b$
   c) $-15k - 15$ **d)** $7x + 2y - 6$

B.   Identifying Terms and Numerical Coefficients

An expression of the type ax^n, where a and n are the known real numbers and x is a variable, is called a term of an expression.

Examples:

$3x^5$ where $a = 3$, $n = 5$, and x is the variable in the term
$-3x^5$ where $a = -3$, $n = 5$, and x is the variable in the term
$9y^2$ where $a = 9$, $n = 2$, and y is the variable in the term

The number a in ax^n is called the coefficient of the term, and x^n is called the variable part.

Examples:

Term	$3y$	$4p$	$\dfrac{-7}{z}$	$-15x^2y^3z$	$-k$	$\dfrac{x}{2}$
Coefficient	3	4	-7	-15	-1	$\dfrac{1}{2}$
Variable Part	y	p	$\dfrac{1}{z}$	x^2y^3z	k	x

C.   Identifying and Combining Like Terms

The terms which differ **only in numerical coefficients** and have identical variable parts are called like terms. Terms which are not like terms are called **unlike terms.**

Warm Up

2.   Decide if the following pairs of terms are like terms.

   a) $2x^6, 7x^6$

Example 2:   Decide if the following pairs of terms are like terms.

   a) $3x^2, -4x^2$ **b)** $4x^3, 4x^2$
   c) $3xy^2z, -5xzy^2$ **d)** $-5xy^2, 5x^2y$
   e) $3x^2, 3y^2$

Solutions:

(a)

$$3x^2, \; -4x^2 \quad \text{Terms}$$

$$x^2 \qquad x^2 \quad \text{Variable Parts}$$

same

Therefore, $3x^2$ and $-4x^2$ are **like terms.**

(b)

$$4x^3, \; 4x^2 \quad \text{Terms}$$

$$x^3 \qquad x^2 \quad \text{Variable Parts}$$

different

Therefore, $4x^3$ and $4x^2$ are **unlike terms.**

(c)

$$3xy^2z \quad -5xzy^2 \quad \text{Terms}$$

$$xy^2z \qquad xzy^2 \quad \text{Variable Parts}$$

same

Therefore, $3xy^2z$ and $-5xzy^2$ are **like terms.**

(d)

$$-5xy^2 \qquad 5x^2y \quad \text{Terms}$$

$$xy^2 \qquad x^2y \quad \text{Variable Parts}$$

different

Therefore, $-5xy^2$ and $5x^2y$ are **unlike terms.**

(e)

$$3x^2, \; 3y^2 \quad \text{Terms}$$

$$x^2 \qquad y^2 \quad \text{Variable Parts}$$

different

Therefore, $3x^2, \; 3y^2$ are **unlike terms.**

b) $3x^3, 3x^4$

c) $15xz^3y, \; -13xyz^3$

d) $3x^2y, \; 4xy^2$

e) $3r^2, \; 2s^2$

Two like terms can be combined by using the distributive law.

- $$5x + 7x = (5 + 7)x$$
  $$= 12x$$

- $$9y - 4y = (9 - 4)y$$
  $$= 5y$$

Warm Up

3. Combine like terms.

a) $8x + 11x$

b) $-9z + 2z$

c) $21r^2 - 32r^2$

d) $3z^2 - 12z + 4z^2$

Answers:

2. a) like   b) unlike c) like
   d) unlike e) unlike
3. a) $19x$ b) $-7z$ c) $-11r^2$
   d) $7z^2 - 12z$

Example 3: Combine like terms in the following algebraic expressions.

Solutions:

To combine like terms, we add or subtract the coefficients.

a) $4x + 7x = (4 + 7)x = 11x$

b) $-7p + 5p = (-7 + 5)p = -2p$

c) $18t^2 - 21t^2 = (18 - 21)t^2 = -3t^2$

d) $22y^2 + 10y - 30y^2 = 22y^2 - 30y^2 + 10y$
$$= (22 - 30)y^2 + 10y = -8y^2 + 10y$$

D. Build expressions from word phrases

Recall we discussed in chapter 1, the conversion of word phrases, and statements into algebraic expressions and equations. We continue the same discussion with slightly different word phrases and statements.

Warm Up

4. The sum of 8, two times a number and three times the number.

Example 4: The sum of 5, seven times a number, and four times the number.

Solution:

Assume unknown number is x.
5 plus seven times a number plus four times the number.

$$5 \ + \ 7 \quad \cdot \quad x \quad + \ 4 \quad \cdot \quad x$$

Simplification:
$$5 + 7x + 4x = 5 + (7x + 4x) \qquad \text{Associative Property}$$
$$= 5 + (7 + 4)x \qquad \text{Distributive Property}$$
$$= 5 + 11x$$

5. Jane uses 5% of her stipend on food, 3% on school materials and another 15% on transportation. Additionally, she spends 5% on miscellaneous. If her told expenditure was 800 dollars, set up an equation which represents this information.

Example 5: Karen spends 10% of her paycheck on food, one-fifteenth of the paycheck on dresses, 5% of the paycheck on utilities, 15% on house rent, and one-fourth on education. She also Invests $200. If the total expenditure is $1,800, set up an equation that represents this information.

Solution:

Unknown: Amount of paycheck $= p$

$$10\% \text{ of } p + \frac{1}{15} \text{ of } p + 5\% \text{ of } p + 15\% \text{ of } p + \frac{1}{4} \text{ of } p + 200 = 1800$$

since the total expenses **equal 1800.**

$$\frac{10}{100}p + \frac{1}{15}p + \frac{5}{100}p + \frac{15}{100}p + \frac{1}{4}p + 200 = 1800$$

This equation is the conversion of the given word problem into symbols.

We can now simplify this equation by combining like terms on the left side of the equation.

$$\text{or} \quad \left(\frac{10}{100} + \frac{1}{15} + \frac{5}{100} + \frac{15}{100} + \frac{1}{4}\right)p + 200 = 1800$$

$$\left(\frac{1}{10} + \frac{1}{15} + \frac{1}{20} + \frac{3}{20} + \frac{1}{4}\right)p + 200 = 1800$$

$$\left(\frac{6}{60} + \frac{4}{60} + \frac{3}{60} + \frac{9}{60} + \frac{15}{60}\right)p + 200 = 1800$$

$$\frac{6+4+3+9+15}{60}p + 200 = 1800$$

$$\frac{37}{60}p + 200 = 1800$$

Example 6: The sum of the following two quantities is 47.

1. Five multiplied by four minus a number.
2. The sum of seven and a number.

Set up an equation that represents this information.

Solution:

Unknown: a number $= x$

First Quantity: 5 **multiplied** by 4 minus a number $= 5 \cdot (4 - x)$

Second Quantity: **Sum** of 7 and the number $= 7 + x$

The sum of $5(4 - x)$ and $(7 + x)$ is equal to 47.

Therefore: $5(4 - x) + (7 + x) = 47$.

This equation is the conversion of the given word problem into symbols. We can now simplify this equation.

Simplification:

$20 - 5x + 7 + x = 47$	Distributive Property
$20 + 7 - 5x + x = 47$	Regroup like terms using commutative property
$27 - 5x + x = 47$	
$27 + (-5 + 1)x = 47$	Distributive Property to combine like terms
$27 - 4x = 47$	

6. The sum of the following two quantities is 41.

   1. 6 multiplied by, one minus a number.

   2. The sum of eight and a number

Answers:

4. $8 + 5x$

5. $\frac{28}{100}p = 800$

6. $14 - 5x = 41$

91

EXERCISE 2.1

Answers:

1. _____
2. _____
3. _____
4. _____
5. _____
6. _____
7. _____
8. _____
9. _____
10. _____
11. _____
12. _____
13. _____
14. _____
15. _____
16. _____
17. _____
18. _____
19. _____
20. _____
21. _____
22. _____
23. _____
24. _____
25. _____
26. _____
27. _____
28. _____
29. _____
30. _____

Simplify the expressions in exercises 1–10.

1. $5 + 3x + 4$
2. $3 + 2x + 7x$
3. $7 - 3x - 9x$

4. $15 - 3x + 5x - 19$
5. $-7 + 2x - 9 + 4x - 3x$

6. $-4 - x - 3x - 9$
7. $4(5 - x) + 7$
8. $3(a - 5) + 4$

9. $6 - 2(x - 3)$
10. $3(4 - x) + 2(x + 4)$

Write down the numerical coefficients of the terms in exercises 11–17.

11. $-15y^2z$
12. $6x$
13. $-7mn$
14. $4pq$

15. $-m$
16. x^5
17. $-x^2yz$

In exercises 18–24, identify the variable part and the numerical coefficient.

18. $2x^2$
19. $2xy$
20. x^2y^2
21. $-3y^2zx$

22. -7
23. x^2
24. -2^2x^2y

In exercises 25–30, identify the pair of like terms.

25. $3x, 7y$
26. $-4p, 8p$
27. $4m^2n, -m^2n$

28. $5m^2n, 5mn^2$
29. $3, -5$
30. $4z^3, -3z^2$

In exercises 31–37, simplify expressions by combining like terms.

31. $-7m + 4m$

32. $5s + 6(s - 3)$

33. $15t^2 + 7(4 - t^2)$

34. $2 + x + 15 - 7x$

35. $3y^2 + 7y + 8x - 4y + 5x - 2y^2$

36. $3(y - 2y^2) + 4(7 - 5y) + 8(y^2 - 7)$

37. $6(3p - 5) - (6p + 4)$

Convert the following word phrases into mathematical expressions. Use x as the variable, and simplify the resulting expression.

38. A number added to the difference of 4 and twice the number.

39. Three times a number subtracted from 8 times the sum of the number and -4.

31. _____

32. _____

33. _____

34. _____

35. _____

36. _____

37. _____

38. _____

39. _____

2.2   ADDITION AND MULTIPLICATION PROPERTIES OF EQUALITY

Upon completion of this section, we will be able to:

  A.   Identify linear equations.
  B.   Use the addition and multiplication properties of equality.
  C.   Use these properties of equality to solve the linear equations.

A.   Identify linear equations

An equation of the type

$$3x + 4 = 0 \quad \text{or} \quad 4x - 5 = 7 - 9x$$

is a linear equation. The main characteristic of a linear equation is that "the exponent of the **variable** part of any term on either side of the equation is "**one**".

Example 1:   Which of the following are linear equations?

  a) $4x - 7 = 2$ **b)** $3 + x^2 - x = 5$
  c) $5(3 - x) + 7 = 2 + 2(x - 4)$

Solutions:

  a) $4x - 7 = 2$ is a linear equation

  b) $3 + x^2 - x = 5$ is **not** a linear equation

  c) $15 - 5x + 7 = 2 + 2x$ is a linear equation

B.   Addition and Multiplication Properties of Equality

When equals are added to equals, they result in equals. This common sense rule is called the **addition property of equality.**

Addition Property of Equality

For any three real numbers, a, b, and c $\qquad a = b \longrightarrow a + c = b + c$

The addition property of equality can be used to show that every *linear equation* in a *variable* x can be written in the form: $\qquad ax = b$ where a and b are real numbers, and $a \neq 0$.

Warm Up

2. Convert to the form $ax = b$.

a) $11x + 7 = 8$

b) $3 + 5x + 3x = 2$

c) $3(x - 2) + 3 = 4$

Example 2: Convert the following linear equations to the form $ax = b$.

a) $4x - 7 = 2$

b) $5(3 - x) + 7 = 2 + 2(x - 4)$

Solutions:

a) $\qquad 4x - 7 = \mathbf{2}$

$\qquad 4x - 7 + \mathbf{7} = 2 + \mathbf{7}$ $\qquad$ – 7 to both sides

$\qquad 4x + 0 = 9$

$\qquad 4x = 9$

Therefore, $4x - 7 = 2$ can be written as $4x = 9$.

b) $\qquad 5(3 - x) + 7 = 2 + 2(x - 4)$

$\qquad \mathbf{15 - 5x + 7} = 2 + \mathbf{2x - 8}$ $\qquad$ Distributive Property

$\qquad -5x + 22 = 2x - \mathbf{6}$ $\qquad$ Combine Like Terms

$\qquad -5x + 22 + (\mathbf{-22}) = 2x - 6 + (\mathbf{-22})$ $\qquad$ Add – 22 to both sides

$\qquad -5x = 2x - 6 + (-22)$

$\qquad -5x = 2x - 28$

$\qquad -5x + (-2x) = 2x - 28 + (-2x)$ $\qquad$ Add – 2x to both sides

$\qquad \longrightarrow -7x = 0 - 28$

$\qquad \longrightarrow -7x = -28$

$\qquad \longrightarrow x = 4$

Multiplication Property of Equality: When equals are multiplied by equals, they result in equals.

$$a = b \longrightarrow ac = bc \qquad (c \neq 0)$$

The addition and multiplication properties of equality can be used to convert any linear equation to the form $x = k$.

Example 3: Convert the following equations to the form $x = k$.

a) $3x = 5$ b) $4x + 3 = 0$

c) $2(x - 3) + 4 = 5x + 7$

Solutions:

a) $3x = 5$

$\frac{1}{3}(3x) = \frac{1}{3} \cdot 5$ Multiply both sides by $\frac{1}{3}$

$\left(\frac{1}{3} \cdot 3\right)x = \frac{1}{3} \cdot 5$ Associative Property

$1 \cdot x = \frac{5}{3}$ or $x = \frac{5}{3}$

b) $4x + 3 = 0$

$4x + 3 + (-3) = 0 + (-3)$ Add –3 to both sides

$4x + [3 + (-3)] = 0 + (-3)$

$4x = -3$

$\frac{1}{4}(4x) = \frac{1}{4}(-3)$ Multiply both sides by $\frac{1}{4}$

$\left(\frac{1}{4} \cdot 4\right)x = \frac{1}{4}(-3)$ Associative Property

$1 \cdot x = \frac{-3}{4}$ or $x = -\frac{3}{4}$

c) $2(x - 3) + 4 = 5x + 7$

$2x - 6 + 4 = 5x + 7$ Distributive Property

$2x - 2 = 5x + 7$

We want all constant terms on the right hand side. Therefore, we add the negative of –2 to both sides. Also, we want all variable terms on the left hand side. Therefore, we add the negative of $5x$ to both sides

$$(2x - 2) + 2 = (5x + 7) + 2$$

$$2x + (-2 + 2) = 5x + (7 + 2) \longrightarrow 2x = 5x + 9$$

$$-5x + 2x = -5x + (5x + 9)$$

$$-5x + 2x = (-5x + 5x) + 9$$

$$-3x = 9 \longrightarrow 3x = -9 \qquad \text{Multiply both sides by -1}$$

$$\frac{1}{3} \cdot 3x = -9 \cdot \frac{1}{3} \longrightarrow \left(\frac{1}{3} \cdot 3\right)x = -3$$

$$\longrightarrow \qquad x = -3$$

C. Solving Linear Equations

Solving an equation means finding the value of the variable (unknown) that makes the equation a true statement. We can solve any equation using the following three steps approach.

Step 1	If need be, simplify both sides of the equation by using the distributive property and combining like terms.
Step 2	Use addition property of equality to convert the equation to the form $ax = b$.
Step 3	Use multiplication property of equality to convert $ax = b$ to the form $x = k$. Then $x = k$ is the required solution.

It is a good practice to check the solution by substituting the value of the variable in the original equation. This substitution should result in a true statement.

Warm Up

4. Solve the equations

a) $3x = 12$

b) $\dfrac{4x}{7} = 3$

Example 4:   Solve the equations

a) $4m = 6$ b) $\dfrac{3x}{5} = 2$

Solutions:

a) *Step 1*   Not needed since both sides of $4m = 6$ are in simplified form.

Step 2   Not needed since the equation is already of the form $ax = b$.

Step 3 $4m = 6$

$\dfrac{1}{4}(4m) = \dfrac{1}{4} \cdot 6$ Multiply both sides by $\frac{1}{4}$

$\left(\dfrac{1}{4} \cdot 4\right)m = \dfrac{1}{4} \cdot 6$ Associative Property

$1 \cdot m = \dfrac{1}{4} \cdot 6$ or $m = \dfrac{6}{4} = \dfrac{3}{2}$

Check: $4m = 6;\ m = \dfrac{3}{2}$ $4\left(\dfrac{3}{2}\right) = 6$ or $\dfrac{12}{2} = 6$ True

b) $\dfrac{3x}{5} = 2$

As in a) above, Steps 1 and 2 are not needed.

Step 3 $\dfrac{5}{3}\left(\dfrac{3}{5}x\right) = \dfrac{5}{3} \cdot 2$ Multiply both sides by $\frac{5}{3}$ inverse of $\frac{3}{5}$

$\left(\dfrac{5}{3} \cdot \dfrac{3}{5}\right)x = \dfrac{5}{3} \cdot 2$ Associative Property

$1 \cdot x = \dfrac{5}{3} \cdot 2$ or $x = \dfrac{10}{3}$

Check: $\dfrac{3}{5}\left(\dfrac{10}{3}\right) = 2$ or $\dfrac{30}{15} = 2 \longrightarrow 2 = 2$ True

96

Example 5:   Solve the equation

a) $2(4x+3) = 3x+5$

b) $3(2x-1) = 4+(3+x)$

Solutions:

a) $2(4x+3) = 3x+5$

Step 1   The left hand side needs to be simplified because of the parentheses.

$$2(4x)+\mathbf{2\cdot 3} = 3x+5 \qquad \text{Distributive Property}$$
$$8x+6 = 3x+5$$

Step 2 $(8x+6)+(-\mathbf{6}) = (3x+5)+(-\mathbf{6}) \qquad \text{Add - 6 to both sides}$

$$8x+[6+(-6)] = 3x+[5+(-6)] \qquad \text{Associative Property}$$
$$8x+0 = 3x+(-1)$$
$$8x = 3x-1$$
$$-3x+8x = -3x+(3x-1) \qquad \text{Add } -3x \text{ to both sides}$$
$$-3x+8x = (-3x+3x)-1 \qquad \text{Associate Property}$$

Step 3 $5x = -1 \qquad\qquad \text{Multiply by } \frac{1}{5} \text{ on both sides}$

$$\frac{\mathbf{1}}{\mathbf{5}}(5x) = \frac{\mathbf{1}}{\mathbf{5}}(-1) \qquad\qquad \text{Combine Like Terms}$$

$$\left(\frac{1}{5}\cdot 5\right)x = -\frac{1}{5} \qquad\qquad \text{Associative Property}$$

$$x = -\frac{1}{5}$$

Check: Checking this solution involves lot of calculations.

> We may therefore use calculator.
> See examples 1-3 (section 2.2-2.3), in Appendix B.

b) $3(2x-1) = 4+(3+x) \longrightarrow 6x-3 = (4+3)+x$

$$\longrightarrow 6x-3 = 7+x$$
$$\longrightarrow 6x-3+\mathbf{3} = 7+x+\mathbf{3}$$
$$\longrightarrow 6x = x+10$$
$$\longrightarrow -\mathbf{x}+6x = -\mathbf{x}+x+10$$
$$\longrightarrow 5x = 10 \longrightarrow x = 2$$

Check: $3(2x-1) = 4+(3+x)$

$$3[2(\mathbf{2})-1] = 4+(3+\mathbf{2}) \qquad \text{or}$$
$$3[3] = 4+5 \qquad \text{or} \quad 9=9 \qquad \text{True}$$

Warm Up

6. Solve the equation

a) $3k - 2k + 4k = 15$

Example 6: Solve the following equations

a) $4t + 5t - 2t + 7t = 35$

b) $3(6x - 2) + 4(3 - 4x) = 2(1 - x)$

Solutions:

a) $4t + 5t - 2t + 7t = 35$

$(4 + 5 - 2 + 7)t = 35$ Distributive Property

$14t = 35$

$\left(\dfrac{1}{14} \cdot 14\right)t = \dfrac{1}{14} \cdot 35$ Multiply by 1/14

$t = \dfrac{35}{14} = \dfrac{5}{2}$

Check the solution by using calculator.

b) $2(3x - 6) - 4(4 + 3x) = x$

b) $3(6x - 2) + 4(3 - 4x) = 2(1 - x)$

$18x - 6 + 12 - 16x = 2 - 2x$

$2x + 6 = 2 - 2x \longrightarrow 2x + 6 + \mathbf{2x} = 2 - 2x + \mathbf{2x}$

$\longrightarrow 4x + 6 = 2$

$\longrightarrow 4x + 6 - \mathbf{6} = 2 - 6$

$\longrightarrow 4x = -4 \longrightarrow \left(\dfrac{\mathbf{1}}{\mathbf{4}} \cdot 4\right)x = \dfrac{\mathbf{1}}{\mathbf{4}}(-4)$

$\longrightarrow x = -1$

7. Translate into symbols and solve. Five times a number added to the negative of five is twenty five.

Example 7: Translate the following sentences into symbols, and solve the resulting equation.

If three times a number is added to 10, the result is 22. What is the Number?

Solution:

Let the unknown number be x .
The problem can be stated as '3 times x plus 10 equals 22'

$3x + 10 = 22$

$3x + 10 + (-\mathbf{10}) = 22 + (-\mathbf{10})$ Add –10

$3x = 12$

$\dfrac{1}{3}(3x) = \dfrac{1}{3} \cdot 12$ or $x = 4$ Multiply by 1/3

Therefore, the required number is 4.

Check: $3 \cdot 4 + 10 = 22 \rightarrow 12 + 10 = 22 \rightarrow 22 = 22$ True

Example 8: When twice a number is subtracted from 11, the result is 1 more than three times the number. Find the number.

8. When thrice a number is subtracted from thirteen, the result is two less than twice the number.

Solution:

Let the unknown number be x.

The problem can be restated as '11 minus $2x$ equals 1 plus $3x$'. *In symbols:*

$11 - 2x = 1 + 3x \longrightarrow 11 - 2x - 3x = 1 + 3x + (-3x)$

$\longrightarrow 11 - 5x = 1 + 0 \longrightarrow 11 - 5x = 1$

$\longrightarrow -11 + 11 - 5x = -11 + 1$

$\longrightarrow 0 - 5x = -10$

$\longrightarrow -5x = -10$

$\longrightarrow \left(-\frac{1}{5}\right)(-5x) = \left(-\frac{1}{5}\right)(-10)$

$\longrightarrow x = 2$

Therefore, the required number is 2.

Answers:

4. a) 4   b) $x = \dfrac{21}{4}$

5. a) $x = -14$ b) $x = \dfrac{21}{2}$

6. a) $k = 3$ b) $x = -4$

7. $x = 6$ 8. $x = 3$

Check: $11 - 2(2) = 1 + 3(2) \rightarrow 11 - 4 = 1 + 6 \rightarrow 7 = 7$ **True**

EXERCISE 2.2

Answers:

Identify the linear equations in exercises 1–6.

1. $3x + 5 = 0$

2. $3x^2 = 5$

3. $3(p + 5) = 4 - p$

4. $5(3y + 2) - 7y = 0$

5. $5t = 0$

6. $3y^2 - 4y + 7 = 0$

Convert the linear equations to the form $ax = b$ in exercises 7–11.

7. $x + 7 = 12$

8. $2y + 4 = 3y$

9. $4 - 3x = 5x - 7$

1. _____

2. _____

3. _____

4. _____

5. _____

6. _____

7. _____

8. _____

9. _____

10. _____

11. _____

12. _____

13. _____

14. _____

15. _____

16. _____

17. _____

18. _____

19. _____

20. _____

21. _____

22. _____

23. _____

24. _____

25. _____

26. _____

27. _____

28. _____

29. _____

30. _____

31. _____

32. _____

10. $3(p+5)-4 = 2(1-p)$ **11.** $2(4-3p)+7(p-2) = 0$

Convert the equations to the form $x = k$ in exercises 12–16.

12. $3x = 5$ **13.** $-4x = 6$ **14.** $2(x+5) = 16$

15. $3x+5 = 11$ **16.** $3(5-2x) = 4+5x$

In exercises 17–30, solve the linear equations and verify your solution.

17. $x+3 = 0$ **18.** $-4x+5 = 0$ **19.** $2x+6 = 3(x-2)$

20. $5x = 8$ **21.** $3p+5 = -1$ **22.** $-5m+8 = 3m-12$

23. $4(t-1) = 2(t+3)$ **24.** $2(z+1)+3(z-2) = 4$

25. $3(2+3r)+4(r-2) = 5$ **26.** $3a+2-2(a-1) = 3(2a+3)$

27. $5s+7s-4s+6s+15 = 27$ **28.** $\dfrac{3}{4}y = 5$

29. $-\dfrac{5}{7}z+6 = 0$ **30.** $\dfrac{5}{9}y = -6$

In exercises 31–32, translate the statements into equations, and solve for the unknown number.

31. When a number is added to 7, the result is 10. What is the number?

32. When a number is multiplied by -3, the result is 9. What is the number?

2.3   MORE ON SOLVING LINEAR EQUATIONS

In the last section we learned how to use addition and multiplication properties to solve linear equations. Recall that solving a linear equation consists of the following three steps:

- Simplification

- Use of addition property to convert the equation to the form $ax = b$

- Use of multiplication property to convert the equation to the form $x = k$

In this section we will examine the effects of the addition and multiplication properties more closely.

Upon completion of this section, we will be able to:

A.   Interpret addition and multiplication properties in terms of subtraction and division, respectively.

B.   Solve equations with fractional co-efficients.

C.   Solve equations with decimal co-efficients.

D.   Recognize equations which have no solutions and those which have infinitely many solutions.

E.   Translate sentences into algebraic expressions.

A.   Addition and Multiplication Properties Revisited

Apply addition property to convert $2x + 3 = 6$ to the form $ax = b$

$$2x + 3 + (-3) = 6 + (-3) \longrightarrow 2x = 6 + (-3)$$

Compare $2x + 3 = 6$ with $2x = 6 + (-3)$

Rule 1:   **Transferring a term** (in a sum)

When a term in a *sum* is transferred to the other side of an equation, it *changes its sign.*

For example:
- $3x + 5 = 7 \longrightarrow 3x = 7 - 5$

- $4x - 3 = 8 \longrightarrow 4x = 8 + 3$

- $4 - x = 5 - 3x \longrightarrow 4 - x + 3x = 5$

  $\longrightarrow -x + 3x = 5 - 4$

Warm Up

1. Transfer the constant terms (terms with no variables) from left side to the right side of the equation.

   a) $7x - 12 = 2$

   b) $3x + 2 = 0$

   c) $4x + 7 = -7$

Example 1:   Transfer the constant terms (terms with no variables) from the left side to the right side of the equation.

   a) $5x + 6 = 0$ b) $7x - 5 = 8x$

   c) $-2x + 9 = 7$

Solutions:

   a) $5x + 6 = 0 \longrightarrow 5x = -6$

   +6 on the left side becomes -6 on the right side

   b) $7x - 5 = 8x \longrightarrow 7x = 8x + 5$

   -5 on the left side becomes $+5$ on the right side

   c) $-2x + 9 = 7 \longrightarrow -2x = 7 - 9$

   +9 on the left side becomes -9 on the right side

Next consider the equation $3x = 5$.

Apply the multiplication property to convert $3x = 5$ to the form $x = k$.

$$\frac{1}{3}(3x) = \frac{1}{3} \cdot 5 \qquad \text{or} \qquad x = \frac{5}{3}$$

Compare $3x = 5$ with $x = \frac{5}{3}$

Note that the factor 3 or the left side becomes a divisor 3 on the right side.

Rule 2:   **Transferring a factor (in a product)**

A factor on one side of the equation can be transferred to the other side as a divisor.

For example, $4x = -5 \longrightarrow x = -\frac{5}{4}$.

Now apply the multiplication property to $\frac{x}{4} = 5$

$$\mathbf{4} \cdot \left(\frac{x}{4}\right) = \mathbf{4} \cdot 5 \qquad \text{Reciprocal of } \frac{1}{4} \text{ is 4. Multiplication property of equality}$$

$$\left(4 \cdot \frac{1}{4}\right)x = 4 \cdot 5 \qquad \text{or} \qquad x = 4 \cdot 5$$

Thus $\frac{x}{4} = 5 \longrightarrow x = 4 \cdot 5$

Rule 3:   **Transferring a divisor**

A divisor on one side of the equation can be transferred to the other side of the equation as a factor.

For example, $\frac{x}{3} = 7 \longrightarrow x = 3 \cdot 7$

Combining the above two rules for multiplication, we get;

$$\frac{ax}{b} = c \longrightarrow ax = bc \longrightarrow x = \frac{bc}{a}$$

Example 2:   Convert the equations to the form $x = k$.

a) $4x = -3$ b) $\dfrac{x}{3} = 2$

c) $\dfrac{3x}{5} = 8$ d) $-\dfrac{4}{7}x + 5 = 11$

Solutions:

a) $4x = -3 \longrightarrow x = -\dfrac{3}{4}$

Factor 4 on left hand side becomes a divisor on the right side

b) $\dfrac{x}{3} = 2 \longrightarrow x = 3 \cdot 2$ or $x = 6$

c) $\dfrac{3}{5} \cdot x = 8 \longrightarrow x = \dfrac{5}{3} \cdot 8$ or $x = \dfrac{40}{3}$

d) $-\dfrac{4}{7}x + 5 = 11 \longrightarrow -\dfrac{4}{7}x = 11 - 5 \longrightarrow -\dfrac{4}{7}x = 6$

$\longrightarrow x = \left(-\dfrac{7}{4}\right)6$

$\longrightarrow x = -\dfrac{42}{4} \longrightarrow x = -\dfrac{21}{2}$

Example 3:   Solve the equation:

$4 - (2x - 3) = 3(x + 2) + 4$

Solution:

Step 1 $4 - (2x - 3) = 3(x + 2) + 4$
$4 - 2x + 3 = 3x + 6 + 4$ Distributive Property
$4 + 3 - 2x = 3x + 6 + 4$ Commutative Property
$7 - 2x = 3x + 10$ Associative Property

Step 2 $-2x = 3x + 10 - 7$ Transfer 7 to the right side
$-2x = 3x + 3$ Transfer $3x$ to the left side
$-3x - 2x = 3$ Combine Like Terms
$-5x = 3$

$x = -\dfrac{3}{5}$ -5 as a factor transfers to the right side as a divisor

Therefore, the solution is $x = -\dfrac{3}{5}$

Warm Up

2. Convert the equations to the $x = k$ form.

a) $\frac{x}{7} = 3$

b) $3x = 5$

c) $\frac{3}{2} \cdot x = 7$

d) $-\frac{5}{6}x + 2 = 5$

3. Solve the equation
$4 + (x + 3) = 4(x + 2) + 3$

Answers:

1. a) $7x = 14$ b) $3x = -2$
c) $4x = -14$

2. a) $x = 21$ b) $x = 1\frac{2}{3}$ c) $x = 4\frac{2}{3}$
d) $x = -3\frac{3}{5}$

3. $x = -1\frac{1}{3}$

B.   Equations with Fractional Coefficient

If coefficients involved in an equation are fractions, we may solve by either of two methods:

   i) apply arithmetic operations on the fractions and solve,

   ii) convert the equation to one with integer coefficients and solve.

An equation with fractional coefficients is converted to one with integer coefficients by multiplying both sides of the equation by the least common denominator of all the fractions.

Warm Up

4. Solve the equation
$\frac{1}{2}x + \frac{1}{3}x = x - \frac{4}{6}$

Example 4: Solve the equation $\frac{3}{5}x - \frac{1}{10}x = x - \frac{5}{2}$.

Method 1: $\quad \frac{3}{5}x - \frac{1}{10}x = x - \frac{5}{2} \longrightarrow \frac{3}{5}x - \frac{1}{10}x - x = -\frac{5}{2}$

$$\longrightarrow \left(\frac{3}{5} - \frac{1}{10} - 1\right)x = -\frac{5}{2} \longrightarrow \frac{6 - 1 - 10}{10}x = -\frac{5}{2}$$

$$\longrightarrow \quad -\frac{5}{10}x = -\frac{5}{2} \longrightarrow x = -\frac{10}{5}\left(-\frac{5}{2}\right)$$

$$\longrightarrow \quad x = \frac{50}{10} \longrightarrow x = 5$$

Therefore, the solution is $x = 5$.

Answers:

4. $x = 4$

Method 2: The least common denominator of all the fractions involved, namely

$\frac{3}{5}, \frac{1}{10}$, and $\frac{5}{2}$ is 10. *Multiply both sides of the equation by 10.*

$$\frac{3}{5}x - \frac{1}{10}x = x - \frac{5}{2}$$

$$10\left(\frac{3}{5}x - \frac{1}{10}x\right) = 10\left(x - \frac{5}{2}\right) \qquad \text{Multiply by l.c.d.}$$

$$10\left(\frac{3}{5}x\right) - 10\left(\frac{1}{10}x\right) = 10x - 10\left(\frac{5}{2}\right) \qquad \text{Distributive Property}$$

$$6x - x = 10x - 25$$

Now solve using the methods learned previously.

$$6x - x - 10x = -25 \qquad \text{Transfer } 10x \text{ to left side}$$

$$-5x = -25 \qquad \text{Combine Like Terms}$$

$$x = \frac{-25}{-5} \quad \text{or} \quad x = 5$$

Check: Substitute $x = 5$ in the **given** equation.

$$\frac{3}{5}(5) - \frac{1}{10}(5) = 5 - \frac{5}{2} \longrightarrow 3 - \frac{1}{2} = 5 - \frac{5}{2}$$

$$\frac{6-1}{2} = \frac{10-5}{2}$$

$$\frac{5}{2} = \frac{5}{2} \qquad \text{True}$$

C.   Equations with Decimal Co-efficients

If an equation involves decimal co-efficients, we may solve by either of the three methods

i)   by using operations with decimal numbers,
ii)   by converting the decimal numbers into fractions or
iii)   by clearing decimals.

To clear decimals, multiply by a suitable power of 10 such as 10, 100, 1000, etc. For example, if the maximum number of decimal places in any of the coefficients is **3** then multiply by 10^3 or 1000.

Example 5:   Solve $.06(10000) + .08x = .072(10000 + x)$

Solution:

The maximum number of decimal places are in .072. There are three decimal places. Therefore, we multiply both sides of the equation by 10^3 or 1,000.

$$\mathbf{1000}(.06)(10000) + \mathbf{1000}(.08x) = \mathbf{1000}(.072)(10000 + x)$$

$$60(10000) + 80x = 72(10000 + x)$$

$$600000 + 80x = 720000 + 72x \quad \text{Transfer 600,000}$$

$$80x = -600000 + 7200000 + 72x$$

$$80x = 120000 + 72x \quad \text{Combine Like Term}$$

$$80x - 72x = 120000 \quad \text{Transfer } 72x \text{ to left side}$$

$$8x = 120000 \quad \text{or} \quad x = \frac{120000}{8} \quad \text{or} \quad x = 15000$$

Therefore, the solution is $x = 15,000$

Note: Equality may be established by comparing the value of each side of the equation.

Left Side: $.06 \times 10000 + .08 \times 15000 = 1800$

Right Side: $.072 \times (10000 + 15000) = 1800$

Since the right hand side and left hand side of the equation have the same value, the solution is correct.

If an equation involves both decimals and fractions, we may first change decimals to fractions.

Example 6:   Solve $\frac{5}{6} + 4x = .5$

Solution:

$$\frac{5}{6} + 4x = \frac{5}{10} \quad \text{The LCD of fractions is 30.}$$

$$\mathbf{30}\left(\frac{5}{6} + 4x\right) = \mathbf{30}\left(\frac{5}{10}\right) \longrightarrow \mathbf{30}\left(\frac{5}{6}\right) + \mathbf{30}(4x) = \mathbf{30}\left(\frac{5}{10}\right)$$

Warm Up

$$25 + 120x = 15 \quad \longrightarrow \quad 120x = 15 - 25$$
$$\longrightarrow \quad 120x = -10$$
$$\longrightarrow \quad x = -\frac{10}{120} \quad \text{or} \quad x = -\frac{1}{12}$$

Therefore, the solution is $x = -\dfrac{1}{12}$

Answers:

5. 199850   6. $x = -\dfrac{1}{60}$

Check: Use calculator, LHS should be $= .5$ RHS $= .5$ (given)

D. Equations with No Solution or Infinitely Many Solutions

All equations encountered so far had only one solution. We shall now give an example of an equation which has *no solution* and an example of an equation which has *infinitely many solutions*.

A linear equation in one variable which has *exactly one* solution is called a **conditional** equation. An equation which is true for all real numbers is called an **identity.** An equation leading to a false statement is called a **contradiction.**

Warm Up

7. Determine which of the following equations is conditional , one with no solution, or the identity.

a) $4(x-3) = 2x + 8$

b) $3(x+2) = x + 7$

Example 7 :   Determine which of the following equations is conditional,   one with no solution, or the identity.

a) $5(x-1) = 4x - 1$

b) $3(x+4) + x = 4x + 12$

c) $5(x-1) + 9 = 5x + 1$

Solutions:

a) $5(x - 1) = 4x - 1$

$5x - 5 = 4x - 1$ Distributive Property

$5x = 4x - 1 + 5$ Transfer -5 to the right side

$5x = 4x + 4$ Combine Like Terms

$5x - 4x = 4$ Transfer $4x$ to the left side

$x = 4$ Combine Like Terms

Therefore, $x = 4$ is the only solution of $5(x-1) = 4x - 1$. Hence the given equation is a **conditional equation.**

b) $3(x+4) + x = 4x + 12$

$3x + 12 + x = 4x + 12 \quad \longrightarrow \quad \mathbf{4x + 12 = 4x + 12}$

Notice that both sides are *identical*. Therefore whatever value we may substitute for x, it will makes the equation true. Thus, $3(x+4) + x = 4x + 12$ has infinitely many solutions, and is therefore an *identity*.

c) $5(x-1)+9 = 5x+1$

$5x-5+9 = 5x+1$

$5x+4 = 5x+1 \longrightarrow -5x+5x+4 = 1$

$0+4 = 1 \longrightarrow 4 = 1$ False

Hence the given equation has no solution and is a contradiction.

Warm Up

c) $2(3x+5)+x = 7x+10$

Answers:
7. a) $x=10$, conditional
   b) conditional   c) Identity

Nature of a linear equation

Identity: If on simplifying, both sides become identical.

Conditional: If on simplifying, the equation can be written in the form $x = k$.

No Solution: If on simplification, the equation results in a false statement.

E. Sentences and Algebraic Expressions

Example 8: The product of two numbers is -8. If one of the numbers is x. What is the other number?

Solution:

$x \cdot (\text{other number}) = -8$ other number $= \dfrac{-8}{x}$

Example 9: The sum of two numbers is 15. If one of the numbers is x, What is the other number?

Solution:

$x + (\text{other number}) = 15$ other number $= 15-x$

Warm Up

8. The product of two numbers is 6. If one of the numbers is x, what is the other.

9. The difference of two numbers is 17. If smaller of the numbers is x, what is the other number.

Answers:
8. $\frac{6}{x}$ 9. $x+17$

EXERCISE 2.3

In exercises 1–4, use addition property of equality to write equations in the form $ax = b$.

1. $4x + 7 = 8$

2. $7 - 2x = 8$

3. $5r = 8 - 4r$

4. $3(2 + 4x) = 3 + 5x$

In exercises 5–15, convert the equations to the form $x = k$.

5. $3x = 5$

6. $7x + 8 = 0$

7. $4 - 5x = 2$

8. $2a - 5 = 3(a + 4)$

9. $6(2y - 1) - 5 = 7(3y - 2) - 24$

Answers:

1. _____

2. _____

3. _____

4. _____

5. _____

6. _____

7. _____

8. _____

9. _____

10. _____

11. _____

12. _____

13. _____

14. _____

15. _____

16. _____

17. _____

18. _____

19. _____

20. _____

21. _____

22. _____

23. _____

24. _____

25. _____

26. _____

27. _____

10. $6k + 9 = -7 + 4k$

11. $2(3z + 4) = 8(1 + z)$

12. $5(3p + 4) = 4(1.5p - 2) + 1$

13. $7(2t + 6) = 9(t + 3) - 5$

14. $8 - 3(5x - 4) = 5(1 - x) - 10$

15. $3x - 2(3 + x) = 5 - 3(4 - x)$

In exercises 16–18, solve the equations. Check your answer with a calculator.

16. $\frac{2}{3}s - \left(s + \frac{1}{4}\right) = \frac{1}{6}(s + 3)$

17. $.2(60) - .50v = .1(60 + v)$

18. $.4(75) + .6t = 2(4.5 + t)$

In exercises 19–23, determine which of the equations is conditional, an identity, or have no solution.

19. $4x + 7 = 2(2x + 8)$ **20.** $3x - 5 = 2(x + 7)$

21. $\frac{2}{3}x + 2 = x - \frac{x-1}{3} + \frac{5}{3}$ **22.** $\frac{x+1}{3} = \frac{x-1}{3}$

23. Given $3a - 2x = 6$, solve for a if $x = 3$.

24. Jeane is t years old now. a) How old will she be in 10 years?
b) How old was she 7 years ago?

Express the answers in terms of t.

25. Two numbers add up to 21. If one of the numbers is m, what is the other number?

26. Product of two numbers is 28. One of the numbers is k. What is the other number?

27. Quotient of two numbers is 27. Second number is n. Find the first number?

2.4   APPLICATIONS OF LINEAR EQUATIONS

Upon completion of this section, we will be able to:

A.   Apply the step by step approach for solving an applied problem.
B.   Solve problems involving only one unknown quantity.
C.   Solve problems involving more than one unknown quantity.

A. Solving Word Problems

We have already discussed how to translate words, phrases, and sentences into mathematical expressions and equations. We shall now discuss some procedures to solve problems using a general and logical thought process: understand the problem, think of a plan, carry out the plan, and look back. These procedures are summarized in the following steps.

Step 1	Read the problem carefully, and identify what is to be found (*the unknown*). Choose a variable to represent the numerical value of the unknown quantity.
Step 2	Write down mathematical expressions for any other unknown quantities using the assigned variable. If possible, draw figures or diagrams. *Diagrams help us to understand the problem better.*
Step 3	Translate the problem into an equation.
Step 4	Solve the equation.
Step 5	Answer the question asked. *Be sure that the answer makes sense and follows the logic of the question.*
Step 6	Verify your answer by using the *original* statement of the problem.

B. Problems Involving Only One Unknown Quantity

Example 1:   The product of 5 and a number, increased by 21 is 141. What is the number?

Solution:

Step 1   Let this number be x.

Step 2   There are no other unknown quantities involved.

Step 3   Translate the problem

Product of 5 and a number,   increased by 21 is 141

$$5x \qquad + \qquad 21 = 141$$

Warm Up

1.   The product of 3 and a number, decreased by 17 is 154. What is the number?

Step 4   Solve the equation $5x + 21 = 141$

$$5x = 141 - 21 \longrightarrow 5x = 120 \longrightarrow x = \frac{120}{5}$$

$$\longrightarrow x = 24$$

Step 5   The required number is 24

Step 6   Product of 5 and 24 is 120. 120 increased by 21 is 141.
Therefore, the answer is verified.

Notes: There is a difference between the following two statements.

a) **The product of 5 and a number, increased by 21** written as an expression is $5x + 21$.

b) **The product of 5, and a number increased by 21** written as an expression is $5(x + 21)$.

Compare the position of the comma in the statements.

Warm Up

2. The sum of a number and 3 multiplied by 4 is the same as 3 times the number increased by 15. Find the number.

| Example 2: |

If the sum of a number and 6 is multiplied by 5, the result is the same as 9 times the number decreased by 2. Find the number.

Solution:

Step 1   Let this number be **x**.

Step 2   There are no other unknown quantities involved.

Step 3   Translate the problem.
The sum of a number and 6, is multiplied by 5, and the result is $(x + 6) \cdot 5$.

Also, 9 times a number, decreased by 2 gives us **$9x - 2$**.

Therefore, the resulting equation is $5(x + 6) = 9x - 2$.

Step 4   Solve the equation

$$5(x + 6) = 9x - 2 \longrightarrow 5x + 30 = 9x - 2$$

$$\longrightarrow 5x = 9x - 2 - 30$$

$$\longrightarrow 5x = 9x - 32$$

$$\longrightarrow -9x + 5x = -32$$

$$\longrightarrow -4x = -32$$

$$\longrightarrow x = \frac{-32}{-4} \text{ or } x = 8$$

Step 5   The required number is 8.

Step 6   Sum of 8 and 6 multiplied by 5 gives:

$$(8 + 6)5 = (14)5 = \mathbf{70}$$

Also, 9 times the number decreased by 2 is: $9(8) - 2 = 72 - 2 = \mathbf{70}$.
Both sides of the equation are equal. The answer is verified.

Answers:

1. 57   **2.** 3

C. Problems Involving More Than One Unknown

Example 3:

A purse contains $6.50 in quarters and dimes. The number of quarters exceeds the number of dimes by 5. Find the number of quarters and dimes.

Warm Up

3. A piggybank contains $8.00 in dimes and quarters. The number of dimes exceeds the number of quarters by 10. Find the number of dimes and quarters.

Solution:

Step 1 *The number of quarters exceeds the number of dimes by 5.*

Let the number of dimes = x.

Step 2 The number of quarters = $x + 5$.

Step 3 Let us convert dimes, quarters, and dollars into cents.

x dimes = $10x$ cents.

$x + 5$ quarters = $25 \cdot (x + 5)$ cents.

The total money in purse = $ 6.50 = 650$ cents

The problem is translated into the following equation:

$$10x + 25(x + 5) = 650$$

Step 4 $10x + 25(x + 5) = 650 \longrightarrow 10x + 25x + 125 = 650$

$\longrightarrow 35x + 125 = 650$

$\longrightarrow 35x = 650 - \mathbf{125}$

$\longrightarrow 35x = 525$

$\longrightarrow x = \dfrac{525}{35}$ or $x = 15$

Step 5 Therefore, there are 15 dimes, and $15 + 5 = 20$ quarters.

Step 6 *Verification:*

i) 20 quarters is 5 more than 15 dimes

ii) 20 quarters = $\dfrac{20}{4}$ dollars = 5 dollars

15 dimes = $\dfrac{15}{10}$ dollars = 1.5 dollars

The total amount is 5 + 1.50 = $6.50

Therefore, the answer is verified.

Note: Do not combine two quantities with different units. Thus 'quarters' and 'dimes' cannot be combined. That is why we converted dimes, quarters, and dollars to the common unit 'cent'.

Warm Up

4. The length of a rectangle is 3 yards more than four times its width. The perimeter is 96 yards. Find its dimensions.

Example 4: The length of a rectangular piece of land is 60 yards more than twice its width. The perimeter is 540 yards. Find its dimensions.

Solution:

Step 1   Assume width $= x$ yards.

Step 2   The length, is 60 yards more than twice the width (x).
Therefore, length $= 2x + 60$.

Step 3   Translate the problem.
Perimeter $= 2(\text{length}) + 2(\text{width})$

$$540 = 2(2x + 60) + 2x$$

Step 4   Solve the equation.

$$2(2x + 60) + 2x = 540 \longrightarrow 4x + 120 + 2x = 540$$

$$6x + 120 = 540 \longrightarrow 6x = 540 - \mathbf{120}$$

$$6x = 420 \longrightarrow x = \frac{420}{6}$$

$$\longrightarrow x = 70$$

Step 5   Therefore, the solution is: width $= x = 70$ yards,
and length $= 2x + 60 = 2(70) + 60 = 140 + 60$
$$= 200 \text{ yards}$$

Step 6   *Verification:*
perimeter $= 2(\text{length} + \text{width})$
$$= 2(200 + 70) = 2(270) = 540 \text{ yards}$$

5. Find the measure of an angle whose supplements is twice its complements.

Example 5: Find the measure of an angle whose supplement is three times its complement.

Solution:

Step 1   Assume angle $= x$ degrees.

Step 2   Supplement $= (180 - x)^0$ and
Complement $= (90 - x)^0$

Step 3   Translate the problem.
The supplement is three times the complement.

$$\downarrow \qquad\qquad \downarrow \quad \downarrow \qquad\qquad \downarrow$$

$$180 - x \;=\; 3 \qquad\qquad (90 - x)$$

Step 4   Solve the equation.

$$180 - x = \mathbf{3}(90 - x) \longrightarrow 180 - x = 270 - 3x$$

$$-x = -\mathbf{180} + 270 - 3x \longrightarrow -x = 90 - 3x$$

$$-x + \mathbf{3}x = 90 \longrightarrow 2x = 90$$

$$x = \frac{90}{2} \quad \text{or} \quad x = 45$$

Step 5   The measure of the angle is $45°$.

Step 6   *Verification:*

The supplement of $45 = 180 - 45 = 135$
The complement of $45 = 90 - 45 = 45$
Three times the complement $= 3(45) = 135$
$$\qquad\qquad\qquad\qquad\qquad = \mathbf{supplement}$$

Example 6:   The sum of the ages of a woman and her daughter is 44 years. Two years ago, the mother was three times as old as her daughter. How old is each one now?

Solution:

Step 1   Let the age of the daughter $= x$ years.

Step 2   Mother's age $= 44 - x$

Step 3   Translate the problem.

Two years ago: Daughter's age $=$ $\mathbf{x} - 2$
              Mother's age $=$ $\mathbf{44} - x - 2$

Two years ago: Mother's age was 3 times daughter's age.

$$44 - x - 2 = 3 \cdot (x - 2)$$

Step 4   Solve the equation.

$$44 - x - 2 = 3(x - 2) \longrightarrow 42 - x = 3(x - 2)$$
$$\longrightarrow 42 - x = 3x - 6$$
$$\longrightarrow -x = -42 + 3x - 6$$
$$\longrightarrow -x - 3x = -48$$
$$\longrightarrow -4x = -48$$
$$\longrightarrow x = 12$$

Step 5   Therefore,   Daughter's age $= 12$ years,
and   Mother's age $= 44 - 12 = 32$ years.

Step 6   *Verification:*

Two years back the daughter's age $= 12 - 2 = 10$ years.
Two years back mother's age $= 32 - 2 = 30$ years.

30 is three times 10.   **True**

Warm Up

6. The sum of the ages of a man and his son is 52 years. Three years later, the sum of twice the son's age and the father's age will be equal to 66 years. Find their present ages.

Warm Up

7. A television camera is sold for $350. If this item was on sale for a discount of 20%, find the original selling price of the television camera.

Example 7: During a clearance sale an electronic store sold a video cassette recorder for $225. If items on sale were discounted by 25%, find the original selling price of the video cassette recorder.

Solution:

Step 1 Let original retail price $= x$.

Step 2 Discount $= 25\%$ of $x = .25x$

Step 3 Translate the problem.

Discounted price $=$ original retail price $-$ discount

Therefore, $225 = x - .25x$

Step 4 Solve the equation.

$$x - .25x = 225 \longrightarrow .75x = 225$$

$$\longrightarrow x = \frac{225}{.75} \longrightarrow x = 300$$

Step 5 The original selling price of the video cassette recorder is $300.

Step 6 *Verification:*

25% discount on $300 = 25\%$ of 300

$.25\,(300) = 75$

Discounted price $= 300 - 75 = \$225$ True

8. A student's scores for three exams were recorded to be 65, 85 and 90. If the average of four scores is 80, what was the fourth score?

Example 8: A patient's temperature was taken at 7 a.m., 11 a.m., 3 p.m., and 7 p.m. The first, second, and fourth readings were 102^0 F, 101.5^0F, and 102.5^0 F respectively. If the average of the four readings was 101.5^0 F, what was the third reading?

Solution:

Step 1 Let third temperature reading $= x^0$ F

Step 2 The average

$$= \frac{\text{sum of the four readings}}{4} = \frac{102 + 101.5 + x + 102.5}{4}$$

Step 3 Translate the problem. The average of the four readings is 101.5.

$$\frac{102 + 101.5 + 102.5 + x}{4} = 101.5$$

114

Step 4   Solve the equation.

$$\frac{102 + 101.5 + 102.5 + x}{4} = 101.5$$

$$\frac{x + 306}{4} = 101.5 \longrightarrow \frac{x}{4} + \frac{306}{4} = 101.5$$

$$\longrightarrow \frac{x}{4} + 76.5 = 101.5$$

$$\longrightarrow \frac{x}{4} = 101.5 - 76.5$$

$$\longrightarrow \frac{x}{4} = 25$$

$$\longrightarrow x = 4(25) \quad \text{or} \quad x = 100$$

Step 5   Third temperature was $100^0 F$.

Verification

The average of 102, 101.5, 100, 102.5

$$= \frac{102 + 101.5 + 100 + 102.5}{4} = \frac{406}{4} = 101.5 \text{ True}$$

Example 9:   A lawn mower uses a mixture of gasoline and oil. For each ounce of oil the mixture contains 15 ounces of gasoline. If the tank holds 80 ounces of the mixture how many ounces each of oil and gasoline are required to fill the tank completely?

Solution:

Step 1   Oil required (in ounces) $= x$

Step 2   Gasoline required (in ounces) $= 15x$

Step 3   Translate the problem.

Total: **The amount of oil and gasoline is 80 ounces**

$$\downarrow \qquad\qquad \downarrow \qquad\quad \downarrow$$

$$x \qquad + \qquad 15x \quad = \quad 80$$

Step 4   Solve the equation

$$x + 15x = 80 \longrightarrow 16x = 80$$

$$\longrightarrow x = \frac{80}{16} \quad \text{or} \quad x = 5$$

Step 5   When the tank is full the quantity of oil required is 5 ounces and the quantity of gasoline required is $80 - 5 = 75$ ounces.

Step 6   *Verification:*

i)   Gasoline $75 = \mathbf{15}(5) = 15$ times the amount of oil TRUE

ii)   Total $75 + 5 = \mathbf{80}$ TRUE

Warm Up

9. A lawn mover uses a mixture of gasoline and fuel. Each quart of fuel is mixed with three quarts of gasoline. If the tank holds 8 quarts. of the mixture how many quarts each of fuel and gasoline are required to fill the tank completely?

Answers:

3. 20 quarters, 30 dimes

4. width: 9 yards, length: 39 yards

5. The angle is zero degrees.

6. The man is 47 and his son is 5.

7. $437.50   **8.** 80

9. 6 quarts of gasoline ; 2 quarts of fuel.

EXERCISE 2.4

Answers:

1. _____

2. _____

3. _____

4. _____

5. _____

6. _____

7. _____

8. _____

9. _____

10. _____

11. _____

12. _____

13. _____

1.   If 6 is added to a number, the result exceeds twice the number by 1. What is the number?

2.   If the sum of an integer and 7 is multiplied by 3, the result is 6 times the original integer. Find the integer.

3.   If 6 is multiplied by the difference between a number and 3, the result is difference between 4 times the number and 2. Find the number.

4.   Find a number which when subtracted from 4 times itself yields 36.

5.   If a dozen rolls cost $2.16, find the price of one roll.

6.   How many $6 hair dryers can be purchased with $256.80 , if the tax is 7%.

7.   A purse contains $2.95 in quarters and dimes. The number of quarters exceeds the number of dimes by 2. Find the number of quarters and dimes in the purse.

8.   A child has $10.45 in quarters and nickels in his piggy bank. If the number of quarters is short of the number of nickels by 11, find the number of each type of coin in the piggy bank.

9.   The length of a rectangle is 3 *cm* less than four times its width. The perimeter of the rectangle is 34 *cm*. Find the dimensions of the rectangle.

10.   A farmer plans to enclose a rectangular field by chain link fencing. The length of the field is 16 yards more than its width. If 140 yards of fencing is required, find the dimensions of the field.

11.   A farmer has 38 more hens than roosters with 150 chickens in all. Find the number of hens and the number of roosters on the farm.

12.   A strip of paper is 57 inches long. It is cut into three pieces. The longer piece is 10 inches longer than the middle-sized piece, and the shortest piece is 10 inches shorter than the middle-sized piece. Find the length of the three pieces.

13.   A lawn mower uses a mixture of gasoline and oil. For each ounce of oil, the mixture contains 16 ounces of gasoline. If the tank holds 85 ounces of mixture, how many ounces of oil and how many ounces of gasoline does it require when full.

14. Find the measure of an angle in degrees. It is given that the complement is one-half of the difference between the supplement and 25^0.

14. _____

15. _____

15. A pharmacist found that he received $\frac{7}{5}$ times as many prescriptions for pain killers as he did for tranquilizers. If on a certain day the pharmacist received 72 prescriptions, how many of these prescriptions of each kind did the receive?

16. _____

16. Find three consecutive integers whose sum is 36.

17. _____

17. Find three consecutive integers such that three times the middle integer exceeds the sum of the other two by 15.

18. In the 1960 United States presidential election, John F. Kennedy received 84 more electoral votes than Richard M. Nixon. Together they received 522 electoral votes. How many votes did each candidate receive?

18. _____

19. _____

19. One side of a triangle is 1 meter more than twice the shortest side, while the second side is 3 meters more than the shortest side. The perimeter of the triangle is 24 meters. Find the length of each side.

20. _____

20. The perimeter of an isosceles triangle is 42 centimeters. Two equal sides are 3 centimeters shorter than the base. Find the dimensions of the triangle.

21. _____

21. The sum of the ages of a mother and a child is 40. If 4 years ago, the mother's age was seven times the child's age, find how old is each one of them?

22. _____

22. At this time Kathy is 20 years old and Linda is 16 years old. How many years ago Kathy was twice as old as Linda?

23. _____

23. A car dealer advertises a $7600 van at a 30% discount for $5500. Is the dealer telling the truth?

24. _____

24. A furniture company declares 30% discount on all items on Father's Day. The discounted price of a dining table is $280. What is the regular price of the dining table?

25. _____

25. Shelia made 85, 84, and 78 on three of the four tests. If her average score for the four tests was 86, what was her score on the fourth test?

2.5   LITERAL EQUATIONS

A literal equation (*or a formula*) is a rule that expresses a relationship between two or more variables. For example, $A = LW$ expresses the relationship between the **A**rea, **L**ength, and **W**idth of a rectangle.

Upon completion of this section, we will be able to:

A.   Solve a literal equation (formula) for one variable when the values of the other variables are given.

B.   Solve a formula for a specified variable in terms of the other variables.

C.   Use formulas for applications.

A.   Solve for One Variable, Given Values of Other Variables

Rule 1:   *Step 1*   Substitute the given values in the formula.

   Step 2   Simplify.

   Step 3   Solve the resulting equation.

   Step 4   Verify your answer.

Warm Up

1. Find the value of the remaining variable.

a) $A = \frac{1}{2} b h$

   $h = 5$, $A = 10$

Example 1:   Find the value of the remaining variable

a) $A = \frac{1}{2} bh;$ $A = 40,$ $b = 10$

b) $A = \frac{1}{3} h(a + 4b + c);$
   $A = 20,$ $h = 5,$ $a = 1,$ $c = 1$

Solutions:

a)   *Step 1*   Substitute in $A = \frac{1}{2} bh$

   $A = 40$ and $b = 10.$ We get $40 = \frac{1}{2}(10)h.$

   Step 2 $\frac{1}{2}(10)h = 40 \longrightarrow 5h = 40$

   Step 3   Solve the equation $5h = 40$

   $\longrightarrow h = \frac{40}{5} \longrightarrow h = 8$

   Step 4   *Verification:*

   Substitute $A = 40,$ $b = 10,$ $h = 8$ in the formula.

   $A = \frac{1}{2} bh$

   $40 = \frac{1}{2}(10)8 \longrightarrow 40 = 5(8) \longrightarrow 40 = 40$ **True**

b) *Step 1* Substitute in $A = \frac{1}{3}h(a + 4b + c)$

$A = 20,\ h = 5,\ a = 1,$ and $c = 1.$

We get $20 = \frac{1}{3}(5)[1 + 4b + 1].$ Substitute

Step 2 $20 = \frac{5}{3}(2 + 4b)$ Simplify

Step 3 Solve the equation. $\frac{5}{3}(2 + 4b) = 20$

$5(2 + 4b) = 60$
$10 + 20b = 60$

$20b = 50 \longrightarrow b = \frac{50}{20} = 2.5$

Step 4 Verification:

$20 = \frac{1}{3}(5)[1 + 4(2.5) + 1]$

$20 = \frac{1}{3}(5)(12) \longrightarrow 20 = 5 \cdot 4$

B. Solve for one Variable in Terms of other Variables

Example 2: If an amount P is invested at simple annual interest rate r, then the amount A available at the end of t years is given by: $A = P + Prt$. Solve for P in terms of A, r, and t.

Solution:

$A = P + Prt$

$= P(1 + rt) \longrightarrow P(1 + rt) = A \longrightarrow P = \frac{A}{(1 + rt)}$

Example 3: Fahrenheit and Celsius scales of temperature are related by the formula $C = \frac{5}{9}(F - 32)$. Express Fahrenheit (F) in terms of Celsius (C).

Solution: $\frac{9}{5}C = F - 32$ Multiply by $\frac{9}{5}$

$\frac{9}{5}C + 32 = F$ Transfer 32

or $F = \frac{9}{5}C + 32$

C.   Use of Formulas for Applications

The examples given below explain the steps that should be followed to solve an application problem. These steps are essentially the same as those mentioned earlier in section 2.4.

Warm Up

4. Area of a square is 25 sq. yards. Find the length of its side.

Example 4:   A rectangular lot has an area of 500 square yards. If the length of the lot is 25 yards, find the width.

Solution:

Step 1   Let the width = x.

Step 2   Draw a figure.

| 500 sq yds | W |

L

Step 3   Use the formula for the area of a rectangle: $A = LW$.

Step 4   Substitute the given values in the formula:
$$500 = 25 \cdot x.$$

Step 5   Solve the equation . $25x = 500$

$$x = \frac{500}{25} \longrightarrow x = 20$$

Step 6   The width of the lot is 20 yards.

Step 7   *Verification:*   Length of the lot   = 25 yards
Width of the lot   = 20 yards
Thus, area of the lot = $25 \cdot 20$
= 500 sq. yards **True**

5. If John has 2000 dollars available at the end of 20 years, with yearly simple interest rate of 5%, what is the principal that he invested?

Example 5:   John wins $1000 in a state lottery. He decides to invest this money in a bank which pays 5% yearly simple interest. How long will it take for the money to double?

Solution:

Step 1   Let the time taken to double the investment = t years.

Step 2   Not applicable

Step 3   The final amount is given by the formula:

$$A = P + Prt.$$

Step 4   Substitute the values: $P = 1000$, $A = 2P = 2000$
$r = 5\% = .05$ time $= t$.

$$2000 = 1000 + 1000(.05)t$$

Step 5   Solve the equation. $1000 + 1000(.05t) = 2000$

$$1000(.05)t = 2000 - 1000$$
$$1000(.05)t = 1000$$

$$50t = 1000 \longrightarrow t = \frac{1000}{50} \longrightarrow t = 20$$

Step 6   The investment will double in 20 years.

Step 7   *Verification:* The interest on $1000 at 5% in 20 years

$$= 1000\,(.05)(20) = 1000.$$

The amount at the end of 20 years $=$ Principal + Interest

$$= 1000 + 1000 = 2000.$$

Example 6:   If two vertically opposite angles have measure $(5x - 27)°$, and $(3x + 11)°$ respectively, find the measure of these angles.

Solution:

Step 1   Not needed

Step 2   Draw the figure.

Step 3   The needed formula (*rule*) is that the measures of vertical opposite angles are equal. Thus, $5x - 27 = 3x + 11$.

Step 4   Not applicable

Step 5   Solve the equation.

$$5x - 27 = 3x + 11 \longrightarrow \quad 5x = 3x + 11 + 27$$
$$\longrightarrow \quad 5x = 3x + 38$$
$$\longrightarrow \quad -3x + 5x = 38$$
$$\longrightarrow \quad 2x = 38$$
$$\longrightarrow \quad x = \frac{38}{2} \quad \text{or} \quad x = 19$$

Step 6   The measure of each of the angle $= 5x - 27$

$$= 5(19) - 27 = 95 - 27 = 68$$

Therefore, the measure of each of the required angle is 68°

Step 7   *Verification:* $5x - 27 = 3x + 11$

$$5(19) - 27 = 3(19) + 11 \longrightarrow 95 - 27 = 57 + 11$$
$$68 = 68 \quad \textbf{True}$$

Warm Up

6. If two vertically opposite angles have the measure $(x + 27)°$ and $(5x - 13)°$ respectively, find the measure of these angles.

Answers:

4. 5 yards 5. $1000

6. The measure of the angle is $37°$

EXERCISE   2.5

In exercises 1–6, solve for the unknown.

1. $A = \dfrac{1}{2}h(b + c); \; A = 30, \, b = 8, \, c = 7$

2. $V = lbh; \; V = 80; \; l = 10, \, h = 2$

Answers:

1. _____

2. _____

3. _____

4. _____

5. _____

6. _____

7. _____

8. _____

9. _____

10. _____

11. _____

12. _____

13. _____

14. _____

15. _____

3. $A = P + \text{Pr}t$; $A = 2440$, $r = 3$, $t = 20$

4. $rp = rq + r$; $r = 20$, $p = 5$

5. $C = \dfrac{5}{9}(F - 32)$; $C = 35$

6. $V = \pi h^2\left(r - \dfrac{h}{3}\right)$, [use $\dfrac{22}{7}$ for π]; $h = 7$, $V = 308$

In exercises 7–12, solve the equations for the indicated variable.

7. $A = \dfrac{1}{2}bh$; for h 8. $p = 2l + 2w$; for l

9. $A = p + prt$; for t 10. $F = \dfrac{9}{5}C + 32$; for C

11. $y = mx + c$; for m 12. $b = a + (n - 1)d$; for n

13.   A rectangular lot has an area of 860 square yards. If the length of the lot is 43 yards.   Find its width.

14.   The perimeter of a sports complex, which is square in shape is 790 meters. Find a side of the complex.

15.   Area of the following trapezium is $52 cm^2$. Find length of the base.

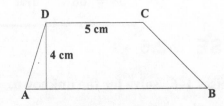

$$\left[\begin{array}{l}\text{Use the formula } A = h(a + b)/2 \text{ where "}a\text{" and "}b\text{" are}\\ \text{lengths of parallel sides and h is the distance between them}\end{array}\right]$$

122

Find the measure of the marked angles.

16. 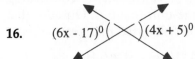 $(6x - 17)^0$ $(4x + 5)^0$

17. 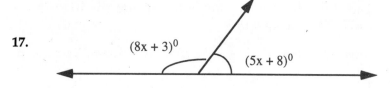 $(8x + 3)^0$ $(5x + 8)^0$

2.6   RATIOS AND PROPORTIONS

If for every three female members on the committee there are four male members then the ratio of females to males in the committee is 3:4 or 3/4. If a motor requires 3 ounces of oil for every 20 ounces of gasoline then the ratio of oil to gasoline in a motor is 3:20 or 3/20. These are examples of ratios. Proportion is an equality relationship of two ratios. In this section we examine some applications concerning ratios and proportions. Methods of solving equations can be effectively used to solve problems involving proportions.

Upon completion of this section we will be able to:

    A.   Write ratios.

    B.   Solve proportions.

    C.   Solve applied problems involving ratios.

A.   Write Ratios

A ratio is a quotient of two quantities. The ratio of a number **a** to a number **b** is written as: $a : b$ or $\dfrac{a}{b}$. Ratios are used to compare two numbers or two quantities. In order to compare two quantities using ratios, their units must be the same. We cannot compute ratios of a quantity in ounces to a quantity in gallons.

Example 1:	Write a ratio for each of the following

    a)   Ratio of 4 dollars to 6 dollars

    b)   Ratio of 4 dimes to 3 quarters

Solutions:

    a)   The ratio of 4 dollars to 6 dollars [same units] $= \dfrac{4}{6}$ or $\dfrac{2}{3}$

Warm Up

1. Write a ratio for the following

    a) Ratio of 8 dollars to 7 dollars.

Warm Up

b) Ratio of 3 dimes to 5 nickels

Answers:

1. a) $\frac{8}{7}$ b) $\frac{6}{5}$

b) The ratio of 4 dimes to 3 quarters [different units]. Since the units 'dimes' and 'quarters' are different we convert the quantities in terms of the same unit (cents). Observe that dimes and quarters can both be converted into cents.

$$4 \text{ dimes} = 4 \cdot 10 = 40 \text{ cents}$$
$$3 \text{ quarters} = 3 \cdot 25 = 75 \text{ cents}$$

Therefore, the ratio of 4 dimes to 3 quarters is 40 to 75 (40 / 75) and not 4 to 3.

Note: Quotients expressing ratios may be reduced. Thus, for example $\frac{40}{75} = \frac{8}{15}$. Therefore, the ratio 40 to 75 and 8 to 15 are same.

B. Proportions

In the note above we observed that the ratios of 40 to 75 and 8 to 15 are equal. This is an example of a proportion.

A proportion is a statement which expresses equality of two ratios. If the two ratios $a{:}b$ and $c{:}d$ *are equal,* then $a{:}b = c{:}d$ which is equivalent to the equation $\frac{a}{b} = \frac{c}{d}$.

$$\text{Notice that} \quad \frac{a}{b} = \frac{c}{d} \longrightarrow \frac{a}{b}(\boldsymbol{bd}) = \frac{c}{d}(\boldsymbol{bd}) \longrightarrow ad = bc$$

Rule: **Cross Multiplication**

The proportion $\frac{a}{b} = \frac{c}{d}$ can be tested by cross multiplication:

$$\frac{a}{b} \diagdown \frac{c}{d} \qquad ad \text{ and } bc \text{ are called } \textit{cross products.}$$

The equality of ratios can be tested from equality of cross products : $ad = bc$

Warm Up

2. Which of the following are proportions.

a) $\frac{6}{7} = \frac{42}{9}$

b) $\frac{9}{12} = \frac{15}{20}$

Example 2: Which of the following are proportions?

a) $\frac{3}{4} = \frac{7}{9}$ b) $\frac{15}{20} = \frac{24}{32}$

Solutions:

a) $\frac{3}{4} = \frac{7}{9} \longrightarrow 3 \cdot 9 = 7 \cdot 4 \longrightarrow 27 = 28$ False

Therefore, $\frac{3}{4} = \frac{7}{9}$ is not a proportion, or the proportion is false.

b) $\frac{15}{20} = \frac{24}{32} \longrightarrow 15 \cdot 32 = 24 \cdot 20 \longrightarrow 480 = 480$ **True**

Therefore, $\frac{15}{20} = \frac{24}{32}$ is a proportion, or the *proportion is true.*

Note: The rule of cross multiplication simply expresses the fact that fractions are equivalent

Example 3:   Find x in the following proportions.

a) $\dfrac{25}{15} = \dfrac{x}{9}$ b) $\dfrac{24}{x} = \dfrac{4}{5}$

Solutions:

a) $\dfrac{25}{15} = \dfrac{x}{9} \longrightarrow 25 \cdot 9 = 15x \longrightarrow 225 = 15x$

$\longrightarrow 15x = 225$

$\longrightarrow x = \dfrac{225}{15}$

$\longrightarrow x = 15$

Verification:

Substitute 15 for x in the proportion. $\dfrac{25}{15} = \dfrac{15}{9} \longrightarrow \dfrac{5}{3} = \dfrac{5}{3}$ True

b) $\dfrac{24}{x} = \dfrac{4}{5} \longrightarrow 24 \cdot 5 = 4x \longrightarrow 120 = 4x$

$\longrightarrow 4x = 120 \longrightarrow x = \dfrac{120}{4}$

$\longrightarrow x = 30$

Verification:

Substitute $x = 30$ in the proportion. $\dfrac{24}{30} = \dfrac{4}{5} \longrightarrow \dfrac{4}{5} = \dfrac{4}{5}$ True

Warm Up

3.   Find x in the following proportions.

a) $\dfrac{3}{5} = \dfrac{x}{15}$

b) $\dfrac{27}{x} = \dfrac{9}{8}$

Answers:

2. a) False   b) True
3. a) $x = 9$ b) $x = 24$

C.   Applications

Recall the six steps for solving word problems (Section 2.4).

Step 1   Read the problem carefully and identify the unknowns.

Step 2   Write down mathematical expressions for the unknowns.

Step 3   Translate the word problem into mathematical symbols.

Step 4   Solve the resulting equation.

Step 5   Respond to the question asked.

Step 6   Carry out the verification.

Example 4:   The length and width of a rectangular lot are in the ratio 5:3. If the perimeter of the lot is 800 yards, find the length and width.

Solution:

Step 1   The unknowns are the length and width of the rectangular lot.

Step 2   The length and width of the lot are in the ratio 5:3.

Let: length = $5x$, width = $3x$.

Warm Up

4.   The length and width of a rectangular field are in the ratio 4:3. If the perimeter of the field is 140 yards find the length and width.

125

Step 3   Therefore, $5x + 5x + 3x + 3x = 800$

$$\left[Perimeter \; = \; length + length + width + width \right]$$

Step 4   The resulting equation is :

$$16x = 800 \longrightarrow x = \frac{800}{16} \longrightarrow x = 50$$

Step 5   Length $= 5x = 5 \cdot 50 = 250$ yards
           Width $= 3x = 3 \cdot 50 = 150$ yards

Step 6   *Verification:*

Perimeter $= 250 + 250 + 150 + 150 = 800$ True

$$\frac{Length}{Width} = \frac{250}{150} = \frac{5}{3} \quad True$$

5. A university maintains a student-teacher ratio of 30:3. If a total of 7260 students are registered for the next spring, how many teachers will be needed to maintain the ratio?

Example 5:   A university maintains a student-teacher ratio of 28:3. If a total of 4172 students are registered for the next spring, how many teachers will be needed to maintain the ratio?

Solution:

Step 1   Let the required number of teachers be x.

Step 2   The ratios of 28:3 and 4172:x are proportions.

Step 3   Therefore, $\dfrac{28}{3} = \dfrac{4172}{x}$.

Step 4   Solve the equation. $28x = 4172(3)$
                                              $= 12516$

$$x = \frac{12516}{28} \quad \text{or} \quad x = 447$$

Step 5   Therefore, 447 teachers are required to maintain the ratio 28:3.

Step 6   *Verification:*

$$\frac{4172}{447} = \frac{28}{3} \longrightarrow \frac{2 \cdot 2 \cdot 7 \cdot 149}{149 \cdot 3} = \frac{28}{3} \longrightarrow \frac{28}{3} = \frac{28}{3} \quad True$$

6. The distance between Charlotte and Atlanta is 250 miles. On a certain map, this represents 6 inches. Raleigh, NC and Columbus, GA are situated 475 miles away. Find the length of the line that connects the two cities on the map.

Example 6:   Distance between Jackson, Mississippi and Atlanta, Georgia is 375 miles. On a certain map this is represented by a length of 9 inches. Memphis and Philadelphia are situated 1000 miles apart. Find the length of the line that connects the two cities on the map.

Solution:

Step 1   To find length which represents the distance between Philadelphia and Memphis on the map. Let this length be x inches.

Step 2   Therefore, the ratios 375:1000 and 9:x form a proportion.

Step 3 Thus, $\dfrac{375}{1000} = \dfrac{9}{x}$.

Step 4 Solve the equation.

$$375x = 9 \cdot 1000 \longrightarrow 375x = 9000$$

$$x = \dfrac{9000}{375} = 24 \text{ inches}$$

Step 5 The length that represents the distance between Memphis and Philadelphia is 24 inches.

Step 6 *Verification:*

$$\dfrac{375}{1000} = \dfrac{9}{24} \longrightarrow \dfrac{15}{40} = \dfrac{3}{8} \longrightarrow \dfrac{3}{8} = \dfrac{3}{8} \text{ True}$$

Example 7: A taxpayer pays a state tax of $500 on an income of $15000. If the tax rate remains the same how much state tax would he have to pay if his income increases by $6000?

Solution:

Step 1 Find the tax on the increased income.

Increased income $= 15000 + 60000 = 21000$

Let the state tax on an income of $21000 $= x$ dollars.

Step 2 The ratios $\dfrac{15000}{21000}$ and $\dfrac{500}{x}$ are a proportion.

Step 3 $\dfrac{15000}{21000} = \dfrac{500}{x}$

Step 4 $\dfrac{15000}{21000} = \dfrac{500}{x} \longrightarrow \dfrac{15}{21} = \dfrac{500}{x}$

$$\longrightarrow 15x = 10500$$

$$\longrightarrow x = \dfrac{10500}{15} \quad \text{or} \quad x = 700$$

Step 5 Therefore, the state tax on the increased income is $700.

Step 6 *Verification:*

$$\dfrac{15000}{21000} = \dfrac{500}{700} \longrightarrow \dfrac{15}{21} = \dfrac{5}{7} \longrightarrow \dfrac{5}{7} = \dfrac{5}{7} \text{ True}$$

Example 8: A certain mixture is made by mixing two ingredients in the ratio 3:5. If it is required to make 10 pounds of the mixture, how much of each ingredient will be needed.

Solution:

Step 1 Find the quantity of each of the ingredients. They are needed in the ratio 3:5.

7. A tax payer pays a state tax of $300 on a income of $9000. If the tax rate remains the same how much state tax would he have to pay if his income increases by 12,000.

8. A certain mixture is made by mixing two ingredients in the ratio 4:5. If it is required to make 20 pounds of mixture, how much of each ingredient will be needed?

127

Warm Up

Answers:

4. The length is 40 yards, width is 30 yards
5. 726 teachers
6. 11.40 inches
7. $700
8. Quantity of first ingredient is 8.88, quantity of second ingredient is 11.12

Step 2   Let the required quantities of the two ingredients be $3x$ and $5x$ respectively.

Step 3 $3x + 5x = 10$

Step 4   Solve the equation $3x + 5x = 10$

$8x = 10$ Combine like terms

$x = \dfrac{10}{8}$ or $x = 1.25$

Step 5   Quantity of the first ingredient
$= 3x = 3(1.25) = 3.75$ lbs

Quantity of the second ingredient
$= 5x = 5(1.25) = 6.25$ lbs

Step 6   *Verification:*

a)   Ratio of 3.75 to 6.25 $= \dfrac{3.75}{6.25} = \dfrac{375}{625} = \dfrac{3}{5}$ True

EXERCISE 2.6

Answers:

1. _____
2. _____
3. _____
4. _____
5. _____
6. _____
7. _____
8. _____
9. _____
10. _____
11. _____
12. _____
13. _____
14. _____
15. _____

In exercises 1–6, change each ratio to a fraction and reduce the fractions. Write the ratio in the lowest terms.

1. Ratio of 12 yards to 20 yards.
2. Ratio of 80°F to 60°F
3. Ratio of 4 yards to 18 feet
4. Ratio of 6 dimes to 9 nickels
5. Ratio of 8 pints to 5 quarts
6. Ratio of 6 days to 9 hours

In exercises 7–12, identify proportions.

7. $\dfrac{4}{9} = \dfrac{24}{29}$

8. $\dfrac{4}{7} = \dfrac{12}{21}$

9. $\dfrac{6}{8} = \dfrac{9}{12}$

10. $\dfrac{7}{10} = \dfrac{10}{7}$

11. $\dfrac{7}{12} = \dfrac{3.5}{6}$

12. $\dfrac{9}{12.5} = \dfrac{18}{25}$

In exercises 13–18, find the value of the unknown from the given proportions.

13. $\dfrac{6}{5} = \dfrac{a}{20}$

14. $\dfrac{4}{7} = \dfrac{24}{k}$

15. $\dfrac{x}{14} = \dfrac{15}{21}$

16. $\dfrac{75}{y} = \dfrac{9}{12}$ **17.** $\dfrac{8}{5} = \dfrac{7}{k}$ **18.** $\dfrac{m}{5} = \dfrac{4}{7}$

16. _____

19. 5 ounces of liver contains 37 grams of protein. How many ounces of liver will provide 111 gms of protein?

17. _____

18. _____

20. Sales tax on a $12 deep fryer is 90¢. How much would the sales tax be on a typewriter which costs $104?

19. _____

21 The distance between Birmingham, Alabama and Atlanta, Georgia is 150 miles. On a map it is shown by a length of 1.2 feet. On the same map the distance between Birmingham, Alabama and Jackson, Mississippi is shown by a length of 2 feet. What is the distance between the two cities.

20. _____

21. _____

22. A small tree 15 feet high casts a shadow 12 feet long. How long is shadow of another tree which is 9 ft 7 inches long?

22. _____

23. Which is a better buy for tomato ketchup:
14 ounces for $.96   or   32 ounces for $1.90

23. _____

24. Which is a better buy for spaghetti sauce:
15 ounces for $1.20   or   32 ounces for $2.40
         or   42 ounces for $3.20

24. _____

2.7   MORE APPLICATIONS

In this section we shall apply the techniques learned so far to solve additional application problems. Recall the steps for solving the word problems.

Upon completing this section we will be able to:

- Solve word problems involving mixtures; percents; simple interest; profit/loss; and distance, rate and time.

Warm Up

Example 1:	How many pounds of Brazilian coffee worth $6 per pound must be mixed with 27 lbs of Colombian coffee worth $4 per pound to produce a mixture worth $4.50 per pound.

1. How many pounds of Chinese coffee worth $10 per pound must be mixed with 30 lbs. of Columbian coffee worth $5 per pound to produce a mixture worth $8.00 per pound?

Solution:

Step 1   Let the quantity of Brazilian coffee needed to be mixed = *x lbs*

Step 2   No diagrams

Warm Up

Step 3   Brazilian coffee: Quantity = x lbs;   total cost = $6x$

Colombian Coffee: Quantity = 27 lbs; total cost =4(27)

Quantity of Mixture: $x + 27$; total cost = $4.50(x + 27)$

Step 4   The problem conveys that $6x + 4 \cdot 27 = 4.50(x + 27)$ since the mixture is obtained by simply adding the two ingredients.

Step 5   Solve the equation.

$$6x + 108 = 4.50x + 121.50$$
$$6x - 4.50x = 121.50 - 108$$
$$1.5x = 13.5$$
$$x = 9 \; lbs$$

Step 6   9 lbs of Brazilian coffee should be mixed with 27 lbs of Colombian coffee so that the mixture costs 4.50 per pound.

Step 7   Verification:

Cost of 9 lbs of Brazilian coffee $= 6 \cdot 9 = \$54$

Cost of 27 lbs of Colombian coffee $= 4 \cdot 27 = \$108$

Cost of the mixture $(9 + 27 = 36 \text{ lbs})$ $= (4.50)36$
$$= \$162$$
$$\$54 + \$108 = \$162 \quad \text{True}$$

2. A chemist has 30 liters of 20% acid solution. What is the amount of pure acid?

Example 2:   A chemist has 50 liters of 30% acid solution. What is the amount of pure acid in the solution?

Solution:

Step 1   Let the amount of pure acid $= x$

Step 2   No diagrams

Step 3   30% means .3

Step 4   The problem conveys that x is 30% of 50.
Thus, $x = (.3)(50)$ or $x = 15$.

Step 5   The equation $x = 15$ is already in the solution form.

Step 6   Therefore, 15 liters of pure acid are contained in the solution.

Step 7   Verification: $\frac{15}{50}(100) = 30\%$

130

Example 3:

A 40% acid solution is mixed with a 75% acid solution to produce 140 liters of a 50% acid solution. How many liters of each acid solution was mixed.

Solution:

Step 1   Let the 40% type of acid solution be x liters. Then the 75% type of acid solution is 140 - x liters.

Step 2   No diagrams.

Step 3   40% means 0.40;   50% means 0.50;   and 75% means 0.75.

Step 4   The problem translates to

$$(40\% \text{ of } x) + (75\% \text{ of } (140 - x)) = (50\% \text{ of } 140)$$

or $.4x + .75(140 - x) = .5(140)$

Step 5 $.4x + (.75)(140) - .75x = .5(140)$

$-.35x + (.75)(140) = .5(140)$

$\longrightarrow -.35 + 105 = 70$

$\longrightarrow -.35x = 70 - 105$

$\longrightarrow -.35x = -35$

$\longrightarrow 35x = 3500 \longrightarrow x = 100$

Step 6   40% acid solution $= x = 100$ liters

75% acid solution $= 140 - x = 140 - 100 = 40$ liters

Step 7   *Verification*

$$40\% \text{ of } 100 = .4(100) = 40$$
$$75\% \text{ of } 40 = .75(40) = 30$$
$$50\% \text{ of } 140 = .5(140) = 70$$
$$40 + 30 = 70 \qquad \textbf{True}$$

Note: You have enough practice in writing the solution with steps. From now onwards we shall discontinue this format. However, to fix your ideas you make a model. We shall also leave the verification to you.

Example 4:

A store marks up 20% profit on a television and sells it for $270. How much was the cost price of the television?

Solution:

Let the cost price of the television be x.

Profit marked up on the television = 20% of $x = .2x$

131

Warm Up

Selling price $=$ cost price $+$ profit $= x + .2x = (1 + .2)x = 1.2x$

Therefore, $1.2x = 270 \longrightarrow \dfrac{12}{10}x = 270 \longrightarrow 12x = 2700$

$$\longrightarrow x = \dfrac{2700}{12} \quad \text{or} \quad x = 225$$

Therefore, the cost price of the television was $225.

Model for the problem

Profit %	x	Cost	= Profit	Cost	+ Profit	= Sales Price
20% =.2	x		.2x	x	.2x	x + .2x

5. Leslie invested $6000 at 15% per year. How much money should she invest at 10% per year so that the annual income from the two investments is 12%.

Example 5: Leslie invested $5000 at 5% per year. How much money should she invest at 8% per year so that annual income from the two investments is 6%?

Solution:

Let the investment at 8% $= x$ dollars

Income from $5000 at 5% $= 5000(.05)(1)$ (I = PRT)

                       $= \$250$

Income from x dollars at 8% $= .08x$

Total desired income $= 6\%$ of the total investment

                       $= .06(x + 5000)$

Total income $=$ income from $5000 at 5% $+$ income from x at 8%.

       or $.06(x + 5000) = 250 + .08x$

               $.06x + 300 = 250 + .08x$

            $.06x - .08x = 250 - 300$

                  $-.2x = -50$

                      $x = 2500$

Therefore, Leslie should invest $2500 at 8%.

6. If investing a certain amount for two years at 6% brings $380 more than investing the same amount at 4% in the same time, find the amount invested.

Example 6: If investing a certain amount for two years at 8% brings $140 more than investing the same amount at 6% in the same time, find the amount to be invested.

Solution:

The difference $140 comes from the difference in the interests, since the amount invested is the same.

Now, let the amount to be invested $= x$.

Interest from 8% for two years $= x(.08)(2) = .16x$ (I = PRT)

Interest from 6% for two years $= x(.06)2 = .12x$

Difference between the interests $= .16x - .12x = .04x$

But the difference is given to be $140.

Therefore, $.04x = 140$ or $x = 3500$

Hence , the amount of money to be invested = $3500.

Example 7:   A part of $12,000 is invested at 5%, and the remaining at 9%. The annual income from the 9% investment is $180 less than the annual income from the 5% investment. How much amount is invested at each rate?

Solution:

Suppose the amount invested at 5% $= x$.
Then the amount invested at 9% $= 12000 - x$.
Interest from 5% investment $= x(.05)(1) = .05x$
Interest from 9% investment $= (12000 - x)(.09)$.
Now the interest from 9% investment is $180 less than the interest from the 5% investment.

Model for the Solution

	Principal	• Rate	= Interest
5% investment	x	.05	$.05x$
9% investment	$12000 - x$	.09	$.09(12000-x)=.05x-180$

Therefore, $(12000 - x)(.09) = .05x - 180$

or $1080 - .09x = .05x - 180$

$1080 + 180 = .05x + .09x$

$1260 = .14x$

$.14x = 1260$ or $x = \dfrac{1260}{.14}$ or $x = 9000$

Therefore, $9000 is invested at 5%, and $3000 $(= 12000 - 9000)$ is invested at 9%

Basic formula for solving distance problems is:

distance = rate • time   or   d = rt

Example 8:   John has to attend a meeting 150 miles away from his place. The meeting starts at 10 a.m. If John drives at an average speed of 60 miles per hour at what time should he leave this place to be at the meeting just in time?

Warm Up

7. A part of $20,000 is invested at 8% and the remaining at 9%.   The annual income from the 9% investment is $200 less than the annual income from the 8% investment. How much of the amount is invested at each rate?

8. Peter has to attend a meeting 200 miles away from his place.   The meeting starts at 11 a.m. If Peter drives at an average speed of 50 miles per hour, at what time should he leave this place to be just at the meeting?

Warm Up

9. A 2nd train leaves Atlanta for New York four hours after the first train. The first train travels at an average speed of 75 mile per hour. How long will it take the second train to overtake the first train if the second train travels at an average speed of 85 miles per hour?

10. A certain amount of money is invested in a bank at 8% simple interest for four years. The proceeds were again invested for two years at 6% simple interest. At the end of 6 years the amount received was 3200. How much money was invested?

Solution:

Suppose John takes t hours to drive to the scheduled place.

Rate	x	Time	=	Distance
60		t		150

Therefore, $60t = 150$ or $t = \dfrac{150}{60} = 2$ hrs and 30 minutes.

Hence, John must leave 2 hrs and 30 minutes before 10:00 a.m., that is at 7:30 am.

Example 9:   A 2nd train leaves Chicago for New York one hour after the first train. The first train travels at an average speed of 60 miles an hour. How long will it take the second train to overtake the first train if the second train travels at an average speed of 80 miles per hour.

Solution:

Suppose the second train travels t hours before it crosses the first train. While the second train travels t hours, the first train would have traveled $(t + 1)$ hours. *When the two trains meet, they will have traveled the same distance.*

Train	Rate	x	Time	=	Distance
First	60		t + 1		60(t + 1)
Second	80		t		80t

Therefore, at the point of overtaking

$$80t = 60(t + 1) \longrightarrow 80t = 60t + 60$$
$$\longrightarrow 80t - 60t = 60$$
$$\longrightarrow 20t = 60$$
$$\longrightarrow t = \frac{60}{20}$$
$$\longrightarrow t = 3$$

It will take the second train 3 hours to overtake the first.

Example 10:   A certain amount of money is invested in a bank at 6% simple interest for four years. The proceeds were again invested for three years at 5% simple interest. At the end of 7 years the amount received was $3422.40. How much money was invested?

Solution:

Let the money invested be x dollars. The first investment earns 6% for four years.

Model for the Problem

	Principal ·	Rate ·	Time	= Interest	Amount = P + I
6%	x	.06	4	.24x	$x + .24x$
5%	$x + .24x$	.05	3	$.05 \times 3(x + .24x)$	$(x + .24x) + .05 \times 3(x + .24x)$

After the first four years:

Interest $= x(.06)(4) = .24x$

The amount received at the end of four years

$$A = P + I = x + .24x = 1.24x$$

Now the interest on the second investment is the amount from $1.24x$ dollars (proceeds of the first investment) invested at 5% for three years. Therefore, on second investment

$$\text{Interest} = 1.24\, x(.05)(3) = .186x$$
$$\text{Final amount} = 1.24x + .186x = 1.426x$$

Now, $1.426x = 3422.40$

Therefore, $x = \dfrac{3422.40}{1.426} = 2400.$

Hence, the amount invested is $2400.

Example 11: A part of $6000 was invested at 6% annual interest and the remaining at 7% annual interest. If, at the end of one year, the total amount received was $6395. How much **money** was invested at each rate?

Solution:

Suppose x dollars were invested at 6%.

Then the amount invested at 7% $= 6000 - x$.

[The total amount to be invested is $6000.]

Model for the Problem

	Principal ·	Rate	= Interest	Amount = P + I
6%	x	.06	.06x	x + .06x
7%	6000 − x	.07	(6000 − x) (.07)	(6000 − x) + (6000 − x) (.07)
Total	6000		.06x + (6000 − x) (.07)	(6000 + .06x + (6000 − x) (.07) = 6395

135

Warm Up

Interest from 6% investment $= x(.06)(1) = .06x$

Interest from 7% investment
$$= (6000 - x)(.07)(1) = (6000 - x)(.07)$$

Total interest earned $= .06x + (6000 - x)(.07)$
$$= .06x + 420 - .07x = 420 - .01x$$

Total amount received after one year $= 6000 + 420 - .01x$
$$= 6420 - .01x$$

But the total amount received is given to be $6395.

Therefore, $6420 - .01x = 6395 \longrightarrow -.01x = 6395 - 6420$

$$\longrightarrow -.01x = -25$$
$$\longrightarrow .01x = 25$$
$$\longrightarrow x = \frac{25}{.01} \longrightarrow x = 2500$$

Therefore, $2500 was invested at 6% and $3500
$(= 6000 - 2500)$ was invested at 7%.

Example 12:   Two cyclists start out at the same time towards each other from points that are 140 miles apart. The first cyclist travels at an average speed of 30 miles per hour, and the second travels at an average speed of 40 miles an hour. After how many hours will they cross each other?

12. Two cyclist start out at the same time toward each other from points that are 170 miles apart. The first cyclist travels at average speed of 40 miles/hr and the second travels at an average speed of 45 miles an hour. After how many hours will they cross each other?

Solution:

Suppose the two cyclists meet after t hours.

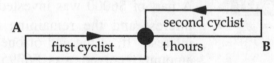

The sum of distances covered by the two cyclists in t hours equals the distance between two points, i.e. 140 miles.

Cyclist	Rate	x	Time	=	Distance
First	30		t		30t
Second	40		t		40t

Therefore, at the point of crossing

$$30t + 40t = 140 \longrightarrow 70t = 140$$
$$t = \frac{140}{70} \longrightarrow t = 2 \text{ hours}$$

The two cyclists will meet after two hours.

Answers:

1. 45 lbs.

2. $x = 6$; 6 liters of pure acid is in the solution

3. 20 liters, 70 liters   **4.** $161.54

5. 9000   **6.** 9500

7. $11764.70 at 8%, $8235.30 at 9%

8. at 7 a.m.

9. $t = 30$ hrs   **10.** $2164.50

11. 2000 at 4% ; 6000 at 5%

12. $t = 2$ hrs

Notes: **1.**   The units of rate and time should be compatible.

For example,
rate =60 miles per hour and time = 4 hours are compatible,
but rate =60 miles per hour and time = 50 minutes are not compatible.

2.   For comparison problems, such as two cars traveling, the units should be carefully looked into.

EXERCISE 2.7

Answers:

1.   Caramels worth $1.75 per pound are mixed with cream chocolates worth $2 per pound to make a 5 pound mixture that will be sold at $1.90 per pound. How many pounds of each are needed?

1. _____

2.   A grocer notices that he has 20 pounds of cashews that are getting stale and not selling for their cost of $6 a pound. He mixes these cashews with peanuts to sell the mixture for $3 per pound. If the peanuts sell for $1.50 a pound, how many pounds of peanuts are needed?

2. _____

3.   Cream has approximately 22% butterfat. How many gallons of cream must be mixed with 2% milk to give 20 gallons of milk containing 4% butterfat?

3. _____

4.   How much pure acid must be mixed with 60 liters of a solution that is 65% acid to obtain a new solution that is 75% acid?

4. _____

5.   How much water must be added to dilute 10 quarts of a solution that is 18% iodine so that the resulting solution will be 15% iodine?

5. _____

6.   A tank contains 40 gallons of water. How many gallons of water should be drained out so that when the remaining water is mixed with 10 gallons of alcohol, the resulting solution has 25% alcohol content?

6. _____

7.   An automobile dealer has $600,000 invested in compact cars and mid-size cars. The profit on the sale of the compact cars is 1%, and the profit on the sale of midsize cars is 16%. How much did the dealer invest in midsize cars if the overall profit on the total investment is 12%.

7. _____

8.   A film shop carrying black and white, and color films has $4000 in inventory. Profit on black and white films is 12% and the profit on color films is 21%. If the annual profit on color films is $150 less than the annual profit on black and white films, how much was invested in each type?

8. _____

9. _____

10. _____

11. _____

12. _____

13. _____

14. _____

15. _____

16. _____

9. A man invested a total of $15000 in two ventures. In one he made a profit of 8%, and in the other he suffered a loss of 4%. His net income from the two investments for the year was $240. How much did he invest in each venture?

10. Torrance split an inheritance between two investments, one paying 7% and the other paying 10%. He invested twice as much at 10% as at 7%. The combined annual income from two investments was $4050. How much did Torrance inherit?

11. Hesse wishes to earn $3500 per year in supplemental income from an inheritance of $40,000. He puts $10,000 in a bank paying 8%. What rate must he earn on the remainder so that his annual income is $3500?

12. Two planes leave the same airport at the same time and travel in the same direction. One plane flies at an average speed of 480 miles per hour and the other at 400 miles per hour. After how many hours will they be 300 miles apart?

13. A boat makes the round trip from main land to a fishing village in 6 hours. If the average speed of the boat while going to the village is 15 miles per hour, and the average speed while returning is 12 miles per hour, find the distance between the village and the mainland.

14. Linda and Kevin went on vacation. They drove to the airport to catch a plane. With an average speed of 55 miles per hour it took them two hours to reach the airport. Their plane cruised at 450 miles per hour. How long were they in the air if they traveled a total of 1460 miles?

15. A motorboat can go 18 miles per hour in still water. If it can go 80 miles downstream in 4 hours. Find the speed of the current. [Speed of the boat downstream = speed of the boat in still water + speed of the current]

16. At 4 p.m. a plane leaves San Francisco for Boston, traveling at an average speed of 500 miles per hour. Two hours later a plane departs from Boston to San Francisco traveling on air-route at an average of 400 miles per hour. The cities are 2800 miles apart, at what time do the planes pass each other? Disregard the time difference between two cities.

2.8   SOLUTIONS OF LINEAR INEQUALITIES

Recall the following facts

1. If we plot two numbers on a number line, the number on the right is greater than the other, and the number on the left is smaller.

2. The inequality symbols for two numbers or expressions are:

$a < b \longrightarrow a$ " is less than" b

$a \leq b \longrightarrow a$ " is less than or equal to" b

$a > b \longrightarrow a$ " is greater than" b

$a \geq b \longrightarrow a$ " is greater than or equal to" b

$a \neq b \longrightarrow a$ " is not equal to" b

Upon completion of this section, we will be able to:

A. Graph intervals on a number line
B. Use the addition property of inequality
C. Use the multiplication property of inequality
D. Solve linear inequalities
E. Solve three-part inequalities
F. Solve applied problems with linear inequalities

A.   Intervals and Their Graphs

Some of the interval graphs and its representation in two different forms are given below.

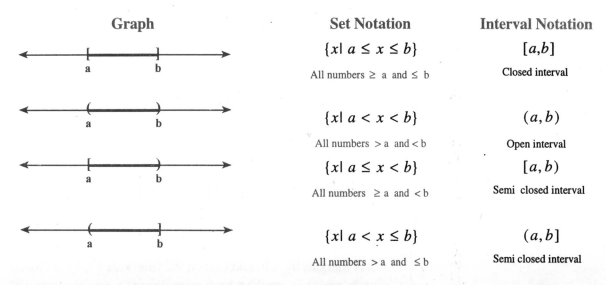

Graph	Set Notation	Interval Notation
	$\{x \mid a \leq x \leq b\}$	$[a,b]$
	All numbers $\geq$ a and $\leq$ b	Closed interval
	$\{x \mid a < x < b\}$	(a,b)
	All numbers $>$ a and $<$ b	Open interval
	$\{x \mid a \leq x < b\}$	$[a,b)$
	All numbers $\geq$ a and $<$ b	Semi closed interval
	$\{x \mid a < x \leq b\}$	$(a,b]$
	All numbers $>$ a and $\leq$ b	Semi closed interval

Note: An interval is represented by a segment of the real line.

139

Warm Up

1. Graph the intervals

a) $[4,6]$

b) $(4,6)$

c) $[4,6]$

Example 1:   Graph the intervals

a) $[3,4]$ b) $(3,4)$ c) $[3,4)$ d) $(3,4]$

Solutions:

a) $[3,4]$ is an example of a **closed interval.** $[3,4]$ represents the set of all real numbers between 3 and 4, *including both 3 and 4. Square brackets represent inclusion of end point.*

Step 1   Mark the numbers 3 and 4 on the real line.

3 and 4 are marked by square brackets since these points are included in the set $[3,4] = \{x \mid 3 \le x \le 4\}$.

Step 2   *Shade the line segment joining 3 and 4. This line segment is the graph of the interval* $[3,4]$.

$[3,4]$ may also be written as $3 \le x \le 4$.

b) $(3,4)$ is an example of an open interval. $(3,4)$ represents the set of all real numbers between 3 and 4; the end points 3 and 4 are **not included.** *{Parentheses represents exclusion of end points.*

Step 1   Mark the numbers 3 and 4 on the real line.

3 and 4 are marked by *parentheses* to emphasize that these points are *not included* in the set $(3,4) = \{x \mid 3 < x < 4\}$.

Step 2   Shade the line between 3 and 4. The shaded region is the graph of the interval $(3,4)$.

$(3,4)$ may also be written as $3 < x < 4$.

c) $[3,4)$ is an example of a *semi-closed* (half – closed) interval. The interval is *closed* on the left since 3 is *included* in the set $[3,4) = \{x \mid 3 \le x < 4\}$ and *open* on the right since 4 is *not included* in the set.

Step 1   Mark 3 and 4 on the real line

3 is marked by a bracket since the intervals $[3,4)$ is closed at 3; and 4 is marked by a parentheses since the interval $[3,4)$ is open at 4.

Step 2   Shade the line between 3 and 4. The shaded region is the graph of the interval $[3,4)$.

$[3,4)$ may also be represented by $3 < x \le 4$.

d) $(3,4]$ is an example of another kind of *semi-closed* interval, *closed* on the right since 4 is *included* in the set $(3,4] = \{x \mid 3 < x \le 4\}$, and open on the left since 3 is *not included* in the set.

d) $(4,6]$

Step 1   Mark 3 and 4 on the real line.

3 is marked by an *left parentheses* since the interval $(3,4]$ is *open* at 3; and 4 is marked by a *right bracket* since the interval $(3,4]$ is *closed* at 4.

Step 2   Shade the line between 3 and 4. The shaded region is the graph of the interval $(3,4]$.

$(3,4]$ may also be represented by $3 < x \le 4$.

Example 2:   Graph the intervals
a) $x > -3$ b) $x \ge -3$
c) $x < -3$ d) $x \le -3$

Solutions:

These are examples of infinite half intervals.

2. Graph the intervals

a) $x > 4$

a)   *Step 1*   Mark -3 on the real line.

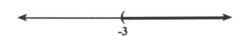

Mark -3 by a *left parentheses* since -3 is not included.

Step 2   Since all numbers greater than -3 lie on to the right of -3, the graph of $x > -3$ is the half line to the right of -3 (-3 not included).

$x > -3$ is also written as $(-3, \infty)$.

b)   The difference between the graphs $x > -3$ and $x \ge -3$ is that in case of $x > -3$, the point -3 is not included in the graph, and in case of $x \ge -3$ the point -3 is included in the graph. The graph of $x \ge -3$ is shown below.

b) $x \ge 4$

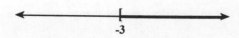

Warm Up

2. c) $x < 4$

    d) $x \leq 4$

Answers:

1.
a)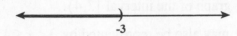
4   6

b)
4   6

c)
4   6

d)
4   6

2.
a)
4

b)
4

c)
4

d)
4

---

c)   The graph of $x < -3$ is shown below.

-3

Notice all numbers which are less than -3 lie to the left of -3, and -3 is *not included.*

$x < -3$ is also denoted by $\left(-\infty, -3\right)$.

d)   The difference between the graphs of $x < -3$ and $x \leq -3$ is similar to the difference between the graphs of $x > -3$ and $x \geq -3$. The graph of $x \leq -3$ is shown below.

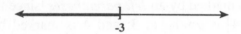
-3

$x \leq -3$ is also denoted by $\left(-\infty, -3\right]$.

B.   Use of Addition Property of Inequality

The solution set of an inequality is the set of all those real numbers which make the inequality true. The inequality $x < 3$ is true for all real numbers less than 3. Inequalities are solved in the same way as equations.

A linear inequality is said to have been solved when it is reduced to the forms:

$$x < k, \quad x \leq k, \quad x > k \quad \text{or} \quad x \geq k.$$

This reduced form is called the **solution** of the inequality.

Addition Property of Inequality

For any three real numbers a, b, c the following pairs of inequalities have the same solutions.

(i) $a < b$ and $a + c < b + c$ (ii) $a \leq b$ and $a + c \leq b + c$

(iii) $a > b$ and $a + c > b + c$ (iv) $a \geq b$ and $a + c \geq b + c$

Note: The Addition Property of Inequality asserts that an inequality does not change when same number is added to both sides of the inequality.

Example 3:   Solve the inequalities.

a) $3 + 4k < 3k + 10$ b) $-4 + 5k \le 6k + 9$

Solutions:

a)

$$3 + 4k < 3k + 10 \qquad \text{Add } -3 \text{ to both sides}$$

$$-\mathbf{3} + 3 + 4k < -\mathbf{3} + 3k + 10 \qquad \text{Simplify}$$

$$4k < 3k + 7 \qquad \text{Add } -3k \text{ to both sides}$$

$$-\mathbf{3k} + 4k < -\mathbf{3k} + 3k + 7 \qquad \text{Combine like terms}$$

$$k < 7$$

In interval notation the solution is $(-\infty, 7)$. The graph of the solution is:

b) $-4 + 5k \le 6k + 9 \quad \longrightarrow \quad -4 + 5k - 9 \le 6k + 9 - 9$

$$-13 + 5k \le 6k \quad \longrightarrow \quad -13 + 5k - \mathbf{5k} \le 6k - \mathbf{5k}$$

$$-13 \le k \qquad \text{or} \qquad k \ge -13$$

In interval notation the solution is $[-13, \infty)$. The graph of the solution is:

C. Multiplication Property of Inequality

Multiplication by a positive number on both sides of the inequality does not affect the solution of an inequality. If a > 0 (**positive number**) then the following pairs of inequalities have the same solutions.

(i) $b < c$ and $ab < ac$ (ii) $b \le c$ and $ab \le ac$

(iii) $b > c$ and $ab > ac$ (iv) $b \ge c$ and $ab \ge ac$

Multiplication or division by a *negative* number *reverses* the inequality symbol.

$$-2 < 1 \quad \longrightarrow \quad 2 > -1 \qquad\qquad \text{Multiplication with } -1 \text{ on both sides changed } < \text{ to } > .$$

becomes

Warm Up

4. Solve the inequalities

a) $5r \geq 20$

b) $-6r < 24$

Answers:

4. a) $r \geq 4$ b) $r > -4$

Example 4:   Solve the inequalities.

a) $4r \leq 16$ b) $-3r > 15$

Solutions:

a) $4r \leq 16$ $\longrightarrow$ $\dfrac{4r}{4} \leq \dfrac{16}{4}$ Divide by 4

   $\longrightarrow$ $r \leq 4$

In interval notation the solution is $(-\infty, 4]$.   The graph of the solution is:

b) $-3r > 15$ $\longrightarrow$ $\dfrac{-3r}{-3} < \dfrac{15}{-3}$ $\longrightarrow$ $r < -5$

Divide by - 3
> becomes <

Divide by - 3

In interval notation the solution is $(-\infty, -5)$. The graph of the solution is shown below.

D.   Solving Linear Inequalities

An inequality is called **linear** if on changing the *inequality sign* $(<, \leq, >, $ or $\geq)$ with an *equality sign* $(=)$, it becomes a linear equation.

1.   A linear inequality can always be written in one of the following forms.

$$ax > b, \ \ ax < b, \ \ ax \leq b, \ \ ax \geq b$$

2. $ax < b \ \longleftrightarrow \ b > ax$ $ax \leq b \ \longleftrightarrow \ b \geq ax$

There are two methods to solve a linear inequality.

Method 1:   Use the addition and multiplication property of inequalities.

Method 2:   Change the inequality to equality, solve the equation, plot the solution of the equation on the number line, and use test point on the number line to graph the solution of the inequality.

We will discuss a few problems by each method separately.

Method 1   Use the addition and multiplication property of inequalities.

> *Step 1*   Use the associative, commutative, and distributive properties of real numbers to combine like terms on both sides of the inequality.
>
> *Step 2*   Use the addition property of inequality to write it in one of the following form; $ax < b$, $ax \le b$, $ax > b$ or $ax \ge b$.
>
> *Step 3*   Use the multiplication property of inequality to further write the inequality in one of the form. $x < k$, $x \le k$, $x > k$ or $x \ge k$. Remember the inequality is reversed if we multiply / divide by a negative number.
>
> *Step 4*   Graph the inequality obtained in *Step 3*.

Example 5:   Solve the inequalities, and graph the solutions.

   a) $5x < 3(x - 4) + 7$

   b) $4x + 5 \ge 7(2x - 3) + 1$

Solutions:

a) $5x < 3(x - 4) + 7$

Step 1 $5x < 3(x - 4) + 7 \longrightarrow 5x < 3x - 5$

Step 2 $\longrightarrow -3x + 5x < -3x + 3x\ 5$

$\longrightarrow 2x < -5$

Step 3 $\longrightarrow \dfrac{1}{2}(2x) < \dfrac{1}{2}(-5) \longrightarrow x < -\dfrac{5}{2}$

Step 4   The graph of $x < -\dfrac{5}{2}$ is the interval $\left(-\infty, -\dfrac{5}{2}\right)$.

-5/2

b) $4x + 5 \ge 7(2x - 3) + 1$

Step 1 $4x + 5 \ge 14x - 21 + 1 \longrightarrow 4x + 5 \ge 14x - 20$

Step 2 $\longrightarrow 4x + 5 - 5 \ge 14x - 20 - 5$

$\longrightarrow 4x \ge 14x - 25$

$\longrightarrow -14x + 4x \ge -14x + 14x - 25$

$\longrightarrow -10x \ge -25$

Step 3 $\longrightarrow -\dfrac{1}{10}(-10x) \le -\dfrac{1}{10}(-25)$

$\longrightarrow x \le \dfrac{5}{2}$

Warm Up

5.   Solve the inequalities and graph the solution.

   a) $3x < 4(x - 1) + 1$

   b) $7x - 6 \ge 5(3x + 9) + 5$

145

Warm Up

6. Solve the inequality
$\frac{5}{3}x - 2 > \frac{17}{7}x + 4$

Step 4   The graph of $x \le \frac{5}{2}$ is the interval $\left(-\infty, \frac{5}{2}\right]$

(test point) 0   5/2

Example 6:   Solve the inequality $\frac{3}{4}x - 4 < \frac{4}{5}x + 1$ and graph the solution.

Solution:

$\frac{3}{4}x - 4 < \frac{4}{5}x + 1$.

This is an inequality which involves fractions.

The least common denominator of the fractions is 20.

$$20\left(\frac{3}{4}x - 4\right) < 20\left(\frac{4}{5}x + 1\right)$$ Multiplication Property

$$20\left(\frac{3}{4}x\right) - 20(4) < 20\left(\frac{4}{5}\right)x + 20(1)$$

$$15x - 80 < 16x + 20 \longrightarrow -x < 100$$

$$\longrightarrow x > -100$$ Multiply by -1

-100

We may use calculator to solve an inequality. See example 2, (section 2.8) in Appendix B.

Method 2   Change the inequality to an equation, solve the equation on the number line, and use a test point on the number line to graph the solution of the inequality.

Step 1   Replace the inequality sign by the equality sign.

Step 2   Solve the equation.

Step 3   Mark the solution obtained in Step 2 on the number line. This divides the line into two parts. (Mark the point with *an open circle* if the inequality is one of the types < or >, and by a solid dot if the inequality is one of the type ≤ or ≥.)

Step 4   Take a test point on either of the two parts of the line *[test point different from the solution]* , and substitute it into the original inequality. If this results is a true statement, the solution is the part of the line containing the test point. If this result is a false statement, then the solution is the part which does not contain the test point.

146

Example 7:

Solve the inequalities and plot the solutions

a) $5x < 3(x-4)+7$

b) $4x+5 \geq 7(2x-3)+1$

Solutions:

a) $5x < 3(x-4)+7$

Step 1 $5x = 3(x-4)+7$

Step 2 Solve the equation

$$5x = 3x - 12 + 7$$
$$5x = 3x - 5$$
$$-3x + 5x = -3x + 3x - 5$$
$$2x = -5 \longrightarrow x = -\frac{5}{2}$$

Step 3

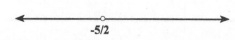
$-5/2$

Step 4 Choose a test point, different from $-\dfrac{5}{2}$.

Let us choose 0 as a test point. The number 0 lies on the right side of the point $-\dfrac{5}{2}$.

Substitute $x = 0$ in $5x < 3(x-4)+7$
$$5(0) < 3(0-4)+7 \longrightarrow 0 < -12 + 7$$
$$\longrightarrow 0 < -5 \qquad \text{False}$$

The graph of the solution is that part which *does not contain* zero.

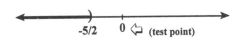
$-5/2 \qquad 0 \Leftarrow$ (test point)

b) $4x+5 \geq 7(2x-3)+1$

Step 1 $4x+5 = 7(2x-3)+1$
$$= 14x - 21 + 1$$

Step 2 $4x+5 = 14x - 20 \longrightarrow -10x = -25$
$$\longrightarrow x = \frac{-25}{-10} \quad \text{or} \quad x = \frac{5}{2}$$

Step 3

$5/2$

Warm Up

Answers:

5. a) $x > 3$ or $(3, \infty)$

   b) $x \leq -7$ or $(-\infty, -7]$

   -7

6. $x < -\dfrac{63}{8}$ or $\left(-\infty, -\dfrac{63}{8}\right)$

   -63/8

7. a) $x < 3$ or $(3, \infty)$

   3

   b) $x \geq 4$ or $[4, \infty)$

   4

Step 4   Take 0 as the test point $\left[0 \neq \dfrac{5}{2}\right]$.

Substitute $x = 0$ in the inequality.

$$4x + 5 \geq 7(2x - 3) + 1$$
$$\longrightarrow \quad 4(0) + 5 \geq 7(2 \cdot 0 - 3) + 1$$
$$\longrightarrow \quad\quad\quad 5 \geq -21 + 1$$
$$\longrightarrow \quad\quad\quad 5 \geq -20 \quad \text{True}$$

The graph of the solution is the part of the line which *contains* zero.

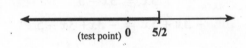

(test point) 0   5/2

E. Three Part Inequalities

Inequalities depicting that a number is between two given numbers are examples of three-part inequalities. Three part inequalities can be solved by using the addition and multiplication properties. These properties are used to reduce the given inequality in the form

$$a < x < b \quad \text{or} \quad a < x \leq b \quad \text{or} \quad a \leq x \leq b \quad \text{or} \quad a \leq x < b.$$

Warm Up

8. Solve the inequalities

   a) $6 < 3x < 9$

   b) $-12 < -6x < 24$

Example 8:   Solve the following three part inequalities

     a) $4 < 2x < 6$ b) $-8 < -4x \leq 12$

Solutions:

a) $4 < 2x < 6 \longrightarrow \dfrac{4}{2} < \dfrac{2x}{2} < \dfrac{6}{2} \longrightarrow 2 < x < 3$

The graph of the solution is the interval (2,3)

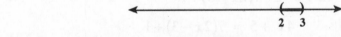

2   3

b) $-8 < -4x \leq 12 \longrightarrow \dfrac{-8}{-4} > \dfrac{-4x}{-4} \geq \dfrac{12}{-4}$ Notice the inequalities symbols are changed

$$\longrightarrow \quad 2 > x \geq -3$$
$$\longrightarrow \quad -3 \leq x < 2$$

The graph of the solution is the interval (−3,2)

-3   2

Example 9: Solve the following three part inequalities

a) $-3 \le 1 - 2x \le 6$ b) $5 \le 3x - 1 < 11$

Solutions:

a) $-3 \le 1 - 2x \le 6$

$-1 - 3 \le -1 + 1 - 2x \le -1 + 6$ Add -1; Addition Property

$-4 \le -2x \le 5$

$\left(-\dfrac{1}{2}\right)(-4) \ge \left(-\dfrac{1}{2}\right)(-2x) \ge -\dfrac{1}{2}(5)$ Multiplication Property $-\dfrac{1}{2}$ is negative

$2 \ge x \ge -\dfrac{5}{2} \longrightarrow -\dfrac{5}{2} \le x \le 2$

The graph of the solution $-\dfrac{5}{2} \le x \le 2$ is the interval $\left[-\dfrac{5}{2}, 2\right]$.

-5/2   2

b) $5 \le 3x - 1 < 11 \longrightarrow 5 + 1 \le 3x < 11 + 1$

$6 \le 3x < 12 \longrightarrow \dfrac{1}{3}(6) \le \dfrac{1}{3}(3x) < \dfrac{1}{3}(12)$

$\longrightarrow 2 \le x < 4$

The graph of the solution $2 \le x < 4$ is the interval $[2, 4)$.

2   4

Warm Up

9. **a)** $-2 \le 2 - 2x \le 6$

b) $7 < 4x - 3 \le 13$

Answers:

8. a) $2 < x < 3$ **b)** $-4 < x < 2$

9. a) $-2 \le x \le 2$ **b)** $\dfrac{5}{2} < x \le 4$

F. Solving an Application Problem

Example 10: Classie has test grades of 78, 84, and 76 on the first three tests in her pre-algebra class. What are the possible scores she can make on the fourth test in order to make at least a letter grade of "B" after the fourth test. A Letter grade "B" or above means an average of at least 80.

Solution:

Suppose the score that Classie makes on the fourth test $= x$.

The average of the four tests $= \dfrac{78 + 84 + 76 + x}{4}$.

Classie's grade will be at least B if $\dfrac{78 + 84 + 76 + x}{4} \ge 80$.

Warm Up

10. Manda scored grades of 78, 65, 43 on her first three exams. What must she make in her last test to get at least an average of 70?

Warm Up

(Average is at least 80)

$$\frac{238 + x}{4} \geq 80 \longrightarrow 4\left(\frac{238 + x}{4}\right) \geq 4(80)$$

$$\longrightarrow 238 + x \geq 320$$

$$\longrightarrow -238 + 238 + x \geq -238 + 320$$

$$\longrightarrow x \geq 82$$

Classie needs to score at least an 82 on the fourth test.

Example 11: Chris has test grades of 75, 89, and 94 on her first three tests. Can she make a letter grade "A" after the fourth test? A Letter grade 'A' means 90 or more.

11. Erin scored grades of 55, 97, 96 on his first three test. Can he still score an average of an A or at least 90 after the fourth test?

Solution:

Suppose that Chris makes x on the fourth test

Then her average of the 4th test will be $= \dfrac{75 + 89 + 94 + x}{4}$

$$= \frac{258 + x}{4}$$

Chris' grade will be an A if

$$\frac{258 + x}{4} \geq 90 \longrightarrow 4\left(\frac{258 + x}{4}\right) \geq 4(90)$$

$$\longrightarrow 258 + x \geq 360 \longrightarrow x \geq 360 - 258 \longrightarrow x \geq 102$$

Answers:

10. $x \geq 94$

11. No, he needs at least 112 to score an A which is above 100.

Since Chris cannot make 102 out of 100, she cannot make an 'A' after the fourth test.

EXERCISE 2.8

Answers:

1. _____
2. _____
3. _____
4. _____
5. _____
6. _____
7. _____
8. _____
9. _____
10. _____

Graph the intervals in exercises 1–8.

1. $(-3, 7]$ **2.** $[0, 6]$ **3.** $(-5, -2]$ **4.** $[-2, 0)$

5. $x \geq 4$ **6.** $x > -3$ **7.** $x < 0$ **8.** $x \leq -1$

In exercises 9–10, use the addition property to write the inequality in the form $ax < b$, or $ax > b$.

9. $3 - 7x \leq 5x + 15$ **10.** $2y + 4 > 3 - 6y$

In exercises 11–14, use the multiplication property to solve the inequalities.

11. $5r \leq 20$ **12.** $-4r \geq 15$ **13.** $-3r < 21$ **14.** $6r > 12$

In exercises 15–21, solve the inequalities, and graph the solution.

15. $-7p < 4p + 22$ **16.** $5(x-1) \leq 3x + 1$

17. $5 - (2-z) > 3z + 5$ **18.** $4(2-3k) \geq 9 - 5(2k-1)$

19. $10x + 5 - (x-15) \leq x + 3 - 23$ **20.** $x + (x-5) \geq x$

21. $(x+3) - (x-3) > x + 1$

Solve the following three-part inequalities in exercises 22–24, and graph the solution in each case.

22. $-2 < -t + 3 < 5$ **23.** $15 > 2x - 7 \geq 9$

24. $-6 \leq -3(x-4) < 24$

25. The $19 wholesale cost of a clock radio added to the profit must not be more than $32 or the radio will not sell. What are the possible profits?

26. Lawanda has test scores of 70, 77, 85. What score on the fourth test would give her an average of 80 or better?

27. Lisa invests $10,000 at 8% annual simple interest. How much more should she invest at 9% so that her annual interest will exceed $1250?

28. The length of a rectangle is 5 feet greater than its width. If the perimeter must be at least 38 feet, but no more than 62 feet, find possible values of the width.

29. A student has test scores of 85, 75, and 98 on the first three tests. Letter grade of 'A" means an average of 90 or more. Can the student make an 'A' after the fourth test?

11. _____

12. _____

13. _____

14. _____

15. _____

16. _____

17. _____

18. _____

19. _____

20. _____

21. _____

22. _____

23. _____

24. _____

25. _____

26. _____

27. _____

28. _____

29. _____

2.9   ABSOLUTE VALUE EQUATIONS AND INEQUALITIES

Recall the definition of the absolute value of a number.

$|x|$ = distance of the number x from the origin.

The distance of -5 and 5 on the number line from the origin is 5.

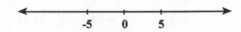

Therefore, $|-5| = 5$ and $|5| = 5$.

We shall use this definition of $|x|$ and solve equations and inequalities of the type.

$$|ax+b| = k \ , \quad |ax+b| \leq k \ , \quad |ax+b| \geq k \ , \ |ax+b| < k \ , \quad |ax+b| > k$$

Upon completion of this section, we will be able to:

A.   Solve simple equations involving absolute value.
B.   Solve simple inequalities involving absolute value.
C.   Identify absolute value equations or inequalities having no solution.

A.   Solution of Equations Involving Absolute Values

Consider the equation $|x+3| = 5$.

By definition this means that the number $x + 3$ is at the distance of 5 unit from the origin. This is equivalent to saying that

$$
\begin{array}{lll}
x+3 = 5 & \text{or} & x+3 = -5 \\
\longrightarrow \quad x = 5-3 & \text{or} & x = -5-3 \\
 = 2 & & = -8
\end{array}
$$

These values of x are the solutions of the equation $|x+3| = 5$. Let us check this.

Check: $x = 2,$ $|2+3| = 5 \longrightarrow |5| = 5$ True

$x = -8,$ $|-8+3| = 5 \longrightarrow |-5| = 5$ True

We can generalize the above observation into the following rule.

> **If $|ax+b| = k$, $k > 0$ then**
>
> $ax+b = k$ **or** $ax+b = -k$

Example 1: Solve the equations.

   a) $|x - 5| = 9$ **b)** $|3x - 4| = 7$

Solutions:

a) $|x - 5| = 9$

$\longrightarrow$ $x - 5 = 9$ or $x - 5 = -9$

$\longrightarrow$ $x = 9 + 5$ or $x = -9 + 5$

$\qquad = 14$ $\qquad\qquad = -4$

The solutions are $x = 14$ and $x = -4$.

Verify the solutions by substituting these values in the original equation.

b) $|3x - 4| = 7$

$\longrightarrow 3x - 4 = 7$ or $3x - 4 = -7$

$\longrightarrow \quad 3x = 11$ or $3x = -3$

$\qquad x = \dfrac{11}{3}$ or $x = -1$

Verify the solutions by substituting these values in original equations.

Example 2: Solve the equations.

   a) $|5 - 3x| = 4$ **b)** $\left|\dfrac{5}{2} - \dfrac{x}{2}\right| = \dfrac{3}{2}$

Solutions:

a) $|5 - 3x| = 4$

$\longrightarrow \quad 5 - 3x = 4$ or $5 - 3x = -4$

$\longrightarrow \quad -3x = -1$ or $-3x = -9$

$\qquad x = \dfrac{1}{3}$ or $x = 3$

Verify the solutions by substituting these values in the original equation.

b) $\left|\dfrac{5}{2} - \dfrac{x}{2}\right| = \dfrac{3}{2}$

$\longrightarrow \quad \dfrac{5}{2} - \dfrac{x}{2} = \dfrac{3}{2}$ or $\dfrac{5}{2} - \dfrac{x}{2} = -\dfrac{3}{2}$

$\longrightarrow \quad 5 - x = 3$ or $5 - x = -3$

$\longrightarrow \quad -x = -2$ or $-x = -8$

$\longrightarrow \quad x = 2$ or $x = 8$

Verify the solutions by substituting these values in the original equations.

Warm Up

1. Solve the equations.

    a) $|x - 7| = 4$

    b) $|2x - 9| = 8$

2. Solve the equations.

    a) $|4 - 5x| = 11$

    b) $\left|\dfrac{7}{3} - \dfrac{x}{2}\right| = \dfrac{11}{6}$

Answers:

1. **a)** $x = 11, 3$ **b)** $x = \dfrac{17}{2}, \dfrac{1}{2}$

2. **a)** $x = -\dfrac{7}{5}, 3$ **b)** $x = 1, \dfrac{25}{3}$

B.   Solution of Inequalities Involving Absolute Values

Consider the equation $|x| < 3$.

By definition this means x is any number at a distance less than 3 units from the origin. This is equivalent to saying x is any point on the number line between -3 and 3.

$$\longrightarrow \quad x > -3 \quad \text{and} \quad x < 3$$

Thus solution to the inequality $|x| < 3$ is $x > -3$ and $x < 3$ or written in a compact form as a double inequality, the solution of $|x| < 3$ is $-3 < x < 3$.

Graphically the solution of $|x| < 3$ is an open interval $(-3, 3)$.

$|x| < 3$:

We can generalize the above observation into the following rule.

> **If $|ax + b| < k$, $k > 0$ then**
>
> $ax + b > -k$ **and** $ax + b < k$

Warm Up

3. Solve the inequalities and graph the solution.

a) $|x - 3| < 13$

b) $|2x - 5| < 9$

Example 3:   Solve the inequalities.

   a) $|x - 5| < 8$ b) $|3x - 7| < 11$

Solutions:

a) $|x - 5| < 8$

$\longrightarrow \qquad x - 5 > -8 \quad \text{and} \quad x - 5 < 8$

$\longrightarrow \qquad\quad x > -3 \quad \text{and} \qquad x < 13$

$\qquad\qquad\quad \text{or} \qquad -3 < x < 13$

The solution is the **open interval** $(-3, 13)$ and its graph is

b) $|3x - 7| < 11$

$\longrightarrow \quad 3x - 7 > -11 \quad \text{and} \quad 3x - 7 < 11$

$\longrightarrow \qquad 3x > -4 \quad \text{and} \qquad 3x < 18$

$\longrightarrow \qquad x > -\dfrac{4}{3} \quad \text{and} \qquad x < 6$

$\qquad\qquad \text{or} \quad -\dfrac{4}{3} < x < 6$

The solution is the **open interval** $\left(-\dfrac{4}{3}, 6\right)$ and its graph is

154

The inequalities in example 3 were strict inequalities, therefore, the solutions were open intervals and did not include the end points. In case of non-strict inequalities, the solutions will include the end points of the solution interval as discussed in the following examples.

Warm Up

Example 4:   Solve the inequalities and graph the solutions.

   a) $|x-3| \leq 12$ **b)** $|2x-4| \leq 7$

4. Solve the inequalities and graph the solutions.

Solutions:

a) $|x-3| \leq 12$

$\longrightarrow$ $x-3 \geq -12$ and $x-3 \leq 12$

$\longrightarrow$ $x \geq -9$ and $x \leq 15$

           or $-9 \leq x \leq 15$

The solution is the **closed interval** $[-9, 15]$ and its graph is

a) $|x-9| \leq 4$

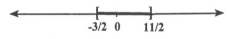

-9   0   15

b) $|2x-4| \leq 7$

$\longrightarrow$ $2x-4 \geq -7$ and $2x-4 \leq 7$

$\longrightarrow$ $2x \geq -3$ and $2x \leq 11$

$\longrightarrow$ $x \geq -\dfrac{3}{2}$ and $x \leq \dfrac{11}{2}$

           or $-\dfrac{3}{2} \leq x \leq \dfrac{11}{2}$

b) $|5x-7| \leq 8$

The solution is the **closed interval** $\left[-\dfrac{3}{2}, \dfrac{11}{2}\right]$ and its graph is

-3/2 0   11/2

Consider now the inequality $|x| > 3$. By definition, this means the distance of x from the origin is greater than 3. This is equivalent to saying that x is any point on the number line either on the left of -3 $(x < -3)$ or on the right of 3 $(x > 3)$.

Thus the solution to the inequality $|x| > 3$ is $x < -3$ **or** $x > 3$.

-3   0   3

Graphically the solutions of $|x| > 3$ are two disjoint intervals $(-\infty, -3)$ or $(3, \infty)$.

We usually write these solutions in the form: $(-\infty, -3) \cup (3, \infty)$.

We can generalize the above observation into the following rule.

If $|ax+b| > k$, $k > 0$ then

$ax+b < -k$ or $ax+b > k$

Warm Up

5. Solve the inequality and graph the solutions.

a) $|3x + 4| > 13$

b) $|5 - 3x| > 14$

Example 5:   Solve the inequalities and graph the solutions.

a) $|2x + 3| > 5$ b) $|3 - 4x| > 9$

Solutions:

a) $|2x + 3| > 5$

$\longrightarrow$ $2x + 3 < -5$ or $2x + 3 > 5$

$\longrightarrow$ $2x < -8$ or $2x > 2$

$\longrightarrow$ $x < -4$ or $x > 1$

Graphically the solution is

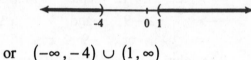

or $(-\infty, -4) \cup (1, \infty)$

b) $|3 - 4x| > 9$

$\longrightarrow$ $3 - 4x < -9$ or $3 - 4x > 9$

$\longrightarrow$ $-4x < -12$ or $-4x > 6$

Recall that if we divide both sides of an inequality by a negative number (-4 in this case) then the inequality symbol is reversed.

$\longrightarrow$ $\dfrac{-4x}{-4} > \dfrac{-12}{-4}$ or $\dfrac{-4x}{-4} < \dfrac{6}{-4}$

$\longrightarrow$ $x > 3$ or $x < -\dfrac{3}{2}$

Graphically the solution is

or $\left(-\infty, -\dfrac{3}{2}\right) \cup (3, \infty)$

Recall if the inequality is non-strict, then we include the end points of the solution interval, as discussed in the following examples.

6. Solve the inequalities and graph the solutions.

a) $|3x - 4| \geq 5$

Example 6:   Solve the inequalities and graph the solutions.

a) $|2x + 3| \geq 5$ b) $|5 - 7x| \geq 26$

Solutions:

a) $|2x - 3| \geq 5$

$\longrightarrow$ $2x - 3 \leq -5$ or $2x - 5 \geq 5$

$\longrightarrow$ $2x \leq -2$ or $2x \geq 10$

$\longrightarrow$ $x \leq -4$ or $x \geq 5$

156

Graph of the solution is

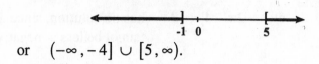

or $(-\infty, -4] \cup [5, \infty)$.

b) $|5 - 7x| \ge 26$

$\longrightarrow \quad 5 - 7x \le -26 \quad$ or $\quad 5 - 7x \ge 26$

$\longrightarrow \quad -7x \le -31 \quad$ or $\quad -7x \ge 21$

Recall division by a negative number reverses the inequality symbol.

$\longrightarrow \quad x \ge \dfrac{31}{7} \quad$ or $\quad x \le -3$

Graph of the solution is

$$\xleftarrow{\qquad\qquad} \overset{-3}{\rule{0pt}{0pt}} \quad 0 \quad \overset{31/7}{\rule{0pt}{0pt}} \xrightarrow{\qquad\qquad}$$

or $(-\infty, -3] \cup \left[\dfrac{31}{7}, \infty\right)$.

Warm Up

b) $|6 - 3x| \ge 7$

Answers:

3. a) $(-10, 16)$ b) $(-2, 7)$

$\xleftarrow{\ (\ \ \ )\ }$ $\xleftarrow{\ (\ )\ }$
   -10   16   -2   7

4. a) $[5, 13]$ b) $\left[-\dfrac{1}{5}, 3\right]$

   5   13   -1/5   3

5. a) $\left(-\infty, -\dfrac{17}{5}\right) \cup (3, \infty)$

   -17/3   3

   b) $(-\infty, -3) \cup \left(\dfrac{19}{3}, \infty\right)$

   -3   19/3

6. a) $\left(-\infty, -\dfrac{1}{3}\right] \cup [3, \infty)$

   -1/3   3

   b) $\left(-\infty, -\dfrac{1}{3}\right] \cup \left[\dfrac{13}{3}, \infty\right)$

   -1/3   13/3

C. Absolute Value Equations, and Inequalities with no Solutions

Recall absolute value of a number is always a non-negative quantity. Consequently, following equations and inequalities have no solutions.

$\quad |2x - 3| = -4 \qquad$ has no solution since a non-negative number never **equals to** -4

$\quad |2x - 3| < -4 \qquad$ has no solution since a non-negative number is never **less than** -4.

Consider now the inequality $\quad |x - 4| > -4$.

This inequality is always true, since left side of the inequality is non-negative and right side is negative and a non-negative number is always greater than a negative number.

Thus solution to the inequality of the type $|x - 4| > -4$ is all real numbers.

Example 7:   Solve the inequalities.

    a) $\quad |x - 2| = -4 \qquad$ **b)** $\quad |2x - 3| = 0$

    c) $\quad |2x - 4| < -3 \qquad$ **d)** $\quad |3x - 4| \ge -5$

Solutions:

    a) $\quad |x - 2| = -4$ has no solution.

    b) $\quad |2x - 3| = 0$

$$\longrightarrow \quad 2x - 3 = 0 \quad \longrightarrow \quad 2x = 3 \quad \longrightarrow \quad x = \frac{3}{2}$$

Warm Up

7.   Solve the inequalities.

    a) $\quad |3x - 5| = -5$

    b) $\quad |5x - 10| = 0$

Warm Up

c) $|3x - 7| < -9$

d) $|5x - 4| > -7$

Answers:
7. a) No solution   b) $x = 2$
   c) No solution   d) $(-\infty, \infty)$

c) $|2x - 4| < -3$ has no solution, since a non-negative cannot be less a negative.

d) $|3x - 4| \geq -5$ is always true. Therefore, all real numbers are solutions or the solution interval is $(-\infty, \infty)$.

EXERCISE 2.9

Answers:

1. _____
2. _____
3. _____
4. _____
5. _____
6. _____
7. _____
8. _____
9. _____
10. _____
11. _____
12. _____
13. _____
14. _____
15. _____
16. _____
17. _____
18. _____
19. _____
20. _____
21. _____

Solve the equations in exercises 1–12,

1. $|x| = 3$
2. $|x - 4| = 2$
3. $|x + 7| - 3 = 6$

4. $|2x - 4| = 5$
5. $|5 - 3x| - 2 = 5$
6. $|x - 4| = 0$

7. $\left| \dfrac{x}{2} - 5 \right| = \dfrac{3}{2}$
8. $\left| \dfrac{2x}{3} - \dfrac{1}{2} \right| = \dfrac{5}{6}$
9. $\left| \dfrac{2}{3} - x \right| = \dfrac{7}{2}$

10. $|7 - x| = -5$
11. $\left| 9x - \dfrac{5}{2} \right| = \dfrac{7}{3}$
12. $\left| 5 - \dfrac{3x}{2} \right| = \dfrac{11}{3}$

In exercises 13–39, solve and graph the inequalities.

13. $|x| < 3$
14. $|x - 2| < 5$
15. $|x + 7| + 4 \leq 8$

16. $|2x - 1| < 5$
17. $|2x - 4| < 7$
18. $|3x - 4| - 5 \leq 3$

19. $|2x - 3| < -3$
20. $|5x - 3| \leq -4$
21. $\left| \dfrac{2x}{3} - \dfrac{1}{2} \right| \leq \dfrac{11}{6}$

158

Answers:

22. $|x| > 3$

23. $|x - 1| > 5$

24. $|x + 5| \geq 6$

25. $|2x - 1| > 7$

26. $|3x - 2| > 13$

27. $|5x - 7| \geq 18$

28. $|x - 7| > -2$

29. $|2x - 9| > 0$

30. $|9x - 7| \geq 0$

31. $\left|\dfrac{2x}{3} - \dfrac{1}{2}\right| \geq \dfrac{5}{2}$

32. $\left|\dfrac{2x}{5} - \dfrac{1}{2}\right| \geq \dfrac{7}{10}$

33. $\left|\dfrac{2x}{7} - \dfrac{1}{2}\right| \geq \dfrac{9}{2}$

34. $|2x + 7| \geq \dfrac{9}{5}$

35. $|5x - 9| \geq -9$

36. $|2x - 5| \leq 0$

37. $|2 - x| \geq 4$

38. $|2 - 3x| \geq 5$

39. $|5 - 2x| \geq -4$

22. _____
23. _____
24. _____
25. _____
26. _____
27. _____
28. _____
29. _____
30. _____
31. _____
32. _____
33. _____
34. _____
35. _____
36. _____
37. _____
38. _____
39. _____

2.10   CHAPTER SUMMARY

Examples

1. We can simplify expressions by combining only the like terms.

1.
$$\underbrace{2x + 3x}\ \underbrace{- 7 + 9} = 5x + 2$$

2. Addition Property:
The **same** number may be added to each side of an equation. This does not change the solution or the original equation.

2.
$$2x + 3 = 0$$
$$2x + 3 + (-3) = 0 + (-3)$$
$$2x = -3$$

3. Multiplication Property:
Both sides of an equation may be multiplied (or divided) by the **same non-zero** number. Again, this does not change the solution of the original equation.

3.
$$2x = -3$$
$$\frac{1}{2} \cdot 2x = \frac{1}{2} \cdot (-3)$$
$$x = -\frac{3}{2}$$

Examples

4. Steps for solving a Linear Equation:

    Step 1   Combine like terms on each side and simplify.

    Step 2   Use the addition property to write the equation in the form $ax = b$

    Step 3   Use the multiplication property of equality to write the equation in the form $x = k$

    Step 4   Verify the solution by substituting it in the original equation.

4. $2x + 4x - 3 = x + 3 + 7$

$6x - 3 = x + 10$

$6x - 3 + 3 = x + 10 + 3$
$6x = x + 13$
$6x + (-x) = x + 13 + (-x)$
$5x = 13$

$\dfrac{1}{5}(5x) = \dfrac{1}{5}13 \;\to\; x = \dfrac{13}{5}$

$6\left(\dfrac{13}{5}\right) - 3 = \dfrac{13}{5} + 10$

$\to \dfrac{78}{5} - 3 = \dfrac{13}{5} + 10$

$\to \dfrac{63}{5} = \dfrac{63}{5}$ True

5. An equation with exactly one solution is called a conditional equation.

6. An equation which on simplification becomes a **true statement** is called an identity. An **identity** is true for all real numbers.

7. An equation which on simplification leads to a **false statement** has **no solution.** Such an equation is called a **contradiction.**

8. **To solve a word problem involving linear equations,** read the problem carefully and follow the steps:

    Step 1   Identify the unknown; choose a variable to represent the unknown.

    Step 2   Write down mathematical expressions for any other unknown quantities using the variable. If possible, draw figures or diagrams.

    Step 3   Translate the problem into an equation

    Step 4   Solve the equation

    Step 5   Answer the question asked. Make sure the solution makes sense in reference to the question.

    Step 6   Verify your answer by using the original statement of the problem.

Literal Equations

9. If values of all but one variable in a formula are given, then the value of the remaining variable can be found by substituting the given values into the formula and solving for the remaining variable.

9. $3xy + 4x^2 = 4x - 4$
find y when $x = 2$

$3(2)y + 4(2)^2 = 4(2) - 4$
$\to 6y + 16 = 8 - 4$
$\to 6y + 16 = 4 \to 6y = -12$
$\to 6y = -12$
$\to y = -2$

10.   A formula can be solved for a specified variable by treating all other variables as constants and then solving the resulting equation for the specified variable.

10.   Solve for F; $C = \dfrac{5}{9}(F - 32)$

$\rightarrow 9C = 5F - 160$

$\rightarrow 5F = 9C + 160$

$\rightarrow F = \dfrac{1}{5}(9C + 160) = \dfrac{9}{5}C + 32$

Ratios and Proportions

11.   To calculate a ratio of two quantities, they must be expressed in the same units, if possible.

11.   Ratio of 5 cents to 2 dollars is:

$\dfrac{5 \text{ cents}}{2 \text{ dollars}} = \dfrac{5 \text{ cents}}{200 \text{ cents}} = \dfrac{5}{200} = \dfrac{1}{40}$

12.   **A proportion is an equality** of two ratios. You can use the method of cross multiplication for solving a proportion.

12.   Ms. Tonya earns \$150 working 12 hours a week. How much does she earn if she works 18 hours ?

$\dfrac{\$x}{\$150} = \dfrac{18 \text{ hours}}{12 \text{ hours}}$

$\rightarrow \dfrac{x}{150} = \dfrac{18}{12} \rightarrow \dfrac{x}{150} = \dfrac{3}{2}$

$\rightarrow 2x = 3 \cdot 150 = 450$

$\rightarrow \quad x = \dfrac{450}{2} = 225$

She earns \$225 working 18 hours a week.

Addition and Multiplication Properties of Inequality

13.   **Addition Property:** If the same number is added to each side of an inequality, the inequality does not change.

13. $3x + 4 \leq 3$

$\rightarrow 3x + 4 + (-4) \leq 3 + (-4)$

$\rightarrow 3x \leq -1$

14.   **Multiplication Property:** Multiplying (or dividing) both sides of an inequality by a negative number reverses the inequality. Multiplying both sides with a positive number does not change the inequality.

14. $-3x \leq 1$

$\rightarrow \dfrac{1}{-3}(-3x) \geq \dfrac{1}{-3}(1)$

$\rightarrow x \geq -\dfrac{1}{3}$

15.   **To solve and graph an inequality**

Step 1   Combine like terms on both sides and simplify.

Step 2   Use the addition property of inequalities to write the inequality in the form $ax < b$, etc.

Step 3   Use the multiplication property of inequalities to further write the inequality in the $x < k$ form etc.

Step 4   Graph the inequality.

15.   Solve $3x + 1 \leq x - 4$

Not needed

$3x + 1 + (-1) \leq x - 4 + (-1)$

$\rightarrow 3x \leq x - 5$

$\rightarrow 3x + (-x) \leq x - 5 + (-x)$

$\rightarrow 2x \leq -5$

$\dfrac{1}{2}(2x) \leq \dfrac{1}{2}(-5)$

$\rightarrow x \leq \dfrac{-5}{2}$

(test point) 0   5/2

Solution of Absolute Value
Equations and Inequalities

Examples

16.-17. To solve $|ax + b| = c$, $c > 0$ we solve two equations

$$ax + b = c \quad \textbf{and} \quad ax + b = -c.$$

If $c > 0$ then this equation has two solutions, if $c = 0$ then one solution.

16. $|2x - 3| = 5$

$\rightarrow 2x - 3 = 5 \quad$ or $\quad 2x - 3 = -5$

$\rightarrow \quad 2x = 8 \quad$ or $\quad\quad 2x = -2$

$\rightarrow \quad\quad x = 4 \quad$ or $\quad\quad\quad x = -1$

17. $|x - 2| = 0$ has one solution $x = 2$

18. To solve $|ax + b| \le k$, $k > 0$ we solve two inequalities

$$ax + b \le k \quad \textbf{and} \quad ax + b \ge -k$$

We can write the solution in a compact form as an interval.

18. $|2x - 3| \le 5$

$\rightarrow 2x - 3 \le 5 \quad$ **and** $\quad 2x - 3 \ge -5$

$\rightarrow \quad 2x \le 8 \quad$ **and** $\quad\quad 2x \ge -2$

$\rightarrow \quad\quad x \le 4 \quad$ **and** $\quad\quad\quad x \ge -1$

Solution is: $[-1, 4]$

19. To solve $|ax + b| \ge k$, $k > 0$ we solve two inequalities

$$ax + b \ge k \quad \textbf{or} \quad ax + b \le -k.$$

We can write the solution in a compact form as the union of two disjoint intervals.

19. $|2x - 3| \ge 5$

$\rightarrow 2x - 3 \ge 5 \quad$ or $\quad 2x - 3 \le -5$

$\rightarrow \quad 2x \ge 8 \quad$ or $\quad\quad 2x \le -2$

$\rightarrow \quad\quad x \ge 4 \quad$ or $\quad\quad\quad x \le -1$

Solution is: $(-\infty, -1] \cup [4, \infty)$

20.
- $|ax + b| = $ (a negative number) has no solution

- $|ax + b| < $ (a negative number) has no solution

- If $|ax + b| \ge $ (a negative number) then all real numbers are solutions.

20.
- $|x - 2| = -4$ has no solution

- $|x - 5| < -3$ has no solution

- Solution of $|2x - 3| \ge -5$ is $(-\infty, \infty)$

2.11 REVIEW EXERCISE

In exercise 1–6, combine like terms and simplify wherever possible.

1. $7x + 4x - 7$

2. $3x - 7 + 2x - 15$

3. $5 - 2x + 9 - 4x$

4. $2(4 - x) + 9x$

5. $x^2 + 3x - 5 - 5(3 - 4x)$

6. $-(4z + 6) + 3(z - 4)$

Solve the equations in exercise 7–17 .

7. $k + 5 = 7$

8. $5 - x = 9$

9. $3x = 4$

10. $-2x = 9$

11. $2x - 4 = 10$

12. $7 - 4x = 11$

13. $10y + 5 = 17$ **14.** $12z - 11 = 61$ **15.** $2p + 3 = 3(p - 5)$

16. $2(x - 3) + 4(x - 12) = -2(x + 27)$ **17.** $\dfrac{1}{3}m - \dfrac{1}{2}m = 4$

Solve the word problems in exercise 18–20 .

18. When five is subtracted from three times a number, the result is nineteen. Find the number.

19. The supplement of an angle measures seven times its complement. Find the measure of the angle.

20. The sum of the ages of a father and his son is 70. The age of the father is 10 years more than twice the age of the son. Find the age of each of them.

Solve the formulas for the specified variable In exercise 21–26 .

21. $V = abh$; for h **22.** $2x - 3y = 4$; for y **23.** $2x - 3y = 4$; for x

24. $\dfrac{x}{2} - \dfrac{a}{5} = 3$; for a **25.** $\dfrac{5}{a} + \dfrac{1}{b} = 7$; for b **26.** $\dfrac{4}{a} + \dfrac{3}{b} = \dfrac{1}{c}$; for a

Write the ratios in exercise 27–32, if possible reduce them to lowest terms where ever possible.

27. 16 feet to 24 feet   **28.** 60 inches to 7 feet   **29.** 2 dollars to 25 cents

30. 2 km to 200 meters (1 km = 1000 meters)   **31.** 5 dimes to 4 nickels

32. 27 inches to 5 feet

In exercise 33–36, identify proportions.

33. $\dfrac{1}{2} = \dfrac{2}{4}$ **34.** $\dfrac{5}{15} = \dfrac{1}{3}$ **35.** $\dfrac{13}{25} = \dfrac{23}{45}$ **36.** $\dfrac{15}{24} = \dfrac{35}{56}$

In exercise 37–42, solve the proportions.

37. $\dfrac{x}{5} = \dfrac{4}{10}$ **38.** $\dfrac{3}{5} = \dfrac{x}{15}$ **39.** $\dfrac{3}{x} = \dfrac{4}{5}$

40. $\dfrac{x - 1}{2} = \dfrac{5}{8}$ **41.** $\dfrac{x}{3} = \dfrac{2x - 1}{5}$ **42.** $\dfrac{2x - 3}{5} = \dfrac{x - 6}{-2}$

Solve the word problems in exercise 43–48.

43. One quart of oil must be mixed with 20 quarts of gasoline. How much oil is needed for 150 quarts of gasoline?

44. Perimeter of a triangle is 38 inches. Longest side of the triangle is 1 inch less than twice the smallest side. Third side is 3 inches more than the smallest side. Find the length of the three sides of the triangle.

45. Two air planes leave San Francisco at the same time in opposite directions. They fly with a speed of 350 miles per hour and 440 miles per hour. In how many hours will they be 1580 miles apart?

46. John invests a part of his savings of $5000 at 6% and the remaining at 7%. The total annual income from the interest is $324. Find the amount of each of the two investments.

47. The distance between two cities on a road map is 12 centimeters. The two cities are actually 150 miles apart. What is the actual distance between two cities which are joined by a 21 centimeter line on this map?

48. Two trains are 480 miles apart. They start at the same time, and travel towards one another. The difference between the speeds of the two trains is 20 miles per hour. If the two trains meet after four hours, find the speed of the faster train.

Solve the inequalities in exercise 49–57, and graph the solution set.

49. $3 + x \geq -9$

50. $3 - x \geq 5$

51. $3x \leq 9$

52. $-3x \leq 12$

53. $4x + 3 < 5$

54. $4 - 5x > 24$

55. $2x + 7 \leq 5(x - 4)$

56. $4 - 5k - 3(2k - 7) > -(k + 2)$

57. $-7 < 3m + 5 \leq 14$

58. The perimeter of a given square is at most 120 feet. Find the possible values for the length of a side.

Solve the equations in exercises 59–64.

59. $|2x - 3| = 9$

60. $|4x - 5| = 11$

61. $\left| \dfrac{x}{2} - \dfrac{2}{3} \right| = \dfrac{5}{6}$

62. $|3x - 9| = 0$

63. $|9 - 2x| = 11$

64. $|5 - 3x| = -4$

Solve the inequalities in exercises 65–76.

65. $|x - 1| < 4$

66. $|2x - 5| \leq 7$

67. $|3x - 7| \leq -2$

68. $\left| 5x - \dfrac{2}{3} \right| < \dfrac{8}{3}$

69. $|x - 2| > 4$

70. $|2x - 3| \geq 3$

71. $|3x - 4| \geq 0$

72. $|9x - 15| \geq -5$

73. $|7x - 9| \geq -4$

74. $|3 - 4x| \geq 5$

75. $|7 - 2x| \geq 14$

76. $|8 - 2x| \geq 17$

2.12   SELF TEST

In exercises 1–2, simplify by combining like terms.

1. $-4x + 7y + 2(3x - 5) + 7$ **2.** $3(x - y) + 4(y - x) - 5(x + y)$

In exercises 3–7, solve each of the equations.

3. $4(p + 3) + 7 = 3p - 1$ **4.** $\dfrac{3}{4}y - 2 = 3$ **5.** $.1(x + 70) + .3x = -1$

6. $4(3x - 5) - 3(x + 2) = 9x + 5$ **7.** $3z + 2(z - 4) = 5z - 8$

In exercises 8–9, solve the proportions.

8. $\dfrac{x}{7} = \dfrac{42}{21}$ **9.** $\dfrac{2m - 1}{5} = \dfrac{3m + 1}{3}$

10.   When three times a number is added to 7, the result is 18. Find the number.

11.   The perimeter of a rectangle is 36 cm. The length of the rectangle is 4 cm more than its width. Find the dimensions of the rectangle.

12.   Given that $(x - 35)^0$ and $(65 + 2x)^0$ are supplementary angles. Determine x.

13.   Solve the formula $S = 2(ab + bh + ah)$ for h.

14.   How many liters of 30% chemical solution must be mixed with 30 liters of 70% solution to get a 60% mixture?

15.   Willie invests some money at 7.5%. He also invests $4000 less than this amount at 6.5%. His total annual income from the interest of these two investments is $1000. How much money is invested at each rate?

In exercises 16–18, solve and graph the inequalities.

16. $-3p > 15$ **17.** $2x + 7 \le -5 + x$ **18.** $3(a + 2) - 5a \le 4(2a - 3)$

19. $-6 \le 3 - 3k < 15$

20.   Lisa has grades of 85, 93, and 89 on her first three tests in Algebra. What possible scores on the fourth test will enable her to achieve an average of 90 or more on the four tests? Assume that her scores cannot be fractional numbers.

Solve the following equations or inequalities.

21. $|2x - 1| = 7$ **22.** $|5 - 2x| = 0$ **23.** $|7 - 2x| = -4$

24. $|3x - 4| \le 7$ **25.** $|5 - 3x| \le -4$ **26.** $|2 - 3x| \le 7$

27. $|x - 2| \ge 4$ **28.** $|2x - 3| \ge -4$

CHAPTER 3

EXPONENTS AND POLYNOMIALS

3.2 Polynomials   _ □ ✕

Ex 4 | Add $6x^4 - 2x^3 + 7x^2 + 5x$ and $-3x^4 + 2x^3 + 4x^2 - 11$.

To **add** polynomials, **combine** their **like terms**.   [Horizontal]   [Vertical]

Horizontal Method

$(6x^4 - 2x^3 + 7x^2 + 5x) + (-3x^4 + 2x^3 + 4x^2 - 11)$

$= (6x^4 - 3x^4) + (-2x^3 + 2x^3) + (7x^2 + 4x^2) + (5x) + (-11)$ ⇐ Pair up like terms

$= 3x^4 + (0)x^3 + (11)x^2 + 5x - 11$ ⇐ Combine like terms

$= 3x^4 + 11x^2 + 5x - 11$ ⇐ Simplify

Vertical Method

Step 1: $6x^4 - 2x^3 + 7x^2 + 5x + 0$

Step 2: $-3x^4 + 2x^3 + 4x^2 + 0x - 11$ ⇐ Combine like terms vertically

Step 3: $\overline{3x^4 + 0x^3 + 11x^2 + 5x - 11}$

$\Rightarrow 3x^4 + 11x^2 + 5x - 11$

S&◁ Exer. ◀   Click On Me or Press Spacebar to Continue   Obj 📋   Exit 📖

CHAPTER 3

EXPONENTS AND POLYNOMIALS

Introduction

The most basic elements of algebra are polynomials. Expressions like $3x + 4$ and $4x - 1 - 2x$ which we have encountered in Chapter 2 are examples of linear polynomials. In this chapter, we will study other polynomials. We will learn how to find the sum, difference, product, and quotient of two polynomials. This chapter is divided into the following sections.

3.1 EXPONENTS

Upon completion of this section we will be able to:

A. Identify and use exponents

B. Use the product rule: $a^m \cdot a^n = a^{m+n}$

C. Use the power rule: $\left(a^m\right)^n = a^{mn}$

A. Exponents

Exponents are used for repeated multiplication.

For example: $2 \cdot 2 \cdot 2 = 2^3$, $x \cdot x = x^2$, $x \cdot x \cdot x = x^3$, $x \cdot x \cdot x \cdot x = x^4$, etc.

For any natural number n, $x^n = \underbrace{x \cdot x \dots x}_{n \text{ factors}}$.

In the exponential expression x^n, x is called the *base* and n is called the *exponent or the power*. x^n is read as "*x raised to the power* of n" or in short, "*x* to the n".

$$x^n \underset{\text{Base}}{\overset{\text{Exponent}}{\rule{0pt}{0pt}}}$$

For any non zero real number x, $x^1 = x$ and $x^0 = 1$.

167

Warm Up

1. Evaluate or expand as appropriate. Indicate the base and the exponent in each case.

a) 3^3

b) 2^4

c) -5^3

d) 2^5

e) $(-5)^2$

f) $(2a)^4$

g) $(-2x)^3$

h) $-(3x)^2$

Answers:

1. a) $27 ; 3 ; 3$ b) $16 ; 2 ; 4$
   c) $-125 ; 5 ; 3$ d) $32 ; 2 ; 5$
   e) $25 ; -5 ; 2$ f) $16a^4 ; 2a ; 4$
   g) $-8x^3 ; -2x ; 3$
   h) $-9x^2 ; 3x ; 2$

Example 1:

Evaluate or expand as appropriate. Indicate the base and exponent in each case.

a) 4^3 b) $(-4)^3$ c) -4^3

d) 4^4 e) $(-4)^4$ f) $(3x)^4$

g) $(-5x)^3$ h) $-(2x)^3$

Solutions:

a) 4^3 : Base = 4, Exponent = 3

$4^3 = 4 \cdot 4 \cdot 4 = 64$

b) $(-4)^3$: Base = -4, Exponent = 3

$(-4)^3 = (-4)(-4)(-4) = -64$

c) -4^3 : Base = 4, Exponent = 3

$-4^3 = -(4 \cdot 4 \cdot 4) = -64$

d) 4^4 : Base = 4, Exponent = 4

$4^4 = 4 \cdot 4 \cdot 4 \cdot 4 = 256$

e) $(-4)^4$: Base = -4, Exponent = 4

$(-4)^4 = (-4)(-4)(-4)(-4) = 256$

f) $(3x)^4$: Base = $3x$, Exponent = 4

$(3x)^4 = (3x)(3x)(3x)(3x)$

$= (3 \cdot 3 \cdot 3 \cdot 3)(x \cdot x \cdot x \cdot x)$

$= 81(x \cdot x \cdot x \cdot x) = 81x^4$

g) $(-5x)^3$: Base = $-5x$, Exponent 3

$(-5x)^3 = (-5x)(-5x)(-5x) = (-5 \cdot -5 \cdot -5)(x \cdot x \cdot x)$

$= -125(x \cdot x \cdot x) = -125x^3$

h) $-(2x)^3 = -[(2x) \cdot (2x) \cdot (2x)] = -(2 \cdot 2 \cdot 2)(x \cdot x \cdot x)$

$= -8(x \cdot x \cdot x) = -8x^3$

Note: In case of $(-x)^n$ the base is $-x$, and we repeatedly multiply $-x$. But in case of $-x^n$, the base is x and we repeatedly multiply x, and then multiply the resulting product by -1.

B. Product Rule

We know, that $3^2 \cdot 3^4 = (3 \cdot 3)(3 \cdot 3 \cdot 3 \cdot 3) = 3 \cdot 3 \cdot 3 \cdot 3 \cdot 3 \cdot 3 = 3^6$. This leads us to the following product rule

> **Product Rule** $\quad a^m \cdot a^n = a^{m+n}$
> In a product when the base is the same, exponents are added.

Example 2:

- $x^3 \cdot x^5 = x^{3+5} = x^8$

- $\left(3x^2\right)\left(5x^3\right) = (3 \cdot 5)\left(x^2 \cdot x^3\right) = 15x^{2+3} = 15x^5$

- $a^2 b^3 a^3 b^4 = \left(a^2 a^3\right)\left(b^3 b^4\right) = a^{2+3} b^{3+4} = a^5 b^7$

Warm Up

2. a) $x^2 \cdot x^3$

b) $\left(2x^5\right)\left(3x^4\right)$

Answers:
2. a) x^5 b) $6x^9$

Notes: The product rule does *not* apply in either of the following situations
1. $3^5 + 3^7 \neq 3^{12}$ It is a sum, not the product .

2. $3^5\, 2^7 \neq 6^{12}$ Base is not the same.

C. Power Rules For Exponents

Consider the following examples:

1. $\left(3^2\right)^4 = 3^2 \cdot 3^2 \cdot 3^2 \cdot 3^2 = 3^{2+2+2+2} = 3^{2 \cdot 4} = 3^8$

Thus $(3^2)^4 = 3^{2 \cdot 4}$. This leads us to the following Power Rule 1.

> **Power Rule 1:** $\left(a^m\right)^n = a^{mn}$,   **for any real number a, and positive integers m and n**

2. $(3 \cdot 5)^2 = (3 \cdot 5)(3 \cdot 5) = (3 \cdot 3)(5 \cdot 5) = 3^2 \cdot 5^2$ This leads us to the Power Rule 2.

> **Power Rule 2:** $(ab)^m = a^m b^m$,   **for two real numbers a, b and positive integers m.**

In other words, when a product is raised to a power each factor is raised to that power.

3. $\left(\dfrac{3}{5}\right)^2 = \dfrac{3}{5} \cdot \dfrac{3}{5} = \dfrac{3 \cdot 3}{5 \cdot 5} = \dfrac{3^2}{5^2}$ This leads us to the Power Rule 3.

> **Power Rule 3:** $\left(\dfrac{a}{b}\right)^m = \dfrac{a^m}{b^m}$,   **for two real numbers a, b $(b \neq 0)$ and positive integers m.**

In other words, when a quotient is raised to a power, both the numerator and denominator are raised to that power.

Warm Up

3. Evaluate:

a) $\left(3^2\right)^2$

b) $(2 \cdot 3)^3$

c) $\left(\dfrac{3}{5}\right)^2$

4. Evaluate:

a) $\left(4x^3\right)^2$

b) $\left(x^2 y^4\right)^3$

c) $\left(2x^3\right)^3 (2y)$

d) $\left(\dfrac{1}{3}\right)^2$

Answers:

3. **a)** 81   **b)** 216   **c)** $\dfrac{9}{25}$

4. **a)** $16x^6$ **b)** $x^6 y^{12}$ **c)** $16x^9 y$ **d)** $\dfrac{1}{9}$

Example 3:

• $\left(2^3\right)^2 = 2^{3 \cdot 2} = 2^6 = 64$ Power Rule 1

• $(2 \cdot 5)^3 = 2^3 \cdot 5^3 = (8)(125) = 1000$ Power Rule 2

• $\left(\dfrac{2}{3}\right)^4 = \dfrac{2^4}{3^4} = \dfrac{16}{81}$ Power Rule 3

Example 4:

• $\left(3x^2\right)^3 = 3^3\left(x^2\right)^3 = 3^3 x^6 = 27x^6$

• $\left(x^2 y^3\right)^4 = \left(x^2\right)^4 \left(y^3\right)^4 = x^8 y^{12}$

• $(4x)^3\left(2x^2\right)^4 = \left(4^3 x^3\right)\left(2^4\left(x^2\right)^4\right) = 4^3 \cdot 2^4 x^3 \cdot x^8 = 1024 x^{11}$

• $\left(\dfrac{x^2}{y^3}\right)^4 = \dfrac{\left(x^2\right)^4}{\left(y^3\right)^4} = \dfrac{x^8}{y^{12}}$

EXERCISE 3.1

Answers:

1. _____

2. _____

3. _____

4. _____

5. _____

6. _____

7. _____

8. _____

9. _____

10. _____

In exercise 1–6, identify the base and exponent for each of the exponential expressions.

1. 3^6

2. -3^6

3. $(-3)^6$

4. $-(-5x)^7$

5. $(5y)^7$

6. $-5y^7$

In exercise 7–10, evaluate the expressions.

7. $\dfrac{2^3 \cdot 4^2}{3^2 \cdot 2^4}$

8. $5^3 - (-5)^3$

9. $3^2 \cdot 2^3$

10. $\left(2^3 + 3^2\right)\left(\dfrac{2}{3}\right)^5$

In exercises 11–18, simplify   as far as possible.

11. $x^2 \cdot x^3 \cdot y \cdot y^5$

12. $\left(16x^2\right)x \cdot x$

13. $\dfrac{x}{y} \cdot \dfrac{x^2}{y} \cdot \dfrac{x^3}{y^2}$

14. $\dfrac{x^2}{y^3} \cdot \dfrac{x^4}{y^2} \cdot \dfrac{x}{y}$

15. $\left(3y^2\right)\left(2y^3\right)$

16. $\left(7a\right)^2\left(-2a\right)^3$

17. $p \cdot p^4 \cdot p^6 \cdot p^5$

18. $\left(6a^0\right)\left(-2a\right)^3$

In exercises 19–25,   identify the true statement.

19. $(-2a)^4 = -16a^4$

20. $(-3b)^3 = -(3b)^3$

21. $\left(-2p^2\right)^4 = 16p^6$

22. $\left(x^2y\right)^4 = x^4y^4$

23. $4^2(-y)^2 = 16y^2$

24. $(2y)^0 = 2$

25. $\left(5m^2\right)^0 = 1$

In exercises 26–28, find the area of the figures.

26.

2x³

3x⁵

rectangle

27.

4m³

square

28.

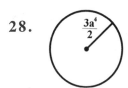

3a⁴/2

11. _____

12. _____

13. _____

14. _____

15. _____

16. _____

17. _____

18. _____

19. _____

20. _____

21. _____

22. _____

23. _____

24. _____

25. _____

26. _____

27. _____

28. _____

3.2   POLYNOMIALS

Upon completion of this section we will be able to:

  A.   Identify a polynomial, its terms, coefficients, and degree
  B.   Evaluate polynomials
  C.   Add polynomials
  D.   Subtract polynomials

Recall that variables are unknown real numbers and therefore can be added or multiplied. Algebraic expressions in one or more variables of the type:

$$2x + 1, \quad 3x^2 - 5x + 7, \quad 3xy^2 + 7x, \; xy^2 + 3xy - 2 \text{ are called polynomials.}$$

The expressions:

$$\frac{2}{x}, \quad \frac{3x}{x^2 + 1}, \quad x^2 + 2x - 1 + \frac{4}{x} \text{ are not polynomials.}$$

A.   Polynomial

A **polynomial** in a *single variable*, say x, is the sum of one or more terms of the form ax^n, where a is a known *real number*, and n is a *whole number*.

  1.   The numerical part (a) of each term of a polynomial is called the **coefficient** of the term.

  2.   The degree of **a term** is the sum of the exponents of the variable factors of the term.

  3.   The degree of **a polynomial** is the largest degree of its terms.

Note: A constant term such as 2 in 3x+2 is a special term whose degree is 0. This is due to the fact that $2 \cdot x^\circ = 2 \cdot 1 = 2$. Notice that the power of x is 0; therefore, the degree is 0.

Example 1:   Write down the terms, degree, and coefficients of the following polynomials.

  a) $3x^7$ **b)** $4x^2 - 3x + 1$ **c)** $2x - 3x^4$

Solution:

Polynomial	Terms	Degree	Coefficients
$3x^7$	$3x^7$	7	3
$4x^2 - 3x + 1$	$4x^2, -3x, 1$	maximum of $\left.\begin{array}{c} 2 \\ 1 \\ 0 \end{array}\right\} = 2$	$4, -3, 1$
$2x - 3x^4$	$2x, -3x^4$	maximum of $\left.\begin{array}{c} 1 \\ 4 \end{array}\right\} = 4$	$2, -3$

Notation: A polynomial is usually written in terms of descending powers of its terms, for example: $-3x^5 + 7x^3 + 8x^2 - 9$. When polynomials are written in this form, the coefficient of the leading term (-3 in this case) is called the **leading coefficient**.

A polynomial with only *one term*, no matter what the exponent, is called a **monomial**. A polynomial with *two terms* is called a **binomial**, and a polynomial with *three terms* is called a **trinomial**. Polynomials with more than three terms are referred to as just **polynomials.**

Example 2:

a) $3x^2$, $-\dfrac{5}{4}x$, 2, x^7 are all examples of monomials.

b) $4x-1$, $\dfrac{2}{3}x^2-3x$, $15x^{20}-2x^7$ are all examples of binomials.

c) $-5x^2+7x+\dfrac{1}{2}$, $10x^5-3x^2+2$, $\sqrt{2}x^{10}-\dfrac{1}{5}x^7+3x^2$ are all examples of trinomials.

B.   Evaluating a Polynomial

A polynomial is essentially an algebraic expression and can be evaluated by simply substituting the value(s) for the variable(s).

Example 3:

Evaluate $4x^3-3x^2+7$ when $x=-3, 0$, and 4.

Solution:

For $x=-3$:
$$4x^3-3x^2+7 = 4(-3)^3-3(-3)^2+7 \quad \text{Substitute } x=-3$$
$$= 4(-27)-3(9)+7 \quad \text{Simplify}$$
$$= -108-27+7 = -128$$

For $x=0$:
$$4x^3-3x^2+7 = 4(0)^3-3(0)^2+7 \quad \text{Substitute } x=0$$
$$= 4\cdot 0-3\cdot 0+7 = 7 \quad \text{Simplify}$$

For $x=4$:
$$4x^3-3x^2+7 = 4(4)^3-3(4)^2+7 \quad \text{Substitute } x=4$$
$$= 4(64)-3(16)+7 = 256-48+7$$
$$= 215$$

Note: Although, a polynomial is an algebraic expression, not every algebraic expression is a polynomial. For example, $\dfrac{3x+1}{4x^2+1}$ is an algebraic expression, but it is not a polynomial. It is however a quotient of two polynomials.

C. Adding Polynomials

There are two methods to add two polynomials

1. Horizontal Method   2. Vertical Method.

The two methods are explained in the following example:

Warm Up

4. Add
$12x^5 - 3x^4 + 2x^3 + 7x - 10$
and $3x^4 + 7x^3 - 2x^2 - x$

Example 4:   Add
$$6x^4 - 2x^3 + 7x^2 + 5x \text{ and } -3x^4 + 2x^3 + 4x^2 - 11$$

Solution:

Recall that terms of an expression that differ only in coefficients are called **like terms**, and like terms can be combined into a single term such as;

$$3x^2 + 4x^2 = (3+4)x^2 = 7x^2$$

Horizontal Method

$$\left(6x^4 - 2x^3 + 7x^2 + 5x\right) + \left(-3x^4 + 2x^3 + 4x^2 - 11\right)$$

$$= \left(6x^4 - 3x^4\right) + \left(-2x^3 + 2x^3\right) + \left(7x^2 + 4x^2\right) + (5x) + (-11) \quad \text{Pair like terms}$$

$$= 3x^4 + 0 \cdot x^3 + 11x^2 + 5x - 11 \quad \text{Combine like terms}$$

$$= 3x^4 + 11x^2 + 5x - 11 \quad \text{Simplify}$$

Vertical Method

Step 1 Write each polynomial in descending order by degree of its terms introducing zero coefficients wherever necessary.

$$6x^4 - 2x^3 + 7x^2 + 5x = 6x^4 - 2x^3 + 7x^2 + 5x + 0$$

$$-3x^4 + 2x^3 + 4x^2 - 11 = -3x^4 + 2x^3 + 4x^2 + 0 \cdot x - 11$$

Step 2 Now write the two polynomials vertically, one below the other, with the like terms in the same column.

$$6x^4 - 2x^3 + 7x^2 + 5x + 0$$
$$-3x^4 + 2x^3 + 4x^2 + 0 \cdot x - 11$$

Step 3 Combine the like terms vertically and simplify

$$\begin{array}{r} 6x^4 - 2x^3 + 7x^2 + 5x + 0 \\ -3x^4 + 2x^3 + 4x^2 + 0x - 11 \\ \hline 3x^4 + 0x^3 + 11x^2 + 5x - 11 \end{array}$$ Combine like terms vertically

$$= 3x^4 + 11x^2 + 5x - 11$$

Answers:

4. $12x^5 + 9x^3 - 2x^2 + 6x - 10$

D.   Subtracting Polynomials

As with real numbers, subtraction of polynomials is defined in terms of addition.

> **Rules for Subtraction:**
>
> Step 1   Change the sign of each term of the second polynomial (the polynomial to be subtracted.)
>
> Step 2   Add the first and the new polynomial.

Example 5:   Simplify
$$\left(3x^7 - 2x^5 + 4x - 1\right) - \left(-4x^6 - 8x^5 + 2x^2 - 7\right)$$

Solution:

Horizontal Method

$\left(3x^7 - 2x^5 + 4x - 1\right) - \left(-4x^6 - 8x^5 + 2x^2 - 7\right)$

$= \left(3x^7 - 2x^5 + 4x - 1\right) + \left(+4x^6 + 8x^5 - 2x^2 + 7\right)$ Step 1

$= 3x^7 + 4x^6 + \left(-2x^5 + 8x^5\right) + \left(-2x^2\right) + 4x + (-1 + 7)$ Step 2

$= 3x^7 + 4x^6 + 6x^5 - 2x^2 + 4x + 6$

Vertical Method

$\left(3x^7 - 2x^5 + 4x - 1\right)$

$= 3x^7 + 0x^6 - 2x^5 + 0x^4 + 0x^3 + 0x^2 + 4x - 1$

$\qquad -\left(- 4x^6 - 8x^5 \qquad\qquad\qquad + 2x^2 \qquad - 7\right)$

$$= \frac{0x^7 + 4x^6 + 8x^5 + 0x^4 + 0x^3 - 2x^2 + 0x + 7}{3x^7 + 4x^6 + 6x^5 + 0x^4 + 0x^3 - 2x^2 + 4x + 6}$$

$= \ 3x^7 + 4x^6 + 6x^5 - 2x^2 + 4x + 6$

Example 6:   Simplify the following polynomials, and compare the degrees of the resulting polynomial with the degrees of the given polynomials.

a) $\left(3y^5 + 4y^3 + 7y^2 - 2y - 1\right) + \left(-3y^5 + 2y^3 + 7y + 6\right)$

b) $\left(x^4 + 3x^3 + 4x^2 + 7x + 1\right) + \left(3x^4 + 4x^2 + 2\right)$

c) $\left(x^3 + 2x - 1\right) - \left(4x^5 - 2x^2 + 7x + 1\right)$

Solutions:

a) $\left(3y^5 + 4y^3 + 7y^2 - 2y - 1\right) + \left(-3y^5 + 2y^3 + 7y + 6\right)$ Combine like terms

$= \left[3y^5 + \left(-3y^5\right)\right] + \left(4y^3 + 2y^3\right) + 7y^2 + (-2y + 7y) + (-1 + 6)$

$= 0 + 6y^3 + 7y^2 + 5y + 5 = 6y^3 + 7y^2 + 5y + 5$ Simplified

Degree of the first polynomial   =   5.
Degree of the second polynomial =   5.
Degree of the sum   =   3.

Warm Up

5.   Simplify:
$$\left(x^6 + 2x^5 - 3x + 2\right) -$$
$$\left(-3x^6 + 4x - 8\right)$$

6.   Simplify:

a) $\left(4y^5 + 3y^3 + 6y^2 - 3y - 4\right)$
$+ \left(-7y^5 - 2y^3 - 6\right)$

175

Warm Up

b) $\left(8x^3 + 7x^2 + 7\right)$
  $+\left(4x^5 - 8x^4 + x^3 + 3\right)$

b) $\left(x^4 + 3x^3 + 4x^2 + 7x + 1\right) + \left(3x^4 + 4x^2 + 2\right)$ Combine like terms

  $= \left(x^4 + 3x^4\right) + 3x^3 + \left(4x^2 + 4x^2\right) + 7x + (1 + 2)$ Simplify

  $= 4x^4 + 3x^3 + 8x^2 + 7x + 3$

  Degree of the first polynomial   = 4.
  Degree of the second polynomial   = 4.
  Degree of the sum   = 4.

c) $\left(x^3 + 2x - 1\right) - \left(4x^5 - 2x^2 + 7x + 1\right)$

  $= \left(x^3 + 2x - 1\right) + \left(-4x^5 + 2x^2 - 7x - 1\right)$

  $= -4x^5 + x^3 + 2x^2 + (2x - 7x) + \left[-1 + (-1)\right]$

  $= -4x^5 + x^3 + 2x^2 - 5x - 2$

  Degree of the first polynomial   = 3.
  Degree of the second polynomial   = 5.
  Degree of the difference   = 5.

Answers:

5. $4x^6 + 2x^5 - 7x + 10$

6.   a) $-3y^5 + y^3 + 6y^2 - 3y - 10$

  b) $4x^5 - 8x^4 + 9x^3 + 7x^2 + 10$

EXERCISE 3.2

Answers:

1. _____

2. _____

3. _____

4. _____

5. _____

6. _____

7. _____

8. _____

9. _____

10. _____

11. _____

12. _____

13. _____

14. _____

In exercises 1–4, identify the algebraic expressions which are polynomials.

1. $3x^2 + 5x - 7$ **2.** $4x + 3 - 7x^2$

3. $3x^2 + \dfrac{1}{x} + 2$ **4.** $\dfrac{3x^3 - 1}{x^2}$

In exercises 5–8, write the polynomials in descending order of powers of the variable. Also find degrees and constant terms in each case.

5. $3x^2 + 7x - 3x^4 + 4x^3$ **6.** $7x^2 + 8x^3 - 5 - 4x^5$

7. $x^4 - 3x^5 + 7x^6 - 9x^8$ **8.** $-6x^4 + 7x^5 - 4x^2 - 2x^3 + 1$

In exercises 9–14, identify monomials, binomials, trinomials, and polynomials. What are their degrees?

9. $3x^2 - 1$ **10.** $4x^3$ **11.** $12x^3 + 3x$

12. $-3x^5 + 7x^2 + 9$ **13.** $15x^{10} + 16x^8 - 7x^4 + 2x$

14. $x^2 + (2x + 1)$

In exercises 15–17, evaluate the polynomials when
(i) $x = 2$ **and**   **(ii)** $x = -2$.

15. $3x^2 - 7x + 5$ **16.** $-4x^3 + 3x^2 + 10$

17. $11x^4 - 9x^3 + 2x^2 + 10x - 5$

Add the polynomials in exercises 18–23.

18. $4x^3 + 7x^2 - 5x,\ \ -3x^2 + 7$

19. $-5x^4 + 7x^3 + 8x - 9,\ \ 6x^4 + 9x^3 + 10x^2 + 9$

20. $4p^2 + 7p - 2,\ \ 3p^2 - 8p + 4$

21. $6z^3 + 7z^2 - 8z,\ \ -8z^3 + 4z^2 + 10z - 2,\ \ 2z^3 + 9z + 2$

22.
$$\begin{array}{r} 5t^3 - 7t^2 + 8t \\ +\ \ 4t^3 - 6t^2 + 4t + 3 \\ \hline \end{array}$$

23.
$$\begin{array}{r} -4r^3 + 7r + 9 \\ +\ \ 6r^3 - 8r^2 + 10 \\ \hline \end{array}$$

Subtract the polynomials in exercises 24–28.

24. $\begin{array}{l} 3x^2 - 4x + 8 \\ 5x^2 + 3x - 8 \end{array}$

25. $\begin{array}{l} 2y^4 - 7y^3 + 8 \\ -6y^4 - 5y^3 + 9 \end{array}$

26. $\left(4t^3 + 7t^2 - 9\right) - \left(5t^4 - 2t^2 + 8t - 1\right)$

27. $\left(-9t^4 + 7t^2 - 1\right) - \left(-9t^4 + 8t^2 + 10\right)$

28. $\left(3n^5 + 4n^3 - 7n^2 + 8\right) - \left(4n^4 - 5n^3 + n^2 - 4\right)$

29.   Determine the perimeter of the triangle whose sides are
$3x^2 + 7x - 2,\ 4x^2 - 5x + 1,$ and $x^3 + x^2 - 2x$

30.   Find the perimeter of a square each of whose sides is
$2x^2 + 4x - 5$.

15. _____

16. _____

17. _____

18. _____

19. _____

20. _____

21. _____

22. _____

23. _____

24. _____

25. _____

26. _____

27. _____

28. _____

29. _____

30. _____

3.3 MULTIPLICATION OF POLYNOMIALS

Every polynomial is a combination of monomials. Two monomials can be multiplied using the associative and commutative properties and the rules for exponents. For example,

$$\left(3x^4\right)\left(2x^6\right) = (3 \cdot 2)(x^4 \cdot x^6) = 6x^{10}$$

Rule: *To multiply two monomials:*

Step 1 Multiply the coefficients.	*Step 2* Multiply the variable parts.

The product of two monomials is a monomial whose coefficient is the number in Step 1, and whose variable part is the variable part in Step 2.

Using the distributive property and multiplication of monomials allows us to multiply two polynomials. Upon completion of this section we will be able to:

- A. Multiply a monomial and a polynomial
- B. Multiply two polynomials
- C. Multiply binomials using the FOIL method

A. Product of a Monomial and a Polynomial

We use the distributive property to multiply a monomial and a polynomial.

Recall: $a\,(b+c) \;=\; a \cdot b + a \cdot c$

Examples:

1. $3x^2\left(4x^3 - 7x\right) = \left(3x^2\right)\left(4x^3\right) - \left(3x^2\right)(7x) = 12x^5 - 21x^3$

2. $-4x^5\left(8x^2 + 9x - 2\right) = \left(-4x^5\right)\left(8x^2\right) + \left(-4x^5\right)(9x) + \left(-4x^5\right)(-2)$

    $$= -32x^7 - 36x^6 + 8x^5$$

3. $x^8\left(-9x^4 + 6x^2 - 7x + 1\right) = x^8\left(-9x^4\right) + x^8\left(6x^2\right) + x^8(-7x) + x^8(1)$

    $$= -9x^{12} + 6x^{10} - 7x^9 + x^8$$

B. Product of Two Polynomials

Two polynomials are multiplied by repeated application of the distributive property.

For example:

$$\overline{(3x^2 + 4x)(4x^2 - 7x + 2)} = (3x^2 + 4x)(4x^2) - (3x^2 + 4x)(7x) + (3x^2 + 4x)(2)$$

$$= (3x^2)(4x^2) + (4x)(4x^2) - \left[(3x^2)(7x) + (4x)(7x)\right] + (3x^2)(2) + (4x)(2)$$

$$= 12x^4 + 16x^3 - (21x^3 + 28x^2) + 6x^2 + 8x \qquad \text{Multiply monomials}$$

$$= 12x^4 + 16x^3 - 21x^3 - 28x^2 + 6x^2 + 8x \qquad \text{Simplify}$$

$$= 12x^4 - 5x^3 - 22x^2 + 8x$$

A working rule for multiplying two polynomials is:

Rule: **Multiplication of Two Polynomials**

Step 1 Multiply each monomial in the first polynomial by every monomial in the second polynomial. [Be careful about signs.]

Step 2 Add and combine like terms obtained in step 1.

Example 4: Multiply $x^2 + 2x - 3$ by $4x^3 - 7x$.

Warm Up

4. Multiply
$$(2x^2 - x - 3)(3x^2 - x)$$

Solution:

There are 3 terms in the first polynomial and 2 terms in the second. Therefore, there will be $3 \cdot 2 = 6$ products in step 1.

Horizontal Method

Step 1 The six products are
$$(x^2)(4x^3), \ (2x)(4x^3), \ (-3)(4x^3), \ x^2(-7x), \ (2x)(-7x),$$
$$(-3)(-7x) \ \text{or} \ 4x^5, \ 8x^4, \ -12x^3, \ -7x^3, \ -14x^2, \ 21x$$

Step 2 Add and combine like terms
$$4x^5 + 8x^4 + (-12x^3) + (-7x^3) + (-14x^2) + 21x$$
$$= 4x^5 + 8x^4 - 19x^3 - 14x^2 + 21x$$

Vertical Method

This method of multiplying two polynomials is usually more convenient. This is explained in the following example.

Step 1 Write the polynomial with the fewer number of terms below the other. Both polynomials are arranged in decreasing order of powers.

Step 2 Multiply $x^2 + 2x - 3$ by $-7x$

Step 3 Multiply $x^2 + 2x - 3$ by $4x^3$.

Step 4 Write polynomials in step 2 and step 3 below each other with like terms lined up.

Step 5 Add the two polynomials in step 4.

$$
\begin{array}{r}
x^2 + 2x - 3 \\
\times \quad 4x^3 - 7x \\
\hline
-7x^3 - 14x^2 + 21x \\
4x^5 + 8x^4 - 12x^3 \\
\hline
4x^5 + 8x^4 - 19x^3 - 14x^2 + 21x
\end{array}
$$

Warm Up

5. Multiply $3x^3 - 2x^2 + 7x - 3$
   by $5x^2 + 3x - 1$

Answers:

4. $6x^4 - 5x^3 - 8x^2 + 3x$

5. $15x^5 - x^4 + 26x^3 + 8x^2 - 16x + 3$

Example 5: Multiply $2x^3 - 7x^2 + 8$ by $x^2 - 4x + 3$

Solution:

Step 1	Write the polynomials
Step 2	Multiply the first polynomial by 3
Step 3	Multiply the first polynomial by $-4x$
Step 4	Multiply the first polynomial by x^2
Step 5	Line up like terms
Step 6	Add the polynomials

$$
\begin{array}{r}
2x^3 - 7x^2 \quad\quad +8 \\
x^2 - 4x + 3 \\
\hline
6x^3 - 21x^2 \quad +24 \\
-8x^4 + 28x^3 \quad\quad -32x \\
2x^5 - 7x^4 \quad\quad + 8x^2 \\
\hline
2x^5 - 15x^4 + 34x^3 - 13x^2 - 32x + 24
\end{array}
$$

C. FOIL Method

There is a special method to multiply two binomials. Since each binomial has 2 terms, there will be four possible terms in the product.

Consider for example, $(2x + 3)(4x + 7)$

We can obtain the four terms of the product as follows:

Multiply the **F**irst terms: $\quad (2x)(4x) = 8x^2$
Multiply the **O**uter terms: $\quad (2x)(7) = 14x$
Multiply the **I**nner terms: $\quad (3)(4x) = 12x$
Multiply the **L**ast terms: $\quad (3)(7) = 21$

Therefore $\quad (2x + 3)(4x + 7) = \underbrace{(2x)(4x)}\ \underbrace{(2x)(7)}\ \underbrace{(3)(4x)}\ \underbrace{(3)(7)}$

$$\text{First} + \text{Outer} + \text{Inner} + \text{Last}$$
$$\mathbf{F} \quad\quad \mathbf{O} \quad\quad \mathbf{I} \quad\quad \mathbf{L}$$

The word **FOIL** is used to remember the various terms of the product of two binomials (**F**: product of **F**irst terms, **O**: product of **O**uter terms, **I**: product of **I**nner terms, **L**: product of **L**ast terms)

Warm Up

6. Multiply $(2x - 3)(x + 1)$
   using the foil method.

Example 6: Multiply $(3x - 7)$ by $(4x + 5)$ using the FOIL method.

Solution:

Step 1

$$(\mathbf{3x - 7})(\mathbf{4x + 5}) = \underbrace{(3x)(4x)}_{\text{First Terms}} + \underbrace{(3x)(5)}_{\text{Outer Terms}} + \underbrace{(-7)(4x)}_{\text{Inner Terms}} + \underbrace{(-7)(5)}_{\text{Last Terms}}$$

$$= 12x^2 + 15x - 28x - 35$$
$$= 12x^2 - 13x - 35$$

Example 7: Multiply $(7a - 3b)$ by $(4a - 5b)$ using the FOIL method.

Solution:

Step 1 $(7a - 3b)(4a - 5b) =$

$$\underbrace{(7a)(4a)}_{F} + \underbrace{(7a)(-5b)}_{O} + \underbrace{(-3b)(4a)}_{I} + \underbrace{(-3b)(-5b)}_{L}$$

$$= 28a^2 - 35ab - 12ab + 15b^2$$
$$= 28a^2 - 47ab + 15b^2$$

Warm Up

7. Multiply
$(3a - 2b)$ by $(6a + 6b)$

Answers:
6. $2x^2 - x - 3$
7. $18a^2 + 6ab - 12b^2$

EXERCISE 3.3

Answers:

In exercises 1–5, find the product of the pairs of monomials.

1. $3x, 5x^4$ 2. $-4x^7, x^8$ 3. $-2x^5, -4x^3$

4. $3x^2, -7x^4$ 5. $-5x^4, -3x$

In exercises 6–10, use distributive law to find products and simplify the results.

6. $2x^2(4x^2 + 7x)$ 7. $-3x^5(x^2 - 3x + 2)$

8. $(6x + 2)(5x^2 - 7x)$

9. $(5x^2 - 3)(8x^9 - 3x^2)$ 10. $(4x + 3y^2)(5x^2 + 8xy^2)$

In exercises 11–18, find products and simplify.

11. $(3q - 1)(4q^2 - 7q)$ 12. $(4x - 8)(3x^5 - 2x^2)$

13. $\left(\frac{4}{5}x^2 - \frac{3}{4}\right)\left(2x - \frac{1}{5}\right)$ 14. $(3x^2 - 5x)(4x^2 + 7x + 1)$

15. $(5x^9 - 3x^2 + 7)(x^3 + x^2)$ 16. $(3x + 5)(3x + 5)$

1. _____
2. _____
3. _____
4. _____
5. _____
6. _____
7. _____
8. _____
9. _____
10. _____
11. _____
12. _____
13. _____
14. _____
15. _____
16. _____

17. _____

18. _____

19. _____

20. _____

21. _____

22. _____

23. _____

24. _____

25. _____

17. $\left(y^3 - 7y\right)\left(y^9 - 10y^6 + 8y\right)$

18. $\left(3x^5 - 5x^3 + 7\right)\left(3x^5 - 5x^3 + 7\right)$

In exercises 19–25, use the FOIL method to find the products.

19. $(4x + 5)(3x - 7)$ 20. $\left(3x^3 + 7x\right)(9x + 5)$

21. $(-3 + 2s)(4 + 3s)$ 22. $(6t + 5)(2t - 3)$

23. $(4k + 5l)(4k - 5l)$ 24. $(4n - 3m)(3n - 4m)$

25. $\left(2y^5 - 3y\right)\left(3y^2 - 7y\right)$

3.4   SPECIAL PRODUCTS

There are some special products which are used frequently. We will examine these special products closely, and observe the patterns for their expansions. Upon completion of this section we will be able to:

     A.   Square binomials
     B.   Find the product of the sum and the difference of two terms
     C.   Expand higher powers of binomials
     D.   Solve application problems

A.   Squares of Binomials

Warm Up

1. Write $(x+3)^2$ in expanded form.

Example 1:   Write $(x+5)^2$ in expanded form.

Solution:

Use FOIL method
$$(x+5)^2 = (x+5)(x+5)$$
$$(x+5)^2 = (x+5)(x+5) = x \cdot x + x \cdot 5 + 5 \cdot x + 5 \cdot 5$$
$$\qquad\qquad\qquad\qquad\qquad\quad \text{F} \qquad \text{O} \qquad \text{I} \qquad \text{L}$$

$= x^2 + 5x + 5x + 5^2$ Simplify

$= x^2 + 2(5x) + 5^2$ Combine like terms

$= x^2 + 10x + 25$

Observe that: $(x+5)^2 =$ Square of the first term + 2 (Product of two terms) + (Square of the second term)

Example 2: Find the product: $(2x - 7)^2$.

Solution: Use FOIL method

$(2x - 7)^2 = (2x - 7)(2x - 7)$

$\qquad = \underset{\text{F}}{(2x)(2x)} - \underset{\text{O}}{(2x)(7)} - \underset{\text{I}}{7(2x)} + \underset{\text{L}}{(7)(7)}$

$\qquad = (2x)^2 - 2[(2x)(7)] + 7^2 = 4x^2 - 28x + 49$

Warm Up

2. Find the product $(3x - 2)^2$

Observe the same pattern as observed in Example 1. We record this pattern as a **RULE 1.**

same sign

RULE 1: For all x and y: $(x + y)^2 = x^2 + 2xy + y^2$

$(x - y)^2 = x^2 - 2xy + y^2$

same sign

Example 3: Use the above rule to expand the following.

a) $(3y + 4z)^2$ **b)** $(4a - 5b)^2$

c) $\left(3m + \dfrac{4}{5}\right)^2$ **d)** $\left(\dfrac{4}{3}x - \dfrac{2}{5}\right)^2$

Warm Up

3. Expand

a) $(4x + 5y)^2$

Solutions:

a)

$(3y + 4z)^2 = (\text{First Term})^2 + 2(\text{Product of Terms}) + (\text{Second Term})^2$

$\qquad\qquad\quad \downarrow \qquad\qquad\quad \downarrow \qquad\qquad\quad \downarrow$

$\qquad = \quad (3y)^2 \quad + \quad 2(3y)(4z) \quad + \quad (4z)^2$

$\qquad = 9y^2 + 24yz + 16z^2$

b) $(3a - 2b)^2$

b)

$(4a - 5b)^2 = (\text{First Term})^2 - 2(\text{Product of Terms}) + (\text{Second Term})^2$

$\qquad\qquad\quad \downarrow \qquad\qquad\quad \downarrow \qquad\qquad\quad \downarrow$

$\qquad = \quad (4a)^2 \quad - \quad 2(4a)(5b) \quad + \quad (5b)^2$

$\qquad = 16a^2 - 40ab + 25b^2$

c) $\left(2z + \dfrac{3}{5}\right)^2$

c)

$\left(3m + \dfrac{4}{5}\right)^2 = (\text{First Term})^2 + 2(\text{Product of Terms}) + (\text{Second Term})^2$

$\qquad\qquad\quad \downarrow \qquad\qquad\quad \downarrow \qquad\qquad\quad \downarrow$

$\qquad = \quad (3m)^2 \quad + \quad 2(3m)\left(\dfrac{4}{5}\right) \quad + \quad \left(\dfrac{4}{5}\right)^2$

$\qquad = 9m^2 + \dfrac{24}{5}m + \dfrac{16}{25}$

d) $\left(\dfrac{3}{2}x - \dfrac{2}{3}\right)^2$

d)

$$\left(\frac{4}{3}x - \frac{2}{5}\right)^2 = (\text{First Term})^2 - 2(\text{Product of Terms}) + (\text{Second Term})^2$$

$$= \left(\frac{4}{3}x\right)^2 - 2\left(\frac{4}{3}x\right)\left(\frac{2}{5}\right) + \left(\frac{2}{5}\right)^2$$

$$= \frac{16}{9}x^2 - \frac{16}{15}x + \frac{4}{25}$$

B. Product of Sum and Difference

Example 4: Find the product: $(x + 5)(x - 5)$.

Solution:

Use FOIL method

$$(x - 5)(x + 5) = x \cdot x + x \cdot 5 + - 5 \cdot x + (5)(-5)$$
$$\qquad\qquad\qquad\quad \text{F} \qquad\quad \text{O} \qquad\quad \text{I} \qquad\quad \text{L}$$

$$= x^2 + 5x - 5x - (5)^2 = x^2 - 5^2 = x^2 - 25$$

We find that the product of the sum and difference of two terms equals the difference of their squares. We state this observation as a **RULE #2**.

Rule 2:   **For all** x **and** y: $(x + y)(x - y) = x^2 - y^2$

Example 5: Write the product in expanded form.

a) $(3p + 4)(3p - 4)$ b) $(2x - 3y)(2x + 3y)$

c) $\left(\dfrac{2}{3}t + \dfrac{4}{5}\right)\left(\dfrac{2}{3}t - \dfrac{4}{5}\right)$

Solutions:

Use the rule for the product of the sum and difference of two terms.

a) $(3p + 4)(3p - 4) = (\text{First Term})^2 - (\text{Second Term})^2$
$$= (3p)^2 - (4)^2 = 9p^2 - 16$$

b) $(2x - 3y)(2x + 3y) = (\text{First Term})^2 - (\text{Second Term})^2$
$$= (2x)^2 - (3y)^2 = 4x^2 - 9y^2$$

c) $\left(\dfrac{2}{3}t + \dfrac{4}{5}\right)\left(\dfrac{2}{3}t - \dfrac{4}{5}\right) = (\text{First Term})^2 - (\text{Second Term})^2$

$= \left(\dfrac{2}{3}t\right)^2 - \left(\dfrac{4}{5}\right)^2 = \dfrac{4}{9}t^2 - \dfrac{16}{25}$

C. Higher Powers

Verify the following rules using rule 1.

> **Rule 3:** **For all** a **and** b: $(a+b)^3 = a^3 + 3a^2b + 3ab^2 + b^3$
>
> $(a-b)^3 = a^3 - 3a^2b + 3ab^2 - b^3$

Observations:

For $(a+b)^3 = a^3 + 3a^2b + 3ab^2 + b^3$
1. *The coefficients are 1,3,3 and 1*
2. *The exponents of **a** are decreasing (3,2,1,0)*
3. *The exponents of **b** are increasing (0,1,2,3)*

For $(a-b)^3 = a^3 - 3a^2b + 3ab^2 - b^3$
The same observations as above apply except that the signs of terms change alternatively.

Example 6: Expand the following

a) $(4a+b)^3$ **b)** $(3s-4t)^3$

Solutions:

a) $(4a+b)^3 = (4a)^3 + 3(4a)^2(b) + 3(4a)(b)^2 + (b)^3$

$= 64a^3 + 48a^2b + 12ab^2 + b^3$

b) $(3s-4t)^3 = (3s)^3 - 3(3s)^2(4t) + 3(3s)(4t)^2 - (4t)^3$

$= 27s^3 - 108s^2t + 144st^2 - 64t^3$

D. Applications

Example 7: Use Rule #1 and 2 to compute the following:

a) $(105)^2$ **b)** $(97)^2$ **c)** $(96)(104)$

Solutions:

a) $105 = 100 + 5$

Therefore, $(105)^2 = (100+5)^2 = (100)^2 + 2(100)(5) + (5)^2$
$= 10000 + 1000 + 25 = 11025$

7. **c)** $(37)(43)$

b) $97 = 100 - 3$

$$(\mathbf{97})^2 = (\mathbf{100-3})^2 = (100)^2 - 2(100)(3) + (3)^2 \qquad \text{Rule #1}$$
$$= 10000 - 600 + 9 = 9409$$

Answers:

7. **a)** 91204 **b)** 1444 **c)** 1591

c) $(96)(104) = (100-4)(100+4) = (100)^2 - (4)^2 \qquad \text{Rule #2}$
$$= 10000 - 16 = 9984$$

EXERCISE 3.4

Answers:

1. _____
2. _____
3. _____
4. _____
5. _____
6. _____
7. _____
8. _____
9. _____
10. _____
11. _____
12. _____
13. _____
14. _____
15. _____
16. _____
18. _____
19. _____
20. _____
21. _____
22. _____
23. _____
24. _____
25. _____
26. _____

In exercises 1–20, use rules 1–3 to write the expressions in the expanded forms.

1. $(x-2)^2$ **2.** $(y+4)^2$ **3.** $(2m-5)^2$

4. $(3t+7)^2$ **5.** $(5m-3n)^2$ **6.** $(7r+5s)^2$

7. $\left(\dfrac{3}{4}x + \dfrac{2}{3}y\right)^2$ **8.** $\left(\dfrac{5}{7}u - \dfrac{4}{5}v\right)^2$ **9.** $(t+6)(t-6)$

10. $(4t+5)(4t-5)$ **11.** $(7x-3y)(7x+3y)$

12. $\left(2x^2 - 1\right)\left(2x^2 + 1\right)$ **13.** $(m-3)^3$

14. $(2x+y)^3$ **15.** $(4x-3y)^3$ **16.** $(x-y)^4$

17. $(3x+2y)^4$ **18.** $\left(x^2 - 1\right)\left(x^2 + 1\right)$

19. $\left(4 + r^2\right)\left(4 - r^2\right)$ **20.** $(3x^2 - y)(3x^2 + y)$

Use rule #1 and 2 to compute the numerical expressions in exercises 21–26:

21. $(206)^2$ **22.** $(92)^2$ **23.** $(1.05)^2$

24. $(.97)^2$ **25.** $(91)(109)$ **26.** $(93)(107)$

3.5   INTEGER EXPONENTS

In section 3.1 we studied whole number exponents. Upon completion of this section we will be able to:

A.	Use negative numbers as exponents
B.	Use the quotient rule for exponents
C.	Use variables as exponents

A.   Negative Exponents

Consider, $\dfrac{4^7}{4^3} = \dfrac{4 \cdot 4 \cdot 4 \cdot 4 \cdot \mathbf{4 \cdot 4 \cdot 4}}{\mathbf{4 \cdot 4 \cdot 4}} = 4 \cdot 4 \cdot 4 \cdot 4 = 4^4 = 4^{7-3} = 4^{7+(-3)} = 4^7 \cdot 4^{-3}$

Thus $\dfrac{4^7}{4^3} = 4^7 \cdot \dfrac{\mathbf{1}}{\mathbf{4^3}} = 4^7 \cdot \mathbf{4^{-3}}$

It follows that we can replace $\dfrac{1}{4^3}$ by 4^{-3} and apply the product rule, namely:

$$\frac{4^7}{4^3} = 4^7 \cdot \frac{1}{4^3} = 4^7 \cdot 4^{-3} = 4^{7+(-3)} = 4^4$$

Therefore for any non-zero real number a and any integer n, $a^{-n} = \dfrac{\mathbf{1}}{\mathbf{a^n}}$

Example 1:   Simplify by writing the answers with positive exponents.

a) 2^{-3} b) $\left(2^3\right)^{-1}$ c) 4^{-4}

d) $\left(5^{-1}\right)^3$ e) $x^{-3},\, x \neq 0$

f) $\dfrac{1}{x^{-4}},\, x \neq 0$ g) $\dfrac{3}{p^{-4}}$

h) $\left(\dfrac{3}{4}\right)^{-3}$

Solutions:

a) $2^{-3} = \dfrac{1}{2^3} = \dfrac{1}{8}$ b) $\left(2^3\right)^{-1} = (8)^{-1} = \dfrac{1}{8^1} = \dfrac{1}{8}$

c) $4^{-4} = \dfrac{1}{4^4} = \dfrac{1}{256}$ d) $\left(5^{-1}\right)^3 = \left(\dfrac{1}{5}\right)^3 = \dfrac{1^3}{5^3} = \dfrac{1}{5^3} = \dfrac{1}{125}$

e) $x^{-3} = \dfrac{1}{x^3}$ f) $\dfrac{1}{x^{-4}} = \dfrac{1}{\dfrac{1}{x^4}} = 1 \cdot \dfrac{x^4}{1} = x^4$

Warm Up

1. Simplify

a) 3^{-4}

b) $\left(3^{-1}\right)^3$

c) $\dfrac{1}{x^{-5}}$

d) $\left(\dfrac{4}{3}\right)^{-2}$

e) $\dfrac{7}{e^{-3}}$

f) x^{-5}

Warm Up

1. g) $\dfrac{4}{x^{-3}}$

h) $\left(\dfrac{2}{5}\right)^{-3}$

g) $\dfrac{3}{p^{-4}} = 3 \cdot \dfrac{1}{p^{-4}} = 3 \cdot \dfrac{1}{\frac{1}{p^4}} = 3 \cdot \dfrac{p^4}{1} = 3p^4$

h) $\left(\dfrac{3}{4}\right)^{-3} = \dfrac{1}{\left(\frac{3}{4}\right)^3} = \dfrac{1}{\frac{3^3}{4^3}} = 1 \cdot \dfrac{4^3}{3^3} = \left(\dfrac{4}{3}\right)^3 = \dfrac{64}{27}$,

Observe that we can change the sign of the exponent by taking the reciprocal of the base. We generalize this observation in the following illustration.

Prove that $\left(\dfrac{a}{b}\right)^{-n} = \left(\dfrac{b}{a}\right)^n$, $a \neq 0$, $b \neq 0$

$$\left(\dfrac{a}{b}\right)^{-n} = \dfrac{1}{\left(\frac{a}{b}\right)^n} = \dfrac{1}{\frac{a^n}{b^n}} = 1 \cdot \dfrac{b^n}{a^n} = \dfrac{b^n}{a^n} = \left(\dfrac{b}{a}\right)^n$$

Thus $\left(\dfrac{a}{b}\right)^{-n} = \left(\dfrac{b}{a}\right)^n$.

Warm Up

2. Simplify and write answer with positive exponent.

a) $\left(\dfrac{2}{3}\right)^{-5}$

b) $\left(\dfrac{5}{y}\right)^{-1}$

c) $\left(\dfrac{1}{4}\right)^{-4}$

3. Simplify and write answers with positive exponents.

a) $\dfrac{x^{-2}y^3z^{-1}}{x^{-4}y^3z^2}$

b) $\left(\dfrac{x^3y^2}{z^{-3}}\right)^{-1}$

Example 2: Simplify and write the answers with positive exponents.

a) $\left(\dfrac{1}{2}\right)^{-3}$ **b)** $\left(\dfrac{2}{x}\right)^{-5}$ **c)** $\left(\dfrac{3}{2}\right)^{-5}$

Solutions:

a) $\left(\dfrac{1}{2}\right)^{-3} = \left(\dfrac{2}{1}\right)^3 = 2^3 = 8$

b) $\left(\dfrac{2}{x}\right)^{-5} = \left(\dfrac{x}{2}\right)^5 = \dfrac{x^5}{2^5} = \dfrac{x^5}{32}$

c) $\left(\dfrac{3}{2}\right)^{-5} = \left(\dfrac{2}{3}\right)^5 = \dfrac{2^5}{3^5} = \dfrac{32}{243}$

Example 3: Simplify and write the answers with only positive exponents.

a) $\dfrac{4^{-2}}{7^{-3}}$ **b)** $\dfrac{x^2}{y^{-3}}$ **c)** $\dfrac{x^{-2}}{y^2}$

d) $\dfrac{x^{-2}y^2}{z^{-2}}$ **e)** $\left(\dfrac{x^2y^{-2}}{z^{-2}}\right)^{-1}$

Solutions:

a) $\dfrac{4^{-2}}{7^{-3}} = \dfrac{7^3}{4^2}$ **b)** $\dfrac{x^2}{y^{-3}} = x^2\left(\dfrac{1}{y^{-3}}\right) = x^2y^3$

c) $\quad \dfrac{x^{-2}}{y^2} = x^{-2}\left(\dfrac{1}{y^2}\right) = \left(\dfrac{1}{x^2}\right)\left(\dfrac{1}{y^2}\right) = \dfrac{1}{x^2 y^2}$

d) $\quad \dfrac{x^{-2}y^2}{z^{-2}} = \dfrac{y^2 z^2}{x^2}$

e) $\quad \left(\dfrac{x^2 y^{-2}}{z^{-2}}\right)^{-1} = \left(\dfrac{x^2 z^2}{y^2}\right)^{-1} = \left(\dfrac{y^2}{x^2 z^2}\right)^{1} = \dfrac{y^2}{x^2 z^2}$

B. Quotient Rule for Exponents

> **For any non-zero real number a, and any integers m and n**
>
> $$\dfrac{a^m}{a^n} = a^{m-n} \quad \text{if } m > n, \quad \text{and} \quad \dfrac{a^m}{a^n} = \dfrac{1}{a^{n-m}} \quad \text{if } n > m$$

Example 4:   Simplify and write the answers with positive exponents.

a) $\quad \dfrac{3^7}{3^3}$ b) $\quad \dfrac{5^3}{5^8}$ c) $\quad \dfrac{6^7}{6^{-3}}$

d) $\quad \dfrac{x^8}{x^{-4}}$ e) $\quad \dfrac{x^2 y^8}{x^6 y^5}$ f) $\quad \dfrac{2^4 x^5}{2^2 x^9}$

Solutions:

a) $\quad \dfrac{3^7}{3^3} = 3^{7-3} = 3^4$

b) $\quad \dfrac{5^3}{5^8} = \dfrac{1}{5^{8-3}} = \dfrac{1}{5^5}$

c) $\quad \dfrac{6^7}{6^{-3}} = 6^{7-(-3)} = 6^{10}$

d) $\quad \dfrac{x^8}{x^{-4}} = x^{8-(-4)} = x^{12}$

e) $\quad \dfrac{x^2 y^8}{x^6 y^5} = \dfrac{y^{8-5}}{x^{6-2}} = \dfrac{y^3}{x^4}$

f) $\quad \dfrac{2^4 x^5}{2^2 x^9} = \dfrac{2^{4-2}}{x^{9-5}} = \dfrac{2^2}{x^4}$

We list all the exponent laws discussed so far. Assume that all denominators and bases of negative exponents are non-zero. Then for all integers m and n,

RULE	EXAMPLE	RULE	EXAMPLE
$a^0 = 1$	$3^0 = 1$	$a^m \cdot a^n = a^{m+n}$	$4^5 \cdot 4^6 = 4^{11}$
$a^{-n} = \dfrac{1}{a^n}$	$3^{-7} = \dfrac{1}{3^7}$	$\left(\dfrac{a}{b}\right)^{-n} = \left(\dfrac{b}{a}\right)^n$	$\left(\dfrac{2}{3}\right)^{-2} = \left(\dfrac{3}{2}\right)^2$
$\left(a^m\right)^n = a^{mn}$	$\left(4^2\right)^6 = 4^{12}$	$\dfrac{a^m}{a^n} = a^{m-n} = \dfrac{1}{a^{n-m}}$	$\dfrac{3^6}{3^8} = 3^{6-8} = 3^{-2} = \dfrac{1}{3^2}$
$\left(\dfrac{a}{b}\right)^m = \dfrac{a^m}{b^m}$	$\left(\dfrac{4}{7}\right)^3 = \dfrac{4^3}{7^3}$	$(ab)^m = a^m b^m$	$(3 \cdot 5)^4 = 3^4 \cdot 5^4$

Warm Up

5. Simplify

a) $\dfrac{4^5 \cdot 4^{-3}}{\left(4^3\right)^{-1}}$

b) $(3x)^3(2x)$

c) $\left(\dfrac{2x^3}{3}\right)^2$

d) $\left[\left(\dfrac{x^2 y^3}{z}\right)^2\right]^{-3}$

e) $\dfrac{x^4}{y^2} \cdot \dfrac{y^3}{xz^3} \cdot \dfrac{z^3}{x^2 y^2}$

Answers:

4. a) 7   b) 177147   c) 4   d) $y^6 x^3$

5. a) 1024   b) $54x^4$ c) $\dfrac{4x^6}{9}$

d) $\dfrac{z^6}{x^{12} y^{18}}$ e) $\dfrac{x}{y}$

Example 5: Simplify the following. The answers must contain only positive exponents.

a) $\dfrac{3^4 \cdot 3^9}{\left(3^2\right)^5}$ b) $(4x)^3(8x)^2$

c) $\left(\dfrac{3x^5}{4}\right)^3$ d) $\left(\dfrac{x^2 y^{-3}}{z^{-2}}\right)^2$

e) $\left[\left(\dfrac{xy^{-2}}{z}\right)^2\right]^3$ f) $\dfrac{x^3}{y^2} \cdot \dfrac{y^3}{xz^2} \cdot \dfrac{z^2}{x^2 y}$

Solutions:

a) $\dfrac{3^4 \cdot 3^9}{\left(3^2\right)^5} = \dfrac{3^{13}}{3^{10}} = 3^{13-10} = 3^3 = 27$

b) $(4x)^3(8x)^2 = \left(2^2 x\right)^3 \left(2^3 x\right)^2 = \left(2^6 x^3\right)\left(2^6 x^2\right)$
$= \left(2^6 \cdot 2^6\right)\left(x^3 \cdot x^2\right) = 2^{12} x^5 = 4096 x^5$

c) $\left(\dfrac{3x^5}{4}\right)^3 = \dfrac{\left(3x^5\right)^3}{4^3} = \dfrac{3^3\left(x^5\right)^3}{4^3} = \dfrac{3^3 x^{15}}{4^3} = \dfrac{27}{64} x^{15}$

d) $\left(\dfrac{x^2 y^{-3}}{z^{-2}}\right)^2 = \left(\dfrac{x^2 z^2}{y^3}\right)^2 = \dfrac{\left(x^2\right)^2 \left(z^2\right)^2}{\left(y^3\right)^2} = \dfrac{x^4 z^4}{y^6}$

e) $\left[\left(\dfrac{xy^{-2}}{z}\right)^2\right]^3 = \left[\left(\dfrac{x}{y^2 z}\right)^2\right]^3 = \left(\dfrac{x}{y^2 z}\right)^6 = \dfrac{x^6}{\left(y^2 z\right)^6} = \dfrac{x^6}{\left(y^2\right)^6 z^6}$
$= \dfrac{x^6}{y^{12} z^6}$

f) $\dfrac{x^3}{y^2} \cdot \dfrac{y^3}{xz^2} \cdot \dfrac{z^2}{x^2 y} = \dfrac{x^{3-1} y^{3-2}}{z^2} \cdot \dfrac{z^2}{x^2 y} = \dfrac{x^2 y}{z^2} \cdot \dfrac{z^2}{x^2 y}$
$= x^{2-2} y^{1-1} z^{2-2} = x^0 y^0 z^0 = 1 \cdot 1 \cdot 1 = 1$

Example 6: Prove that $\left(2^2\right)^3 \neq 2^{2^3}$

Solution:

$\left(2^2\right)^3 = 2^6 = 64$ and $2^{2^3} = 2^8 = 256$

Therefore $\left(2^2\right)^3 \neq 2^{2^3}$

C. Variables as Exponents

All the rules of exponents for real numbers are also applicable when exponents are variables.

Example 7: Simplify by using the rules of exponents.

a) $4x^m \cdot 2x^4$ b) $(3y^2)^z$ c) $\dfrac{t^{5k}}{t^{3k}}$

d) $a^{x-y} \cdot a^{y-z} \cdot a^{z-x}$

e) $(a^{x+y})^{(x-y)} \cdot (a^{y+z})^{(y-z)} \cdot (a^{z+x})^{(z-x)}$

Solutions:

a) $4x^m \cdot 2x^4 = (4 \cdot 2)(x^m \cdot x^4) = 8x^{m+4}$

b) $(3y^2)^z = 3^z(y^2)^z = 3^z y^{2z}$

c) $\dfrac{t^{5k}}{t^{3k}} = t^{5k-3k} = t^{2k}$

d) $a^{x-y} \cdot a^{y-z} \cdot a^{z-x} = a^{(x-y)+(y-z)+(z-x)} = a^0 = 1$

e) $(a^{x+y})^{(x-y)} \cdot (a^{y+z})^{(y-z)} \cdot (a^{z+x})^{(z-x)}$

$= a^{(x+y)(x-y)} \cdot a^{(y+z)(y-z)} \cdot a^{(z+x)(z-x)}$

$= a^{x^2-y^2} \cdot a^{y^2-z^2} \cdot a^{z^2-x^2}$

$= a^{(x^2-y^2)+(y^2-z^2)+(z^2-x^2)} = a^0 = 1$

EXERCISE 3.5

Evaluate the numerical expressions in exercises 1–4.

1. $\left(\dfrac{1}{2}\right)^{-2}$

2. $\left(\dfrac{2}{3}\right)^3$

3. $\left(-\dfrac{4}{5}\right)^3$

4. $\left(-\dfrac{3}{5}\right)^{-4}$

In exercises 5–17, write the expressions with positive exponents. Assume that no denominator is zero.

5. $(x^{-4})^5$

6. $(x^{-3}y^2)^3$

7. $(r^{-2}sr^3s^4)^3$

8. $\dfrac{k^9 k^{-2}}{(k^2)^4}$

9. $\dfrac{2}{a^{-4}}$

10. $\left(\dfrac{3a^{-2}b^4}{5a^2b^{-3}}\right)^0$

11. $\left(\dfrac{-3x^{-4}y^2}{5x^2y^4}\right)^3$

12. $\dfrac{(4y)^3}{y^3}$

13. $\dfrac{3k^{-4}l^5}{3^{-2}k^{-6}l^{-2}}$

14. $\left(\dfrac{a^3}{b^2}\right)^6$

Answers:

1. _____
2. _____
3. _____
4. _____
5. _____
6. _____
7. _____
8. _____
9. _____
10. _____
11. _____
12. _____
13. _____
14. _____

15. _____

16. _____

17. _____

18. _____

19. _____

20. _____

21. _____

22. _____

23. _____

24. _____

25. _____

26. _____

27. _____

28. _____

29. _____

30. _____

31. _____

32. _____

15. $\dfrac{x^6\left(x^4\right)^{-2}}{\left(x^{-2}\right)^2}$ 16. $\dfrac{2x^{-2}y^3}{(4xy^{-3})^2}$ 17. $\dfrac{2^{-5}x^2y^{-3}}{2^{-8}x^{-3}y^2}$

In exercises 18–20, evaluate the expressions for $x = 2$, $y = -3$ **with and without calculator.** See example 2, page 446 in Appendix B for use of the calculator.

18. $\dfrac{x^3}{y^{-2}}$ 19. $\left(\dfrac{x}{y^2}\right)^{-2}$ 20. $\left(-x^{-1}y\right)^3$

Simplify the expressions in exercises 21–26. Write the answer in terms of positive exponents.

21. $(2x^{-2}y^2)^{-2}$ 22. $(-2x^2y)^{-3}$

23. $x^y \cdot x^{3y} \cdot x^{-8y} \cdot x^{-10y}$ 24. $4^k \cdot 4^{2k} \cdot 4^{-5k} \cdot 4^{-3}$ $(k \geq 2)$

25. $x^y \cdot y^x \cdot x^{3y} \cdot y^{3x} \cdot x^{y^2} \cdot y^{x^2}$

26. $\left(m^{x-y}\right)^{(x+y)}\left(m^{y-z}\right)^{(y+z)}\left(m^{z-t}\right)^{(z+t)}\left(m^{t-x}\right)^{(t+x)}$

Evaluate the numerical expressions in exercises 27–29.

27. $2^2 \cdot 3^{-2} + 3^2 \cdot 2^{-3}$ 28. $5 \cdot 4^{-2} - 3 \cdot 2^{-3}$

29. $2 \cdot 5^{-2} - 3^{-1} \cdot 3^{-2}$

In exercises 30–32, simplify and write in terms of positive exponents.

30. $\left(\dfrac{5}{x}\right)^{-2}$ 31. $\left(\dfrac{x}{y^2}\right)^{-2} \cdot \left(\dfrac{y}{x^2}\right)$ 32. x^{2^3}

3.6   THE QUOTIENT OF TWO POLYNOMIALS

Dividing a polynomial by a monomial is rather simple. It can be done by using the distributive law and the rules of exponents. We shall also explain the method of long division, similar to the one we studied in arithmetic, for finding the quotient of two polynomials. Upon completion of this section we will be able to:

    A.   Divide a polynomial by a monomial
    B.   Divide a polynomial by a polynomial

A.   Dividing a Polynomial by a Monomial

Dividing a polynomial by a monomial is similar to multiplying a polynomial by the reciprocal of the monomial. We can use the distributive law.

$$\frac{a+b}{c} = \frac{1}{c} \cdot (a+b) = \frac{1}{c} \cdot a + \frac{1}{c} \cdot b = \frac{a}{c} + \frac{b}{c}.$$

Thus
$$\frac{a+b}{c} = \frac{a}{c} + \frac{b}{c}$$

To divide a polynomial by a monomial, we divide each term of the polynomial by the monomial.

Example 1:   Simplify the following.

a) $\dfrac{16x^4 - 8x^2 + 12x}{4x^2}$

b) $\dfrac{6y^{10} - 3y^6 + 4y^3 + 8y}{3y^3}$

c) $\dfrac{16m^4 - 12m^3 + 4m^2 + 8m - 9}{4m^2}$

Solutions:

a) $\dfrac{16x^4 - 8x^2 + 12x}{4x^2} = \dfrac{16x^4}{4x^2} - \dfrac{8x^2}{4x^2} + \dfrac{12x}{4x^2} = 4x^2 - 2 + \dfrac{3}{x}$

b) $\dfrac{6y^{10} - 3y^6 + 4y^3 + 8y}{3y^3} = \dfrac{6y^{10}}{3y^3} - \dfrac{3y^6}{3y^3} + \dfrac{4y^3}{3y^3} + \dfrac{8y}{3y^3}$

$= 2y^7 - y^3 + \dfrac{4}{3} + \dfrac{8}{3y^2}$

c) $\dfrac{16m^4 - 12m^3 + 4m^2 + 8m - 9}{4m^2}$

$= \dfrac{16m^4}{4m^2} - \dfrac{12m^3}{4m^2} + \dfrac{4m^2}{4m^2} + \dfrac{8m}{4m^2} - \dfrac{9}{4m^2}$

$= 4m^2 - 3m + 1 + \dfrac{2}{m} - \dfrac{9}{4m^2}$

Warm Up

1.   Simplify the following

a) $\dfrac{27x^4 - 18x^2 + 9x}{3x^3}$

b) $\dfrac{20y^6 - 4y^3 + 4y}{4y^4}$

c) $\dfrac{45y^5 + 25y^4 + 10y^3}{5y^3}$

193

Warm Up

2. Using Instruction from example 2.

$$\frac{Polynomial}{2x^3} = 4x^2 - 15x + 3$$

Answers:

1. a) $9x - \dfrac{6}{x} + \dfrac{3}{x^2}$ b) $5y^2 - \dfrac{1}{y} + \dfrac{1}{y^3}$

   c) $9y^2 + 5y + 2$

2. $8x^5 - 30x^4 + 6x^3$

Example 2: Find the polynomial, which when divided by $3x^2$, yields $4x^3 - 5x^2 - 7$ as a quotient.

Solution:

$$\frac{Polynomial}{3x^2} = 4x^3 - 5x^2 - 7. \text{ Multiply both sides by } 3x^2$$

$$\left(\frac{Polynomial}{3x^2}\right)3x^2 = \left(4x^3 - 5x^2 - 7\right)3x^2$$

$$\begin{aligned}
Polynomial &= \left(4x^3\right)\left(3x^2\right) - \left(5x^2\right)\left(3x^2\right) - (7)\left(3x^2\right) \\
&= 12x^5 - 15x^4 - 21x^2.
\end{aligned}$$

B. Quotient of Two Polynomial

Let us recall the method of long division for whole numbers.

$$\text{Divisor} \overline{)\begin{array}{c} \text{Quotient} \\ \text{Dividend} \end{array}}$$
$$\overline{\text{Remainder}}$$

Divisor x Quotient + Remainder = Dividend

Warm Up

3. Divide 6235 by 17.

Example 3: Divide 34245 by 21.

Solution:

Step 1 $21\overline{)34245}$ $\longrightarrow$

Step 2 21 divides into 34 one time.
$$\begin{array}{r} 1 \\ 21\overline{)34245} \end{array}$$

Step 3 Subtract 21 from 34
$$\begin{array}{r} 1 \\ 21\overline{)34245} \\ \underline{21} \\ 13 \end{array}$$

Step 4 Bring down the next digit.
$$\begin{array}{r} 1 \\ 21\overline{)34245} \\ \underline{21} \\ 132 \end{array}$$

Step 5 21 goes into 132 six times
$$\begin{array}{r} 16 \\ 21\overline{)34245} \\ \underline{21} \\ 132 \\ \underline{126} \end{array}$$

Step 6 Subtract 126 from 132
$$\begin{array}{r} 16 \\ 21\overline{)34245} \\ \underline{21} \\ 132 \\ \underline{126} \\ 6 \end{array}$$

Step 7 Bring down the next digit.
$$\begin{array}{r} 16 \\ 21\overline{)34245} \\ \underline{21} \\ 132 \\ \underline{126} \\ 64 \end{array}$$

Step 8 21 divides into 64 three times.
$$\begin{array}{r} 163 \\ 21\overline{)34245} \\ \underline{21} \\ 132 \\ \underline{126} \\ 64 \\ \underline{63} \end{array}$$

Step 9 Subtract 63 from 64
$$\begin{array}{r} 163 \\ 21\overline{)34245} \\ \underline{21} \\ 132 \\ \underline{126} \\ 64 \\ \underline{63} \\ 1 \end{array}$$

Step 10 Bring down the next digit.
$$\begin{array}{r} 1630 \\ 21\overline{)34245} \\ \underline{21} \\ 132 \\ \underline{126} \\ 64 \\ \underline{63} \\ 15 \end{array}$$

Step 11   Since 15 is smaller than 21, 21 divides 15 zero times.

$$
\begin{array}{r}
1630 \\
21\overline{)34245} \\
\underline{21} \\
132 \\
\underline{126} \\
64 \\
\underline{63} \\
15 \\
\underline{0} \\
15
\end{array}
$$

Answer: When 34245 is divided by 21, the quotient is 1630, and the remainder is 15.

Check: (Quotient) x (Divisor) + Remainder = Dividend
$(1630)21 + 15 = 34245 \;\rightarrow\; 34230 + 15 = 34245$
$\rightarrow\; 34245 = 34245$ True!

Note 1:   The remainder is the result of the last subtraction, when there are no more digits to bring down.

Long division for polynomials is carried out the same way as division for numbers. However, before carrying out the long division for polynomials, make sure that:

1.   The dividend and the divisor are both written in terms of *descending powers*.
     For example: $4x^3 + 7x^2 - 3x$.

2.   Missing terms in the dividend are with a zero coefficient.
     For example $5x^4 - 7x^2 + 8$ is written as $5x^4 + 0 \cdot x^3 - 7x^2 + 0 \cdot x + 8$

Example 4:   Divide $x^2 + 11x + 30$ by $x + 5$.

Solution:

Notice that both the dividend $\left[x^2 + 11x + 30\right]$ and the divisor $[x + 5]$ are written in terms of descending powers of x, and the dividend has no missing exponents in x. We can now use the division algorithm (long division).

Step 1 $\longrightarrow$ *Step 2*

Divide $x^2 + 11x + 30$ by $x + 5$.

$$x + 5\overline{)x^2 + 11x + 30}$$

$$
x + 5\overline{)\begin{array}{l}x \\ x^2 + 11x + 30 \\ x^2 + 5x\end{array}} \quad \left[x(x+5) = x^2 + 5x\right]
$$

Step 3   *Step 4*

$$
x + 5\overline{)\begin{array}{l}x \\ x^2 + 11x + 30 \\ \underline{x^2 + 5x} \\ 6x\end{array}} \quad \text{Subtract}
$$

$$
x + 5\overline{)\begin{array}{l}x \\ x^2 + 11x + 30 \\ \underline{x^2 + 5x} \\ 6x + 30\end{array}}
$$
Bring down the next term

195

Answers:

3. When 6235 is divided by 17, quotient is 366 and the remainder is 15.

4 Quotient is $3x + 4$ and remainder is -2.

Step 5

$$x + 5 \overline{\smash{\big)}\, \begin{array}{c} x + 6 \\ x^2 + 11x + 30 \end{array}}$$

$$\underline{x^2 + 5x}$$

$$6x + 30$$

$$\mathbf{6x + 30}$$

$[6(x + 5) = 6x + 30]$

Step 6

$$x + 5 \overline{\smash{\big)}\, \begin{array}{c} x + 6 \\ x^2 + 11x + 30 \end{array}}$$

$$\underline{x^2 + 5x}$$

$$6x + 30$$

$$\underline{6x + 30}$$

$$0$$

Subtract

Quotient $= x + 6$, Remainder $= 0$

Note: The division process terminates when the remainder is either zero or the degree of the remainder is less than the degree of the divisor.

Step 7 *Verification*

(Divisor) · (Quotient) + Remainder = Dividend

$(x + 5)(x + 6) + 0 = x^2 + 11x + 30$

$x^2 + 5x + 6x + 30 = x^2 + 11x + 30$ True

EXERCISE 3.6

Answers:

1. _____

2. _____

3. _____

4. _____

5. _____

6. _____

7. _____

8. _____

9. _____

10. _____

11. _____

12. _____

Find the quotients in exercises 1–10.

1. $\dfrac{21x^4}{3x^2}$

2. $\dfrac{16x^7 y}{2x^5 y}$

3. $\dfrac{(-2y)^3 z^2}{2y^2 z}$

4. $\dfrac{15s^2 t^3}{-5st^2}$

4. $\dfrac{15s^2 t^3}{-5st^2}$

5. $\dfrac{4m^3 - 3m^2 + 5}{2m}$

6. $\dfrac{6k^5 - k^4 + 3k^2 + 9k + 10}{3k^2}$

7. $\dfrac{24x^6 y^7 - 12x^5 y^{12} + 36xy}{48x^2 y^3}$

8. $\dfrac{4x^3 y^{-2} + 8x^{-2} y^2 - 12y^4}{12x^{-1} y^{-1}}$

9. $\dfrac{2s^{2k} - 3s^{k+3} - 6s^{k+1}}{s^k}$

10. $\dfrac{3a^{2x} - 5a^x b^{2y+1} - 6b^{4y-1}}{a^x b^{y-1}}$

In exercises 11 and 12, identify the divisor, dividend, quotient, and remainder.

11. $\left(8k^4 - 12k^3 - 2k^2 + 7k - 6\right) \div (2k - 3) = 4k^3 - k + 2$

12. $\dfrac{-6m - m^2 + m^4}{m^2 - 2} = m^2 + 1 + \dfrac{-6m + 2}{m^2 - 2}$

In exercises 13–28, use long division to find the quotient and remainder.

13. $\dfrac{x^2 + 7x + 12}{x + 4}$ 14. $\dfrac{x^2 - 6x + 9}{x - 3}$ 15. $\dfrac{6y^2 - y - 12}{2y - 3}$

16. $\dfrac{9t^2 + 2t^3 + 5t - 6}{2t + 3}$ 17. $\dfrac{3x + 5x^2 + x^3 + x^4 + 6}{x + 2 + x^2}$

18. $\dfrac{3x^2 + 13x + 16x^4 + 3}{4x + 3}$ 19. $\dfrac{27a^3 + 8}{3a + 2}$

20. $\dfrac{64b^3 - 27}{16b^2 + 12b + 9}$ 21. $\dfrac{x^4 - 1}{x^2 + 1}$ 22. $\dfrac{t^5 - 32}{t - 2}$

23. $2x + 3\overline{\smash{\big)}\,6x^3 + 23x^2 + 27x + 9}$

24. $2x + 5\overline{\smash{\big)}\,16x^2 - 10x + 16x^3 - 5}$

25. $\dfrac{x^5 + 3x + 2}{x^3 + 2x + 1}$ 26. $\dfrac{2y^2 - 5y - 3}{2y + 4}$

27.   What polynomial when divided by $4x - 2$ yields the quotient $3x^2 - 7x + 5$?

28.   A polynomial, when divided by $4 - x^2$ yields $4x^3 - 7x + 2$ as a quotient and $2x - 3$ as a remainder. Find the polynomial ?

13. _____

14. _____

15. _____

16. _____

17. _____

18. _____

19. _____

20. _____

21. _____

22. _____

23. _____

24. _____

25. _____

26. _____

27. _____

28. _____

3.7   SCIENTIFIC NOTATION

The scientific notation is a convenient way of expressing very large or very small numbers. In scientific notation, numbers are written in the form $a \times 10^n$ where $1 \le |a| < 10$ and a is written in decimal form.

Upon completion of this section we will be able to:

 A.   Express numbers in scientific notation
 B.   Convert numbers from scientific notation to the standard notation
 C.   Use scientific notations in calculations

A.   Express Numbers in Scientific Notation

Observe that

a) $53.9 = 5.39 \times 10$ b) $539.72 = 5.3972 \times 10^2$

c) $.053 = 5.3 \times 10^{-2}$ d) $5.39 = 5.39 \times 10^0$.

The numbers on the right side of '=' sign are the scientific notation version of the number on the left side of the '=' sign. These observations lead us to the following rule.

> **Rule:**   **To convert a number from standard notation to scientific notation,**
>
> **Step 1** Move the decimal to the right of the first non zero digit.
>
> **Step 2** a) If the decimal is moved n places to the left then multiply by 10^n.
>   b) If the decimal is moved n places to the right then multiply by 10^{-n}.

Warm Up

1. Convert to scientific notation.

a)   4384

b)   43.84

c)   438.4

d)   .4384

Answers:

1. a) 4.384×10^3 b) 4.384×10^1
   c) 4.384×10^2 d) 4.384×10^{-1}

Example 1:   Convert the following to scientific notation.

a)   37.54   b) 375.4   c) −3754
d)   .3754   e) .03754   f) −.003754

Solutions:

a) **37.54:**   Move the decimal **to the left by 1** digit and **multiply by 10^1** Thus, $37.54 = 3.754 \times 10^1$.

b) **375.4:**   Move the decimal **to the left by 2** digits and **multiply by 10^2** Thus, $375.4 = 3.754 \times 10^2$.

c) **−3754.0**: Move the decimal **to the left by 3** digits and **multiply by 10^3** Thus, $-3754 = -3.754 \times 10^3$.

d) **.3754 :**   Move the decimal **to the right by 1** digit and **multiply by 10^{-1}** Thus, $.3754 = 3.754 \times 10^{-1}$.

e) **.03754:**   Move the decimal **to the right by 2** places and **multiply by 10^{-2}** Thus, $.03754 = 3.754 \times 10^{-2}$.

f) **−.003754:** Move the decimal **to the right by 3** places and **multiply by 10^{-3}** Thus, $-.003754 = -3.754 \times 10^{-3}$.

> We may verify the answers with calculator. See example 1, page 516

B.   Converting from Scientific Notation to Standard Notation

To convert a number in scientific notation to a regular decimal number, all that is required is to reverse the process.

In $a \times 10^n$ if n is positive then move the decimal in " a " to the right by n digits; otherwise move it to the left by n digits.

Example 2:   Convert the following into standard notation.

$$\textbf{a)} \qquad 2.75 \times 10^3 \qquad \textbf{b)} \qquad -4.03 \times 10^{-4}$$

Solutions:

a) 2.75×10^3:   Move the decimal in 2.75 three digits to the right.

$2.75 \times 10^3 = 2750$

b) -4.03×10^{-4}:   Move the decimal in -4.03 four digits to the left.

$-4.03 \times 10^{-4} = -.000403$

Warm Up

2. Convert into standard form.

a) 3.5×10^{-3}

b) 2.8×10^4

Answers:

2. **a)** 0.0035   **b)** 28000

C.   Applications

Example 3:   Light travels 300,000,000 meters per second. A light year is the distance that light travels in one year. Use scientific notation to express the number of meters traveled in one light year.

Solution:

$300,000,000 = 3.0 \times 10^8$

Number of seconds in one year $= \ 365 \times 24 \times 60 \times 60$

$= \ 365 \times 24 \times 60 \times 60$ Express each factor in scientific notation

$= 31536000 = 3.1536 \times 10^7$

Number of meters traveled in one light year:

$=$ (Number of meters traveled in one second) $\times$ (Number of seconds in one year)

$= \left(3 \times 10^8\right) \times \left(3.1536 \times 10^7\right)$

$= (3 \times 3.1536)10^{15} = \ 9.4608 \times 10^{15}$ meters

Warm Up

3. A plane travels at 3,000 miles per hour. Express this value in scientific notations.

Answer:

3. 3×10^3 mi/hr

EXERCISE 3.7

Answers:

1. _____

2. _____

3. _____

4. _____

5. _____

6. _____

7. _____

8. _____

9. _____

10. _____

11. _____

12. _____

13. _____

14. _____

15. _____

16. _____

17. _____

18. _____

In exercises 1–10, write in scientific notation.

1. 4501   **2.** 95.37   **3.** −847.509   **4.** 400.09

5. .034   **6.** .00809   **7.** $.0529 \times 10^5$

8. 775×10^5 **9.** $.0037 \times 10^{-3}$ **10.** .000000678

In exercises 11–18, write in standard notation:

11. 7.86×10^2 **12.** 3.59×10^5 **13.** 4.9705×10^4

14. 5.2349×10^{-1} **15.** -3.457×10^2 **16.** -3.456×10^{-3}

17. 5.7095×10^{-8} **18.** 9.725×10^{-4}

3.8   CHAPTER SUMMARY

1.   Assume that no denominator is zero. Then for positive integers m and n:

Rule	**Examples:**
$a^m \cdot a^n = a^{m+n}$	**1.** $2^5 \cdot 2^3 = 2^{5+3} = 2^8$
$\left(a^m\right)^n = a^{mn}$	$\left(2^5\right)^4 = 2^{20}$
$(ab)^m = a^m b^m$	$(2x)^4 = 2^4 x^4$
$\left(\dfrac{a}{b}\right)^m = \dfrac{a^m}{b^m}$	$\left(\dfrac{3}{P}\right)^4 = \dfrac{3^4}{P^4}$

Examples:

2. **The degree of a polynomial** is the maximum of the exponents in each term.

2. Degree of $4x^3 - 5x + 2$ is 3.

3. **Addition of polynomials:** We can add polynomials by combining their like terms. We may use the *horizontal method* or the *vertical method.*

3. $(3x^3 + 5x^2 + 3x - 7) + (x^3 + 5x - 4)$

Horizontal Method

$(3x^3 + 5x^2 + 3x - 7) + (x^3 + 5x - 4)$

$= (3+1)x^3 + 5x^2 + (3+5)x + (-7-4)$

$= 4x^3 + 5x^2 + 8x - 11$

Vertical Method

$3x^3 + 5x^2 + 3x - 7$

$x^3 \qquad\quad + 5x - 4$

$\overline{4x^3 + 5x^2 + 8x - 11}$

4. **Subtraction of polynomials:** We change the signs of the terms in the second polynomial (the one to be subtracted), and add the resulting polynomial and the first polynomial.

4. $(2x^2 - 3x + 5) - (x^2 + 4x - 7)$

Horizontal Method

$(2x^2 - 3x + 5) - (x^2 + 4x - 7)$

$= 2x^2 - 3x + 5 + (-x^2 - 4x + 7)$

$= x^2 - 7x + 12$

Vertical Method

$\begin{array}{ccc} 2x^2 - 3x + 5 & & 2x^2 - 3x + 5 \\ -(x^2 + 4x - 7) & \rightarrow & -x^2 - 4x + 7 \\ \hline & & x^2 - 7x + 12 \end{array}$

5. **Evaluating a polynomial:** We can evaluate a polynomial for a given value of the variable by direct substitution of the given value for the variable.

5. Evaluate $2x^2 + 5x - 7$ for $x = 2$

$2(2)^2 + 5(2) - 7 = 8 + 10 - 7 = 11$

6. **Multiplying two polynomials:** We multiply each monomial in the first polynomial by each monomial in the second polynomial, and simplify by combining like terms.

6. $(x^2 + 2x + 3)(x + 5)$

$= x^2 \cdot x + x^2 \cdot 5 + 2x \cdot x + 2x \cdot 5 + 3 \cdot x + 3 \cdot 5$

$= x^3 + 5x^2 + 2x^2 + 10x + 3x + 15$

$= x^3 + 7x^2 + 13x + 15$

7. **Multiplying two binomials:** We use the FOIL method to multiply two binomials.

7. $(3x+5)(4x-3)$

$= (3x)(4x) + (3x)(-3) + (5)(4x) + (5)(-3)$

First Terms Outer Terms Inner Terms Last Terms

$= 12x^2 - 9x + 20x - 15 = 12x^2 + 11x - 15$

8. **Special Products:**

$(a + b)^2 = a^2 + 2ab + b^2$

$(a - b)^2 = a^2 - 2ab + b^2$

$(a + b)(a - b) = a^2 - b^2$

8. $(4x+3y)^2 = (4x)^2 + 2(4x)(3y) + (3y)^2$

$\qquad\qquad = 16x^2 + 24xy + 9y^2$

$(3p-5)^2 = (3p)^2 - 2(3p)(5) + (5)^2$

$\qquad\quad = 9p^2 - 30p + 25$

$(3x+5y)(3x-5y) = (3x)^2 - (5y)^2$

$\qquad\qquad\qquad = 9x^2 - 25y^2$

$$(a+b)^3 = a^3 + 3a^2b + 3ab^2 + b^3$$

$$(a-b) = a^3 - 3a^2b + 3ab^2 - b^3$$

$(x+2)^3$

$= (x)^3 + 3(x)^2(2) + 3(x)(2)^2 + (2)^3$

$= x^3 + 6x^2 + 12x + 8$

$(x-2)^3$

$= (x)^3 - 3(x)^2(2) + 3(x)(2)^2 - (2)^3$

$= x^3 - 6x^2 + 12x - 8$

9. **Integer exponents:** We assume $a \neq 0$, $b \neq 0$ and m and n are integers

Rules:

$$a^{-n} = \frac{1}{a^n}$$

$$a^0 = 1$$

$$\frac{a^m}{a^n} = a^{m-n}$$

$$\left(\frac{a}{b}\right)^{-n} = \left(\frac{b}{a}\right)^n$$

9.

$3^{-5} = \frac{1}{3^5} = \frac{1}{243}$

$(-13)^0 = 1$

$\frac{5^7}{5^3} = 5^{7-3} = 5^4$

$\left(\frac{2}{3}\right)^{-2} = \left(\frac{3}{2}\right)^2 = \frac{3^2}{2^2} = \frac{9}{4}$

10. **Quotient of a polynomial and a monomial:** We divide each term of the polynomial by the monomial, and simplify.

10.

$\frac{4x^3 - 6x^2 + 8x - 2}{2x}$

$= \frac{4x^3}{2x} - \frac{6x^2}{2x} + \frac{8x}{2x} - \frac{2}{2x}$

$= 2x^2 - 3x + 4 - \frac{1}{x}$

11. **Quotient of a polynomial and a polynomial:** We perform division with polynomials in the same way as we perform long division on large numbers.

$$\text{Divisor } \overline{)\text{ Divident}}^{\text{Quotient}}$$

$$\cdots\cdots$$
$$\text{Remainder}$$

11.

Divisor $\times$ Quotient + Remainder = Dividend

$\frac{\text{Dividend}}{\text{Divisor}} = \text{Quotient} + \frac{\text{Remainder}}{\text{Divisor}}$

12. **Writing in scientific notation:**

We use a two step method

Step 1: Move the decimal to the right of the one's digit.

Step 2: If the decimal is moved n digits to the left, multiply by 10^n. If the decimal is moved n places to the right multiply by 10^{-n}.

12. 0.00035: Move the decimal to the right by 4 places and multiply by 10^{-4}
$0.00035 = 3.5 \times 10^{-4}$

456.9: Move the decimal to the left by two places and multiply by 10^2
$456.9 = 4.569 \times 10^2$

3.9   REVIEW EXERCISE

Evaluate the numerical expressions in exercises 1-4.

1. $\dfrac{2^3 \cdot 3^4}{4^2}$

2. $\dfrac{-2^2 \cdot 5^3}{10^2}$

3. $\dfrac{(-2)^2(-3)^3}{6^2}$

4. $\left(-5^3\right)^2\left(\dfrac{2}{5}\right)^3$

In exercises 5-8, write each of the following in exponent form.

5. $(27x^2)(2xy)(3y)$

6. $3(2x^2)(2x)^2$

7. $\dfrac{x^3}{y^2} \cdot \dfrac{y^6}{x^9}$

8. $\dfrac{x}{y^2} \cdot \dfrac{y^4}{z^2} \cdot \dfrac{z}{x^3 z}$

In exercises 9-10, evaluate the polynomial for the given value of x.

9. $5x^4 - 7x + 1$ for $x = 2$

10. $2x^3 - 4x^2 + 5$ for $x = -1$

In exercises 11-12, write in descending powers, and find the degree of the polynomial.

11. $4x^3 - 7x - 5x^7 + 3x^2 - 2$

12. $5x^5 - 7x + 5x^2 - 5 + 3x^4$

In exercises 13-20, perform the indicated operations.

13. **Add:** $3p^2 - 5p + 3$ and $4p^3 - 3p^2 + 2$

14. **Subtract:** $3x^3 + 5x^2 + 4x$ from $4x^4 - 3x^2 + 7x$

15 **Subtract:** $4p^3 - 3p^2 + 2p$ from $3p^2 - 5p + 3$

16. **Product** $2x$ and $-7x^3$

17. **Product** $4x^3(3x^2 - 5x + 2)$

18. **Product** $(3x^3 + 5x + 1)(7x^2 - 2x)$

19. **Product by FOIL Method** $(5y^2 - 3y)(3y - 2)$

20. **Product by FOIL Method** $(4x^2 + 3x)(3x - 5)$

Simplify using the special products in exercises 21-23.

21. $\left(\dfrac{4}{5}x + 3y^2\right)^2$

22. $\left(\dfrac{3}{2}x^2 - 7\right)^2$

23. $(5x + 3y^2)(5x - 3y^2)$

24. Use the sum of square formula to find the value of $(6.05)^2$.

In exercises 25-28, simplify and write the answers with positive exponents.

25. $\dfrac{x^3 \cdot x^{-2}}{x^4}$

26. $\dfrac{a^{-2} \cdot b^3}{a^5 b^{-5}}$

27. $\dfrac{(2a^{-1})^2 \cdot (3a^{-2})}{b^{-4}b^2}$

28. $\dfrac{(6p^{-2})(2q^{-5})^2}{p^{-3}(q^2)^4}$

203

29. Simplify $\left(a^{x+y}\right)^{(x+y)} \cdot \left(a^{x-y}\right)^{(x-y)} \cdot \left(a^{\frac{x}{y}}\right)^{\frac{x}{y}}$ **30.** Simplify $\dfrac{24x^4}{-15x^2}$

31. Write as the sum of three terms $\dfrac{4t^3 - 6t^2 + 8t}{6t^2}$.

In exercises 32–34, find the quotient and the remainder.

32. $\dfrac{4a^2 - 5a + 7}{2a - 3}$ **33.** $\dfrac{5x^3 + 4x - 3}{x^2 - x - 1}$ **34.** $\dfrac{y^4 + 4y^3 + 6y^2 + 7}{y^2 + 2}$

35. Write in scientific notation. **a)** 1,357,000 **b)** .00357

36. Write without exponents. **a)** $\left(3 \times 10^{-5}\right)\left(2.7 \times 10^7\right)$ **b)** $\dfrac{4 \times 10^5}{8 \times 10^8}$

3.10 SELF TEST

1. Simplify : $\dfrac{3^{-2} \cdot 5^3}{3 \cdot 5}$

2. Find the value of the polynomial $3x^3 + 2x^2 - x - 2$ for $x = -1$.

3. Write in scientific notation:. **a)** 9784 **b)** .000235

4. Write in standard notation. **a)** 2.7×10^5 **b)** 9.8×10^{-3}

Which of the resulting polynomials, in exercises 5–7, is a monomial, binomial, trinomial or a polynomial of higher degree? Find the degree of each.

5. $\left(3x^2 + 5x - 7\right) + \left(4x^2 + 1\right)$ **6.** $(2x + 1)(2x - 1)$ **7.** $\left(3x^2\right)\left(5x^3\right)$

8. Add: $\begin{array}{l} 4x^3 + 7x - 1 \\ 5x^4 + 9x^2 + 8x + 4 \end{array}$ **9.** Subtract: $\begin{array}{l} 5x^3 - 7x^2 + 2 \\ 3x^2 + 5x - 1 \end{array}$

10. Simplify: $\left(5x^3 + 2x^2 - 3x\right) - \left(2x^4 + 4x^2 - 2x + 1\right) + \left(x^4 + 2x + 2\right)$.

11. Multiply $5x^3\left(-3x^4 + 2x^2 - 3\right)$ **12.** Multiply $\left(3x^2 + 5x - 7\right)\left(4x^3 + 6x + 1\right)$

13. Write as a sum of four terms $\dfrac{-6x^3 + 8x^2 + 8x - 2}{2x^2}$

14. Find the quotient and remainder $x^2 + x + 1 \overline{\smash{)}15x^5 - 7x^3 + 8x^2 + 9}$

15. Apply the special product formulas to simplify : 4.07×3.93

CHAPTER 4

FACTORING, QUADRATIC EQUATIONS AND INEQUALITIES

4.2 Factoring Trinomials

Factoring Trinomials $ax^2 + bx + c$, $a \neq 1$

| Observations | Strategy |

Step 1: **Factor out** the G.C.F., if any.

Step 2: **Write** the polynomial in **descending powers** of the variable, and **insert** the **missing terms** with **zero coefficient**, if needed.

Step 3: **Find CI** such that their **sum** is **b** and **product** is **ac** (product of a and c).

> a $\Rightarrow$ **Leading coefficient** in $ax^2 + bx + c$.
> b $\Rightarrow$ **Coefficient of middle term** in $ax^2 + bx + c$.
> c $\Rightarrow$ **Constant term** in $ax^2 + bx + c$.

Step 4: **Split** the **middle term** using the **CI**.

Step 5: **Factor** by **grouping**.

S&◁» Exer.   Click On Me or Press Spacebar to Continue   Obj Exit

CHAPTER 4

FACTORING, QUADRATIC EQUATIONS AND INEQUALITIES

Introduction

In Chapters 1 – 3, we learned about algebraic expressions and the difference between an algebraic expression and an equation. In this chapter we shall discuss procedures for expressing simple polynomials, of degree two or three as a product of linear polynomials. This process is generally referred to as **factoring polynomials**. We shall then use these factoring procedures to solve equations of degree two, usually referred as solving quadratic equations by factoring. We shall close this chapter after briefly discussing solutions of quadratic inequalities.

This Chapter is divided into the following sections:

4.1   FACTORS

Recall that a number m is a factor of a number n if n is a multiple of m.

For example, **12 is a multiple of 2**, so 2 is a factor of 12. Factoring is a process which is the opposite of finding products. For example:

$$2 \cdot 6 = 12 \qquad \text{Product}$$
$$12 = 2 \cdot 6 \qquad \text{Factors}$$

Similarly, we can talk of factoring polynomials. In this section we shall learn how to factor polynomials. Upon completion of this section we will be able to:

A.   Find the Greatest Common Factor of the terms of a polynomial.
B.   Factor out the Greatest Common Factor.
C.   Factor a polynomial by grouping.

A.   Greatest Common Factor

A **Common Factor** of two or more integers is a number which is a factor of each of the given numbers.

The greatest among the *common factors* of a set of numbers is called their **greatest common factor** (g.c.f.) or **greatest common divisor** (g.c.d.).

Warm Up

1. Find the greatest common factor of 22, 165, and 33.

Example 1: Find the greatest common factor of 12, 32, and 40.

Solution:

The factors of 12 are   1, **2**, 3, **4**, 6, 12
The factors of 32 are   1, **2**, **4**, 8, 16, 32
The factors of 40 are   1, **2**, **4**, 5, 8, 10, 20, 40

The number 4 is the largest number that divides evenly all the three given numbers.

Thus the greatest common divisor or greatest common factor is 4: g.c.f. = 4.

The following rule gives us a general method for find g.c.f.

Rule: We use four step approach to find the greatest common factor of a set of numbers.

Step 1   Write the prime factorization of each number.

Step 2   Select the common primes in each factorization.

Step 3   Use smallest of the exponents for each common prime.

Step 4   Multiply the common primes with the selected (least) exponents.

If there is no common prime factor, we say g.c.d. is 1, and the given numbers are called **co-prime**.

Warm Up

2. Find the greatest common factor of:

a) 12, 36

b) 28, 20

c) 15, 45 and 60

d) 120, 440 and 280

Example 2: Find the greatest common factor of:
a) 18, 35   **b)** 48, 40
c) 12, 32, 40   **d)** 840, 180, 300.

Solutions:

a)   *Step 1* $18 = 2 \cdot 3^2$, $35 = 5 \cdot 7$.

     Step 2   There are no common prime factors. Therefore the g.c.f. of 18 and 35 is 1.

b)   *Step 1* $48 = 2^4 \cdot 3$, $40 = 2^3 \cdot 5$.

     Step 2   The only common prime factor is 2.

     Step 3   The least of the exponents of 2 (the smaller of 3 and 4) is 3.

     Step 4   Therefore, the g.c.f. of 48 and 40 is $2^3 = 8$.

c)   *Step 1* $12 = 2^2 \cdot 3$, $32 = 2^5$, $40 = 2^3 \cdot 5$.

     Step 2   The only common prime factor is 2.

     Step 3   The least of the exponents of 2 (the smallest of 2, 3 and 5) is 2.

     Step 4   Therefore, the greatest common factor of 12, 32 and 40 is $2^2 = 4$.

d)   *Step 1* $840 = 2^3 \cdot 3 \cdot 5 \cdot 7$ $180 = 2^2 \cdot 3^2 \cdot 5$

$300 = 2^2 \cdot 3 \cdot 5^2$

Step 2   The common primes factors are 2, 3, and 5.

Step 3   The least of the exponents of **2** is **2**.

The least of the exponents of **3** is **1**.

The least of the exponents of **5** is **1**.

Therefore, the greatest common factor of 840, 180, and 300 is

$$2^2 \cdot 3^1 \cdot 5^1 = 4 \cdot 3 \cdot 5 = 60$$

Warm Up

2. e) 26, 39, and 52

Example 3:   Find the Greatest Common Factor of

a) $12x^3,\ 45x^8,\ -9x^2$

b) $x^3y^2,\ x^4y^5, xy^6$

c) $6x^2y^3,\ 8x^2,\ 24x^3y$

3. Find the greatest common factor of:

a) $3x^3, 12x, 18x^4$

Solutions:

a)   Factor out each term completely

$12x^3 = 2 \cdot 2 \cdot \mathbf{3} \cdot \mathbf{x} \cdot \mathbf{x} \cdot x$

$45x^8 = \mathbf{3} \cdot 3 \cdot 5 \cdot \mathbf{x} \cdot \mathbf{x} \cdot x \cdot x \cdot x \cdot x \cdot x \cdot x$

$-9x^2 = -3 \cdot \mathbf{3} \cdot \mathbf{x} \cdot \mathbf{x}$

b) x^3z^2, xz, xyz

The greatest common factor of $12x^3,\ 45x^8$, and $-9x^2$ is $3x^2$.
Each monomial has one factor of 3 and two factors of x .

Before working parts b) and c), we list the steps for finding greatest common factor of monomials.

Answers:

1. 11 **2. a)** 12 **b)** 4 **c)** 15 **d)** 40 **e)** 13

3. a) $3x$ **b)** xz

Step 1	Find the greatest common factor of the coefficients of the monomials.
Step 2	Determine the exponents of various variables in each monomial.
Step 3	Take the minimum of the exponents for each variable. Write each variable raised to respective minimum exponent.
Step 4	The greatest common **factor** is then the product of all quantities determined in Steps 1 and 3.

b)   Monomials: $x^3 y^2,\ x^4 y^5,\ xy^6$

Step 1   Coefficients: 1, 1, 1
Greatest common factor of coefficients $= 1$

Steps 2 & 3

Monomial	Exponent of x	Exponent of y
x^3y^2	3	2
x^4y^5	4	5
xy^6	1	6
Minimun	**1**	**2**

Step 4   Greatest common factor

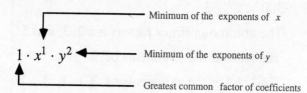

Therefore g.c.f. $= xy^2$

c)   Monomials: $6x^2y^3$, $8x^2$, and $24x^3y$. They can be rewritten as $6x^2y^3$, $8x^2y^0$ and $24x^3y$. Since $y^0 = 1$.

Step 1   The greatest common factor of coefficients 6, 8, and 24:

$$6 = 2 \cdot 3$$
$$8 = 2 \cdot 2 \cdot 2 \qquad \text{The g.c.f.} = 2$$
$$24 = 2 \cdot 2 \cdot 2 \cdot 3$$

Steps 2 & 3

Monomial	Exponent of x	Exponent of y
$6x^2y^3$	2	3
$8x^2y^0$	2	0
$24x^3y$	3	1
Minimun	**2**	**0**

Step 4   Greatest common factor $2x^2y^0 = 2x^2$

B.   Factoring out the greatest common factor

The greatest common factor of the various terms can be used to write the polynomial in the factored form (as a product). To do this we use distributive property backwards.

For example, consider the polynomial $8x^3 - 12x^2$. The greatest common factor of its term $8x^3$ and $-12x^2$ is $\mathbf{4x^2}$.

Thus

$$8x^3 - 12x^2 = \left(\mathbf{4x^2}\right)(2x) - \left(\mathbf{4x^2}\right)(3)$$
$$= \mathbf{4x^2}(2x - 3). \qquad \text{Distributive Property}$$

To factor out greatest common factor of a polynomial;

Step 1   Find the greatest common factor of the terms of the polynomial.

Step 2   Write each term with the greatest common factor (obtained in Step 1) as a factor.

Step 3   Use the distributive property backwards.

Example 4: Factor out the greatest common factor

a) $15x^5 + 25x^3 - 45x^2$ b) $25r^3s + 15rs^3$

c) $3a(a^2 + 4) - 2(a^2 + 4)$

d) $10a^2 + 12b + 14$

Warm Up

4. Factor out the greatest common factor.

a) $2x^3 + 12x^2 - 6x^4$

Solutions:

a) $15x^5 + 25x^3 - 45x^2$

Step 1 Various terms of the polynomial are $15x^5$, $25x^3$, $-45x^2$
The greatest common factor of 15, -25 and 45 is **5**.
The minimum of the exponents of x in $15x^5$, $25x^3$, and $-45x^2$ is **2**.

The greatest common factor is $\mathbf{5x^2}$.

b) $35x^3y + 14xy^2$

Step 2 $15x^5 = (\mathbf{5x^2})(3x^3)$ $25x^3 = (\mathbf{5x^2})(5x)$
$45x^2 = (\mathbf{5x^2})(9)$

Step 3 $15x^5 + 25x^3 - 45x^2$
$= (\mathbf{5x^2})(3x^3) + (\mathbf{5x^2})(5x) - (\mathbf{5x^2})(9)$ Factor out g.c.f.
$= (\mathbf{5x^2})(3x^3 + 5x - 9)$ Distributive Property

b) $25r^3s + 15rs^3$

c) $2a(a+4) - (a+4)$

Step 1 The two terms of the polynomial are $25r^3s$ and $15rs^3$
The greatest common factor of 25 and 15 is **5**.
The minimum of the exponents of r is **1**.
The minimum of the exponents of s is **1**.

Therefore, the greatest common factor of these various terms is $\mathbf{5\,rs}$.

Step 2 $25r^3s = (\mathbf{5rs})(5r^2)$ $15rs^3 = (\mathbf{5rs})(3s^2)$

Step 3 $25r^3s + 15rs^3 = (\mathbf{5rs})(5r^2) + (\mathbf{5rs})(3s^2)$ Factor out g.c.f.
$= \mathbf{5rs}(5r^2 + 3s^2)$ Distributive Property

d) $15a^2 + 105b + 35d$

c) $a^2 + 4$ is the greatest common factor of $3a(a^2 + 4)$ and $2(a^2 + 4)$.

Thus $3a(a^2 + 4) - 2(a^2 + 4) = (3a)(a^2 + 4) - (2)(a^2 + 4)$
$= (a^2 + 4)(3a - 2)$

Warm Up

Answers:

4. a) $2x^2(x+6-3x^2)$

   b) $7xy(5x^2+2y)$

   c) $(a+4)(2a-1)$

   d) $5(3a^2+21b+7d)$

d) $10a^2 + 12b + 14$

Step 1   The three terms are $10a^2$, $12b$, and 14. The greatest common factor of $10a^2$, $12b$, and 14 is $2a^0 b^0 = 2$

Step 2 $10a^2 = 2(5a^2)$, $12b = 2(6b)$, $14 = 2 \cdot (7)$

Step 3 $10a^2 + 12b + 14 = 2(5a^2) + 2(6b) + 2 \cdot (7)$
$= 2(5a^2 + 6b + 7)$

C. Factor By Grouping

Let us examine Example 4(c).

$$3a(a^2 + 4) - 2(a^2 + 4) = 3a^3 - 2a^2 + 12a - 8$$

We cannot factor the polynomial on right hand side by factoring out the greatest common factor. However, this polynomial was actually factored as $(a^2 + 4)(3a - 2)$. How do we get this factorization if we start with the polynomial $3a^3 - 2a^2 + 12a - 8$ instead? We can *rewrite* the polynomial as $\underbrace{(3a^3 + 12a)} - (2a^2 + 8)$. In fact, we have *regrouped* the terms.

Now, $(3a^3 + 12a) = 3a(a^2 + 4)$ and $(2a^2 + 8) = 2(a^2 + 4)$.

When we factor each of these groups, we have a common factor, namely, $a^2 + 4$.

Thus $3a^3 - 2a^2 + 12a - 8 = (3a^3 + 12a) - (2a^2 + 8)$
$= 3a(a^2 + 4) - 2(a^2 + 4) = (a^2 + 4)(3a - 2)$

Alternatively,

$3a^3 - 2a^2 + 12a - 8 = (3a^3 - 2a^2) + (12a - 8)$
$= a^2(3a - 2) + 4(3a - 2)$
$= (3a - 2)(a^2 + 4)$

This process of factoring an expression in groups of terms is called **factoring by grouping**.

Notes: **1.**   There is no hard and fast rule for factoring by grouping. The terms should be so grouped that the different groups have a factor in common.

2.   There are many polynomials which cannot be factored at all. A polynomial that cannot be factored is called *a prime polynomial*.

Warm Up

5. Factor the following

   a) $5x + 3 + 10ax + 6a$

Example 5:   Factor the following by grouping.

a) $3x + 5 + 9ax + 15a$ b) $y^2 + 4y + 8y + 32$

c) $3ab - 8a - 6b + 16$

d) $3at^2 + 3bt^2 + a + 5bt + 5at + b$

e) $x^4 + 2x^3 + x^2 + x + 1$

Solutions:

Method 1

a) $3x + 5 + 9ax + 15a$

$= (3x + 5) + (9ax + 15a)$ Grouping

$= 1 \cdot (3x + 5) + 3a(3x + 5)$ Factor the groups

$= (1 + 3a)(3x + 5)$ Distributive Property

Method 2

$3x + 5 + 9ax + 15a$

$= (3x + 9ax) + (5 + 15a)$

$= 3x(1 + 3a) + 5(1 + 3a)$

$= (3x + 5)(1 + 3a)$

Method 1

b) $y^2 + 4y + 8y + 32$

$= (y^2 + 4y) + (8y + 32)$ Grouping

$= y(y + 4) + 8(y + 4)$ Factor the groups

$= (y + 8)(y + 4)$ Distributive Property

Method 2

$y^2 + 4y + 8y + 32$

$= (y^2 + 8y) + (4y + 32)$

$= y(y + 8) + 4(y + 8)$

$= (y + 8)(y + 4)$

b) $x^2 + 6x + x + 6$

c) $3ab - 8a - 6b + 16$

$= (3ab - 8a) - (6b - 16)$ Grouping

$= a(3b - 8) - 2(3b - 8)$ Factor the groups

$= (a - 2)(3b - 8)$ Distributive Property

$3ab - 8a - 6b + 16$

$= (3ab - 6b) - (8a - 16)$

$= 3b(a - 2) - 8(a - 2)$

$= (3b - 8)(a - 2)$

c) $x^3 + 2x^2 + x + 2$

d) $3at^2 + 3bt^2 + a + 5bt + 5at + b$

$(3at^2 + 3bt^2) + (5bt + 5at) + (a + b)$

$= 3t^2(a + b) + 5t(a + b) + 1(a + b)$

$= (3t^2 + 5t + 1)(a + b)$

$3at^2 + 3bt^2 + a + 5bt + 5at + b$

$= (3at^2 + 5at + a) +$

$\qquad (3bt^2 + 5bt + b)$

$= a(3t^2 + 5t + 1) +$

$\qquad b(3t^2 + 5t + 1)$

$= (a + b)(3t^2 + 5t + 1)$

d) $3ab + 3ac + 3b^2 + 3bc$

e) $x^6 + 3x^4y^2 + x^2y^4 + 3y^6$

e) $x^4 + 2x^3 + x^2 + x + 1$

$= (x^4 + x^3) + (x^3 + x^2) + (x + 1)$

$= x^3(x + 1) + x^2(x + 1) + 1(x + 1)$

$= (x^3 + x^2 + 1)(x + 1)$

$x^4 + 2x^3 + x^2 + x + 1$

$= (x^4 + 2x^3 + x^2) + (x + 1)$

$= x^2(x^2 + 2x + 1) + (x + 1)$

$= x^2(x + 1)^2 + (x + 1)$

$= (x + 1)\left[x^2(x + 1)1\right]$

$= (x + 1)(x^3 + x^2 + 1)$

Answers:

5. a) $(2a + 1)(5x + 3)$

   b) $(x + 1)(x + 6)$

   c) $(x^2 + 1)(x + 2)$

   d) $3(a + b)(b + c)$

   e) $(x^4 + y^4)(x^2 + 3y^2)$

EXERCISE   4.1

Answers:

1. _____

2. _____

3. _____

4. _____

5. _____

6. _____

7. _____

8. _____

9. _____

10. _____

11. _____

12. _____

13. _____

14. _____

15. _____

16. _____

17. _____

18. _____

19. _____

20. _____

21. _____

22. _____

In exercises 1–6, find the greatest common factor.

1.   4, 30, 42   **2.**   30, 45, 75

3. $36, 48m, 60m^2$ **4.** $15m$, $12n^2, 30p$

5. $16m^2n^3, 36m^3n^5, 24mn^2$ **6.** $28x^4y^3, 42x^3y^2, 63xy^5$

In exercises 7–10, provide the missing factor.

7. $36 = 4(\ )$ **8.** $5x^2 = x(\ )$

9. $3x^4y^5 = 3x^2 (\ )$ **10.** $24p^4q^5 = 3p^3q^2(\ )$

In exercises 11–14, identify the expression which is completely factored?

11. $3a^2 + 4a$ **12.** $4(3x^2y - 2x)$ **13.** $(3p - q)(p + q)$

14. $2(m - 1) + mn(m - 1)$

In exercises 15–22, factor out the greatest common factor.

15. $4x + 6x^3$ **16.** $28x^2 + 42x^3$ **17.** $8y^3 - 4y^5$

18. $11y^2 - 12z^3$ **19.** $25m^5 - 50m^4 + 100m^3$

20. $45m^2n^3 - 36mn^2 + 63m^3n$ **21.** $3a(1 - 5b) - 4b(1 - 5b)$

22. $r(r - 2s) - s(2s - r)$

In exercises 23–32, factor by grouping.

23. $x^2 + 5y - xy - 5x$

24. $ar + br - a - b$

25. $x^2 + 2xy + 3x + 6y$

26. $x^2y - x^2 - 3y + 3$

27. $x^4 - 2x^3 + x^2 + x - 1$

28. $m^4 + 4m^3 + 4m^2 + 2m + 4$ $\left[\text{Split } 4m^3 = 2m^3 + 2m^3\right]$

29. $x^3 - 1$ $\left[\text{Hint: Write } x^3 - 1 = x^3 - x^2 + x^2 - x + x - 1\right]$

30. $a^2 - b^2$ $\left[\text{Hint: Write } a^2 - b^2 = a^2 - ab + ab - b^2\right]$

31. $2n^4p - 2n^2 - n^3p^2 + np + 3mn^3p - 3mn$

32. $3a^2 + 6a + 3a^6 + 12a^5 + 12a^4$

23. _____
24. _____
25. _____
26. _____
27. _____
28. _____
29. _____
30. _____
31. _____
32. _____

4.2   FACTORING TRINOMIALS

In this section we shall learn how to factor trinomials of the form $ax^2 + bx + c$, where $a, b,$ and c are integers.

Upon completion of this section, we will be able to

A. Identify trinomials of the type $ax^2 + bx + c$ which can be factored.
B. Factor trinomials of the form $x^2 + bx + c$.
C. Factor trinomials of the form $ax^2 + bx + c$, $a \neq 1$.
D. Factor those trinomials which can be reduced to the above form.

A.   When can "$ax^2 + bx + c$" be Factored?

A trinomial $ax^2 + bx + c$ (notice the degree is 2) can be factored in rationals only if $b^2 - 4ac$ is **a perfect square**. We shall prove this important fact in later chapters. In this section, the phrase "can be factored" means can be factored using rational numbers.

Warm Up

1. Identify which of the trinomials can be factored.

a) $x^2 - 3x - 4$

b) $x^2 + 2x + 4$

c) $x^2 + 6x + 5$

Answers:

1.   a) can be factored

b) cannot be factored

c) can be factored

Example 1:   Identify which of the trinomials can be factored.

a) $x^2 - 5x + 4$ b) $x^2 + 3x - 5$ c) $5y^2 + 7y + 2$

Solutions:

a) $x^2 - 5x + 4$ Compare this with $ax^2 + bx + c$.
Here, $a = 1$, $b = -5$, $c = 4$ and

$$b^2 - 4ac = (-5)^2 - 4(1)(4) = 25 - 16 = 9$$

Since 9 is a **perfect square** $(3^2 = 9)$, therefore $x^2 - 5x + 4$ can be factored.

b) $x^2 + 3x - 5$
Here, $a = 1$, $b = 3$, $c = -5$, and

$$b^2 - 4ac = (3)^2 - 4(1)(-5) = 9 + 20 = 29$$

Since 29 is **not a perfect square,** therefore $x^2 + 3x - 5$ cannot be factored.

c) $5y^2 + 7y + 2$
Here $a = 5$, $b = 7$, $c = 2$ and

$$b^2 - 4ac = (7)^2 - 4(5)(2) = 49 - 40 = 9$$

Since 9 is a **perfect square,** therefore $5y^2 + 7y + 2$ can be factored.

B.   Factoring Trinomials of the type $x^2 + bx + c$ $(a = 1)$

Recall

$$(x + p)(x + q) = x^2 + px + qx + pq$$
$$= x^2 + (p + q)x + pq$$

Therefore $x^2 + (p + q)x + pq = (x + p)(x + q)$,

Whenever we are given a trinomial to factor, we compare it with the above.

For example: Consider the trinomial $x^2 - 5x + 4$.
Compare $x^2 - 5x + 4$ with $x^2 + (p + q)x + pq$
$$-5 \quad = \quad p + q$$
$$4 \quad = \quad pq$$

We need to find two integers whose sum is -5 and product is 4. We call these integers as **critical integers** (CI). By trial and error we may find the two integers that meets our requirement.

Integer	Sum	Product	Do the integers satisfy the requirements?
1, −4	−3	−4	No
−6, 1	−5	−6	No
−4, −1	−5	4	Yes

Therefore $p = -4$ and $q = -1$. So $x^2 - 5x + 4 = (x + p)(x + q)$
$$= (x - 4)(x - 1)$$

Observations:

1.   An expression of degree two of the type $x^2 + bx + c$, if factorable, has two linear factors of the type $x + p$ and $x + q$.

2.   If we know the numbers p and q then we know the factors of $x^2 + bx + c$.

3.   Given $x^2 + bx + c = (x + p)(x + q)$, then $p + q = b$, and $pq = c$

This suggests the following rule for factorization of trinomials of the type $x^2 + bx + c$.

Step 1   Make sure that the trinomial has all the three terms, written in the standard form. If not, provide the missing term with zero coefficient and rearrange the terms.

$$x^2 + 3x \quad \longrightarrow \quad x^2 + 3x + 0$$
$$x^2 - 4 \quad \longrightarrow \quad x^2 + 0x - 4$$
$$2x + x^2 \quad \longrightarrow \quad x^2 + 2x + 0$$

Step 2   Find *two* critical integers, whose product is the constant term (c) and the sum is the coefficient of the middle term (b)

Step 3   Split the x - term into two parts using the two **CI**.

Step 4   Factor by grouping.

Alternatively we can factor using the following steps.

Step 1   The same as Step 1 above

Step 2   Find CI's, the same way as above

Step 3   If p and q are the critical integers then
$x + p$ and $x + q$ are the factors.
Thus $x^2 + bx + c = (x + p)(x + q)$

This alternative approach is applicable only if the leading coefficient (coefficient of x^2 form) is 1.

Example 2:   Factor $x^2 - 5x + 4$.

Solution:

Step 1   Not needed.   The polynomial is already written in the form $x^2 + bx + c$.

Step 2   Here $b = -5$, $c = 4$.

We are to find two numbers whose product is 4 (positive) and the sum is -5 (negative). Both the numbers must be negative. (why?)
Stop and think.

Warm Up

2.   **a)** Factor $x^2 - 3x - 4$.

Warm Up

2. b) Factor $x^2 + 7x + 6$

Integers	Product	Sum
$-2, -2$	4	-4
$-1, -4$	4	-5

Therefore, the integers -1 and -4 meet our requirements.

Step 3 $x^2 - 5x + 4$

$= x^2 - 4x - 1 \cdot x + 4$ Split x term

Step 4 $= (x^2 - 4x) - (x - 4)$ Grouping

$= x(x - 4) - 1 \cdot (x - 4)$ Factor each group

$= (x - 4)(x - 1)$ Factor again

Alternatively
Since -1 and -4 are CIs,
$x^2 - 5x + 4$
$= (x - 1)(x - 4)$

3. Factor the following:

a) $x^3 + 2x$

b) $y^2 - 9$

Example 3:   Factor the following trinomials.

a) $x^2 + 3x$ **b)** $y^2 - 16$

c) $x^2 + 8x + 12$

d) $z^2 - 3z - 4$ **e)** $t^2 - 2at - 3a^2$

Solutions:

a) *Step 1* $x^2 + 3x = x^2 + 3x + 0$

Step 2   The CI are 3 and 0, since the product has to be zero.

Step 3 $x^2 + 3x = x^2 + 3x + 0x + 3 \cdot 0$

Step 4 $= x(x + 3) + 0(x + 3)$
$= (x + 0)(x + 3)$
$= x(x + 3)$

Alternatively
Since 3 and 0 are the CIs,

$x^2 + 3x = (x + 0)(x + 3)$
$= x(x + 3)$.

Note: x is the greatest common factor of x^2 and $3x$. Therefore, we can directly factor out x and write $x^2 + 3x = x \cdot x + 3 \cdot x = x(x + 3)$.

b) *Step 1* $y^2 - 16 = y^2 + 0 \cdot y - 16$

Step 2   The CI, whose product is -16 and the sum 0, are 4 and -4.

Step 3 $y^2 - 16 = y^2 + 0 \cdot y - 16$
$= y^2 + 4y - 4y - 16$ Split the middle term

Step 4 $= (y^2 + 4y) - (4y + 16)$ Grouping
$= y(y + 4) - 4(y + 4)$ Factor out g.c.f
$= (y - 4)(y + 4)$ Factor again

Alternatively

Since 4 and -4 are the CIs,
$y^2 - 16$
$= (y + 4)(y - 4)$.

Note: Later in section 4.3, we shall see how $y^2 - 16$ can be factored directly as $(y - 4)(y + 4)$.

c) *Step 1* Not needed since $x^2 + 8x + 12$ is already in the desired form.

Step 2 We need two integers whose sum is 8 and product is 12. These integers will both be *positive* since in this case c $(= 12)$ is *positive*, and b $(= 8)$ is also positive.

Integers	Product	Sum
1, 12	12	13
2, 6	**12**	**8**
3, 4	12	7

The CI are 2 and 6.

Step 3 $x^2 + \mathbf{8x} + 12 = x^2 + \mathbf{2x} + \mathbf{6x} + 12$

Step 4 $= \left(x^2 + 2x\right) + \left(6x + 12\right)$

$= x(x + 2) + 6(x + 2)$

$= (x + 2)(x + 6)$

Alternatively

Since 2 and 6 are the CIs

$x^2 + 8x + 12$

$= (x + 2)(x + 6)$.

d) $z^2 - 3z - 4$

Step 1 Not needed.

Step 2 We have to find two integers whose sum is -3 and the product is -4. Since here $c(= -4)$ is negative, the two integers will have *opposite* signs.

Integers	Product	Sum
$-1, 4$	-4	3
$1, -4$	**-4**	**-3**

The CIs are 1 and -4.

Step 3 $z^2 - \mathbf{3z} - 4$ Split

$= z^2 - \mathbf{4z} + z - 4$

Step 4 $= \left(z^2 - 4z\right) + (z - 4)$ Grouping

$= z(z - 4) + \mathbf{1}(z - 4)$ Factor out g.c.f.

$= (z - 4)(z + 1)$ Factor again

Alternatively

Since 1 and -4 are the CIs,

$z^2 - 3z - 4$

$= (z + 1)(z - 4)$.

e) $y^2 - 5ay + 6a^2$

e) $t^2 - 2at - 3a^2$

In this case, there are two variables t and a. We concentrate on t only and find out two terms whose sum is $-2a$ and product is $-3a^2$.

Step 1   Not needed since the terms are arranged according to descending powers of t and no term is missing.

Step 2   Find CI, whose sum is $-2a$, and whose product is $-3a^2$. Such terms are $-3a$ and a.

$$-3a + a = -2a, \qquad (-3a)(a) = -3a^2$$

Answers:

2.   a) $(x-4)(x+1)$ b) $(x+1)(x+6)$

3.   a) $x(x^2+2)$ b) $(y+3)(y-3)$
   c) $(x+4)(x-2)$
   d) $(r+5)(r-1)$
   e) $(y-2a)(y-3a)$

Step 3 $t^2 - 2at - 3a^2 = t^2 - 3at + at - 3a^2$

Step 4 $= (t^2 - 3at) + (at - 3a^2)$ Grouping

$= t(t - 3a) + a(t - 3a)$ Factor out g.c.f.

$= (t - 3a)(t + a)$

Alternatively

Since -3a and a are the CIs,

$t^2 - 2at - 3a^2$
$= (t - 3a)(t + a).$

C.   **Factoring Trinomials** $ax^2 + bx + c = 0, \quad a \neq 1.$

Consider the product $(3x - 4)(x - 2)$. We expand this product using FOIL method.

$$(3x - 4)(x - 2) = 3x^2 - 6x - 4x + 8$$
$$= 3x^2 - 10x + 8$$

Let us write the above results in the reverse order.

$$3x^2 - 10x + 8 = 3x^2 - 6x - 4x + 8 = (3x - 4)(x - 2)$$

Observations:

1.   *The expression* $3x^2 - 10x + 8$ *is factored by separating the middle term into two parts* $(-10x = -6x - 4x)$. *We use two numbers* -6 *and* -4.

2.   *The product of* -6 *and* -4 *is the same as the product of the leading coefficient and the constant terms.* $(-6)(-4) = 3 \cdot 8$

3.   *The sum of* -6 *and* -4 *is the coefficient of the middle term.*

These observations suggest the following steps for factoring a polynomial of the form $ax^2 + bx + c$.

Step 1   Factor out the g.c.f., if any.

Step 2   Write the polynomial in descending powers of the variable, and insert the missing terms with zero coefficient.

Step 3   Find CI such that their sum is b and the product is ac (product of a and c).

$a =$ Leading coefficient in $ax^2 + bx + c$

$b =$ Coefficient of the middle term in $ax^2 + bx + c$

$c =$ Constant term in $ax^2 + bx + c$

Step 4   Split the middle term using the CI.

Step 5   Factor by grouping.

Example 4:   Factor the following polynomials.

a) $3x^2 + 7x + 4$ b) $4a^2 + 4a - 3$

c) $6y - 45 + 3y^2$ d) $-10x^2 - 11x + 6$

Warm Up

4. Factor the following polynomials:

Solutions:

a) $3x^2 + 7x + 4$

a) $4x^2 + 4x + 1$

Step 1 & 2   Not needed

Step 3 $b = 7$ and $ac = 12$. We need to find two integers whose sum is 7 and product is 12. These integers should both be positive. Why? **STOP** and **THINK**. The CI are 3 and 4.

Step 4 $3x^2 + \mathbf{7x} + 4 = 3x^2 + \mathbf{3x} + \mathbf{4x} + 4$

Split the middle term

Step 5 $= \left(3x^2 + 3x\right) + \left(4x + 4\right)$ Grouping

$= 3x(x + 1) + 4(x + 1)$ Factor out g.c.f.

$= (x + 1)(3x + 4)$ Factor again

b) $4a^2 + 4a - 3$

b) $6a^2 + 7a - 3$

Step 1 & 2   Not needed.

Step 3   We need to find two integers whose sum is 4 and product is $4(-3) = -12$. Notice that the two integers must have opposite signs. Why? **STOP** and **THINK**. Now -2, and 6 are two such integers. Their sum is 4, and their product is -12.

Step 4 $4a^2 + \mathbf{4a} - 3 = 4a^2 - \mathbf{2a} + \mathbf{6a} - 3$

Split the middle term

Step 5 $= \left(4a^2 - 2a\right) + \left(6a - 3\right)$ Grouping

$= 2a(2a - 1) + 3(2a - 1)$ Factor out g.c.f.

$= (2a - 1)(2a + 3)$

Warm Up

c) $7p^2 + 12p + 5$

c) $6y - 45 + 3y^2$

Step 1 $3(2y - 15 + y^2)$

Step 2   Rewrite $3(y^2 + 2y - 15)$

Step 3   We need to find two integers, whose sum is 2 and product is $1(-15) = -15$. The integers must have opposite signs. Why? **STOP** and **THINK**. Now 5 and -3 are two such integers. Their sum is $5 + (-3) = 2$ and their product is $5(-3) = -15$.

Step 4 $3[y^2 + 2y - 15] = 3(y^2 + 5y - 3y - 15)$ Split the middle term

Step 5 $\qquad\qquad = 3[(y^2 + 5y) - (3y + 15)]$ Grouping

$\qquad\qquad\qquad = 3[y(y + 5) - 3(y + 5)]$

$\qquad\qquad\qquad = 3[(y + 5)(y - 3)] = 3(y + 5)(y - 3)$

d) $-2x^2 - x + 45$

d) $-10x^2 - 11x + 6$

Step 1 $-1(10x^2 + 11x - 6)$

Step 2   Not needed

Step 3   First, we shall factor $10x^2 + 11x - 6$. We need two integers whose sum is 11 and have a product of $10(-6) = -60$. The two integers must have opposite signs. Why? The integers are 15 and -4.

Step 4 $10x^2 + 11x - 6 = 10x^2 + 15x - 4x - 6$ Split the middle term

Step 5 $\qquad\qquad = (10x^2 + 15x) - (4x + 6)$ Grouping

$\qquad\qquad\qquad = 5x(2x + 3) - 2(2x + 3)$ Factor out g.c.f.

$\qquad\qquad\qquad = (2x + 3)(5x - 2)$ Factors

Therefore, $-10x^2 - 11x + 6 = -1 \cdot (10x^2 + 11x - 6)$

$\qquad\qquad\qquad = -(5x - 2)(2x + 3)$

$\qquad\qquad\qquad = (2 - 5x)(2x + 3)$

Answers:

4. a) $(2x + 1)(2x + 1)$

  b) $(2a + 3)(3a - 1)$

  c) $(7p + 5)(p + 1)$

  d) $(9 - 2x)(x + 5)$

D. Miscellaneous Examples

Warm Up

5. Factor the following:

a) $-3x^2 + x^3 + 2x$

Example 5:   Factor the following.

a) $x^3 - 6x^2 + 5x$ 　　　　　 b) $2a^4 + 4a^3 - 30a^2$

c) $3y(y + 5) + 2(y + 5)(y^2 - 1)$ 　d) $z^4 + 2z^2 - 15$

Solutions:

a) $x^3 - 6x^2 + 5x = x(x^2 - 6x + 5)$ Factor out g.c.f.

Now we factor $x^2 - 6x + 5$.

$x^2 - 6x + 5 = x^2 - 5x - x + 5$ Step 2 and 3

$\qquad = \left(x^2 - 5x\right) - (x - 5)$ Step 4

$\qquad = x(x - 5) - 1(x - 5)$

$\qquad = (x - 1)(x - 5)$

Therefore, $x^3 - 6x^2 + 5x = x\left(x^2 - 6x + 5\right)$

$\qquad\qquad\qquad\qquad = x(x - 1)(x - 5)$

b) $2a^4 + 4a^3 - 30a^2 = 2a^2\left(a^2 + 2a - 15\right)$ Factor out g.c.f.

Now we factor $a^2 + 2a - 15$. The CIs are 5 and -3.

Also the leading coefficient is 1.

b) $a^4 + 9a^3 - a^2 - 9a$

Therefore $a^2 + 2a - 15 = (a + 5)(a - 3)$ Alternative approach

and $2a^4 + 4a^3 - 30a^2 = 2a^2\left(a^2 + 2a - 15\right)$

$\qquad\qquad\qquad\qquad = 2a^2(a - 3)(a + 5)$

c) $3y(y + 5) + 2(y + 5)\left(y^2 - 1\right) = 3y(y + 5) + 2\left(y^2 - 1\right)(y + 5)$

$\qquad\qquad\qquad\qquad\qquad = (y + 5)\left[3y + 2\left(y^2 - 1\right)\right]$

$\qquad\qquad\qquad\qquad\qquad = (y + 5)\left(3y + 2y^2 - 2\right)$

c) $2\left(3x^2 + 2x + 1\right) + (3x - 1)$

Now we factor $3y + 2y^2 - 2$.

$3y + 2y^2 - 2 = 2y^2 + 3y - 2$ The CIs are 4, -1

$\qquad\qquad = 2y^2 + 4y - y - 2$

$\qquad\qquad = \left(2y^2 + 4y\right) - (y + 2)$

$\qquad\qquad = 2y(y + 2) - 1 \cdot (y + 2)$

$\qquad\qquad = (y + 2)(2y - 1)$

Therefore,

$3y(y + 5) + 2(y + 5)\left(y^2 - 1\right) = (y + 5)\left(3y + 2y^2 - 2\right)$

$\qquad\qquad\qquad\qquad\qquad = (y + 5)(y + 2)(2y - 1)$

d) $z^4 + 2z^2 - 15 = \left(z^2\right)^2 + 2z^2 - 15$

Substitute $z^2 = y$.

$z^4 + 2z^2 - 15 = y^2 + 2y - 15$

We factor $y^2 + 2y - 15$ and then replace y by z^2.

The CIs are 5 and -3

Therefore $y^2 + 2y - 15 = (y + 5)(y - 3)$

$\qquad z^4 + 2z^2 - 15 = \left(z^2 + 5\right)\left(z^2 - 3\right)$

d) $y^5 + 7y^3 + 10y$

Answers:

5. **a)** $x(x - 1)(x - 2)$

$\quad$ **b)** $a(a + 9)(a + 1)(a - 1)$

$\quad$ **c)** $(6x + 1)(x + 1)$

$\quad$ **d)** $y\left(y^2 + 5\right)\left(y^2 + 2\right)$

EXERCISE 4.2

Answers:

1. _____

2. _____

3. _____

4. _____

5. _____

6. _____

7. _____

8. _____

9. _____

10. _____

11. _____

12. _____

13. _____

14. _____

15. _____

16. _____

17. _____

18. _____

19. _____

20. _____

21. _____

22. _____

23. _____

24. _____

25. _____

26. _____

27. _____

In exercises 1–4, determine which trinomial can be factored.
[Use the criterion that $b^2 - 4ac$ must be a perfect square.]

1. $x^2 - 5x - 14$ **2.** $2x^2 - 3x + 4$

3. $2x^2 - 3x - 2$ **4.** $-5p^2 + 4p + 1$

In exercises 5–9, complete the factoring.

5. $x^2 + 8x + 15 = (x + 3)\ (\quad)$

6. $x^2 + 15x + 56 = (x + 8)(\quad)$

7. $t^2 - 2t - 15 = (\quad)(t - 5)$

8. $3r^2 - 8r - 3 = (r - 3)\ (\quad)$

9. $4y^3 - 10y^2 - 6y = 2y(2y\quad)(\quad - 3)$

In exercises 10–51, factor the trinomials.

10. $x^2 - 9x - 22$ **11.** $x^2 - 10x + 25$ **12.** $z^2 - z - 30$

13. $x^2 - x - 6$ **14.** $x^2 + x - 6$ **15.** $x^2 - 5x + 6$

16. $x^2 - 5x + 4$ **17.** $x^2 - 3x - 4$ **18.** $x^2 + 3x - 4$

19. $x^2 - 4x - 5$ **20.** $x^2 + 4x - 5$ **21.** $x^2 - 6x + 5$

22. $x^2 - 5x - 14$ **23.** $x^2 + 5x - 14$ **24.** $x^2 - 9x + 14$

25. $x^2 + 4x - 21$ **26.** $x^2 - 4x - 21$ **27.** $x^2 - 10x + 21$

28. $2x^2 + 5x - 3$ **29.** $2x^2 - 5x - 3$ **30.** $3x^2 - 5x - 2$

31. $3x^2 + 5x - 2$ **32.** $4x^2 - 7x - 15$ **33.** $4x^2 + 7x - 15$

34. $6x^2 + 7x - 3$ **35.** $6x^2 - 7x - 3$ **36.** $6x^2 - 11x + 3$

37. $6x^2 + 11x + 3$ **38.** $6x^2 - 5x + 1$ **39.** $6x^2 - x - 1$

40. $6x^2 + x - 1$ **41.** $6x^2 + 5x + 1$ **42.** $10x^2 + 11x - 6$

43. $10x^2 - 11x - 6$ **44.** $10x^2 + 19x + 6$

45. $10x^2 - 19x + 6$ **46.** $-r^2 + 4r + 32$

47. $-40t - 75 - 5t^2$ **48.** $a^2x^3 - 12ax^3 + 35x^3$

49. $12a^3b^4 - 4a^2b^5 - ab^6$ **50.** $18x^3y - 3x^2y^2 - 105xy^2$

51. $21x^4 - 10x^3 - 16x^2$

28. _____

29. _____

30. _____

31. _____

32. _____

33. _____

34. _____

35. _____

36. _____

37. _____

38. _____

39. _____

40. _____

41. _____

42. _____

43. _____

44. _____

45. _____

46. _____

47. _____

48. _____

49. _____

50. _____

51. _____

4.3   SPECIAL FACTORIZATIONS

Recall that a number is called a *perfect square* if it is the square of an integer. For example, 4 is a perfect square $\left[4 = 2^2\right]$. Similarly, a number is called a *perfect cube* if it is a cube (third power) of an integer. Thus -8 is a perfect cube since $-8 = (-2)^3$.

Perfect squares less than 200 are: 1, 4, 9, 16, 25, 36, 49, 64, 81, 100, 121, 144, 169, 196.
Perfect squares are never negative.

Perfect cubes between 1 and 1000 are: 1, 8, 27, 64, 125, 216, 343, 512, 729, 1000.

Perfect cubes between -1000 and -1 **are:** $-1, -8 -27, -64, -125, -216, -343,$ $-512, -729, -1000$
Perfect cubes can be positive or negative

Expressions containing variables with even exponents such as $x^8 x^6$ are also perfect squares since $x^8 y^6 = \left(x^4 y^3\right)^2$. Again, an expression of the type $x^6 y^3$ is a perfect cube since $x^6 y^3 = \left(x^2 y\right)^3$.

In the last chapter, we learnt that
$$(a - b)(a + b) = a^2 - b^2$$
$$(a + b)^2 = a^2 + 2ab + b^2$$
$$(a - b)^2 = a^2 - 2ab + b^2$$
$$(a + b)\left(a^2 - ab + b^2\right) = a^3 + b^3$$
$$(a - b)\left(a^2 + ab + b^2\right) = a^3 - b^3$$

We shall use these products to perform special factorizations. Upon completion of this section we will be able to:

    A.   Factor the Difference of Two Squares.
    B.   Factor a Perfect Square Trinomial.
    C.   Factor the Sum of Two Cubes.
    D.   Factor the Difference of Two Cubes.

A.   Difference of Two Squares

$$(a - b)(a + b) = a^2 - b^2 \longrightarrow a^2 - b^2 = (a - b)(a + b)$$

Warm Up

1. Factor

   a) $9y^2 - 4$

   b) $z^2 - \dfrac{16}{9}$

Example 1:   Factor.

   a) $x^2 - 36$ **b)** $y^2 - \dfrac{9}{4}$ **c)** $9z^2 - 25$

   d) $16x^2 - 25y^2$ **e)** $16x^4 - 25y^2$

   f) $16x^4 - 81y^4$ **g)** $(a + b)^2 - c^2$

   h) $x^4 - 1$ **i)** $3m^4 n - 48n$

Solutions:

a) $x^2 - 36 = (x)^2 - (6)^2$ Difference of two squares

$\qquad = (x - 6)(x + 6)$ $a^2 - b^2 = (a-b)(a+b)$

c) $8m^2n - 32n$

b) $y^2 - \dfrac{9}{4} = (y)^2 - \left(\dfrac{3}{2}\right)^2$ Difference of two squares

$\qquad = \left(y - \dfrac{3}{2}\right)\left(y + \dfrac{3}{2}\right)$ $a^2 - b^2 = (a-b)(a+b)$

d) $x^6 - 4$

c) $9z^2 - 25 = (3z)^2 - 5^2 = (3z - 5)(3z + 5)$ $a^2 - b^2 = (a-b)(a+b)$

d) $16x^2 - 25y^2 = (4x)^2 - (5y)^2 = (4x - 5y)(4x + 5y)$

e) $(a + b)^4 - c^2$

e) $16x^4 - 25y^2 = (4x^2)^2 - (5y)^2 = (4x^2 - 5y)(4x^2 + 5y)$

f) $16x^4 - 81y^4 = (4x^2)^2 - (9y^2)^2 = (4x^2 - 9y^2)(4x^2 + 9y^2)$

$\qquad = \left[(2x)^2 - (3y)^2\right](4x^2 + 9y^2)$

$\qquad = (2x - 3y)(2x + 3y)(4x^2 + 9y^2)$

f) $81z^2 - 121y^2$

g) $(a + b)^2 - c^2 = (a + b - c)(a + b + c)$

Answers:

1. **a)** $(3y + 2)(3y - 2)$

h) $x^4 - 1 = (x^2)^2 - 1^2 = (x^2 - 1)(x^2 + 1)$

$\qquad = \left[(x)^2 - (1)^2\right](x^2 + 1)$

$\qquad = (x - 1)(x + 1)(x^2 + 1)$

b) $\left(z + \dfrac{4}{3}\right)\left(z - \dfrac{4}{3}\right)$

c) $8n(m + 2)(m - 2)$

d) $(x^3 + 2)(x^3 - 2)$

e) $\left[(a+b)^2 - c\right]\left[(a+b)^2 + c\right]$

i) $3m^4n - 48n = 3n(m^4 - 16) = 3n(m^2 - 4)(m^2 + 4)$ [Why?]

$\qquad = 3n(m - 2)(m + 2)(m^2 + 4)$ [Why?]

f) $(9z + 11y)(9z - 11y)$

Note: Whereas $m^2 - 4$ is a difference of two squares, and can be factored,

$m^2 + 4$ **cannot** be factored!

B. Perfect Square Trinomials

Perfect square trinomials can be factored according to the following rules

same

same

$$a^2 + 2ab + b^2 = (a + b)^2 \qquad\qquad a^2 - 2ab + b^2 = (a - b)^2$$

Notice that, in $a^2 + 2ab + b^2$, two of the terms are perfect squares, and the third term is *twice* the product of the quantities whose squares the other two terms are, as in the following illustration.

$$\underbrace{(3a)^2}_{\text{Perfect Square}} + 2\underbrace{(3a)(5b)}_{\text{Product}} + \underbrace{(5b)^2}_{\text{Perfect Square}}$$

$$= (3a + 5b)^2$$

For example,

$$\underbrace{16x^2}_{\substack{\text{Perfect Square}\\(4x)^2}} + \underbrace{40x}_{\substack{\text{Twice the product}\\2(4x)(5)}} + \underbrace{25}_{\substack{\text{Perfect Square}\\5^2}}$$

$$= (4x + 5)^2$$

A similar observation can be made about $a^2 - 2ab + b^2$.

Warm Up

2. Factor the trinomials

a) $9x^2 + 42x + 49$

b) $x^2 + 4x + 4$

c) $x^2 + 8x + 16$

Example 2:   Factor the trinomials.

a) $x^2 - 6x + 9$ b) $x^2 + 6x + 9$

c) $4x^2 - 28x + 49$

d) $9a^2 + 30ab + 25b^2$ e) $\dfrac{4}{9}x^4 - \dfrac{2}{3}x^2 + \dfrac{1}{4}$

Solutions:

a) $x^2 - 6x + 9 =$

$$\underbrace{x^2}_{\substack{\text{Perfect Square}\\x^2}} - \underbrace{6x}_{\substack{\text{Twice the product}\\2\,(x)\,(3)}} + \underbrace{9}_{\substack{\text{Perfect Square}\\3^2}}$$

$$= (x - 3)^2$$

b) $x^2 + 6x + 9 =$

$$\underbrace{x^2}_{\substack{\text{Perfect Square}\\x^2}} + \underbrace{6x}_{\substack{\text{Twice the product}\\2\,(x)\,(3)}} + \underbrace{9}_{\substack{\text{Perfect Square}\\3^2}}$$

$$= (x + 3)^2$$

Observations:

The sign of the middle term of the perfect square trinomial is the same as the sign between the two terms under the square.

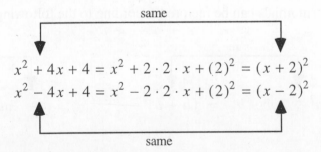

226

c) $4x^2 - 28x + 49 =$

$$\underbrace{4x^2}_{\substack{\text{Perfect Square}\\(2x)^2}} - \underbrace{28x}_{\substack{\text{Twice the product}\\2\ (2x)\ (7)}} + \underbrace{49}_{\substack{\text{Perfect Square}\\(7)^2}}$$

$$= (2x - 7)^2$$

d) $9a^2 + 30ab + 25b^2 =$

$$\underbrace{9a^2}_{\substack{\text{Perfect Square}\\(3a)^2}} + \underbrace{30\ ab}_{\substack{\text{Twice the product}\\2\ (3a)\ (5b)}} + \underbrace{25b^2}_{\substack{\text{Perfect Square}\\(5b)^2}}$$

$$= (3a + 5b)^2$$

e) $\dfrac{4}{9}x^4 - \dfrac{2}{3}x^2 + \dfrac{1}{4} = \left(\dfrac{2}{3}x^2\right)^2 - 2\left(\dfrac{2}{3}x^2\right)\left(\dfrac{1}{2}\right) + \left(\dfrac{1}{2}\right)^2$

$$= \left(\dfrac{2}{3}x^2 - \dfrac{1}{2}\right)^2$$

Warm Up

2. d) $25y^2 + 90y + 81$

e) $\dfrac{1}{4}x^2 - x + 1$

Answers:

2. a) $(3x + 7)^2$ **b)** $(x + 2)^2$

c) $(x + 4)^2$ **d)** $(5y + 9)^2$

e) $\left(\dfrac{1}{2}x - 1\right)^2$

C. Sum of Two Cubes

The sum of two cubes can be factored with the help of the following formula.

$$a^3 + b^3 = (a + b)(a^2 - ab + b^2)$$

same sign   opposite sign

This result may be verified by expanding the product on the right.

Note: Recall that sum of two squares cannot be factored.

Example 3: Factor each of the following expressions

a) $x^3 + 8$ **b)** $8x^3 + 27$

c) $64p^6 + 27q^3$ **d)** $8m^6 + 125n^6$

e) $64a^6 + 729b^6$

Warm Up

3. Factor each of the following expressions

a) $x^3 + 27$

Solutions:

a) $x^3 + 8 = x^3 + 2^3 = (x + 2)\left(x^2 - 2x + 2^2\right)$ $a^3 + b^3$

$$= (x + 2)(x^2 - 2x + 4)$$ $= (a + b)(a^2 - ab + b^2)$

Note: $x^2 - 2x + 4$ is not a perfect square. However, $x^2 - 4x + 4 = x^2 - 2(x)(2) + 2^2$ is a perfect square.

Warm Up

b) $27x^3 + 64$

c) $8p^6 + 1$

d) $64x^6 + 125y^6$

Answers:

3. a) $(x+3)(x^2 - 3x + 9)$

   b) $(3x+4)(9x^2 - 12x + 16)$

   c) $(2p^2 + 1)(4p^4 - 2p^2 + 1)$

   d) $(4x^2 + 5y^2)(16x^4 - 20x^2y^2 + 25y^4)$

b) $8x^3 + 27 = (2x)^3 + 3^3$ Sum of two cubes
$$= (2x + 3)\left[(2x)^2 - (2x)(3) + 3^2\right] \qquad a^3 + b^3$$
$$= (2x + 3)(4x^2 - 6x + 9) \qquad = (a+b)(a^2 - ab + b^2)$$

c) $64p^6 + 27q^3 = \left(4p^2\right)^3 + \left(3q\right)^3$ Sum of two cubes
$$= \left(4p^2 + 3q\right)\left[\left(4p^2\right)^2 - \left(4p^2\right)(3q) + \left(3q\right)^2\right]$$
$$= \left(4p^2 + 3q\right)\left[16p^4 - 12p^2q + 9q^2\right]$$

d) $8m^6 + 125n^6 = \left(2m^2\right)^3 + \left(5n^2\right)^3$ Sum of two cubes
$$= \left(2m^2 + 5n^2\right)\left[\left(2m^2\right)^2 - \left(2m^2\right)\left(5n^2\right) + \left(5n^2\right)^2\right]$$
$$= \left(2m^2 + 5n^2\right)\left(4m^4 - 10m^2n^2 + 25n^4\right)$$

e) $64a^6 + 729b^6 = \left(4a^2\right)^3 + \left(9b^2\right)^3$ Sum of two cubes
$$= \left(4a^2 + 9b^2\right)\left[\left(4a^2\right)^2 - \left(4a^2\right)\left(9b^2\right) + \left(9b^2\right)^2\right]$$
$$= \left(4a^2 + 9b^2\right)\left(16a^4 - 36a^2b^2 + 81b^4\right)$$

Note : $4a^2 + 9b^2$ is a sum of two squares, namely $(2a)^2 + (3b)^2$.
It *cannot* be factored.

D.   Difference of Two Cubes

The difference of two cubes can be factored with the help of the following formula.

$$a^3 - b^3 = (a-b)(a^2 + ab + b^2)$$

Same sign   Opposite sign

The result may be verified by expanding the product on the right

Warm Up

4. Factor each of the following
    expressions.

    a) $x^3 - 27$

Example 4:   Factor each of the following expressions.

a) $x^3 - 8$ b) $8x^3 - 27$

c) $64p^6 - 27q^3$ d) $8m^6 - 125n^6$

e) $64a^6 - 729b^6$

Solutions:

a) $x^3 - 8 = (x)^3 - 2^3$ Difference of two cubes
$$= (x - 2)\left[(x)^2 + 2(x) + (2)^2\right]$$
$$= (x - 2)(x^2 + 2x + 4)$$

b) $8x^3 - 27 = (2x)^3 - 3^3$ Difference of two cubes

$\qquad = (2x - 3)\left[(2x)^2 + (2x)(3) + 3^2\right]$

$\qquad = (2x - 3)(4x^2 + 6x + 9)$

c) $64p^6 - 27q^3 = \left(4p^2\right)^3 - (3q)^3$ Difference of two cubes

$\qquad = \left(4p^2 - 3q\right)\left[\left(4p^2\right)^2 + \left(4p^2\right)(3q) + (3q)^2\right]$

$\qquad = \left(4p^2 - 3q\right)\left(16p^4 + 12p^2q + 9q^2\right)$

d) $8m^6 - 125n^6 = \left(2m^2\right)^3 - \left(5n^2\right)^3$ Difference of two cubes

$\qquad = \left(2m^2 - 5n^2\right)\left[\left(2m^2\right)^2 + \left(2m^2\right)\left(5n^2\right) + \left(5n^2\right)^2\right]$

$\qquad = \left(2m^2 - 5n^2\right)\left[4m^4 + 10m^2n^2 + 25n^4\right]$

Warm Up

b) $27x^3 - 64$

c) $8p^6 - 1$

d) $64x^6 - 125y^6$

Answers:

4.   a) $(x - 3)(x^2 + 3x + 9)$

     b) $(3x - 4)(9x^2 + 12x + 16)$

     c) $\left(2p^2 - 1\right)\left(4p^4 + 2p^2 + 1\right)$

     d) $\left(4x^2 - 5y^2\right)\left(16x^4 + 20x^2y^2 + 25y^4\right)$

Note: $2m^2 - 5n^2$ is not a difference of square, in rationals, since 2 and 5 are not perfect squares.

General Strategy for Factoring a Polynomial

Step 1   Look for the g.c.f. of all the terms, other than 1. If the g.c.f. is **1** then proceed to step 2 with the given polynomial. If the g.c.f. is other than **1** then factor it out and proceed with the reduced polynomial to step 2.

Given polynomial = g.c.f. [Reduced Polynomial]

Step 2   If the given polynomial or the reduced polynomial has only two terms then check if it is one of the following three forms.

     a)   Difference of two squares

     b)   Difference of two cubes

     c)   Sum of two cubes

Step 3   If the expression has only three terms then check if it is one of the following forms.

     a)   Perfect Square: $a^2 + 2ab + b^2$ or $a^2 - 2ab + b^2$

     b)   Trinomial with leading coefficient 1: $x^2 + bx + c$

     c)   Trinomial with leading coefficient not 1: $ax^2 + bx + c$

Step 4   If the expression has more than three terms then try to factor by grouping method

Step 5   Check if each factor can be factored any further. Factoring always means factoring completely.

EXERCISE 4.3

Answers:

1. _____

2. _____

3. _____

4. _____

5. _____

6. _____

7. _____

8. _____

9. _____

10. _____

11. _____

12. _____

13. _____

14. _____

15. _____

16. _____

17. _____

18. _____

19. _____

20. _____

21. _____

22. _____

23. _____

24. _____

25. _____

26. _____

27. _____

28. _____

29. _____

In exercises 1–16, factor the binomials completely, wherever possible.

1. $x^2 - 9$ **2.** $4x^2 - 25$ **3.** $16a^2 + b^2$ **4.** $81a^2 - 25b^2$

5. $2a^2 - 8b^2$ **6.** $3x^2 - 12y^2$ **7.** $2 - 8t^2$ **8.** $18 - 50a^2$

9. $xy^2 - x^3$ **10.** $2a^2b - 18b^3$ **11.** $5a^3 - 20ab^2$ **12.** $3t^2 - 27$

13. $a^2bc - b^3c$ **14.** $m^4 - 81$ **15.** $9p^2 + 4q^2$ **16.** $r^4 - 49$

In exercises 17–29, factor the following.

17. $x^2 - 6x + 9$ **18.** $x^2 + 8x + 16$ **19.** $a^2 + 10a + 25$

20. $r^2 - 14r + 49$ **21.** $y^2 - 7y + \dfrac{49}{4}$ **22.** $t^2 + 5t + \dfrac{25}{4}$

23. $2x^2 - 8x + 8$ **24.** $3a^2 + 18a + 27$ **25.** $a^2b - 2ab^2 + b^3$

26. $16a^2 + 24ab + 9b^2$ **27.** $49z^2 - 28zt + 4t^2$

28. $9x^2 + 48x^2y + 64x^2y^2$ **29.** $a^2b^2x^2 - 20a^2b^2x + 100a^2b^2$

In exercises 30–32, fill in the blanks so that the resulting expression is a perfect square.

30. $x^2 + 6x + 25$ **31.** $x^2 - 16x + 100$ **32.** $x^2 - 4x + 13$

In exercises 33–40, factor using formulas for the sum or difference of two cubes.

33. $x^3 - 1$ **34.** $x^3 + 27$ **35.** $27a^3 - b^3$

36. $64r^3 + 125s^3$ **37.** $125x^3 + 8y^3$ **38.** $729p^3 - 1000q^3$

39. $(x + y)^3 + (x - y)^3$ **40.** $8x^6 + 64y^6$

30. _____

31. _____

32. _____

33. _____

34. _____

35. _____

36. _____

37. _____

38. _____

39. _____

40. _____

4.4   SOLVING QUADRATIC EQUATIONS BY FACTORING

An equation is called a **quadratic equation** or a **second degree equation** if it can be written in the form $ax^2 + bx + c = 0$, where a, b, and c, are real numbers, and $a \neq 0$. (if a = 0 the equation reduces to a linear equation $bx + c = 0$).

As with linear equations, solving a quadratic equation means finding numbers which make the equation true upon substitution. For example $x = -1$ is a solution of $4x^2 + 3x - 1 = 0$ because $4(-1)^2 + 3(-1) - 1 = 0$ is a true statement.

In this section we will see show how factoring can be used to solve quadratic equations.

Upon completion of this section we should be able to:

     A.   Define Zero Factor Property.
     B.   Solve Quadratic Equations.
     C.   Use Zero Factor Property for more than two Factors.

A. Zero-Factor Property

If a and b are real numbers, then $ab = 0 \longrightarrow a = 0$ or $b = 0$.

This property can be stated differently: If the product of two factors is zero then either of these two or both can be zero.

Warm Up

1. Find the value(s) of x in $(x-3)(3x-2)=0$.

Answers:

1. $x=3$, $x=\dfrac{2}{3}$

Example 1:   Given $(x-4)(3x+2)=0$, find the value(s) of x?

Solution:

$$(x-4)(3x+2)=0 \longrightarrow x-4 = 0 \text{ or } 3x+2 = 0$$
Zero-factor property

Notice $x-4=0$ and $3x+2=0$ are linear equations.

$$x-4 = 0 \quad \text{or} \quad 3x+2 = 0$$
$$x = 4 \qquad\qquad 3x = -2$$
$$x = -2/3$$

Thus $(x-4)(3x+2)=0 \longrightarrow x=4$ or $x=-\dfrac{2}{3}$.

B.   Solving Quadratic Equations

We use a four step approach for solving quadratic equations by factoring.

Step 1   Write the equation in the *standard form*: $ax^2+bx+c=0$.

Step 2   Factor the trinomial ax^2+bx+c .

Step 3   Equate each factor to zero and solve for the unknown (x)

Step 4   Check the solutions by substituting in the *original* equation.

Warm Up

2. Write the following equations in standard form.

a) $2x^2-x=3$

b) $4x^2=3(x-2)$

c) $x^2=x+5$

d) $2x=x^2+1$

Example 2:   Write the following equations in the standard form.

a) $3x^2-5x=7$ b) $2x^2=4(x-5)$
c) $3x=x^2-2$ d) $x^2=-5$

Solutions:

a)
$$3x^2-5x=7$$
$$3x^2-5x+(-7)=7+(-7)$$
$$3x^2-5x-7=0$$

b)
$$2x^2=4(x-5)$$
$$2x^2=4x-20$$
$$2x^2-4x+20=0$$

c)
$$3x=x^2-2$$
$$-x^2+3x=-2 \qquad \text{Transfer } x^2 \text{ to left side}$$
$$-x^2+3x+2=0 \qquad \text{Transfer } -2 \text{ to left side}$$

d)
$$x^2=-5$$
$$x^2+5=0 \qquad\qquad \text{Transfer } -5 \text{ to left side}$$

Example 3: Solve the following equations.

a) $x^2 - 3x - 4 = 0$ b) $x^2 + 5x = 14$

c) $3y^2 - 48 = 0$ d) $9p^2 = 25$

e) $3z^2 = 5z$ f) $2x^2 - x - 10 = 0$

g) $x^2 + 4x + 4 = 0$

3. Solve the following equations.

a) $2x^2 - x - 3 = 0$

Solutions:

a) $x^2 - 3x - 4 = 0$

Step 1   Not needed. The equation is already in the standard form

Step 2 $x^2 - 3x - 4 = (x - 4)(x + 1)$ Factor

Step 3 $(x - 4)(x + 1) = 0$

Therefore, $x - 4 = 0$ or $x + 1 = 0$ Zero Factor Property

$\longrightarrow$ $x = 4$ or $x = -1$

The solutions are 4 and -1.

Step 4   Check the solutions: $x^2 - 3x - 4 = 0$

$x = 4$: $(4)^2 - 3(4) - 4 = 0$

$\longrightarrow 16 - 12 - 4 = 0$ True

$x = -1$: $(-1)^2 - 3(-1) - 4 = 0$

$\longrightarrow 1 + 3 - 4 = 0$ True

b) $x^2 + 5x = 14$

b) $x^2 - 2x + 1 = 0$

Step 1 $x^2 + 5x - 14 = 0$

Step 2 $(x + 7)(x - 2) = 0$ Factor

Step 3 $x + 7 = 0$ or $x - 2 = 0$ Zero Factor Property

$\longrightarrow x = -7$ or $x = 2$

The solutions are -7 and 2.

Step 4   Check the solutions: $x^2 + 5x - 14 = 0$

$x = -7$: $(-7)^2 + 5(-7) - 14 = 0$

$49 - 35 - 14 = 0$ True

$x = 2$: $(2)^2 + 5(2) - 14 = 0$

$4 + 10 - 14 = 0$ True

Warm Up

c) $9z^2 = 16$

c) $3y^2 - 48 = 0$

Step 1   Not needed

Step 2 $3y^2 - 48 = 3(y^2 - 16) = 3(y - 4)(y + 4)$

Step 3 $y - 4 = 0$ or $y + 4 = 0 \longrightarrow y = 4$ or $y = -4$

The solutions are 4 and -4.

Step 4   Check the solutions: $3y^2 - 48 = 0$

$y = \mathbf{4}$: $3(\mathbf{4})^2 - 48 = 0$

$\longrightarrow 48 - 48 = 0$ **True**

$y = -\mathbf{4}$: $3(-\mathbf{4})^2 - 48 = 0$

$\longrightarrow 48 - 48 = 0$ **True**

d) $x^2 + 8x + 16 = 0$

d) $9p^2 = 25$

Step 1 $9p^2 - 25 = 0$

Step 2 $9p^2 - 25 = (3p - 5)(3p + 5)$ Factor

Step 3 $3p - 5 = 0$ or $3p + 5 = 0 \longrightarrow p = \dfrac{5}{3}$ or $p = -\dfrac{5}{3}$

The solutions are $\dfrac{5}{3}$ and $-\dfrac{5}{3}$.

Step 4   Check the solutions: $9p^2 - 25 = 0$

$p = \dfrac{5}{3}$: $9\left(\dfrac{5}{3}\right)^2 - 25 = 0 \longrightarrow 25 - 25 = 0$ **True**

$p = -\dfrac{5}{3}$: $9\left(-\dfrac{5}{3}\right)^2 - 25 = 0 \longrightarrow 25 - 25 = 0$ **True**

e) $4z^2 = 8z$

e) $3z^2 = 5z$

Step 1 $3z^2 - 5z = 0$

Step 2 $3z^2 - 5z = z(3z - 5)$ Factor

Step 3 $z = 0$ or $3z - 5 = 0$

$z = 0$ or $z = \dfrac{5}{3}$

The solutions are **0** and $\dfrac{5}{3}$.

Step 4   Check the solutions: $3z^2 - 5z = 0$

$z = \mathbf{0}$: $3(0)^2 - 5(0) = 0 \longrightarrow 0 = 0$ **True**

$z = \dfrac{5}{3}$: $3\left(\dfrac{5}{3}\right)^2 - 5\left(\dfrac{5}{3}\right) = 0 \longrightarrow 3\left(\dfrac{25}{9}\right) - 5\left(\dfrac{5}{3}\right) = 0$

$\longrightarrow \dfrac{25}{3} = \dfrac{25}{3}$ **True**

f) $2x^2 - x - 10 = 0$

f) $2x^2 + 3x - 5$

Step 1   Not needed

Step 2 $2x^2 - x - 10 = (2x - 5)(x + 2)$

Step 3 $2x - 5 = 0$ or $x + 2 = 0$

$2x = 5$ or $x = -2$

$x = \dfrac{5}{2}$ and $x = -2$

The solutions are $\dfrac{5}{2}$ and $-\mathbf{2}$.

Step 4   Check the solutions: $2x^2 - x - 10 = 0$

$x = \dfrac{5}{2}$: $2\left(\dfrac{5}{2}\right)^2 - \left(\dfrac{5}{2}\right) - 10 = 0 \longrightarrow 2 \cdot \dfrac{25}{4} - \dfrac{5}{2} - 10 = 0$

$\longrightarrow 10 - 10 = 0$ **True**

$x = -\mathbf{2}$: $2(-\mathbf{2})^2 - (-\mathbf{2}) - 10 = 0$

$2 \cdot 4 + 2 - 10 = 0 \longrightarrow 10 - 10 = 0$ **True**

g) $x^2 + 4x + 4 = 0$

g) $y^2 - 6y + 9 = 0$

Step 1   Not needed

Step 2 $x^2 + 4x + 4 = (x + 2)^2 = (x + 2)(x + 2)$

Answers:

Step 3 $x + 2 = 0$ or $x + 2 = 0$

$\longrightarrow x = -2$ and $x = -2$

The solutions are -2 and -2 (repeated).

2. a) $2x^2 - x - 3 = 0$

b) $4x^2 - 3x + 6 = 0$

c) $x^2 - x - 5 = 0$

d) $x^2 - 2x + 1 = 0$

Step 4   Check the solutions: $x^2 + 4x + 4 = 0$

$x = -\mathbf{2}$: $(-\mathbf{2})^2 + 4(-\mathbf{2}) + 4 = 0$

$4 + (-8) + 4 = 0 \longrightarrow 0 = 0$ **True**

3. a) $\dfrac{3}{2}, -1$ **b)** $1, 1$ **c)** $-\dfrac{4}{3}, \dfrac{4}{3}$

d) $-4, -4$ **e)** $0, 2$ **f)** $-\dfrac{5}{2}, 1$

g) $3, 3$

C. Zero Factor Property for more than two Factors

Zero - factor property can be extended to more than two numbers. For example if $a \cdot b \cdot c = 0$ then $a = 0$ or $b = 0$ or $c = 0$.

Warm Up

4. Solve the following equations.

a) $(3x + 7)(x^2 + x - 12) = 0$

Example 4: Solve the following equations

a) $(2x + 5)(x^2 - x - 12) = 0$

b) $4y^3 - y = 0$

c) $(z^2 - 4)(z^2 - 9) = 0$

Solutions:

a) $(2x + 5)(x^2 - x - 12) = 0$

Since $x^2 - x - 12 = (x - 4)(x + 3)$.

$(2x + 5)(x^2 - x - 12) = 0 \longrightarrow (2x + 5)(x - 4)(x + 3) = 0$

The zero-factor property gives us;

$$2x + 5 = 0 \qquad \text{or} \qquad x - 4 = 0 \qquad \text{or} \quad x + 3 = 0$$
$$\longrightarrow \qquad 2x = -5 \qquad \text{or} \qquad x = 4 \qquad \text{or} \qquad x = -3$$
$$\longrightarrow \qquad x = -\frac{5}{2} \qquad \text{or} \qquad x = 4 \qquad \text{or} \qquad x = -3$$

Hence the solutions of $(2x + 5)(x^2 - x - 12) = 0$ are $\dfrac{-5}{2}$, **4**, and **- 3.**

We leave the verification of the solutions as an exercise.

b) $8y^3 - 32y = 0$

b) $4y^3 - y = 0$

$4y^3 - y = y(4y^2 - 1) = y(2y - 1)(2y + 1)$

The given equation becomes $y(2y - 1)(2y + 1) = 0$

The zero - factor property gives us;

$$y = 0 \qquad \text{or} \qquad 2y - 1 = 0 \qquad \text{or} \qquad 2y + 1 = 0$$
$$\longrightarrow \qquad y = 0 \qquad \text{or} \qquad 2y = 1 \qquad \text{or} \qquad 2y = -1$$
$$\longrightarrow \qquad y = 0 \qquad \text{or} \qquad y = \frac{1}{2} \qquad \text{or} \qquad y = -\frac{1}{2}$$

Hence the solutions of $4y^3 - y = 0$ are 0, $\dfrac{1}{2}$, $-\dfrac{1}{2}$.

Checking of the solutions is left as an exercise.

c) $(x^2 - 16)(x^2 - 81) = 0$

c) $(z^2 - 4)(z^2 - 9) = 0$

$(z^2 - 4)(z^2 - 9) = (z^2 - 2^2)(z^2 - 3^2)$

$= (z - 2)(z + 2)(z - 3)(z + 3)$

The given equation becomes $(z-2)(z+2)(z-3)(z+3)=0$

$\longrightarrow$ $z-2=0$ or $z+2=0$ or $z-3=0$ or $z+3=0$

$\longrightarrow$ $z=2$ or $z=-2$ or $z=3$ or $z=-3$

Hence the solutions of $(z^2-4)(z^2-9)=0$ are ± 2 and ± 3

EXERCISE 4.4

Answers:

Solve the equations in exercises 1-9.

1. $(x-5)(3x+4)=0$

2. $(2x+3)(3x+5)=0$

3. $(3x-1)(x^2+3)=0$

4. $t(t-2)=0$

5. $(t+1)(2t-3)=0$

6. $t^2-4=0$

7. $2x^2-18=0$

8. $ay^2-9a=0$ $(a \neq 0)$

9. $2x(x-5)(x-7)=0$

Solve the equations in exercises 10-21.

10. $x^2-7x+10=0$

11. $x^2+10x+24=0$

12. $y^2=6y+7$

13. $t^2+2=-3t$

14. $9m^2=64$

15. $25p^2-20p+4=0$

16. $2z^2-z=10$

17. $15x^2=7x$

18. $x(x-9)=22$

19. $\frac{5}{2}x-1-x^2=0$

20. $z^2=\frac{1}{2}(z+1)$

21. $10=r(6r-7)$

1. _____

2. _____

3. _____

4. _____

5. _____

6. _____

7. _____

8. _____

9. _____

10. _____

11. _____

12. _____

13. _____

14. _____

15. _____

16. _____

17. _____

18. _____

19. _____

20. _____

21. _____

Answers:

22. _____

23. _____

24. _____

25. _____

26. _____

27. _____

28. _____

29. _____

30. _____

Solve the equations in exercises 22-30.

22. $2x^2 + x^3 = 0$

23. $4t^3 - 25t = 0$

24. $t^3 - 8t^2 - 9t = 0$

25. $7x^4 = 2x^2\left(x + \dfrac{5}{2}\right)$

26. $3x = -4x^2(3x + 5)$

27. $x^4 - 17x^2 + 16 = 0$

28. $y^4 - 5y^2 = 36$

29. $x^2 + 1 = 0$

30. $y^4 - 16 = 0$

4.5   APPLICATIONS OF QUADRATIC EQUATIONS

In this section we shall consider some simple application problems and show how solutions of quadratic equations helps in solving some practical problem. Upon completion of this section we will be able to solve problems concerning numbers and geometry using quadratic equations

The overall strategy for solving these problems remains the same. *Read the problem carefully; draw a diagram if possible, translate the words and phrases to mathematical symbols and expressions, solve the mathematical component, interpret your answers, and check the solution.*

Application to Number Theory

Warm Up

1. The product of two consecutive integers is 6. Find the integers.

Example 1:   The product of two consecutive integers is 156. Find the integers.

Solution:

If the *smaller* of the two integers is n, then the *next consecutive* integer is $n + 1$.

The product of n and $n + 1$ is $n(n + 1)$.

It is given that $n(n + 1) = 156$.

Therefore, the solution of the problem depends on solving the equation $n(n + 1) = 156$.

$n^2 + n = 156 \quad \longrightarrow \quad n^2 + n - 156 = 0$

$\longrightarrow \quad (n - 12)(n + 13) = 0$

$\longrightarrow \quad n - 12 = 0 \quad$ or $\quad n + 13 = 0 \quad$ <small>Zero – Factor Property</small>

$\longrightarrow \quad n = 12 \quad$ or $\quad n = -13 \quad$ <small>Solutions of the Equation</small>

The two integers are n and $n + 1$. When $n = 12$, the two integers are 12 and 13. When $n = -13$, the two integers are -13 and -12. Therefore, there are two solutions to the problem.

1.   Either the two integers are 12 and 13.
2.   Or the two integers are -12 and -13.

Verify that in each case the product is 156.

Application to Geometry

Example 2:   The length of a rectangle is three times its width. The area of the rectangle is 147 square centimeters Find the dimensions of the rectangle.

Solution:

Suppose width of the rectangle $= x$ cms.
Then the length of the rectangle $= 3x$ cms.
Area of the rectangle $= (3x)x$ sq. cms.

But the area is given to be 147 square centimeters.

Therefore,

$(3x)x = 147 \longrightarrow 3x^2 = 147$

$\longrightarrow \quad 3x^2 - 147 = 0$

$\longrightarrow \quad 3(x^2 - 49) = 0$

$\longrightarrow \quad 3(x - 7)(x + 7) = 0$

$\longrightarrow \quad x - 7 = 0 \quad$ or $\quad x + 7 = 0$ Zero – Factor Property

$\longrightarrow \quad x = 7 \qquad$ or $\quad x = -7$ Solutions of the Equation

The width cannot be negative. Therefore, the only choice is $x = 7$.   Hence, the dimensions of the rectangle are

Width $= x = 7$ centimeters.   Length $= 3x = 3(7) = 21$ centimeters.

Verify that your solution is correct: Area $=$ (Width) (Length) $= 7 \cdot 21$
                                                                             $= 147$ **True**

Warm Up

2.   The length of a rectangle is twice its width. The area of the rectangle is 8 square cm. Find the dimensions of the rectangle.

In our next problem we shall use the *Pythagorean Formula*. Recall for a right triangle:

$(\text{Hypotenuse})^2 = (\text{Base})^2 + (\text{Height})^2$

$d^2 = b^2 + h^2$

Example 3:   One side of a rectangle is 7 cms more than the other. If the diagonal of the rectangle is 13 cms, find the dimensions of the rectangle.

Solution:

Suppose the smaller side $= x$ cm.

Then the longer side $= x + 7$ cm.

Warm Up

3.   Base of the right triangle is 6 cm more than the height. The area of the triangle is 216 cm^2. Find the length of its base and its height.

Warm Up

By the Pythagorean formula:

$$(\text{diagonal})^2 = (\text{length})^2 + (\text{width})^2$$

$$(13)^2 = (x+7)^2 + x^2$$

$$x^2 + (x+7)^2 = 13^2$$

$$\longrightarrow x^2 + (x^2 + 14x + 49) = 169$$

$$\longrightarrow 2x^2 + 14x + 49 - 169 = 0$$

$$\longrightarrow 2x^2 + 14x - 120 = 0$$

$$\longrightarrow 2(x-5)(x+12) = 0$$

$$\longrightarrow x - 5 = 0 \quad \text{or} \quad x + 12 = 0$$

$$\longrightarrow x = 5 \quad \text{or} \quad x = -12$$

Solution of the Problem:

$x = -12$ is not a possible solution, because no side of the rectangle can be negative. Therefore $x = 5$ is the only solution.

Thus the smaller side = **5 cms** and the longer side $= 5 + 7 = $ **12 cm.**

4. Height of triangle is 2 times its base. The area of the triangle is 196 cm^2. Find the base and height of the triangle.

Example 4: Height of a triangle is 4 times its base. The area of the triangle is 288 square centimeters. Find the base and the height of the triangle.

Solution:

Suppose base $= x$ cm. Then height $= 4x$ cm.

$$\textbf{Area of triangle} = \frac{1}{2}(\textbf{base})(\textbf{height})$$

$$= \frac{1}{2}x(4x) = 2x^2$$

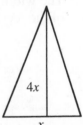

But it is given that the area = 288 square centimeters. Therefore,

$$2x^2 = 288 \longrightarrow x^2 = 144 \longrightarrow x^2 - 144 = 0$$

$$\longrightarrow (x-12)(x+12) = 0$$

$$\longrightarrow x - 12 = 0 \quad \text{or} \quad x + 12 = 0$$

$$\longrightarrow x = 12 \quad \text{or} \quad x = -12$$

$x = -12$ is not a feasible solution.

Hence Base $= x = $ **12** *cm* Height $= 4x = $ **48** *cm*

Example 5: The product of the measures of two complementary angles is 1400^0. Find the measure of the greater angle.

Solution:

Let the measure of the greater angle $= x$

Then the measure of smaller angle $= 90 - x$ angles are complementary

Product of the two measures $= (90 - x)x$

Product of the two measures $= 1400^0$.   Given

Therefore,

$(90-x)x = 1400 \longrightarrow 90x - x^2 = 1400 \longrightarrow x^2 - 90x + 1400 = 0$

$\longrightarrow (x-70)(x-20) = 0$

$\longrightarrow x - 70 = 0 \quad$ or $\quad x - 20 = 0$

$\longrightarrow x = 70 \quad$ or $\quad x = 20$

The two angles are 20^0 and 70^0. The measure of the greater angle $= 70^0$.

Warm Up

5. The product of the measure of two complementary angles is 1800. Find the measure of the greater angle.

Answers:

1. –2, –3 and 2, 3
2. 2, 4
3. base = 24 cm ; height = 18 cm
4. base = 14, height = 28
5. $60°$

EXERCISE 4.5

Solve the following Word Problems

Answers:

1. Product of two consecutive even integers is 168. Find the integers.

   1. _____

2. Product of two consecutive odd integers is 323. Find the integers.

   2. _____

3. If the sum of the squares of three consecutive integers is 194, find the integers.

   3. _____

4. If the sum of the squares of two consecutive even integers is 100, determine the integers.

   4. _____

5. If the product of two consecutive integers is 132, find the integers.

   5. _____

6. A positive number added to the square of the preceding number equals 73. What is the number?

   6. _____

7. One side of a rectangle is 5 meters longer than the other. If the area of the rectangle is 126 square meters, determine the dimensions of the rectangle.

   7. _____

8. _____

9. _____

10. _____

11. _____

12. _____

13. _____

14. _____

15. _____

16. _____

8. A rectangle with an area of 112 square yards has length 6 yards more than its width. Find the perimeter of the rectangle.

9. The area of a square is numerically equal to two times its perimeter.   Determine the length of a side of the square.

10. The width of a rectangular floor is 3 feet less than its length. If the area of the floor is 108 square feet, determine the dimensions of the floor.

11. The base of a triangle is 2 feet more than twice its height. If the area of the triangle is 12 square feet, determine its base and height.

12. Find the width of a strip that has been mowed around a rectangular lawn 60 feet by 80 feet if half of the lawn remains to be mowed.

13. The longer leg of a right triangle is 1 inch longer than the shorter leg. The hypotenuse is 1 inch shorter than twice the length of the shorter leg. Find the length of the longer leg.

14. A lot has the shape of a right triangle. The difference between the two legs is 2 meters. The hypotenuse is 6 meters less than twice the length of the longer leg. Find the length of the shorter leg.

15. Two supplementary angles have measures whose product is 7931. Find the measures of the two angles.

16. Product of two complementary angle measures is 2016 . What is the measure of the greater angle?

4.6   SOLVING QUADRATIC INEQUALITIES

A quadratic inequality can always be written in one of the following forms:

$$ax^2 + bx + c < 0, \quad ax^2 + bx + c > 0, \quad ax^2 + bx + c \le 0, \quad ax^2 + bx + c \ge 0.$$

Upon completion of this section we will be able to:

    A.   Solve Quadratic Inequalities.
    B.   Solve Quadratic Inequalities with Two Critical Points.
    C.   Solve Quadratic Inequalities with One or No Critical Points.

A. Solving a Quadratic Inequality

Consider the equation: $x^2 - 5x + 4 = 0$

Its solutions are $x = 4$ and $x = 1$. The points 1 and 4 divide the number line into three regions:

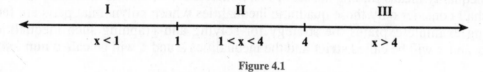

Figure 4.1

Region I: The set of all numbers less than 1.
Region II: The set of all numbers between 1 and 4, and
Region III: Set of all numbers greater than 4.

We shall examine the behavior of $x^2 - 5x + 4$ in these regions. We should not expect $x^2 - 5x + 4$ to become zero at any point other than 1 and 4 (why?).

The signs of the polynomial in different (I, II, III) regions are discussed in the following table.

Point	Region	Value	Sign of Value
–4	I	$(-4)^2 - 5(-4) + 4 = 40$	Positive
–2	I	$(-2)^2 - 5(-2) + 4 = 18$	Positive
–1	I	$(-1)^2 - 5(-1) + 4 = 10$	Positive
0	I	$(0)^2 - 5(0) + 4 = 4$	Positive
2	II	$(2)^2 - 5(2) + 4 = -2$	Negative
2.5	II	$(2.5)^2 - 5(2.5) + 4 = -2.25$	Negative
3	II	$(3)^2 - 5(3) + 4 = -2$	Negative
3.5	II	$(3.5)^2 - 5(3.5) + 4 = -1.25$	Negative
5	III	$(5)^2 - 4(5) + 5 = 10$	Positive
6	III	$(6)^2 - 4(6) + 5 = 17$	Positive
8	III	$(8)^2 - 4(8) + 5 = 37$	Positive
10	III	$(10)^2 - 4(10) + 5 = 65$	Positive

243

A careful examination of the table shows:

- All values of the polynomial in the same region have a common sign.
- The signs alternate between positive and negative in successive regions.

Solving an inequality means finding the set of real numbers for which the inequality is true. In this section we shall consider only those quadratic inequalities whose polynomial parts are factorable. The following example explains the strategy for solving and graphing such inequalities. The inequalities > and < will be called **strict** and the inequalities $\geq$ and $\leq$ will be called **non - strict**.

Warm Up

1. Solve the inequality
$$x^2 + 5x + 4 \geq 0$$

Answers:

1. $x \geq -1$; $x \leq -4$

Example 1: Solve the inequality $x^2 - 5x + 4 \geq 0$ and graph the solution.

Solution:

First of all we solve $x^2 - 5x + 4 = 0$.
$$x^2 - 5x + 4 = (x-4)(x-1) \quad \longrightarrow \quad (x-4)(x-1) = 0$$
$$\longrightarrow \quad x - 4 = 0 \quad \text{or} \quad x - 1 = 0$$
$$\longrightarrow \quad x = 4 \quad \text{or} \quad x = 1$$

We call the solutions of the equation the **critical points** of the inequality.
Therefore, 1 and 4 are critical points of $x^2 - 5x + 4 \geq 0$.
Next we mark the critical points on the number line.

Region I   Region II   Region III

(test point) ⇨ 0   1   4

These points are marked by solid dots since the inequality is *non - strict*. These points divide the number line into three regions. We will determine the sign of the polynomial in any one region say Region I. For this, we choose a **test point** different from the critical point 1. We choose **0** as a test point and evaluate the polynomial at $x = \mathbf{0}$.

$$x^2 - 5x + 4 = (0)^2 - 5(0) + 4 = 4 > 0$$

Since, $x = 0$ lies in the region I, the polynomial in region I has *positive* sign. Also since the signs in the regions alternate, the sign in the next region II is negative, and in the region III is positive.

I   II   III

Positive 1   Negative   4 Positive

Thus, the points in regions I and III satisfy the inequality $x^2 - 5x + 4 \geq 0$. Therefore, the solution of the inequality is:

$$x \leq 1 \quad \text{or} \quad x \geq 4.$$

and the graph of the inequality is:

1   4

B. Quadratic Inequalities with Two Critical Points

We use the following steps to solve quadratic inequalities where the polynomial has two distinct factors.

Step 1	Write the inequality in one of the standard forms with the right side equal to zero.
Step 2	Change the inequality to an equation, and solve the equation to obtain *critical points*.
Step 3	Mark the critical points on the number line to determine the regions.
Step 4	Choose a test point *different* from the critical points in anyone of the regions. Evaluate the polynomial at the test point and identify its sign.
Step 5	Determine the region to which the test point belongs. In this region the sign of the polynomial is the same as in step 4.
Step 6	Determine the sign of the polynomial in other two regions. Recall signs alternate in successive regions.
Step 7	Identify the regions whose sign matches the inequality. Write down the solutions, and mark (shade) the regions that form solutions. Use parentheses for a strict inequality and square brackets for a non-strict inequality.

Example 2:   Solve and graph the following inequalities:

a) $x^2 - 25 < 0$ b) $x^2 - 6x \le 16$

c) $3m^2 + 7m > -2$ d) $3p - 4p^2 \ge 0$

Warm Up

2. Solve the following inequalities.

a) $x^2 - 9 \ge 0$

Solutions:

a) $x^2 - 25 < 0$

Step 1   Not needed.

Step 2 $x^2 - 25 = 0 \longrightarrow (x - 5)(x + 5) = 0$

$\longrightarrow x - 5 = 0$ or $x + 5 = 0$

$\longrightarrow$ $x = 5$ or $x = -5$

The critical Points are -5 and 5.

Step 3

$$\text{I} \qquad\qquad \text{II} \qquad\qquad \text{III}$$

-5   5

Inequality is strict

Step 4   Choose 0 as a *test point*.

When $x = 0$

$$x^2 - 25 = (0)^2 - 25 = -25 < 0$$

Step 5   The test point 0 is in region II, and the sign for region II is *negative*.

245

Step 6

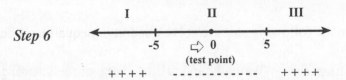

$$-5 \qquad \overset{\Rightarrow}{} 0 \qquad 5$$
(test point)

$+ + + +$ $- - - - - - - - - - - -$ $+ + + +$

Step 7 The sign for region II matches with the inequality $x^2 - 25 < 0$. Therefore, solution of the inequality is $-5 < x < 5$. The graph of the inequality is

$$\text{(} \underline{\qquad\qquad} \text{)}$$
$$ -5 \qquad\qquad 5$$

b) $x^2 - 3x \leq 4$

b) $x^2 - 6x \leq 16$

Step 1 $\qquad x^2 - 6x \leq 16 \longrightarrow x^2 - 6x - 16 \leq 0$

Step 2 $\qquad x^2 - 6x - 16 = 0 \longrightarrow (x-8)(x+2) = 0$

$\longrightarrow x - 8 = 0 \ \text{ or } \ x + 2 = 0$

$\longrightarrow \qquad x = 8 \ \text{ or } \qquad x = -2$

Step 3

$$ -2 \qquad\qquad\qquad 8$$

Inequality is non-strict

Step 4 Choose 0 as a *test point* When $x = 0$
$x^2 - 6x - 16 = (0)^2 - 6(0) - 16 = -16 < 0$

Step 5 Test point 0 is in region II and the sign for region II is *negative*.

Step 6

$$\qquad -2 \quad 0 \overset{\Leftarrow}{} \text{(test point)} \quad 8$$

$+ + + + +$ $- - - - - - - - - - -$ $+ + +$

Step 7 The sign for region II matches with the inequality $x^2 - 6x \leq 16$. Therefore, the solution of the inequality is $-2 \leq x \leq 8$. The graph of the inequality is:

$$ -2 \qquad\qquad\qquad 8$$

Warm Up

c) $3m^2 + 7m > -2$

2.   c) $2x^2 + 3x > 5$

Step 1 $3m^2 + 7m > -2 \longrightarrow 3m^2 + 7m + 2 > 0$

Step 2 $3m^2 + 7m + 2 = 0 \longrightarrow (3m+1)(m+2) = 0$

$\longrightarrow \quad 3m + 1 = 0 \quad$ or $\quad m + 2 = 0$

$\longrightarrow \quad\quad 3m = -1 \quad$ or $\quad\quad m = -2$

$\longrightarrow \quad\quad m = -\dfrac{1}{3} \quad$ or $\quad\quad m = -2$

Step 3

$$\underset{\quad\quad\quad -2 \quad\quad -1/3}{\overset{\text{I} \quad\quad \text{II} \quad\quad\quad \text{III}}{\longleftarrow\!\!\!-\!\!\!-\!\!\!-\!\!\!-\!\!\!-\!\!\!-\!\!\!\longrightarrow}} \quad \text{Inequality is strict}$$

Step 4   Choose 0 as a *test point*.

$x = 0 :\quad 3m^2 + 7m + 2 = 3(0)^2 + 7(0) + 2 = 2 > 0$

Step 5   Test point 0 is in region III, and the sign for region III is *positive*.

Step 6

$$\underset{\quad\quad -2 \quad\quad -1/3 \quad 0 \;\Leftarrow\; \text{(test point)}}{\overset{\text{I} \quad\quad \text{II} \quad\quad\quad\quad \text{III}}{\longleftarrow\!\!\!-\!\!\!-\!\!\!-\!\!\!-\!\!\!-\!\!\!-\!\!\!\longrightarrow}}$$

$$+\;+\;+\;+ \quad -\;-\;-\;- \quad +\;+\;+\;+\;+\;+\;+\;+\;+$$

Step 7   The signs in the regions I and III match with the inequality $3m^2 + 7m > -2$. Therefore, the solution of the inequality is

$$m < -2 \quad \text{or} \quad m > -\frac{1}{3}.$$

The graph of the inequality is

d) $4z - 8z^2 \geq 0$

d) $3p - 4p^2 \geq 0$

Step 1 $3p - 4p^2 \geq 0 \longrightarrow -4p^2 + 3p \geq 0$

Step 2 $-4p^2 + 3p = 0 \longrightarrow p(-4p + 3) = 0$

$\longrightarrow p = 0 \quad$ or $\quad -4p + 3 = 0$

$\longrightarrow p = 0 \quad$ or $\quad -4p = -3$

$\longrightarrow p = \mathbf{0} \quad$ or $\quad p = \dfrac{3}{4}$

The critical points are **0** and $\dfrac{3}{4}$.

Step 3

$$\underset{}{\overset{\text{I} \qquad \text{II} \qquad \text{III}}{\longleftrightarrow}}$$
$$0 \quad 3/4$$

Step 4   Choose 1 as *test point*.
We *cannot choose 0 as test point since it is a critical point*.
When $p = 1 \quad -4p^2 + 3p = -4(1)^2 + 3(1)$
$$= -4 + 3 = -1 < 0$$

Step 5   Test point 1 is in region III, and the sign for region III is negative.

Step 6

I   II   III
$$\longleftrightarrow$$
$$0 \quad 3/4 \ 1 \ \Leftarrow \ \textbf{(test point)}$$
$$- - - - - - - - - - - \quad + + + \quad - - - - - - - -$$

Step 7   The sign for region II matches with the inequality $3p - 4p^2 \geq 0$.

Therefore, the solution of the inequality is: $0 \leq p \leq \dfrac{3}{4}$.

The graph of the inequality is

$$0 \quad 3/4$$

C. Inequalities with One or No Critical Point

Example 3: Solve the inequalities.

a) $(x-1)^2 > 0$ b) $-(y-3)^2 \geq 0$

c) $x^2 - 4x + 4 < 0$

Warm Up

3. Solve the inequalities

a) $(x-2)^2 \geq 0$

Solutions:

a) $(x-1)^2 > 0$ $(x-1)^2 = 0$

$x - 1 = 0$

$x = 1$

This inequality has only one critical point, and, therefore, cannot be solved by the steps listed above.   However, we know that $(x-1)^2$ is a perfect square, and therefore it is zero at $x = 1$, and is *positive* for all other values of x. [Recall that square of a real number can never be negative].

Hence $(x-1)^2 > 0$ holds for all $x \neq 1$.

The graph of this inequality is the entire real line except $x = 1$.

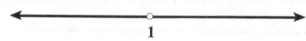

b) $-(y-3)^2 \geq 0$

$(y-3)^2$ is zero only at $y = 3$, and is positive for all other values of y. Therefore, $-(y-3)^2 = 0$ at $y = 3$, and is *negative* for all other values of y. Therefore $-(y-3)^2 \geq 0$ is true only when $y = 3$.

Graph of this inequality is just one point $y = 3$.

b) $-(z+3)^2 \geq 0$

c) $x^2 - 4x + 4 < 0$ $\longrightarrow$ $(x-2)^2 < 0$

$(x-2)^2$ is zero at $x = 2$, and *positive* for all other values of x.

Thus $(x-2)^2$ is never negative.

Hence $(x-2)^2 < 0$ is not true for any value of x. The inequality has no solution.

c) $x^2 + 6x + 9 < 0$

Warm Up

4. $x^2 + x + 12 > 0$

Example 4:   Solve the inequality: $x^2 + 2x + 10 > 0$

Solution:

To determine the critical points we equate the polynomial to zero and solve

$$x^2 + 2x + 10 = 0 \qquad \textbf{....... (1)}$$
$$a = 1, \quad b = 2, \quad c = 10$$

Therefore $b^2 - 4ac = 4 - 40 = -36 < 0$.   Since $b^2 - 4ac < 0$, the quadratic equation **(1)** has no real number solution. We shall prove this point in later chapters.

This is a case of an inequality with no critical points. In such cases either the polynomial is positive for all values of the variable or negative for all values of the variable. We shall discuss this fact in more details in chapter 9. Check the positive or negative characteristic with a test point.

For example, when $x = 0$, $x^2 + 2x + 10 = 10$, which is positive. Hence the inequality $x^2 + 2x + 10 > 0$ is true for all values of x. The graph of the inequality is the whole number line.

EXERCISE 4.6

Answers:

1. _____
2. _____
3. _____
4. _____
5. _____
6. _____
7. _____
8. _____
9. _____
10. _____
11. _____
12. _____
13. _____

In exercises 1–4, write the inequalities in the standard form.

1. $2x \geq 3x^2 - 5$ 2. $5x^2 + 3x < -5$

3. $0 > 2x - 25 - 7x^2$ 4. $3 \leq x + x^2$

Find critical points of the inequalities in exercises 5–9.

5. $2x^2 - 7x + 3 \leq 0$ 6. $x^2 > 5x + 6$ 7. $3y^2 + 5y < 2$

8. $x^2 + 8x + 16 \geq 0$ 9. $4x^2 + 9 > 0$

In exercises 10–14, solve the inequalities and graph the solutions.

10. $(x + 3)(x - 7) \geq 0$ 11. $(z + 4)(z + 8) \leq 0$

12. $(t - 3)(t + 2) > 0$ 13. $(2p + 1)(p - 5) < 0$

14. $(4p+5)(7-3p) \leq 0$

In exercises 15 – 27, solve the inequalities and graph the solutions.

15. $x^2 + 5x + 4 \leq 0$　　　　**16.** $y^2 - 10y + 24 \geq 0$

17. $t^2 + 9t + 20 \leq 0$　　　　**18.** $z^2 + 11z + 30 \leq 0$

19. $8 + 7x \geq x^2$　　　　**20.** $2m^2 + 7m > 4$

21. $5q^2 \leq 2 - 3q$　　　　**22.** $4x^2 > 9$

23. $3x^2 \leq 27$　　　　**24.** $4x - x^2 \geq 4$

25. $3r^2 + 18r + 27 < 0$　　　　**26.** $x^2 - 14x + 49 \geq 0$

27. $9t^2 + 18t + 9 > 0$

14. _____

15. _____

16. _____

17. _____

18. _____

19. _____

20. _____

21. _____

22. _____

23. _____

24. _____

25. _____

26. _____

27. _____

4.7　　CHAPTER SUMMARY

FACTORS

Examples

1.　Finding the greatest common factor of a list of monomials

1.　*Find the greatest common factor of*
$24x^3y^2z, \quad 36x^2y^4, \quad 60x^2yz^2$

　　Step 1　Find the greatest common factor of the coefficients of monomials.

Coefficients: 24, 36, 60
Greatest Common Factor of Coefficients = 12.

　　Step 2　Determine exponents of various variables in each monomial.

Exponent of x: 3, 2, 2;
Exponent of y: 2, 4, 1;
Exponent of z: 1, 0, 2;

　　Step 3　Take the minimum of the exponents for each variable. Write each variable raised to the respective minimum exponent.

Minimum exponent of $x = 2 \rightarrow x^2$
Minimum exponent of $y = 1 \rightarrow y$
Minimum exponent of $z = 0 \rightarrow z^0$

Examples

Step 4   The greatest common factor is the product of all quantities determined in the above three steps.

Greatest Common Factor $= 12\,x^2 y^1 z^0 = 12x^2 y$

2. Factoring by Grouping

Step 1   Group the terms in such a way that each of the groups has a common factor.

Step 2   Use the distributive property to factor each group of terms

Step 3   If all the groups share a common factor, then use distributive property to factor out this common factor

Step 4   If all the groups do not share a common factor, try regrouping and repeat the steps 1 thru 3 again.

2.   *Factor:* $15x^3 + 2y^2 - 6x^2 y - 5xy$

$= \left(15x^2 - 6x^2 y\right) + \left(2y^2 - 5xy\right)$

$= 3x^2 \left(5x - 2y\right) + y\left(2y - 5x\right)$

$= 3x^2 \left(5x - 2y\right) + y\left(2y - 5x\right)$

$= \left(5x - 2y\right)\left(3x^2 - y\right)$

FACTORING TRINOMIALS

3. The trinomial $ax^2 + bx + c$ can be factored only if $b^2 - 4ac$ is a perfect square.

3.   (i) $3x^2 + 5x - 7$: $a = 3,$ $b = 5,$ $c = -7$
$b^2 - 4ac = 25 - 4(3)(-7) = 109$

Since 109 is not a perfect square, the trinomial is not factorable.

4. Factoring $x^2 + bx + c$

Step 1   Complete the missing terms, if necessary.

Step 2   Find two CI so that their sum is b and their product is c.

Step 3   Split the middle term using the integers from Step 2.

Step 4   Factor by grouping

4.   Factor: $x^2 + 7x + 6$

Here, $b = 7,$ $c = 6.$

The CI are 6 and 1: $\mathbf{6 \cdot 1 = 6}$ and $\mathbf{6 + 1 = 7}$.

$x^2 + \mathbf{6x} + x + 6$

$\left(x^2 + 6x\right) + \left(x + 6\right) = x\left(x + 6\right) + 1\left(x + 6\right)$

$= \left(x + 1\right)\left(x + 6\right)$

5. Factoring $x^2 + bx + c$, an alternative approach

Step 1   Write the expression in standard *form*

Step 2   Find two numbers (CIs) whose sum is b and product is c.

Step 3   If CIs are p and q then
$$x^2 + bx + c = (x + p)(x + q)$$

5.   Factor $x^2 + 7x + 6$
$x^2 + 7x + 6$
$b = 7,$ $c = 6$
CIs are $p = 1,$ $q = 6$
$\because 6 + 1 = 7$ and $6 \cdot 1 = 6$

$x^2 + 7x + 6 = \left(x + 6\right)\left(x + 1\right)$

Examples

6. **Factoring $ax^2 + bx + c$, $a \neq 1$**

6. Factor: $12x^2 - 17x - 5$

Step 1	Factor out the g.c.f., if any.
Step 2	Complete missing terms, if any.
Step 3	Find two CIs such that their sum is b and their product is ac.
Step 4	Split the middle term using the integers found on Step 2.
Step 5	Factor by grouping.

$a = 12, \quad b = -17, \quad c = -5$

The CI are -20 and 3.
$b = -17, \qquad a \cdot c = -60.$

$-20 + 3 = -17 \quad$ and $\quad (-20)(3) = -60.$

$12x^2 - 17x - 5 = 12x^2 - 20x + 3x - 5$

$\qquad = 4x(3x - 5) + 1(3x - 5)$
$\qquad = (3x - 5)(4x + 1)$

SPECIAL FACTORIZATIONS

7. $\quad a^2 - b^2 = (a - b)(a + b)$

7. $9x^2 - 49 = (3x)^2 - 7^2 = (3x - 7)(3x + 7)$

8. $\quad a^2 + 2ab + b^2 = (a + b)^2$

8. $4x^2 + 4x + 1 = (2x)^2 + 2(2x)(1) + 1^2 = (2x + 1)^2$

9. $\quad a^2 - 2ab + b^2 = (a - b)^2$

9. $4x^2 - 4x + 1 = (2x)^2 - 2(2x)(1) + 1^2 = (2x - 1)^2$

10. $\quad a^3 + b^3 = (a + b)(a^2 - ab + b^2)$

10. $8p^3 + 27 = (2p)^3 + 3^3$
$\qquad = (2p + 3)\left[(2p)^2 - (2p)(3) + 3^2\right]$
$\qquad = (2p + 3)(4p^2 - 6p + 9)$

11. $\quad a^3 - b^3 = (a - b)(a^2 + ab + b^2)$

11. $27r^3 - 1 = (3r)^3 - 1^3$
$\qquad = (3r - 1)\left[(3r)^2 + (3r)(1) + 1^2\right]$
$\qquad = (3r - 1)(9r^2 + 3r + 1)$

APPLICATIONS OF FACTORING

12. If $(2x - 3)(3x + 1) = 0$,
then $2x - 3 = 0$ or $3x + 1 = 0$

12. **The Zero - Factor Property**

If a and b are real numbers such that $ab = 0$, then either $a = 0$ or $b = 0$.

13. **Three step approach to solve Quadratic Equations by Factoring**

13. Solve: $6x^2 - x = 1$

| Step 1 | Write the equation in the standard form $ax^2 + bx + c = 0$ |
| Step 2 | Factor $ax^2 + bx + c$ into *linear factors*. |

$6x^2 - x - 1 = (2x - 1)(3x + 1)$

Examples

Step 3 Equate each factor to zero and solve.

$$(2x-1)(3x+1)=0$$
$$\longrightarrow \quad 2x-1=0 \quad \text{or} \quad 3x+1=0$$
$$\longrightarrow \quad 2x=1 \quad \text{or} \quad 3x=-1$$
$$\longrightarrow \quad x=\frac{1}{2} \quad \text{or} \quad x=-\frac{1}{3}$$

QUADRATIC INEQUALITIES

14. Seven step approach to solve a quadratic inequality

Solve the inequality $3x^2 + 5x \geq 2$

14. Solve the inequality.

Step 1 Write the inequality in one of the standard forms with the right side equal to zero.

$$3x^2 + 5 \geq 2 \longrightarrow 3x^2 + 5x - 2 \geq 0$$

Step 2 Change the inequality to an equation, and solve the equation for critical points.

$$3x^2 + 5x - 2 = 0$$
$$(x+2)(3x-1)=0$$
$$x+2=0 \quad \text{or} \quad 3x-1=0$$
$$x=-2 \quad \text{or} \quad x=\frac{1}{3}$$

Step 3 Mark the critical points on the number line.

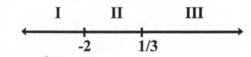

Step 4 Choose a test point, and evaluate the polynomial at the test point. [The test point must be different from the critical points.]

Test point $= 0$
$3x^2 + 5x - 2$
$3(0)^2 + 5(0) - 2 = -2 \leq 0$

Step 5 Determine the region to which the test point belongs. The sign in this region is the same as the sign of the value is step 4.

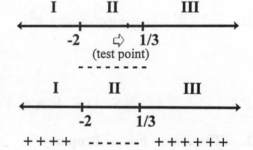

Step 6 Assign positive or negative signs to each region. In most cases, signs alternate in successive regions.

Step 7 Identify the regions whose sign matches with the inequality. Write down the solution and shade the regions that form solutions. Use parentheses for a strict inequality and square brackets for a non-strict inequality.

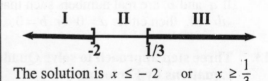

The solution is $x \leq -2$ or $x \geq \frac{1}{3}$

4.8 REVIEW EXERCISE

In exercises 1–4, find the greatest common factor of the monomials

1. $9, \ 75, \ 90$

2. $16, \ 25, \ 49$

3. $12p^3q, \ 16p^2q^2, \ 28p^4qr^2, \ 36p^5q^3s$

4. $15x^2y, \ 25xz^2, \ 9y^2z^2$

In exercises 5–8, factor out the greatest common factor.

5. $27x^3 - 36x^2$

6. $63y^2 - 14z^2$

7. $30p^2q^3 + 45p^4q^2 - 75pq^4$

8. $4s(3s - 5t) - 5t^2(5t - 3s)$

In exercises 9–12, factor by grouping.

9. $12x^2 - 15x - 20y + 16xy$

10. $12x^3 - 4x^2y + 3xy - y^2$

11. $r^4 + 3r^3 + 3r^2 + 7r - 6$

12. $3x^5 - 3x^3y - 2x^2y^2 + 2y^3 + x^2 - y$

In exercises 13–14, complete the blanks.

13. $x^2 + 2x - 15 = (x + 5)(\quad)$

14. $12x^2 + 13x - 14 = (\quad + 7)(\quad - 2)$

In exercises 15–38, factor completely.

15. $x^2 + 6x - 16$

16. $x^2 - 6x + 8$

17. $36x^2 - 1$

18. $16t^2 + 8t + 1$

19. $8y^2 - 6y - 2$

20. $3p^2 - 10p - 8$

21. $2x^3 - 5x^2 - 3x$

22. $(x - 1)^2 + 5(x - 1) + 6$

23. $x^4 + x^2 - 6$

24. $2x^4 - 7x^2 - 4$

25. $x^2 + 3x + 6$

26. $3x^2 + 5x + 8$

27. $p^2 - 16$

28. $4a^2 - 49$

29. $4p^2 + 25$

30. $x^4 - 36$

31. $16x^4 - 81$

32. $y^2 - 8y + 16$

33. $2z^2 + 12z + 18$

34. $x^2 - 5x + \dfrac{25}{4}$

35. $9x^2 + 30xy + 25y^2$

36. $27x^3 - 125y^3$

37. $8r^3s^3 + 27t^3$

38. $216a^3b^6 - 125c^6$

In exercises 39–50, solve the equations.

39. $(x + 4)(3x - 5) = 0$

40. $(2x + 3)(x^2 + 1) = 0$

41. $p^2 + 15p + 50 = 0$

42. $p^2 - 15p + 50 = 0$

43. $x^2 - 15x = 100$

44. $2m^2 + m = 0$

45. $4x^2 + 4x + 1 = 0$

46. $x^2 = 12 - x$

47. $2x^2 + 5x + 3 = 0$

48. $2 + y = 6y^2$

49. $x^4 + 8x^2 + 15 = 0$

50. $x^4 - 13x^2 + 36 = 0$

51.   Product of two consecutive odd integers is 143. Find the integers.

52.   Sum of the squares of two consecutive numbers is 221. Find the numbers.

53.   When square of a whole number is added to 4 times the next number the result is 81. Find the number.

54.   The area of a rectangular window is 154 square feet. If the width is 3 feet less than the length, find the dimensions.

55.   A piece of wire is 12 feet in length, and is to be cut into two pieces. Each of these pieces will then be bent into squares such that the sum of their areas is 5 square feet. How long will the two pieces be?

56.   The hypotenuse of a right triangle is 1 inch longer than the longer leg. The shorter leg is 8 inches shorter than the hypotenuse. Find the length of the three sides of the triangle.

57.   Two cars leave at the same time. One car travels north, and the other car travels west. When the car traveling west had gone 24 miles, the distance between the two cars was 4 miles more than three times the distance covered by the car traveling north. Find the distance traveled by the car heading north.

58.   The product of the measures of two supplementary (sum = 180°) angles is 5600^0. Find the measure of the greater angle.

In exercises 59–61, find the critical points of the following inequalities.

59. $x^2 + x - 12 \geq 0$ **60.** $x^2 < 4x + 12$ **61.** $3x^2 + 5 > 0$

In exercises 62–70, solve and graph the inequalities

62. $(x + 4)(x - 2) \leq 0$ **63.** $y^2 + 6y \geq 0$ **64.** $6x^2 < 5x + 6$

65. $4x^2 + 3 > 0$ **66.** $x^2 + 4x + 4 < 0$ **67.** $-(x - 2)^2 \geq 0$

68. $x(x + 7) > -12$ **69.** $4x^2 + 6x + 9 \leq 0$ **70.** $x^2 - 25 \leq 0$

4.9   SELF TEST

Factor out the greatest common factor.

1. $24x^3y^4 + 40x^2y - 64xy^2$ **2.** $3a(4b - a) + 5b(a - 4b)$

Factor by grouping.

                                                           3. $12x^2 + 20x - 15y - 9xy$

4. $12x^3 - 4x^2y + 9xy - 3y^2 - 6x + 2y$ **5.** $8p^2 - 2pq - 3q^2 - 20p + 15q$

Complete the factorization.

                                                           6. $6x^2 - 7x - 20 = (2x\ \ )(\ \ )$

Factor completely the polynomials.

7. $25a^2 - 10a + 1$ **8.** $3x^2 + 4$ **9.** $x^3 - 3x^2 - 18x$

10. $8x^2 - 2x - 15$ **11.** $12p^2 - 27q^2$ **12.** $x^2 + x + 1$

13. $8m^3 + n^6$

Solve the following equations.

14. $x^2 - 3x = 18$ **15.** $6x^2 + 10x - 4 = 0$ **16.** $x^4 = 4x^2 + 45$

17. $6x^3 + 7x^2 = 10x$

18. The difference of two whole numbers is 2. If two times the square of the smaller number added to three times the square of the larger number equals 140, find the numbers.

19. The triangular sail of a schooner has an area of 30 square meters. The base of the sail is 4 meters less than the height of the sail. Find the height of the sail.

20. A ladder is leaning against a wall. The distance of the bottom of the ladder from the wall is 4 feet less than the length of the ladder. The top of the ladder from the floor is 2 feet less than the length of the ladder. Determine the length of the ladder.

21. Explain why $\left(4x^2 - 9\right)(3x + 5)$ is not a complete factorization of $12x^3 + 20x^2 - 27x - 45$

Solve the inequalities

22. $x^2 + 1 \leq 0$ **23.** $3x^2 + 5x - 12 \leq 0$ **24.** $3t^2 + 2t \leq 8$

CHAPTER 5

RATIONAL EXPRESSIONS

5.4 Least Common Denominator of Rational Expressions □ ▣ ✕

Ex 1

Find the least common multiple of:

⦿ $x^3 - x^2$, and $x^2 - 2x + 1$.

○ $3x^3 - 27x$, $4x^4 + 12x^3$, and $(x - 3)^2(y - 1)$.

Step 1: **Factor** the polynomials.

$$x^3 - x^2 \Rightarrow x^2(x - 1).$$

$$x^2 - 2x + 1 \Rightarrow (x - 1)^2.$$

Step 2:

Factors	x	$x - 1$
Highest Power	2	2

Step 3: **Least common multiple** $= (x)^2(x - 1)^2$.

S&◁» Exer.   ❋ Click On Me or Press Spacebar to Continue   Obj   Exit

CHAPTER 5

RATIONAL EXPRESSIONS

We know that arithmetic fractions such as $\frac{3}{7}, \frac{6}{4}, -\frac{2}{5}$ are *quotients of two integers,* with the divisor not equal to zero. These are also called *rational numbers.* In the same way *rational expressions* are *quotients of two polynomials.* Rational expressions can be added, subtracted, multiplied, and divided in much the same way as arithmetic fractions. In this chapter we study rational expressions.

This chapter is divided into the following sections.

5.1   EVALUATING RATIONAL EXPRESSIONS

Recall that expressions of the type: $3x + 1$, $5x^2 + 4x - 7$, and $5t^3 - 7t^2 + 17t - 5$ where all the exponents of the variables are whole numbers are called polynomials. A ratio of two polynomials is called a **rational expression.**

$$\text{Examples:} \quad \frac{-5x}{7}, \quad \frac{3b}{9 - y}, \quad \frac{2z^2 + 1}{3z + 5} \quad \text{and} \quad \frac{t^3}{t^2 + 2} \quad \text{are rational expressions.}$$

Upon completion of this section we will be able to:

   A.   Determine the values of the variables for which a rational expression is not defined.

   B.   Evaluate rational expressions.

A. When a Rational Expression is Not Defined

We know that division by zero is not possible. Therefore a rational expression is said to be *undefined* or *not defined* at the real number "**a**" if on substituting "a" for the variable the denominator of the rational expression becomes zero.

To determine the values for which a rational expression is not defined, we proceed as follows:

| Step 1 | Set the denominator of the rational expression to zero. |
| Step 2 | Solve the equation obtained in step 1. |

The solutions of the equation are the values for which the rational expression is not defined.

Warm Up

1. Determine the values for which the expressions are not defined.

a) $\dfrac{4}{x^4 + 6}$

b) $\dfrac{4x + 5}{x - 6}$

c) $\dfrac{4y}{2y - 3}$

d) $\dfrac{t^2 + 4}{t^2 - 16}$

e) $\dfrac{5z - 1}{z^2 - 3z - 4}$

Answers:

1. a) defined for all values of x

b) $x = 6$ c) $y = \dfrac{3}{2}$ d) $t = 4, -4$

e) $z = 4, -1$

Example 1: For each of the following rational expressions determine the values for which the expressions are not defined.

a) $\dfrac{3x}{x^2 + 5}$ b) $\dfrac{x^2 - 1}{x + 7}$ c) $\dfrac{2y}{3y - 2}$

d) $\dfrac{t^2 + 1}{t^2 - 9}$ e) $\dfrac{5z}{z^2 - 6z + 8}$

Solutions:

a) $\dfrac{3x}{x^2 + 5}$: $x^2 + 5 = 0$ [Set the denominator to zero.]

The equation $x^2 + 5 = 0$ has no real solution, since $x^2 + 5 > 0$ for all x. Therefore, the rational expression is *defined for all* values of x. There are no points at which this rational expression is not defined.

b) $\dfrac{x^2 - 1}{x + 7}$: $\quad x + 7 = 0 \longrightarrow x = -7$ Steps 1 and 2

Therefore, the rational expression $\dfrac{x^2 - 1}{x + 7}$ is not defined for $x = -7$.

c) $\dfrac{2y}{3y - 2}$: $\quad 3y - 2 = 0 \longrightarrow 3y = 2 \longrightarrow y = \dfrac{2}{3}$ Steps 1 and 2

Therefore, the rational expression $\dfrac{2y}{3y - 2}$ is not defined for $y = \dfrac{2}{3}$.

d) $\dfrac{t^2 + 1}{t^2 - 9}$: $\quad t^2 - 9 = 0 \longrightarrow (t - 3)(t + 3) = 0 \longrightarrow t = 3$ or $t = -3$

Therefore, the rational expression $\dfrac{t^2 + 1}{t^2 - 9}$ is not defined for $t = 3$ or $t = -3$.

e) $\dfrac{5z}{z^2 - 6z + 8}$: $\quad z^2 - 6z + 8 = 0 \longrightarrow (z - 2)(z - 4) = 0$

$\longrightarrow z - 2 = 0$ or $z - 4 = 0$

$\longrightarrow z = 2$ or $z = 4$

Therefore, the rational expression $\dfrac{5z}{z^2 - 6z + 8}$ is not defined for $z = 2$ and $z = 4$.

B. Evaluating a Rational Expression

To evaluate a rational expression for a given value, substitute the value for the variable in the expression and simplify. For example, the value of $\dfrac{2x}{x^2-4}$ for $x=1$ is:

$$\frac{2(1)}{(1)^2-4}=\frac{2}{1-4}=\frac{2}{-3}=-\frac{2}{3}.$$

Example 2: Find the numerical value of each of the following rational expressions for the given values of the variables.

a) $\dfrac{5x-7}{2x^2+3x-1}$; $\quad x=2$

b) $\dfrac{3p^2-7}{p^3+p^2+p+4}$; $\quad p=-1$

Solutions:

a) **Substitute 2 for x** in $\dfrac{5x-7}{2x^2+3x-1}$

$$\frac{5(2)-7}{2(2^2)+3(2)-1}=\frac{10-7}{2(4)+6-1}=\frac{3}{8+6-1}=\frac{3}{13}.$$

b) **Substitute -1 for p** in $\dfrac{3p^2-7}{p^3+p^2+p+4}$

$$\frac{3(-1)^2-7}{(-1)^3+(-1)^2+(-1)+4}=\frac{3(1)-7}{-1+1-1+4}=\left(\frac{-4}{3}\right)=-\frac{4}{3}$$

Warm Up

2. Find the numerical value of each of the following rational expressions for the given values of the variable.

a) $\dfrac{3x+2}{x^2+3x+4}$; $x=3$

b) $\dfrac{5p^2-1}{3p^4+p^3+2p^2+4}$; $p=-1$

Answers:

2. a) $\dfrac{1}{2}$ b) $\dfrac{1}{2}$

EXERCISE 5.1

Find values of the variable in exercises 1–8, for which the rational expression is not defined.

1. $\dfrac{3x}{2x^2+1}$

2. $\dfrac{4}{5x}$

3. $\dfrac{3x^2+1}{5x-2}$

4. $\dfrac{5x-7}{x+3}$

5. $\dfrac{2t}{t^2-1}$

6. $\dfrac{1}{y^2-5y+6}$

7. $\dfrac{13p}{p^2+36}$

8. $\dfrac{5z-3}{z^2+11z+30}$

Answers:

1. _____
2. _____
3. _____
4. _____
5. _____
6. _____
7. _____
8. _____

In exercises 9–16, evaluate the rational expressions for the indicated value.

9. _____

10. _____

11. _____

12. _____

13. _____

14. _____

15. _____

16. _____

9. $\dfrac{3x-5}{2x}$; $x = 5$

10. $\dfrac{5x^2-6x}{2x}$; $x = -4$

11. $\dfrac{y^2+1}{y^2-1}$; $y = 2$

12. $\dfrac{t+8}{t^2-4t+3}$; $t = -1$

13. $\dfrac{2p-1}{3p^2+4p-5}$; $p = 0$

14. $\dfrac{-4a+6}{3-5a+7a^2}$; $a = 1$

15. $\dfrac{4x^2+3x-1}{2x^2+5x+9}$; $x = -2$

16. $\dfrac{2x^2-1}{x^3+4x^2+1}$; $x = 3$

5.2   SIMPLIFYING RATIONAL EXPRESSIONS

Recall that a fraction is said to be in lowest terms if the numerator and the denominator have no common factor other than 1. In other words a fraction is in lowest terms if the greatest common factor of the numerator and the denominator is 1. For example: $\dfrac{3}{5}$ and $-\dfrac{15}{7}$ are in lowest terms but $\dfrac{2}{4}$ is not. In exactly the same way we say:

A *rational expression* $\dfrac{P}{Q}$ $(Q \neq 0)$ is in **lowest terms** if the greatest common factor of P [numerator] and Q [denominator] is 1.

Upon completion of this section we will be able to:

    A.   Identify fundamental property of rational expressions

    B.   Write rational expressions in lowest terms.

A.   Fundamental Property of Rational Expressions

Rational expressions represent real numbers for all permissible values of the variable. For this reason properties of real numbers also apply to rational expressions. Recall an important property of rational numbers: $\dfrac{ak}{bk} = \dfrac{a}{b}$ *for all non-zero numbers k. This property when applied to rational expressions give us the following property:*

Fundamental Property of Rational Expressions:

$$\frac{PK}{QK} = \frac{P}{Q}$$ for all rational expressions $\frac{P}{Q}$, and for any non zero number or expression K.

B. Writing a Rational Expression in Lowest Terms

Recall the steps used in writing a fraction in lowest terms. For example to write $\frac{16}{24}$ in lowest terms we:

1. Factor $16 = 2 \cdot 2 \cdot 2 \cdot 2$

2. Factor $24 = 2 \cdot 2 \cdot 2 \cdot 3$

3. Find the greatest common factor $= 2 \cdot 2 \cdot 2$

4. Simplify by dividing the numerator and denominator by greatest common factor;

   i.e.: $\frac{16}{24} = \frac{2 \cdot 8}{3 \cdot 8} = \frac{2}{3}$.   Fundamental property

We follow the same steps to write a rational expression in lowest terms.

Step 1	Factor the numerator completely.
Step 2	Factor the denominator completely.
Step 3	Determine the greatest common factor of the numerator and the denominator.
Step 4	Divide the numerator and the denominator by the greatest common factor.

Notes: 1. Simplifying a rational expression also means writing the rational expression in lowest terms.
2. Step 4 is, in fact, applying the fundamental property of rational expressions.

Example 1:   Write the following in lowest terms

a) $\dfrac{36}{63}$ b) $\dfrac{12x^5}{18x^3}$

c) $\dfrac{4x - 20}{7x - 35}$ d) $\dfrac{4 - y}{-2y + 8}$

Warm Up

1. Write the following in lowest terms.

a) $\dfrac{63}{90}$

Solutions:

a) $\dfrac{36}{63}$:

Step 1 $36 = 2 \cdot 2 \cdot 3 \cdot 3$ Factor the numerator

Step 2 $63 = 3 \cdot 3 \cdot 7$ Factor the denominator

Step 3   Greatest common factor of 36 and 63
$= 3 \cdot 3 = 9.$

Step 4 $\dfrac{36}{63} = \dfrac{9 \cdot 4}{9 \cdot 7} = \dfrac{4}{7}$ Divide the numerator and denominator by the g.c.f.

263

Warm Up

b) $\dfrac{9x^7}{15x^3}$

c) $\dfrac{6x+42}{5x+35}$

d) $\dfrac{1-y}{-4y+4}$

2. Simplify each of the following rational expressions.

a) $\dfrac{t^2-4}{t+2}$

b) $\dfrac{12x^5}{18x^3}$:

Step 1 $12x^5 = 2 \cdot \mathbf{2} \cdot \mathbf{3} \cdot x \cdot x \cdot x \cdot x \cdot x$ Factor the numerator

Step 2 $18x^3 = \mathbf{2} \cdot \mathbf{3} \cdot 3 \cdot x \cdot x \cdot x$ Factor the denominator

Step 3   Greatest common factor $= \mathbf{2} \cdot \mathbf{3} \cdot x \cdot x \cdot x = 6x^3$

Step 4 $\dfrac{12x^5}{18x^3} = \dfrac{(\mathbf{6x^3})(2x^2)}{(\mathbf{6x^3})(3)} = \dfrac{2x^2}{3}$ Divide the numerator and denominator by g.c.f.

c) $\dfrac{4x-20}{7x-35}$:

Step 1 $4x-20 = 4(x-5) = 2 \cdot 2(\mathbf{x-5})$ Factor the numerator

Step 2 $7x-35 = 7(\mathbf{x-5})$ Factor the denominator

Step 3   Greatest common factor $= \mathbf{x-5}.$

Step 4 $\dfrac{4x-20}{7x-35} = \dfrac{4(x-5)}{7(x-5)} = \dfrac{4}{7}$ Divide the numerator and denominator by g.c.f.

d) $\dfrac{4-y}{-2y+8} = \dfrac{4-y}{2(4-y)} = \dfrac{1}{2}$

Example 2:   Simplify each of the following rational expressions

a) $\dfrac{t^2-9}{t-3}$ b) $\dfrac{2z^2+11z+12}{3z^2+11z-4}$

c) $\dfrac{(a^3-b^3)(a+b)}{(a^3+b^3)(a-b)}$ d) $\dfrac{x^3+5x^2+6x}{x^2-2x-8}$

Solutions:

a) $\dfrac{t^2-9}{t-3}$:

Step 1 $t^2-9 = (t)^2-(3)^2 = (t-3)(t+3)$ Factor the numerator

Step 2 $t-3 = t-3$ Factor the denominator

Step 3   Greatest common factor $= t-3$

Step 4 $\dfrac{t^2-9}{t-3} = \dfrac{(t-3)(t+3)}{t-3} = t+3$ Divide the numerator and denominator by g.c.f.

b) $\dfrac{2z^2 + 11z + 12}{3z^2 + 11z - 4}:$

Step 1 $2z^2 + 11z + 12 = 2z^2 + 8z + 3z + 12$ The CIs are 8 and 3
$$= \left(2z^2 + 8z\right) + (3z + 12)$$
$$= 2z(z + 4) + 3(z + 4)$$
$$= (z + 4)(2z + 3)$$

Step 2 $3z^2 + 11z - 4 = 3z^2 - z + 12z - 4$ The CIs are -1 and 12
$$= \left(3z^2 - z\right) + (12z - 4)$$
$$= z(3z - 1) + 4(3z - 1)$$
$$= (3z - 1)(z + 4)$$

Step 3   Greatest common factor $= z + 4$

Step 4 $\dfrac{2z^2 + 11z + 12}{3z^2 + 11z - 4} = \dfrac{(2z + 3)(z + 4)}{(3z - 1)(z + 4)} = \dfrac{2z + 3}{3z - 1}$

c) $\dfrac{\left(a^3 - b^3\right)(a + b)}{\left(a^3 + b^3\right)(a - b)} = \dfrac{(a - b)\left(a^2 + ab + b^2\right)(a + b)}{(a + b)\left(a^2 - ab + b^2\right)(a - b)}$

$$= \dfrac{a^2 + ab + b^2}{a^2 - ab - b^2}$$

d) $\dfrac{x^3 + 5x^2 + 6x}{x^2 - 2x - 8} = \dfrac{x\left(x^2 + 5x + 6\right)}{(x + 2)(x - 4)}$

$$= \dfrac{x(x + 2)(x + 3)}{(x + 2)(x - 4)}$$

$$= \dfrac{x(x + 3)}{(x - 4)} = \dfrac{x^2 + 3x}{x - 4}$$

EXERCISE 5.2

Answers:

1. _____

2. _____

3. _____

4. _____

5. _____

6. _____

7. _____

8. _____

9. _____

10. _____

11. _____

12. _____

13. _____

14. _____

15. _____

16. _____

17. _____

18. _____

19. _____

20. _____

21. _____

In exercises 1–10, write the rational expressions in lowest terms.

1. $\dfrac{12}{18}$

2. $\dfrac{15x^4}{3x^2}$

3. $\dfrac{-26p^3q^5}{39p^4q}$

4. $\dfrac{\left(2x^3\right)^3}{5x^4}$

5. $\dfrac{24t-30}{12}$

6. $\dfrac{7a(a-b)}{21(a-b)}$

7. $-\dfrac{3p(p-4)}{8-2p}$

8. $\dfrac{9t^2(s-t)}{12t(t-s)^2}$

9. $\dfrac{3(a+4)}{(a+4)(2a-1)}$

10. $\dfrac{x^2-y^2}{x-y}$

In exercises 11–21, simplify the rational expressions.

11. $\dfrac{3x-6}{x^2-4x+4}$

12. $\dfrac{3y^2-6y}{-9y+18}$

13. $\dfrac{2t^3+19t^2-21t}{2t^2+21t}$

14. $\dfrac{x^3+1}{x^3+a}, \quad a \neq 1$

15. $\dfrac{(a-b)^3}{a^2-2ab+b^2}$

16. $\dfrac{2x^2-2y^2}{x^2+2y+2x+xy}$

17. $\dfrac{p^2-3p+9}{p^3+27}$

18. $\dfrac{16p^2-25q^2}{16p^2-40pq+25q^2}$

19. $\dfrac{16p^2-25q^2}{16p^2-40q+25q^2}$

20. $\dfrac{4x^2+8x+3}{6+x-2x^2}$

21. $\dfrac{6t^2-7t-5}{2t^2+5t+2}$

5.3 MULTIPLICATION AND DIVISION OF RATIONAL EXPRESSIONS

Multiplication and division of rational expressions is performed in exactly the same way as multiplication and division of arithmetic fractions.

Upon completion of this section will be able to :

A.   Multiply rational expressions.

B.   Divide rational expressions.

A. Multiplication of Rational Expressions

Recall how two fractions are multiplied.

$$\frac{10}{9} \cdot \frac{21}{25} = \frac{10 \cdot 21}{9 \cdot 25} = \frac{(2 \cdot 5)(3 \cdot 7)}{(3 \cdot 3)(5 \cdot 5)} = \frac{2 \cdot 3 \cdot 5 \cdot 7}{3 \cdot 3 \cdot 5 \cdot 5} = \frac{14}{15}$$

To multiply two rational expressions we follow the steps:

Step 1	Multiply the numerators.
Step 2	Multiply the denominators.
Step 3	The numerator of the product is the product of the numerators of the two expressions. The denominator of the product is the product of the denominators of the two expressions.
Step 4	Reduce the answer in step 3 to lowest terms.

Example 1: Multiply and write your answer in lowest terms.

a) $\dfrac{x^2 - 7x + 12}{x} \cdot \dfrac{x^2}{x-3}$ b) $\dfrac{a-b}{3b} \cdot \dfrac{b^3}{(a-b)^2}$

Solutions:

a) $\dfrac{x^2 - 7x + 12}{x} \cdot \dfrac{x^2}{x-3}$

Step 1   The product of numerators $= \left(x^2 - 7x + 12\right)\left(x^2\right).$

Step 2   The product of denominators $= x(x-3).$

Step 3 $\dfrac{x^2 - 7x + 12}{x} \cdot \dfrac{x^2}{x-3} = \dfrac{\left(x^2 - 7x + 12\right)\left(x^2\right)}{x(x-3)}$ Reduce to lowest terms

$= \dfrac{(x-3)(x-4)x \cdot x}{x(x-3)}$

$= x(x-4)$

Warm Up

1. Multiply and write your answers in lowest terms.

a) $\dfrac{4x^2 + 16x + 15}{3x} \cdot \dfrac{9x^2}{2x+5}$

Warm Up

b) $\dfrac{(x+y)^3 \cdot y^2}{y \cdot (x+y)}$

b) $\dfrac{a-b}{3b} \cdot \dfrac{b^3}{(a-b)^2} = \dfrac{(a-b)(b^3)}{(3b)(a-b)^2}$ Reduce to lowest terms.

$= \dfrac{(a-b)b \cdot b \cdot b}{(3b)(a-b)(a-b)}$ Factor numerator and denominator

$= \dfrac{b \cdot b}{3(a-b)} = \dfrac{b^2}{3(a-b)}$

2. Multiply and simplify

Example 2:   Multiply and simplify.

a) $\dfrac{4x+12}{6x^3 + 24x^2} \cdot \dfrac{4x^2 + 16x}{x+3}$

a) $\dfrac{3x^2 - 12}{6-3x} \cdot \dfrac{2x^2 - 4x}{x+2}$

b) $\dfrac{x^2 + 2x - 3}{6x^2 + 5x + 1} \cdot \dfrac{2x^2 - 5x - 3}{2x^2 - 2} \cdot \dfrac{6x^2 + 4x - 2}{x^2 - 2x - 3}$

Solutions:

a) $\dfrac{3x^2 - 12}{6-3x} \cdot \dfrac{2x^2 - 4x}{x+2} = \dfrac{(3x^2 - 12)(2x^2 - 4x)}{(6-3x)(x+2)}$

$= \dfrac{[3(x^2 - 4)][2x(x-2)]}{3(2-x)(x+2)}$

$= \dfrac{3 \cdot 2x(x-2)(x+2)(x-2)}{-3\,(x-2)(x+2)}$

$= \dfrac{2x(x-2)}{-1}$

$= -2x(x-2) = -2x^2 + 4x$

$= 4x - 2x^2$

b) $\dfrac{x^2 + 5x + 4}{x^2 - x - 6} \cdot \dfrac{x^2 + 5x + 6}{x^2 - 1}$

$\dfrac{2x^2 + 3x - 5}{x^2 + x - 6}$

b) $\dfrac{x^2 + 2x - 3}{6x^2 + 5x + 1} \cdot \dfrac{2x^2 - 5x - 3}{2x^2 - 2} \cdot \dfrac{6x^2 + 4x - 2}{x^2 - 2x - 3}$

$= \dfrac{(x^2 + 2x - 3)(2x^2 - 5x - 3)(6x^2 + 4x - 2)}{(6x^2 + 5x + 1)(2x^2 - 2)(x^2 - 2x - 3)}$

$= \dfrac{[(x+3)(x-1)][(2x+1)(x-3)][(2)(3x-1)(x+1)]}{[(3x+1)(2x+1)][(2)(x-1)(x+1)][(x+1)(x-3)]}$

$= \dfrac{(x+3)(3x-1)(2)(x-1)(2x+1)(x-3)(x+1)}{(3x+1)(x+1)(2)(2x+1)(x-1)(x+1)(x-3)}$

$= \dfrac{(x+3)(3x-1)}{(3x+1)(x+1)}$

Answers:

1. a) $3x(2x+3)$ b) $y(x+y)^2$

2. a) $\dfrac{-8}{3x}$ b) $\dfrac{(x+4)(2x+5)}{(x-3)(x-2)}$

Note: When multiplying the numerators and denominators of the two rational expressions we *do not* *expand* the products. They need to be factored for simplification.

B. Division of Rational Expressions

Recall that in order to divide, for example, $\dfrac{2}{3}$ by $\dfrac{5}{12}$ we multiply $\dfrac{2}{3}$ by the reciprocal of $\dfrac{5}{12}$.

Thus $\dfrac{2}{3} \div \dfrac{5}{12} = \dfrac{2}{3} \cdot \dfrac{12}{5} = \dfrac{2 \cdot 12}{3 \cdot 5} = \dfrac{2 \cdot 2 \cdot 2 \cdot 3}{3 \cdot 5} = \dfrac{8}{5}$ Reciprocal of $\dfrac{5}{12}$ is $\dfrac{12}{5}$

Also recall that the reciprocal of a fraction is obtained by swapping the numerator and the denominator of the fraction. We use the same definition for the reciprocal of a rational expression.

If $\dfrac{R}{S}$ is a non zero rational expression, then the **reciprocal** of $\dfrac{R}{S}$ is defined to be $\dfrac{S}{R}$.

To divide a rational expression $\dfrac{P}{Q}$ by a non-zero expression $\dfrac{R}{S}$, or to simplify $\dfrac{P}{Q} \div \dfrac{R}{S}$,

we use the following steps:

Step 1	Multiply $\dfrac{P}{Q}$ and the reciprocal of $\dfrac{R}{S}$.
Step 2	Simplify the product to the lowest terms.

Example 3: Simplify and write your answer in lowest terms.

a) $\dfrac{4p^2}{15pq^3} \div \dfrac{8pq^2}{21p^2q^3}$ b) $\dfrac{x^2-4}{x} \div (x+2)$

Warm Up

3. Simplify and write your answers in lowest terms.

a) $\dfrac{24x^2y^3}{7y} \div \dfrac{6xy}{35x}$

Solutions:

a) $\dfrac{4p^2}{15pq^3} \div \dfrac{8pq^2}{21p^2q^3}$:

Step 1 $\dfrac{4p^2}{15pq^3} \div \dfrac{8pq^2}{21p^2q^3} = \dfrac{4p^2}{15pq^3} \cdot \dfrac{21p^2q^3}{8pq^2}$

$\downarrow$ Divide $\downarrow$ Multiply

Step 2 $= \dfrac{(4p^2)(21p^2q^3)}{(15pq^3)(8pq^2)} = \dfrac{(4 \cdot 21)(p^2p^2q^3)}{(15 \cdot 8)pq^3pq^2}$

$= \dfrac{2 \cdot 2 \cdot 3 \cdot 7p^2 \cdot p^2 \cdot q^3}{3 \cdot 5 \cdot 2 \cdot 2 \cdot 2p^2 \cdot q^3 \cdot q^2} = \dfrac{7p^2}{10q^2}$

b) $\dfrac{x^2-4}{x} \div (x+2)$:

Step 1 $\dfrac{x^2-4}{x} \div (x+2) = \dfrac{x^2-4}{x} \cdot \dfrac{1}{x+2}$

$\downarrow$ Divide $\downarrow$ Multiply

Step 2 $= \dfrac{x^2-4}{x(x+2)} = \dfrac{(x-2)(x+2)}{x(x+2)} = \dfrac{x-2}{x}$

b) $\dfrac{3x^2-27}{x} \div (x+3)$

4. Simplify and write your expression in lowest terms.

a) $\dfrac{\dfrac{x^2 - 36}{x^2 + 2x - 8}}{\dfrac{x^2 + 5x - 6}{x^2 - 4x + 4}} \div$

b) $\left(4t^2 - 9\right) \div \dfrac{t^2 - t - 6}{t - 3}$

$\div \dfrac{2t + 3}{t + 2}$

Example 4:   Simplify and write your answer in lowest terms.

a) $\dfrac{x^2 - 9}{x^2 - 8x + 12} \div \dfrac{x^2 - 6x + 9}{x^2 - 4}$

b) $\left(4t^2 - 9\right) \div \dfrac{2t^2 + 5t + 3}{t + 2} \div (2t - 3)$

Solutions:

a) $\dfrac{x^2 - 9}{x^2 - 8x + 12} \underset{\underset{\text{Divide}}{\downarrow}}{\div} \dfrac{x^2 - 6x + 9}{x^2 - 4} = \dfrac{x^2 - 9}{x^2 - 8x + 12} \underset{\underset{\text{Multiply}}{\downarrow}}{\cdot} \dfrac{x^2 - 4}{x^2 - 6x + 9}$

$$= \dfrac{\left(x^2 - 9\right)\left(x^2 - 4\right)}{\left(x^2 - 8x + 12\right)\left(x^2 - 6x + 9\right)}$$

$$= \dfrac{(x - 3)(x + 3)(x - 2)(x + 2)}{(x - 2)(x - 6)(x - 3)(x - 3)}$$

$$= \dfrac{(x + 3)(x + 2)}{(x - 6)(x - 3)}$$

b)   Recall the order of operations. Perform the division from left to right.

$$\left(4t^2 - 9\right) \underset{\underset{\text{Divide}}{\downarrow}}{\div} \dfrac{2t^2 + 5t + 3}{t + 2} \div (2t - 3) = \left(4t^2 - 9\right) \underset{\underset{\text{Multiply}}{\downarrow}}{\cdot} \dfrac{t + 2}{2t^2 + 5t + 3} \div (2t - 3)$$

$$= \dfrac{\left(4t^2 - 9\right)(t + 2)}{2t^2 + 5t + 3} \underset{\underset{\text{Divide}}{\downarrow}}{\div} (2t - 3) = \dfrac{\left(4t^2 - 9\right)(t + 2)}{2t^2 + 5t + 3} \underset{\underset{\text{Multiply}}{\downarrow}}{\cdot} \dfrac{1}{2t - 3}$$

$$= \dfrac{\left(4t^2 - 9\right)(t + 2)}{\left(2t^2 + 5t + 3\right)(2t - 3)} = \dfrac{(2t - 3)(2t + 3)(t + 2)}{(2t + 3)(t + 1)(2t - 3)} = \dfrac{t + 2}{t + 1}$$

Example 5:   Perform the indicated operations and simplify.

a) $\dfrac{2a^2 + 5a - 3}{a^2 + 2a - 3} \div \left(\dfrac{a^2 + 2a - 35}{a^2 - 6a + 5} \div \dfrac{a^2 - 9a + 14}{2a^2 - 5a + 2}\right)$

b) $\dfrac{z^2 - z - 6}{z^2 - 4} \div \left(\dfrac{z^2 - 8z + 15}{z^2 - z - 2} \cdot \dfrac{z^2 + 3z + 2}{z^2 - 3z - 10}\right)$

Solutions:

Recall that we have to simplify first the expressions within the grouping symbols.

a)

$$\frac{2a^2 + 5a - 3}{a^2 + 2a - 3} \div \left(\frac{a^2 + 2a - 35}{a^2 - 6a + 5} \div \frac{a^2 - 9a + 14}{2a^2 - 5a + 2} \right)$$

$$= \frac{2a^2 + 5a - 3}{a^2 + 2a - 3} \div \left(\frac{a^2 + 2a - 35}{a^2 - 6a + 5} \cdot \frac{2a^2 - 5a + 2}{a^2 - 9a + 14} \right)$$

$$= \frac{2a^2 + 5a - 3}{a^2 + 2a - 3} \div \frac{\left(a^2 + 2a - 35\right)\left(2a^2 - 5a + 2\right)}{\left(a^2 - 6a + 5\right)\left(a^2 - 9a + 14\right)}$$

$$= \frac{2a^2 + 5a - 3}{a^2 + 2a - 3} \cdot \frac{\left(a^2 - 6a + 5\right)\left(a^2 - 9a + 14\right)}{\left(a^2 + 2a - 35\right)\left(2a^2 - 5a + 2\right)}$$

$$= \frac{\left(2a^2 + 5a - 3\right)\left(a^2 - 6a + 5\right)\left(a^2 - 9a + 14\right)}{\left(a^2 + 2a - 3\right)\left(a^2 + 2a - 35\right)\left(2a^2 - 5a + 2\right)} \quad \text{Multiply}$$

$$= \frac{(2a - 1)(a + 3)(a - 5)(a - 1)(a - 2)(a - 7)}{(a - 1)(a + 3)(a + 7)(a - 5)(2a - 1)(a - 2)} \quad \text{Factor}$$

$$= \frac{(a - 1)(a - 2)(a + 3)(a - 5)(2a - 1)(a - 7)}{(a - 1)(a - 2)(a + 3)(a - 5)(2a - 1)(a + 7)} \quad \text{Rearrange the terms}$$

$$= \frac{a - 7}{a + 7}$$

b)

$$\frac{z^2 - z - 6}{z^2 - 4} \div \left(\frac{z^2 - 8z + 15}{z^2 - z - 2} \cdot \frac{z^2 + 3z + 2}{z^2 - 3z - 10} \right) \quad \begin{array}{l}\text{Multiply inside}\\ \text{the parentheses}\end{array}$$

$$= \frac{z^2 - z - 6}{z^2 - 4} \div \left(\frac{z^2 - 8z + 15}{z^2 - z - 2} \cdot \frac{z^2 + 3z + 2}{z^2 - 3z - 10} \right) \quad \text{Simplify division}$$

$$= \frac{z^2 - z - 6}{z^2 - 4} \cdot \frac{\left(z^2 - z - 2\right)\left(z^2 - 3z - 10\right)}{\left(z^2 - 8z + 15\right)\left(z^2 + 3z + 2\right)} \quad \text{Multiply}$$

$$= \frac{\left(z^2 - z - 6\right)\left(z^2 - z - 2\right)\left(z^2 - 3z - 10\right)}{\left(z^2 - 4\right)\left(z^2 - 8z + 15\right)\left(z^2 + 3z + 2\right)}$$

$$= \frac{(z - 3)(z + 2)(z - 2)(z + 1)(z - 5)(z + 2)}{(z - 2)(z + 2)(z - 3)(z - 5)(z + 1)(z + 2)} \quad \text{Factor}$$

$$= 1 \quad \text{Simplify}$$

Warm Up

5. Perform the indicated operations and simplify.

a) $\left[\dfrac{4x^2 + 4x + 1}{3x + 5} \div \dfrac{2x^2 + 3x + 1}{3x^2 + 8x + 5} \right]$
$\div \dfrac{(2x + 1)(x + 3)}{2x + 3}$

b) $\dfrac{x^2 + x - 6}{x^2 - 1}$
$\div \left[\dfrac{x^2 - 8x + 15}{x^2 + 3x - 4} \div \dfrac{x^2 - 4x + 5}{x^2 + 7x + 12} \right]$

Answers:

3. **a)** $20x^2 y$ **b)** $\dfrac{3(x - 3)}{x}$

4. **a)** $\dfrac{x^2 - 8x + 12}{x^2 + 3x - 4}$ **b)** $2t - 3$

5. **a)** $\dfrac{2x + 3}{x + 3}$ **b)** $\dfrac{x - 2}{x - 3}$

EXERCISE 5.3

Answers:

1. _____

2. _____

3. _____

4. _____

5. _____

6. _____

7. _____

8. _____

9. _____

10. _____

11. _____

12. _____

13. _____

14. _____

15. _____

16. _____

17. _____

18. _____

19. _____

20. _____

21. _____

In exercises 1–5, perform the multiplication and write your answers in lowest terms.

1. $\dfrac{3x^2}{20} \cdot \dfrac{4}{x^2}$

2. $\dfrac{7a^3}{15a^2} \cdot \dfrac{25a^4}{14a^3}$

3. $\dfrac{x^2y^2}{p^2q} \cdot \dfrac{p^{-1}q^3}{x^3}$

4. $\dfrac{3x^2y^2}{5x^3y^5} \cdot \dfrac{10x^5y^{-3}}{9xy^{-2}}$

5. $\dfrac{3r^2s}{10r^3} \cdot \dfrac{15r^2}{7rs^2} \cdot \dfrac{21r^2s^2}{r^4}$

In exercises 6–10, perform the division and simplify.

6. $\dfrac{3p^2}{8p^4} \div \dfrac{6p^3}{24p^4}$

7. $\dfrac{25x^8}{9x^4} \div \dfrac{15x^5}{10x^2}$

8. $\dfrac{5a^3}{\left(4a^2\right)^2} \div \dfrac{15a^2}{8a^4}$

9. $\dfrac{3p^2q^2}{6p^2q^3} \cdot \dfrac{-4p^6q^{-2}}{18p^{-3}q} \div \dfrac{36p}{18q^{-2}}$

10. $\dfrac{14m^5}{2n^2} \div \dfrac{28m^4}{8n^3} \div \dfrac{5m^2n^3}{2m^3n^{-1}}$

In exercises 11–25, perform the indicated operations and simplify.

11. $\dfrac{a^2+2a+1}{a} \cdot \dfrac{a^2+a}{a^2-1}$

12. $\dfrac{6(x+2)}{3(x-1)^2} \cdot \dfrac{9(x-1)}{(x+2)}$

13. $\dfrac{2a-5}{3} \div \dfrac{5-2a}{9}$

14. $\dfrac{t^2-36}{t-3} \cdot \dfrac{t^2-9}{t+6}$

15. $\dfrac{x^2-4}{2a-ax} \div \dfrac{x^2+4x+4}{a(2+x)}$

16. $\left(2a^2-9a-5\right) \div \dfrac{2a^2+a}{a}$

17. $\dfrac{3t^2-5t-2}{4t^2-3t-1} \div \dfrac{3t^2+7t+2}{5t^2-3t-2}$

18. $\dfrac{2x+3}{2x+4} \cdot \dfrac{x^2-4}{x+1}$

19. $\dfrac{6y^2}{y^2-y-6} \cdot \dfrac{y+2}{3y}$

20. $\dfrac{z^2+2z-15}{z^2-z-2} \div \dfrac{z^2+3z-10}{z^2+4z+3}$

21. $\dfrac{3a^2-2a}{3a+2} \div (2-3a) \div \dfrac{3a}{3a-3}$

22. $\dfrac{x^2 - 9}{6x^2 + x - 1} \cdot \dfrac{2x^2 + 5x + 2}{x^2 + 4x + 3} \div \dfrac{x^2 - 3x}{x^2 - x - 2}$

22. _____

23. $\dfrac{t^2 + 10t + 25}{t^2 + 10t} \div \dfrac{t + 5}{t + 10} \cdot \dfrac{10t}{t^2 + 15t + 30}$

23. _____

24. $\dfrac{4z^2 - 10z + 6}{z^3 - 3z^2} \div \dfrac{2z - 3}{z^2} \cdot \dfrac{z - 3}{2z - 2}$

24. _____

25. $\dfrac{p^2 - 4}{p^2 - p^6} \div \left(\dfrac{p^2 - 3p - 10}{p^2 - 8p + 15} \cdot \dfrac{p^2 - p - 2}{p^2 + 3p + 2} \right)$

25. _____

5.4   LEAST COMMON DENOMINATOR OF RATIONAL EXPRESSIONS

Our next goal is to define addition and subtraction of rational expressions. This is done exactly the same way as for arithmetic fractions. Recall that we needed the *least common denominator* to add or subtract two fractions with different denominators. In this section we develop the concept of the *least common denominator* of two rational expressions.

Upon completion of this section we will be able to:

     A.   Find the least common denominator (l.c.d) of rational expressions
     B.   Rewrite a rational expression with a given new denominator.

Least Common Denominator

As in the case of arithmetic fractions, the **least common denominator** of two rational expressions is simply the *least common multiple of their denominators*. The least common multiple of two polynomials is, as the name indicates, the smallest of the common multiples of the polynomials.

To find the least common multiple of two polynomials, we follow the steps given below:

Step 1	Factor each polynomial completely.
Step 2	Determine the different factors and their maximum exponents in various factorizations.
Step 3	The product of the different factors each raised to its maximum exponent, as determined in step 2, is the least common multiple (l.c.m.) of the polynomials.

Warm Up

1. Find the least common multiple of :

   a) $x+1$ and x^3-x

   b) $(x-2)y$, x^2+2x-8, x^2+6x+8

2. Find the least common denominator.

   a) $\dfrac{1}{a+3}$ and $\dfrac{1}{a-3}$

Example 1:   Find the least common multiple of :

a) x^3-x^2, and x^2-2x+1

b) $3x^3-27x$, $4x^4+12x^3$, and $(x-3)^2(y-1)$

Solutions:

a) x^3-x^2, and x^2-2x+1

Step 1   Factor the polynomials. $x^3-x^2 = x^2(x-1)$,
$$x^2-2x+1 = (x-1)^2$$

Step 2

Factors	x	$x-1$
Highest Power	2	2

Step 3   Least common multiple $= (x)^2(x-1)^2$

b) $3x^3-27x$, $4x^4+12x^3$, and $(x-3)^2(y-1)$

Step 1   Factor the polynomials.

$$3x^3-27x = 3x(x^2-9) = 3x(x-3)(x+3)$$

$$4x^4+12x^3 = 4x^3(x+3) = 2^2x^3(x+3)$$

$$(x-3)^2(y-1) = (x-3)^2(y-1)$$

Step 2

Factors	3	2	x	$x-3$	$x+3$	$y-1$
Highest Power	1	2	3	2	1	1

Step 3   Least common multiple

$$= 3^1 \cdot 2^2 \cdot x^3(x-3)^2(x+3)(y-1)$$
$$= 12x^3(x-3)^2(x+3)(y-1)$$

Example 2:   Find the least common denominator of:

a) $\dfrac{4}{a-4}$, and $\dfrac{7}{a-6}$ b) $\dfrac{t}{t-3}$, and $\dfrac{2}{3-t}$

Solutions:

a)   The denominators are: $a-4$ and $a-6$

Step 1   Factor the denominators. $a-4 = a-4$, $a-6 = a-6$

Step 2

Factors	$a-4$	$a-6$
Highest Power	1	1

Step 3   l.c.d. $= (a-4)(a-6)$

274

b)   The denominators are: $t - 3$ and $3 - t$

Step 1   Factor the denominators
$$t - 3 = t - 3, \quad 3 - t = -(t - 3)$$

Step 2

Factor	$t - 3$
Highest Power	1

Step 3   l. c. d. $= t - 3$

Example 3:   Find the least common denominator of the following rational expressions.

a) $\dfrac{1}{x-1}, \ \dfrac{x+2}{x^2 - 2x + 1}, \quad$ and $\quad \dfrac{4x}{x^2 - 1}$

b) $\dfrac{2x-1}{x^2 + 8x + 12}, \dfrac{x}{x^2 - 36}, \quad$ and $\quad \dfrac{3 - 5x}{x^3 + 12x^2 + 36x}$

Solutions:

a)   The denominators are: $x - 1, \ x^2 - 2x + 1, \quad$ and $\quad x^2 - 1$

Step 1   Factor the denominators.
$$x - 1 = x - 1$$
$$x^2 - 2x + 1 = (x - 1)^2$$
$$x^2 - 1 = (x - 1)(x + 1)$$

Step 2

Factors	$x - 1$	$x + 1$
Highest Power	2	1

Step 3   Least Common Denominator $= (x - 1)^2 (x + 1)^1$
$$= (x + 1)(x - 1)^2$$

b)   The denominators are:
$$x^2 + 8x + 12, \ x^2 - 36, \quad \text{and} \quad x^3 + 12x^2 + 36x$$

Step 1   Factor the denominators.
$$x^2 + 8x + 12 = (x + 2)(x + 6)$$
$$x^2 - 36 = (x - 6)(x + 6)$$
$$x^3 + 12x^2 + 36x = x(x^2 + 12x + 36) = x(x + 6)^2$$

Step 2

Factors	x	$x + 2$	$x - 6$	$x + 6$
Highest Power	1	1	1	2

1. a) $x(x^2 - 1)$
    b) $y(x + 4)(x + 2)(x - 2)$
2. a) $(a + 3)(a - 3)$
    b) $(x - 1)$
3. a) $(x + 2)(x - 2)^2$
    b) $x(x + 2)(x - 4)(x + 4)^2$

Step 3   LCD $= x(x + \cdot 2)(x - 6)(x + 6)^2$

B.   Rewriting Rational Expressions with a Given Denominator

A rational expression can always be rewritten with a **new denominator which is a multiple of the old one** by using the fundamental property of rational expressions. We show this with the help of some examples.

Warm Up

4. Rewrite each of the following rational expressions with a new denominator as indicated.

a) $\dfrac{3}{5}$; 30

b) $\dfrac{2z}{5y}$; $10x^2y$

Example 4:   Rewrite each of the following rational expressions with a new denominator as indicated.

a) $\dfrac{4}{15}$; 90   b) $\dfrac{3y}{4z}$; $8xz^2$

c) $\dfrac{15t}{t^2 - 7t}$; $t^4 - 10t^3 + 21t^2$

d) $\dfrac{p-3}{p+4}$; $p^2 - 16$

e) $\dfrac{1}{q^2 - q + 1}$; $(q+1)(q^3 + 1)$

Use the following steps:

Step 1	Find the quotient: $\dfrac{\text{new denominator}}{\text{old denominator}} = k.$
Step 2	Multiply the given fraction by $\dfrac{k}{k}$. Fundamental property
Step 3	Simplify and expand if necessary.

Solutions:

a) $\dfrac{4}{15}$; **90**

Step 1 $\dfrac{\text{new denominator}}{\text{old denominator}} = \dfrac{90}{15} = 6$

Step 2 $\dfrac{4}{15} = \dfrac{4}{15} \cdot \dfrac{6}{6}$

Step 3 $\dfrac{4}{15} \cdot \dfrac{6}{6} = \dfrac{24}{90}$

b) $\dfrac{3y}{4z}$; $8xz^2$

Step 1 $\dfrac{\text{new denominator}}{\text{old denominator}} = \dfrac{8xz^2}{4z} = 2xz$

Step 2 $\dfrac{3y}{4z} = \dfrac{3y}{4z} \cdot \dfrac{2xz}{2xz}$

Step 3 $= \dfrac{6xyz}{8xz^2}$

276

c) $\dfrac{15t}{t^2 - 7t}$; $t^4 - 10t^3 + 21t^2$

Step 1 $\dfrac{t^4 - 10t^3 + 21t^2}{t^2 - 7t} = \dfrac{t^2(t^2 - 10t - 21)}{t(t-7)} = \dfrac{t \cdot t(t-3)(t-7)}{t(t-7)}$

$= t(t-3) = t^2 - 3t$

Step 2 $\dfrac{15t}{t^2 - 7t} = \dfrac{15t}{t^2 - 7t} \cdot \dfrac{t^2 - 3t}{t^2 - 3t}$

Step 3 $= \dfrac{15t(t^2 - 3t)}{(t^2 - 7t)(t^2 - 3t)} = \dfrac{15t^3 - 45t^2}{t^4 - 10t^3 + 21t^2}$

d) $\dfrac{p-3}{p+4}$; $p^2 - 16$

Step 1 $\dfrac{p^2 - 16}{p+4} = \dfrac{(p-4)(p+4)}{p+4} = p - 4$

Step 2 $\dfrac{p-3}{p+4} = \dfrac{p-3}{p+4} \cdot \dfrac{p-4}{p-4}$

Step 3 $= \dfrac{(p-3)(p-4)}{(p+4)(p-4)} = \dfrac{p^2 - 7p + 12}{p^2 - 16}$

e) $\dfrac{1}{q^2 - q + 1}$; $(q+1)(q^3 + 1)$

Step 1 $\dfrac{(q+1)(q^3+1)}{q^2 - q + 1} = \dfrac{(q+1)(q+1)(q^2 - q + 1)}{q^2 - q + 1} = (q+1)^2$

Step 2 $\dfrac{1}{q^2 - q + 1} = \dfrac{1}{q^2 - q + 1} \cdot \dfrac{(q+1)^2}{(q+1)^2}$ Fundamental property

Step 3 $= \dfrac{(q+1)^2}{(q^2 - q + 1)(q+1)^2}$

$= \dfrac{(q+1)^2}{(q+1)\big[(q+1)(q^2 - q + 1)\big]}$ $(q+1)(q^2 - q + 1) = (q^3 + 1)$

$= \dfrac{(q+1)^2}{(q+1)(q^3 + 1)}$

5. Find the least common denominator of the following rational expressions and rewrite them with the l.c.d. as new denominator.

$$\frac{3}{x^2 - 9}, \quad \frac{1}{x^2 - x - 6}, \text{ and}$$

$$\frac{x}{x^2 + 5x + 6}$$

Example 5: Find the least common denominator of the following rational expressions and rewrite them with the l.c.d. as the new denominator.

$$\frac{x}{x^2 - 4}, \quad \frac{1}{x^2 + 3x + 2}, \quad \frac{5}{x^2 - x - 2}$$

Solution:

$$x^2 - 4 = (x - 2)(x + 2)$$
$$x^2 + 3x + 2 = (x + 1)(x + 2)$$
$$x^2 - x - 2 = (x + 1)(x - 2)$$

Factors	$x - 2$	$x + 2$	$x + 1$
Highest Power	1	1	1

Therefore the l.c. d. of the given rational expressions is:

$$(x - 2)(x + 2)(x + 1) = \left(x^2 - 4\right)(x + 1).$$

We write each fraction with the l.c.d as the new denominator.

For $\dfrac{x}{x^2 - 4}$:

$$\frac{\text{new denominator}}{\text{old denominator}} = \frac{(x - 2)(x + 2)(x + 1)}{x^2 - 4}$$

$$= \frac{(x - 2)(x + 2)(x + 1)}{(x - 2)(x + 2)} = x + 1$$

Therefore, $\dfrac{x}{x^2 - 4} = \dfrac{x}{x^2 - 4} \cdot \dfrac{x + 1}{x + 1} = \dfrac{x(x + 1)}{\left(x^2 - 4\right)(x + 1)}$

For $\dfrac{1}{x^2 + 3x + 2}$:

$$\frac{\text{new denominator}}{\text{old denominator}} = \frac{(x - 2)(x + 2)(x + 1)}{x^2 + 3x + 2}$$

$$= \frac{(x - 2)(x + 2)(x + 1)}{(x + 1)(x + 2)} = x - 2$$

Therefore, $\dfrac{1}{x^2 + 3x + 2} = \dfrac{1}{x^2 + 3x + 2} \cdot \dfrac{x - 2}{x - 2}$

$$= \frac{x - 2}{\left(x^2 + 3x + 2\right)(x - 2)}$$

$$= \frac{x - 2}{(x + 1)(x + 2)(x - 2)}$$

$$= \frac{x - 2}{(x + 1)\left(x^2 - 4\right)}$$

For $\dfrac{5}{x^2 - x - 2}$:

$$\frac{\text{new denominator}}{\text{old denominator}} = \frac{(x - 2)(x + 2)(x + 1)}{(x + 1)(x - 2)}$$

$$= \frac{(x - 2)(x + 2)(x + 1)}{x^2 - x - 2} = x + 2$$

Therefore, $\dfrac{5}{x^2-x-2} = \dfrac{5}{x^2-x-2} \cdot \dfrac{x+2}{x+2}$

$$= \dfrac{5(x+2)}{(x^2-x-2)(x+2)}$$

$$= \dfrac{5x+10}{(x+1)(x-2)(x+2)}$$

$$= \dfrac{5x+10}{(x+1)(x^2-4)}$$

Warm Up

Answers:

4. a) $\dfrac{18}{30}$ b) $\dfrac{4x^2z}{10x^2y}$ c) $\dfrac{13t^2-39t}{t^3-8t^2+15}$

  d) $\dfrac{p^2-8p+15}{p^2-9}$

5. $\dfrac{3x+6}{(x+2)(x^2-9)}$, $\dfrac{x+3}{(x+2)(x^2-9)}$,

  $\dfrac{x^2-3x}{(x+2)(x^2-9)}$

EXERCISE 5.4

Answers:

In exercises 1–5, find the least common denominator.

1. $\dfrac{3}{a}$, $\dfrac{2}{b}$

2. $\dfrac{x+4}{x^2}$, $\dfrac{x-2}{x}$

3. $\dfrac{2x^2}{x-1}$, $\dfrac{3}{x^2-5x+4}$

4. $\dfrac{1}{p-4}$, $\dfrac{2}{4-p}$

5. $\dfrac{1}{t^2+4t-12}$, $\dfrac{-2}{t^2+t-30}$, $\dfrac{4t}{t^2+2t-24}$

In exercises 6–15, find the least common denominator and rewrite the expressions with the l.c.d. as the new denominator.

6. $\dfrac{2}{3x-6}$, $\dfrac{1}{2x-4}$

7. $\dfrac{1}{8x+16}$, $\dfrac{2}{x^2+x-2}$

8. $\dfrac{2+t}{t^2-4}$, $\dfrac{1}{t-2}$

9. $\dfrac{2p}{p^2-3p-4}$, $\dfrac{1}{p+1}$

10. $\dfrac{2a+1}{a^2+3a}$, $\dfrac{1}{a^2-9}$

11. $\dfrac{x}{x^3+27}$, $\dfrac{-2}{x^2+6x+9}$

12. $\dfrac{3}{x+2}$, $\dfrac{1}{x-4}$

13. z, $\dfrac{1}{z}$

14. $\dfrac{3}{t+1}$, $\dfrac{2}{t^2}$, $\dfrac{t}{t-1}$

15. $\dfrac{m-2}{m^2-5m}$, $\dfrac{2m}{m^2-25}$, $\dfrac{1}{m^2+5m}$

1. _____

2. _____

3. _____

4. _____

5. _____

6. _____

7. _____

8. _____

9. _____

10. _____

11. _____

12. _____

13. _____

14. _____

15. _____

5.5   ADDITION AND SUBTRACTION

Recall that in Chapter 1 we examined how to add or subtract two fractions. To add two fractions with the same denominator we simply add the numerator and place the sum over the common denominator.

$$\text{Thus } \frac{3}{5} + \frac{4}{5} = \frac{3+4}{5} = \frac{7}{5}.$$

To add two fractions with different denominators, we first find l.c.d of the two fractions, then rewrite the two fractions with the l.c.d. as the new denominator, and finally add the fractions.

$$\text{Thus } \frac{5}{6} + \frac{1}{8} = \frac{5}{6} \cdot \frac{4}{4} + \frac{1}{8} \cdot \frac{3}{3} \quad \text{l.c.d.} = 24$$

$$= \frac{20}{24} + \frac{3}{24} = \frac{20+3}{24} = \frac{23}{24}$$

Addition and subtraction of rational expressions are performed in the same way. Upon completion of this section we will be able to:

    A.   Add rational expressions with the like denominators.

    B.   Add rational expressions with different denominators.

    C.   Subtract rational expressions.

A.   Adding Two Rational Expressions with Like Denominator

To add two rational expressions $\dfrac{P}{Q}$ and $\dfrac{R}{Q}$ with the same denominator, add the numerators, place the sum over the common denominator, and reduce the resulting rational expression $\dfrac{P+R}{Q}$ to lowest terms if possible.

Warm Up

1. Perform addition

    a) $\dfrac{3}{x+2} + \dfrac{2x}{x+2}$

    b) $\dfrac{11t}{(t+3)^2} + \dfrac{2t}{(t+3)^2}$

Answers:

1. a) $\dfrac{2x+3}{x+2}$ b) $\dfrac{13t}{(t+3)^2}$

Example 1:   Perform addition

  a) $\dfrac{4}{x+1} + \dfrac{5x}{x+1}$ b) $\dfrac{4t}{(t+1)^2} + \dfrac{4}{(t+1)^2}$

Solutions:

a) $\dfrac{4}{x+1} + \dfrac{5x}{x+1} = \dfrac{4+5x}{x+1} = \dfrac{5x+4}{x+1}$ Same denominator

b) $\dfrac{4t}{(t+1)^2} + \dfrac{4}{(t+1)^2} = \dfrac{4t+4}{(t+1)^2} = \dfrac{4(t+1)}{(t+1)^2} = \dfrac{4}{t+1}$ Same denominator

B.   Adding Rational Expressions With Different Denominators

To add rational expressions with different denominators, we follow the steps given below:

Step 1	Find the least common denominator.
Step 2	Rewrite each expression with the l.c.d. as the common denominator.
Step 3	Add the fractions in the rewritten form.
Step 4	Write the answers in the lowest terms.

Example 2:   Add the following rational expressions.

a) $\dfrac{5}{4x} + \dfrac{2}{3x}$ b) $\dfrac{2}{x} + \dfrac{3}{y}$

c) $\dfrac{4x}{x+3} + \dfrac{-5x}{x-3}$

d) $\dfrac{x}{x^2 - 2x + 1} + \dfrac{3}{x^2 - 1}$

e) $\dfrac{2}{3y(y+3)} + \dfrac{y-1}{y^2(y-4)}$

f) $t + 2 + \dfrac{1}{t-2}$

g) $\dfrac{3a}{2a-1} + \dfrac{a-1}{a(a+3)} + \dfrac{a}{2a^2 + 5a - 3}$

Warm Up

2.   Add the following rational expressions.

a) $\dfrac{3}{2x} + \dfrac{1}{6x}$

Solutions:

a) $\dfrac{5}{4x} + \dfrac{2}{3x}$:

Step 1   Find the l.c.d. of $\dfrac{5}{4x}$ and $\dfrac{2}{3x}$:

$$\left.\begin{cases} 4x = 2 \cdot 2 \cdot x \\ 3x = 3x \end{cases}\right\}$$

l.c.d. $= 2 \cdot 2 \cdot 3x = \mathbf{12x}$

Step 2 $\dfrac{5}{4x} = \dfrac{5}{4x} \cdot \dfrac{\mathbf{3}}{\mathbf{3}} = \dfrac{15}{12x}$ $\dfrac{12x}{4x} = 3$

$\dfrac{2}{3x} = \dfrac{2}{3x} \cdot \dfrac{\mathbf{4}}{\mathbf{4}} = \dfrac{8}{12x}$ $\dfrac{12x}{3x} = 4$

Step 3 $\dfrac{5}{4x} + \dfrac{2}{3x} = \dfrac{15}{\mathbf{12x}} + \dfrac{8}{\mathbf{12x}} = \dfrac{\mathbf{15+8}}{12x} = \dfrac{23}{12x}$

Step 4   The resulting fraction cannot be reduced.

Warm Up

b) $\dfrac{4}{r} + \dfrac{5}{s}$

c) $\dfrac{2}{x-4} + \dfrac{5x}{x+4}$

d) $\dfrac{2x}{x^2-4x+4} + \dfrac{3}{x^2-4}$

b) $\dfrac{2}{x} + \dfrac{3}{y}$:

Step 1   The l.c.d. of $\dfrac{2}{x}$ and $\dfrac{3}{y}$ is xy

Step 2 $\dfrac{2}{x} = \dfrac{2}{x} \cdot \dfrac{y}{y} = \dfrac{2y}{xy}$ $\dfrac{xy}{x} = y$

$\dfrac{3}{y} = \dfrac{3}{y} \cdot \dfrac{x}{x} = \dfrac{3x}{xy}$ $\dfrac{xy}{y} = x$

Step 3 $\dfrac{2}{x} + \dfrac{3}{y} = \dfrac{2y}{xy} + \dfrac{3x}{xy} = \dfrac{2y + 3x}{xy}$

Step 4   The resulting fraction cannot be reduced.

c) $\dfrac{4x}{x+3} + \dfrac{-5x}{x-3}$:

Step 1   The l.c.d. of $\dfrac{4x}{x+3}$ and $\dfrac{-5x}{x-3}$ is $(x+3)(x-3)$

Step 2 $\dfrac{4x}{x+3} = \dfrac{4x}{x+3} \cdot \dfrac{x-3}{x-3} = \dfrac{4x(x-3)}{(x+3)(x-3)}$ $\dfrac{\text{l.c.d}}{x+3} = x-3$

$\dfrac{-5x}{x-3} = \dfrac{-5x}{x-3} \cdot \dfrac{x+3}{x+3} = -\dfrac{5x(x+3)}{(x-3)(x+3)}$ $\dfrac{\text{l.c.d}}{x-3} = x+3$

Step 3 $\dfrac{4x}{x+3} + \dfrac{-5x}{x-3} = \dfrac{4x(x-3)}{(x+3)(x-3)} + \dfrac{-5x(x+3)}{(x+3)(x-3)}$

$= \dfrac{4x(x-3) + [-5x(x+3)]}{(x+3)(x-3)}$

$= \dfrac{\left(4x^2 - 12x\right) + \left(-5x^2 - 15x\right)}{x^2 - 9}$

$= \dfrac{-x^2 - 27x}{x^2 - 9}$

Step 4   The resulting fraction cannot be reduced.

d) $\dfrac{x}{x^2 - 2x + 1} + \dfrac{3}{x^2 - 1}$:

Step 1   Find l.c.d. of the two fractions.

$$x^2 - 2x + 1 = (x-1)^2$$

$$x^2 - 1 = (x-1)(x+1)$$

$$\text{l.c.d.} = (x+1)(x-1)^2$$

Step 2   The first fraction:

$$\frac{x}{x^2 - 2x + 1} = \frac{x}{x^2 - 2x + 1} \cdot \frac{x+1}{x+1} \qquad \frac{\text{l.c.d}}{x^2-2x+1} = x+1$$

$$= \frac{x(x+1)}{(x-1)^2(x+1)}$$

The second fraction:

$$\frac{3}{x^2 - 1} = \frac{3}{x^2 - 1} \cdot \frac{x-1}{x-1} \qquad \frac{\text{l.c.d}}{x^2-1} = x-1$$

$$= \frac{3(x-1)}{\left(x^2-1\right)(x-1)} = \frac{3(x-1)}{(x+1)(x-1)(x-1)}$$

$$= \frac{3(x-1)}{(x+1)(x-1)^2}$$

Step 3 $\dfrac{x}{x^2 - 2x + 1} + \dfrac{3}{x^2 - 1} = \dfrac{x(x+1)}{(x-1)^2(x+1)} + \dfrac{3(x-1)}{(x-1)^2(x+1)}$

$$= \frac{x(x+1) + 3(x-1)}{(x-1)^2(x+1)}$$

$$= \frac{x^2 + 4x - 3}{(x-1)^2(x+1)}$$

Step 4   The resulting fraction cannot be reduced.

e) $\dfrac{2}{3y(y+3)} + \dfrac{y-1}{y^2(y-4)}$:

Step 1   Find l.c.d. of the two fractions.

$$3y(y+3) = 3y(y+3)$$

$$y^2(y-4) = y^2(y-4)$$

$$\text{l.c.d.} = 3y^2(y-4)(y+3)$$

Step 2   The first fraction:

$$\frac{2}{3y(y+3)} = \frac{2}{3y(y+3)} \cdot \frac{y(y-4)}{y(y-4)} \qquad \frac{\text{l.c.d}}{3y(y+3)} = y(y-4)$$

$$= \frac{2y(y-4)}{3y^2(y+3)(y-4)}$$

The second fraction:

$$\frac{y-1}{y^2(y-4)} = \frac{y-1}{y^2(y-4)} \cdot \frac{3(y+3)}{3(y+3)} \qquad \frac{\text{l.c.d}}{y^2\ (y-4)} = 3(y+3)$$

$$= \frac{3(y-1)(y+3)}{3y^2(y+3)(y-4)}$$

Warm Up

2. (contd)

Step 3 $\dfrac{2}{3y(y+3)} + \dfrac{y-1}{y^2(y-4)}$

$$= \dfrac{2y(y-4)}{3y^2(y+3)(y-4)} + \dfrac{3(y-1)(y+3)}{3y^2(y+3)(y-4)}$$

$$= \dfrac{2y(y-4) + 3(y-1)(y+3)}{3y^2(y+3)(y-4)}$$

$$= \dfrac{2y^2 - 8y + 3y^2 + 6y - 9}{3y^2(y+3)(y-4)} = \dfrac{5y^2 - 2y - 9}{3y^2(y+3)(y-4)}$$

Step 4   The resulting fraction cannot be reduced.

f) $t + 3 + \dfrac{1}{t-3}$

f) $t + 2 + \dfrac{1}{t-2} = \dfrac{t+2}{1} + \dfrac{1}{t-2}$ l.c.d. $= t-2$

$$= \dfrac{t+2}{1} \cdot \dfrac{t-2}{t-2} + \dfrac{1}{t-2} \cdot \dfrac{1}{1} = \dfrac{(t+2)(t-2)}{t-2} + \dfrac{1}{t-2}$$

$$= \dfrac{(t+2)(t-2) + 1}{t-2}$$

$$= \dfrac{t^2 - 4 + 1}{t-2} = \dfrac{t^2 - 3}{t-2}$$

g) $\dfrac{4a}{3a-1} + \dfrac{a+2}{a^2(a+4)}$

g) $\dfrac{3a}{2a-1} + \dfrac{a-1}{a(a+3)} + \dfrac{a}{2a^2+5a-3}$

Find the l.c.d of the fractions:

$$2a - 1 \ = \ 2a - 1$$
$$a(a+3) \ = \ a(a+3)$$
$$2a^2 + 5a - 3 \ = \ (2a-1)(a+3)$$

Therefore, the l. c. d. $= a(2a-1)(a+3).$

Now we rewrite the fractions with the l.c.d. as the common denominator and add.

$$\dfrac{3a}{2a-1} + \dfrac{a-1}{a(a+3)} + \dfrac{a}{2a^2+5a-3}$$

$$= \dfrac{3a}{2a-1} \cdot \dfrac{a(a+3)}{a(a+3)} + \dfrac{a-1}{a(a+3)} \cdot \dfrac{2a-1}{2a-1} + \dfrac{a}{2a^2+5a-3} \cdot \dfrac{a}{a}$$

$$\downarrow \qquad\qquad\qquad \downarrow \qquad\qquad\qquad \downarrow$$

$$\tfrac{a(2a-1)(a+3)}{2a-1} = a(a+3) \qquad \tfrac{a(2a-1)(a+3)}{a(a+3)} = 2a-1 \qquad \tfrac{a(2a-1)(a+3)}{2a^2+5a-3} = a$$

$$= \dfrac{3a^2(a+3)}{a(2a-1)(a+3)} + \dfrac{(a-1)(2a-1)}{a(2a-1)(a+3)} + \dfrac{a^2}{a(2a-1)(a+3)}$$

$$= \dfrac{3a^2(a+3) + (a-1)(2a-1) + a^2}{a(2a-1)(a+3)} = \dfrac{3a^3 + 9a^2 + 2a^2 - 3a + 1 + a^2}{a(2a-1)(a+3)}$$

$$= \dfrac{3a^3 + 12a^2 - 3a + 1}{a(2a-1)(a+3)}$$

Example 3:   Add.

a) $\dfrac{x}{x^2-9}+\dfrac{3}{9-x^2}$ b) $\dfrac{1}{x+1}+\dfrac{2x}{1-x^2}$

Warm Up

3.   Add

a) $\dfrac{3x}{x^2-4}+\dfrac{4}{4-x^2}$

Solutions:

a) $\dfrac{x}{x^2-9}+\dfrac{3}{9-x^2}:$

The l.c.d. of the two fractions is x^2-9.

$x^2-9=x^2-9,$

$9-x^2=-1(x^2-9)$

Therefore, $\dfrac{x}{x^2-9}+\dfrac{3}{9-x^2}=\dfrac{x}{x^2-9}+\dfrac{3}{9-x^2}\cdot\dfrac{-1}{-1}$

$=\dfrac{x}{x^2-9}+\dfrac{-3}{x^2-9}$

$=\dfrac{x-3}{x^2-9}=\dfrac{x-3}{(x-3)(x+3)}=\dfrac{1}{x+3}$

b) $\dfrac{2}{x+3}+\dfrac{x}{9-x^2}$

b) $\dfrac{1}{x+1}+\dfrac{2x}{1-x^2}:$

Find the l.c.d. of the fractions:

$x+1=1+x$, $1-x^2=(1-x)(1+x)$, l.c.d.$=(1-x)(1+x)$

$\dfrac{1}{x+1}+\dfrac{2x}{1-x^2}=\dfrac{1}{1+x}\cdot\dfrac{1-x}{1-x}+\dfrac{2x}{1-x^2}$

$=\dfrac{1-x}{1-x^2}+\dfrac{2x}{1-x^2}=\dfrac{1-x+2x}{1-x^2}$

$=\dfrac{1+x}{1-x^2}$

$=\dfrac{1+x}{(1-x)(1+x)}=\dfrac{1}{1-x}$

Answers:

2. a) $\dfrac{5}{3x}$ b) $\dfrac{4s+5r}{rs}$

c) $\dfrac{5x^2-18x+8}{x^2-16}$

d) $\dfrac{2x^2+7x-6}{(x+2)(x-2)^2}$

e) $\dfrac{2y^3-2y^2+3y+2}{y^3(y+2)(y-3)}$ f) $\dfrac{t^2-8}{t-3}$

g) $\dfrac{4a^4+16a^3+3a^2+5a-2}{a^2(a+4)(3a-1)}$

3. a) $\dfrac{3x-4}{x^2-4}$ b) $\dfrac{x-6}{x^2-9}$

C. Subtracting Rational Expressions

Recall the definition of subtraction for two fractions. For example, $\dfrac{3}{5}-\dfrac{1}{3}$ is defined to be the sum of $\dfrac{3}{5}$ and the additive inverse of $\dfrac{1}{3}$. For any two rational expressions $\dfrac{P}{Q}$ and $\dfrac{R}{S}$,

$\dfrac{P}{Q}-\dfrac{R}{S}=\dfrac{P}{Q}+\dfrac{-R}{S}$, that is the sum of $\dfrac{P}{Q}$ and the additive inverse of $\dfrac{R}{S}$.

Warm Up

4.   Subtract

a) $\dfrac{4}{q} - \dfrac{5}{q}$

b) $\dfrac{3}{5x} - \dfrac{2}{20y}$

c) $\dfrac{3}{2x(x+2)} - \dfrac{x-3}{x^3(x+4)}$

d) $\dfrac{x+5}{x-5} - \dfrac{x-10}{5-x}$

Example 4:   Subtract.

a) $\dfrac{4}{2q} - \dfrac{5}{2q}$

b) $\dfrac{3}{10x} - \dfrac{4}{15y}$

c) $\dfrac{4}{3x(x+3)} - \dfrac{x-1}{x^2(x-2)}$

d) $\dfrac{x+6}{x-3} - \dfrac{x-12}{3-x}$

e) $\dfrac{3}{t+2} + \dfrac{2}{t-2} - \dfrac{t-1}{t^2-4}$

Solutions:

a) $\dfrac{4}{2q} - \dfrac{5}{2q}$: The additive inverse of $\dfrac{5}{2q} = \dfrac{-5}{2q}$

Therefore, $\dfrac{4}{2q} - \dfrac{5}{2q} = \dfrac{4}{2q} + \dfrac{-5}{2q} = \dfrac{4+(-5)}{2q} = \dfrac{-1}{2q} = -\dfrac{1}{2q}$

b) $\dfrac{3}{10x} - \dfrac{4}{15y} = \dfrac{3}{10x} + \dfrac{-4}{15y} = \dfrac{3}{10x} \cdot \dfrac{3y}{3y} + \dfrac{-4}{15y} \cdot \dfrac{2x}{2x}$ l.c.d. $= 30\,xy$

  (↓ Subtract)   (↓ Add)

$= \dfrac{9y}{30xy} + \dfrac{-8x}{30xy} = \dfrac{9y+(-8x)}{30xy} = \dfrac{9y-8x}{30xy}$

c) $\dfrac{4}{3x(x+3)} - \dfrac{x-1}{x^2(x-2)} = \dfrac{4}{3x(x+3)} + \dfrac{-(x-1)}{x^2(x-2)}$ l.c.d. $= 3x^2(x-2)(x+3)$

  (↓ Subtract)   (↓ Add)

$= \dfrac{4}{3x(x+3)} \cdot \dfrac{x(x-2)}{x(x-2)} + \dfrac{-(x-1)}{x^2(x-2)} \cdot \dfrac{3(x+3)}{3(x+3)}$

$= \dfrac{4x(x-2)}{3x^2(x-2)(x+3)} + \dfrac{-3(x-1)(x+3)}{3x^2(x-2)(x+3)}$

$= \dfrac{4x(x-2) + [-3(x-1)(x+3)]}{3x^2(x-2)(x+3)}$

$= \dfrac{4(x^2-2x) - 3(x^2+2x-3)}{3x^2(x-2)(x+3)}$

$= \dfrac{4x^2-8x-3x^2-6x+9}{3x^2(x-2)(x+3)} = \dfrac{x^2-14x+9}{3x^2(x-2)(x+3)}$

d) $\dfrac{x+6}{x-3} - \dfrac{x-12}{3-x} = \dfrac{x+6}{x-3} + \dfrac{-(x-12)}{3-x}$

$= \dfrac{x+6}{x-3} + \dfrac{-(x-12)(-1)}{x-3}$

$= \dfrac{x+6+x-12}{x-3} = \dfrac{2x-6}{x-3}$

$= \dfrac{2(x-3)}{x-3} = 2$

e) $\dfrac{3}{t+2}+\dfrac{2}{t-2}-\dfrac{t-1}{t^2-4}=\dfrac{3}{t+2}+\dfrac{2}{t-2}+\dfrac{-(t-1)}{t^2-4}$ l.c.d. $=t^2-4$
$=(t-2)(t+2)$

$\qquad\qquad\quad\downarrow\qquad\qquad\quad\downarrow$
$\qquad\qquad$ Subtract $\qquad\quad$ Add

$\quad=\dfrac{3}{t+2}\cdot\dfrac{t-2}{t-2}+\dfrac{2}{t-2}\cdot\dfrac{t+2}{t+2}+\dfrac{-(t-1)}{t^2-4}$

$\quad=\dfrac{3(t-2)}{(t+2)(t-2)}+\dfrac{2(t+2)}{(t-2)(t+2)}+\dfrac{1-t}{t^2-4}$

$\quad=\dfrac{3t-6}{t^2-4}+\dfrac{2t+4}{t^2-4}+\dfrac{1-t}{t^2-4}$

$\quad=\dfrac{3t-6+2t+4+1-t}{t^2-4}=\dfrac{4t-1}{t^2-4}$

EXERCISE 5.5

In exercise 1–26, perform the indicated operations. Write your answer in lowest terms.

1. $\dfrac{2}{x}+\dfrac{3}{x}$ $\qquad$ **2.** $\dfrac{4}{x}-\dfrac{7}{x}$ $\qquad$ **3.** $\dfrac{3}{x^2}+\dfrac{4x+1}{x^2}$

4. $\dfrac{2}{y+1}+\dfrac{2y}{y+1}$ $\qquad$ **5.** $\dfrac{x^2}{x^3-1}-\dfrac{1}{x^3-1}$ $\qquad$ **6.** $\dfrac{t^2+4t}{t+2}+\dfrac{4}{t+2}$

7. $\dfrac{4x}{(x-3)^2}-\dfrac{12}{(x-3)^2}$ $\qquad$ **8.** $\dfrac{4x}{(x-3)^2}-\dfrac{(9-x)(x-1)}{(x-3)^2}$

9. $\dfrac{x}{8}+\dfrac{5}{12}$ $\qquad$ **10.** $\dfrac{4}{3}-\dfrac{2}{x}$ $\qquad$ **11.** $\dfrac{x-3}{x}+\dfrac{2x-1}{2x}$

12. $\dfrac{1}{y}+\dfrac{3}{y^2}$ $\qquad$ **13.** $\dfrac{4}{x-2}-\dfrac{5}{2-x}$ $\qquad$ **14.** $\dfrac{1}{x-y}-\dfrac{2y}{x^2-y^2}$

15. $\dfrac{3a}{9a^2-4b^2}-\dfrac{1}{3a+2b}$

Answers:

1. _____

2. _____

3. _____

4. _____

5. _____

6. _____

7. _____

8. _____

9. _____

10. _____

11. _____

12. _____

13. _____

14. _____

15. _____

16. _____

17. _____

18. _____

19. _____

20. _____

21. _____

22. _____

23. _____

24. _____

25. _____

26. _____

16. $\left(\dfrac{r+s}{r-s}\right)^2 + 1$

17. $\dfrac{2}{z-4} - \dfrac{z+12}{z^2-16}$

18. $2x+5 - \dfrac{x^2+2x-15}{x-3}$

19. $\dfrac{2-t}{9t+6} + \dfrac{t-2}{6t+4}$

20. $\dfrac{4x}{x^2+2x-3} - \dfrac{5x}{x^2+5x+6}$

21. $\dfrac{m}{m-1} - \dfrac{1}{m} + 1$

22. $\dfrac{16}{r^2 s} + \dfrac{1}{rs} - \dfrac{6}{rs^2}$

23. $\dfrac{2x+3}{5x} - \dfrac{2x-1}{10x} + \dfrac{4}{x}$

24. $\dfrac{5}{a+1} - \dfrac{1}{a^2-1} + \dfrac{2}{a-1}$

25. $\dfrac{16x-x^2}{x^2-4} + \dfrac{2x+3}{2-x} + \dfrac{3x-2}{x+2}$

26. $\dfrac{1}{x+1} - \left(\dfrac{1}{x-1} - \dfrac{1}{x^2-1}\right)$

5.6   COMPLEX FRACTIONS

A rational expression with fractions in the numerator or the denominator is called a **complex fraction.**

For example: $\dfrac{\dfrac{3}{5}}{\dfrac{4}{7}}$, $\dfrac{3+\dfrac{4}{5}}{1\dfrac{2}{3}-\dfrac{5}{2}}$, and $\dfrac{2-\dfrac{3}{x}}{\dfrac{3}{x^2}+\dfrac{5}{x}}$ are all complex fractions.

After studying this section, we will be able to simplify complex fractions using two different methods.

METHOD 1: Simplification of Complex Fractions:

Step 1	Find the l.c.d. of all fractions appearing in numerator and denominator.
Step 2	Multiply the numerator and the denominator by the l.c.d. Simplify the numerator and denominator.
Step 3	Write in lowest terms.

Example 1: Simplify: **a)** $\dfrac{1\frac{2}{7}}{\frac{6}{11}}$ **b)** $\dfrac{\frac{xy}{z^2}}{\frac{x^3}{y^2z}}$ **c)** $\dfrac{x-\frac{1}{x}}{2+\frac{1}{x}}$

1. Simplify

   a) $\dfrac{2\frac{1}{5}}{\frac{3}{10}}$

Solutions:

a) $\dfrac{1\frac{2}{7}}{\frac{6}{11}} = \dfrac{\frac{9}{7}}{\frac{6}{11}}$

Step 1 The l.c.d. of the fractions $\dfrac{9}{7}$ and $\dfrac{6}{11}$ is 77.

Step 2 Multiply the numerator and the denominator by l.c.d

$$\dfrac{\frac{9}{7}}{\frac{6}{11}} = \dfrac{\left(\frac{9}{7}\right)(77)}{\left(\frac{6}{11}\right)(77)} = \dfrac{9\cdot 11}{7\cdot 6} = \dfrac{99}{42}$$

Step 3 Express in lowest terms $\dfrac{99}{42} = \dfrac{3\cdot 33}{2\cdot 3\cdot 7} = \dfrac{33}{14}$

b) $\dfrac{\frac{xy}{z^2}}{\frac{x^3}{y^2z}}$ The l.c.d of $\dfrac{xy}{z^2}$ and $\dfrac{x^3}{y^2z}$ is y^2z^2.

Multiply the numerator and the denominator by the l.c.d

$$\dfrac{\frac{xy}{z^2}}{\frac{x^3}{y^2z}} = \dfrac{\left(\frac{xy}{z^2}\right)(y^2z^2)}{\frac{x^3}{y^2z}(y^2z^2)} = \dfrac{xy^3}{x^3z} = \dfrac{y^3}{x^2z}$$

b) $\dfrac{\frac{z^2}{xy}}{\frac{y^2z}{x^3y}}$

c) $\dfrac{x-\frac{1}{x}}{2+\frac{1}{x}}$: The l.c.d. of the fractions in the numerator and denominator is x.

c) $\dfrac{x^2-\frac{1}{x}}{3+\frac{1}{x}}$

Multiply the numerator and the denominator by the l.c.d.

$$\dfrac{x-\frac{1}{x}}{2+\frac{1}{x}} = \dfrac{\left(x-\frac{1}{x}\right)x}{\left(2+\frac{1}{x}\right)x} = \dfrac{x\cdot x-\frac{1}{x}\cdot x}{2\cdot x+\frac{1}{x}\cdot x} = \dfrac{x^2-1}{2x+1}$$

METHOD 2:   Simplification of Complex Fractions

Step 1	Simplify the numerator.
Step 2	Simplify the denominator.
Step 3	Divide the numerator by the denominator.

For Example: $\dfrac{\dfrac{4}{7}}{\dfrac{2}{3}} = \dfrac{4}{7} \div \dfrac{2}{3} = \dfrac{4}{7} \cdot \dfrac{3}{2}$

Simplify and write in lowest terms. $\dfrac{4}{7} \cdot \dfrac{3}{2} = \dfrac{12}{14} = \dfrac{6}{7}$

Now we simplify expressions in example 1 by method 2.

Warm Up

2. Simplify the complex fractions

   a) $\dfrac{2\dfrac{1}{5}}{\dfrac{3}{10}}$

   b) $\dfrac{\dfrac{z^2}{xy}}{\dfrac{y^2 z}{x^3 y}}$

Example 2:   Simplify the complex fractions.

a) $\dfrac{1\dfrac{2}{7}}{\dfrac{6}{11}}$ b) $\dfrac{\dfrac{xy}{z^2}}{\dfrac{x^3}{y^2 z}}$ c) $\dfrac{x - \dfrac{1}{x}}{2 + \dfrac{1}{x}}$

Solutions:

a) $\dfrac{1\dfrac{2}{7}}{\dfrac{6}{11}} = \dfrac{\dfrac{9}{7}}{\dfrac{6}{11}}$

   Steps 1   Not needed.

   Step 2   Not needed.

   Step 3 $\dfrac{\dfrac{9}{7}}{\dfrac{6}{11}} = \dfrac{9}{7} \div \dfrac{6}{11}$ Divide numerator by denominator

           $= \dfrac{9}{7} \cdot \dfrac{11}{6} = \dfrac{9 \cdot 11}{7 \cdot 6} = \dfrac{3 \cdot 3 \cdot 11}{7 \cdot 2 \cdot 3} = \dfrac{33}{14}$ Compare with example 1*a*

b) $\dfrac{\dfrac{xy}{z^2}}{\dfrac{x^3}{y^2 z}} = \dfrac{xy}{z^2} \div \dfrac{x^3}{y^2 z} = \dfrac{xy}{z^2} \cdot \dfrac{y^2 z}{x^3} = \dfrac{xy^3 z}{z^2 x^3} = \dfrac{y^3}{zx^2}$ Compare with example 1*b*

c)
$$\dfrac{x - \dfrac{1}{x}}{2 + \dfrac{1}{x}}$$

c)
$$\dfrac{x^2 - \dfrac{1}{x}}{3 + \dfrac{1}{x}}$$

Step 1   Simplify the numerator,

$$x - \frac{1}{x} = x \cdot \frac{x}{x} - \frac{1}{x} = \frac{x^2}{x} - \frac{1}{x} = \frac{x^2 - 1}{x}$$

Step 2   Simplify the denominator,

$$2 + \frac{1}{x} = 2 \cdot \frac{x}{x} + \frac{1}{x} = \frac{2x}{x} + \frac{1}{x} = \frac{2x + 1}{x}$$

Step 3   Divide the numerator by the denominator.

$$\frac{x - \dfrac{1}{x}}{2 + \dfrac{1}{x}} = \frac{x^2 - 1}{x} \div \frac{2x + 1}{x} = \frac{x^2 - 1}{x} \cdot \frac{x}{2x + 1}$$

$$= \frac{(x^2 - 1)x}{x(2x + 1)} = \frac{x^2 - 1}{2x + 1}$$

Example 3:   Simplify the following complex fraction by both methods.

$$\frac{\dfrac{x}{x - y} - \dfrac{y}{x + y}}{x^2 - y^2}$$

3.   Simplify the following expression by both methods:

$$\frac{\dfrac{a}{a + b} + \dfrac{b}{a - b}}{\dfrac{1}{a - b} - \dfrac{1}{a + b}}$$

Solution:

Method #1

Step 1   l.c.d. of the numerator and the denominator is
$$(x - y)(x + y) = x^2 - y^2$$

Step 2   Multiply the numerator and the denominator by the l.c.d.

$$\frac{\dfrac{x}{x-y} - \dfrac{y}{x+y}}{\left(x^2 - y^2\right)} = \frac{\left(\dfrac{x}{x-y} - \dfrac{y}{x+y}\right)\left(x^2 - y^2\right)}{\left(x^2 - y^2\right)\left(x^2 - y^2\right)}$$

$$= \frac{\dfrac{x}{x - y} \cdot \left(x^2 - y^2\right) - \dfrac{y}{x + y} \cdot \left(x^2 - y^2\right)}{\left(x^2 - y^2\right)^2}$$

$$= \frac{x(x + y) - y(x - y)}{\left(x^2 - y^2\right)^2}$$

$$= \frac{x^2 + xy - yx + y^2}{\left(x^2 - y^2\right)^2} = \frac{x^2 + y^2}{\left(x^2 - y^2\right)^2}$$

Step 3   Not Needed.

Warm Up

Method #2

Step 1   Simplify the numerator.

$$\frac{x}{x-y} - \frac{y}{x+y} = \frac{x}{x-y} \cdot \frac{x+y}{x+y} - \frac{y}{x+y} \cdot \frac{x-y}{x-y}$$

$$= \frac{x(x+y)}{(x-y)(x+y)} - \frac{y(x-y)}{(x+y)(x-y)}$$

$$= \frac{x(x+y) - y(x-y)}{x^2 - y^2}$$

$$= \frac{x^2 + xy - yx + y^2}{x^2 - y^2} = \frac{x^2 + y^2}{x^2 - y^2}$$

Step 2   Simplify the denominator. Not needed.

Step 3   Divide the numerator by the denominator.

$$\frac{\dfrac{x}{x-y} - \dfrac{y}{x+y}}{x^2 - y^2} = \frac{\dfrac{x^2 + y^2}{x^2 - y^2}}{x^2 - y^2}$$

$$= \frac{x^2 + y^2}{x^2 - y^2} \div \left(x^2 - y^2\right)$$

$$= \frac{x^2 + y^2}{x^2 - y^2} \cdot \frac{1}{x^2 - y^2} = \frac{x^2 + y^2}{(x^2 - y^2)^2}$$

Answers:

1. a) $\dfrac{22}{3}$ b) $\dfrac{x^2 z}{y^2}$ c) $\dfrac{x^3 - 1}{3x + 1}$

2. a) $\dfrac{22}{3}$ b) $\dfrac{x^2 z}{y^2}$ c) $\dfrac{x^3 - 1}{3x + 1}$

3. $\dfrac{a^2 + b^2}{2b}$

EXERCISE 5.6

Answers:

1. _____

2. _____

3. _____

4. _____

5. _____

6. _____

7. _____

8. _____

9. _____

In exercises 1–3, use method 1 to simplify the complex fractions.

1. $\dfrac{\dfrac{1}{5}}{\dfrac{2}{9}}$

2. $\dfrac{\dfrac{1}{4} - \dfrac{1}{5}}{\dfrac{3}{6}}$

3. $\dfrac{\dfrac{2}{3} + \dfrac{4}{5}}{\dfrac{1}{3}}$

In exercises 4–5, use method 2 to simplify the complex fractions.

4. $\dfrac{\dfrac{5}{6}}{-\dfrac{5}{4}}$

5. $\dfrac{\dfrac{1}{6} - \dfrac{2}{7}}{\dfrac{1}{7}}$

In exercises 6–20, use any method to simplify the complex fractions.

6. $\dfrac{\dfrac{p^2}{q}}{5\dfrac{p}{q^2}}$

7. $\dfrac{\dfrac{t+3}{t}}{\dfrac{t-4}{2}}$

8. $\dfrac{\dfrac{6}{x}}{\dfrac{1+x}{4x^5}}$

9. $\dfrac{\dfrac{1}{x} - x}{\dfrac{x^2 - 1}{3}}$

10. $\dfrac{\dfrac{y+4}{y}}{\dfrac{1}{y}+\dfrac{1}{5}}$

11. $\dfrac{\dfrac{1}{a}-\dfrac{1}{b}}{\dfrac{a}{b}-\dfrac{b}{a}}$

10. _____

11. _____

12. $\dfrac{t-1-\dfrac{2}{t}}{\dfrac{2t^2}{3}}$

13. $\dfrac{1-a-\dfrac{2}{a}}{\dfrac{6}{a^2}+\dfrac{1}{a}-1}$

12. _____

13. _____

14. $\dfrac{x^2-16}{\dfrac{1}{4}-\dfrac{1}{x}}$

15. $\dfrac{2+\dfrac{1}{x}}{1-\dfrac{2}{x}}$

14. _____

15. _____

16. $\dfrac{\dfrac{a}{b}+\dfrac{1}{a}}{\dfrac{a}{b}-\dfrac{1}{a}}$

17. $\dfrac{\dfrac{1}{x^2-4}+\dfrac{1}{x-2}}{3-\dfrac{1}{x-2}}$

16. _____

17. _____

18. $t+\dfrac{t}{1-\dfrac{t+1}{t}}$

19. $\dfrac{\dfrac{1}{m^2-1}+\dfrac{2}{m^2+4m+3}}{\dfrac{2}{m^2+2m-3}+\dfrac{1}{m+3}}$

18. _____

19. _____

20. $\dfrac{2a}{a-\dfrac{a}{3-\dfrac{1}{2}}}$

20. _____

5.7   EQUATIONS CONTAINING RATIONAL EXPRESSIONS

The statements $\dfrac{3}{x-1} + \dfrac{2x}{x+1} = 2,$ or $\dfrac{2}{y^2-9} + \dfrac{1}{y+3} = \dfrac{y}{y-3}$ are examples of equations containing rational expressions.

Upon completion of this section we will be able to:

    A.   Solve equations containing rational expressions.

    B.   Solve for a particular Unknown

A. Solving Equations containing Rational Expressions

In order to solve an equation containing rational expressions, our first aim is to clear the equation of all fractions. The best way to do this is to multiply both sides of the equation by the l.c.d. of the rational expressions appearing in the equation.

Steps to solve an equation involving rational expressions.

Step 1	Find the l.c.d. of all rational expressions appearing in the equation.
Step 2	Multiply both sides of the equation by the l.c.d. and simplify until the resulting equation is without fractions.
Step 3	Solve the resulting equation.
Step 4	Verify the answer(s) obtained in step 3 by substituting the solution in the original equation. Reject any solution that makes any denominator zero.

Warm Up

1. $\dfrac{4}{x-2} + \dfrac{3x}{x+2} = 3$

Example 1:   Solve $\dfrac{3}{x-1} + \dfrac{2x}{x+1} = 2.$

Solution:

Step 1   The l.c.d of the rational terms in the given equation is: $(x-1)(x+1)$.

Step 2 $\left(\dfrac{3}{x-1} + \dfrac{2x}{x+1}\right)(x-1)(x+1) = 2(x-1)(x+1)$

$\dfrac{3(x-1)(x+1)}{x-1} + \dfrac{2x(x-1)(x+1)}{x+1} = 2(x-1)(x+1)$

$3(x+1) + 2x(x-1) = 2(x-1)(x+1)$

Step 3 $3x + 3 + 2x^2 - 2x = 2(x^2 - 1)$

$2x^2 + x + 3 = 2x^2 - 2$

$-2x^2 + 2x^2 + x = -2 - 3$

$x = -5$

Thus $x = -5$ is possibly a solution of the equation.

Step 4 Checking: Substitute -5 for x in the original equation.

$$\frac{3}{x-1} + \frac{2x}{x+1} = 2$$

$$\frac{3}{-5-1} + \frac{2(-5)}{-5+1} = 2 \longrightarrow -\frac{3}{6} + \frac{-10}{-4} = 2$$

$$\longrightarrow -\frac{1}{2} + \frac{5}{2} = 2 \longrightarrow 2 = 2 \quad \text{True}$$

Thus $x = 2$ is a solution.

Example 2: Solve the following equations.

a) $2 - \dfrac{4}{x} = \dfrac{x+1}{5}$ b) $-\dfrac{2a}{a+1} = 1 + \dfrac{2}{a+1}$

c) $\dfrac{2}{t^2-1} - \dfrac{1}{2} = \dfrac{1}{t-1}$

Warm Up

2. Solve the following equations.

a) $\dfrac{2a}{a-3} = \dfrac{3}{a-3} - 1$

Solutions:

a) $2 - \dfrac{4}{x} = \dfrac{x+1}{5}$

Step 1 The l.c.d. of rational expressions is $5x$.

Step 2 $\left(2 - \dfrac{4}{x}\right)5x = \left(\dfrac{x+1}{5}\right)5x$ Multiply both sides by the l.c.d.

$$10x - \left(\dfrac{4}{x}\right)5x = (x+1)x \longrightarrow 10x - 20 = x^2 + x$$

Step 3 $-x^2 + 10x - 20 = x$

$-x^2 + 10x - 20 - x = 0$

$\longrightarrow -x^2 + 9x - 20 = 0$ Multiply both sides by -1

$\longrightarrow x^2 - 9x + 20 = 0$ Factor

$\longrightarrow (x-4)(x-5) = 0$

$\longrightarrow x - 4 = 0 \ \text{ or } \ x - 5 = 0$

$\longrightarrow x = 4 \ \text{ or } \ x = 5 \ \text{ are the solutions.}$

Thus the possible solutions are $x = 4$ and $x = 5$.

Step 4 Check the solutions:

$x = 4$: Substitute 4 for x in the original equation.

$$2 - \frac{4}{4} = \frac{4+1}{5} \longrightarrow 1 = 1 \quad \text{True}$$

$x = 5$: Substitute 5 for x in the original equation.

$$2 - \frac{4}{5} = \frac{5+1}{5} \longrightarrow \frac{6}{5} = \frac{6}{5} \quad \text{True}$$

Thus $x = 4$ and $x = 5$ are solutions.

Warm Up

b) $3 - \dfrac{4}{x} = \dfrac{x}{2}$

b)　　　$-\dfrac{2a}{a+1} = 1 + \dfrac{2}{a+1}$

Step 1　The l.c.d. of the rational expressions is $a+1$.

Step 2　$-\dfrac{2a}{a+1}(a+1) = \left(1 + \dfrac{2}{a+1}\right)(a+1)$　Multiply both sides by the l.c.d.

$-2a = (a+1) + \left(\dfrac{2}{a+1}\right)(a+1) \longrightarrow -2a = a+1+2$

Step 3　$-2a = a+3 \longrightarrow -2a - a = 3 \longrightarrow -3a = 3$

$\longrightarrow a = \dfrac{3}{-3} = -1$

Step 4　Check the solutions: Substitute -1 for a in the original equation.

$$-\dfrac{2a}{a+1} = 1 + \dfrac{2}{a+1}$$
$$\dfrac{-2(-1)}{-1+1} = 1 + \dfrac{2}{-1+1}$$

Notice that upon substitution, $a = -1$ makes the denominator zero. Therefore, -1 is an extraneous solution. Since -1 was the only candidate for a solution, the given equation has *no solution*.

c) $\dfrac{2}{a+1} + \dfrac{1}{a-1} = 1$

c)　　　$\dfrac{2}{t^2-1} - \dfrac{1}{2} = \dfrac{1}{t-1}$

Step 1　The l.c.d. of the rational expressions is $2(t^2-1)$

Step 2　$\left(\dfrac{2}{t^2-1} - \dfrac{1}{2}\right)[2(t^2-1)] = \left(\dfrac{1}{t-1}\right)[2(t^2-1)]$　Multiply both sides by l.c.d.

$\left(\dfrac{2}{t^2-1}\right)[2(t^2-1)] - \dfrac{1}{2}[2(t^2-1)] = \dfrac{2(t^2-1)}{t-1}$

$4 - (t^2-1) = 2(t+1) \longrightarrow 5 - t^2 = 2t+2$

$-t^2 - 2t + 3 = 0 \longrightarrow t^2 + 2t - 3 = 0$

Step 3　$t^2 + 2t - 3 = 0 \longrightarrow (t-1)(t+3) = 0$　Factor

$\longrightarrow t-1 = 0 \text{ or } t+3 = 0$

$\longrightarrow t = 1 \text{ or } t = -3$

Step 4　Checking the solutions:

$t = 1$:　Substituting 1 for t makes the denominator 0 on both sides.

Therefore, $t = 1$ is an **extraneous solution.**

296

$t = -3$: Substitute -3 for t in the original equation.

$$\frac{2}{(-3)^2 - 1} - \frac{1}{2} = \frac{1}{-3 - 1} \quad \longrightarrow \quad \frac{2}{9 - 1} - \frac{1}{2} = \frac{1}{-4}$$

$$\frac{2}{8} - \frac{1}{2} = -\frac{1}{4} \quad \longrightarrow \quad \frac{2 - 4}{8} = -\frac{1}{4}$$

$$-\frac{2}{8} = -\frac{1}{4} \quad \longrightarrow \quad -\frac{1}{4} = -\frac{1}{4} \quad \text{True}$$

Thus $t = -3$ is the only solution of the equation.

Warm Up

Answers:

1. 10   2. a) 2 b) 2, 4 c) 0, 3

B. Solving for a Particular Unknown

Example 3: Solve the following equation for b. $\dfrac{2}{c} = \dfrac{1}{a} + \dfrac{1}{b}$

Solution:

The l.c.d. of the rational expressions is **abc**.

Multiply both sides of the formula by abc.

$$\left(\frac{2}{c}\right)abc = \left(\frac{1}{a} + \frac{1}{b}\right)abc$$

$$\frac{2abc}{c} = \frac{abc}{a} + \frac{abc}{b} \quad \longrightarrow \quad 2ab = bc + ac$$

$2ab - bc = ac$ Collect all terms containing **b** on one side.

$(2a - c)b = ac$ Factor out b

$b = \dfrac{ac}{2a - c}$ Solve for b

Example 4: Solve for F: $C = \dfrac{5}{9}(F - 32)$.

Solution:

$$9C = 9\frac{5}{9}(F - 32) \quad \longrightarrow \quad 9C = 5(F - 32)$$

$$= 5F - 160$$

$$9C + 160 = 5F \quad \text{or} \quad 5F = 9C + 160 \quad \longrightarrow \quad F = \frac{9}{5}C + 32$$

Warm Up

3. Solve the equation for b.
$$\frac{3}{c} = \frac{1}{2a} + \frac{1}{b}$$

4. Solve for F:
$$K = \frac{5}{9}(F - 32) + 273$$

Answers:

3. $b = \dfrac{2ac}{6a - c}$ 4. $F = (k - 273)\dfrac{9}{5} + 32$

EXERCISE 5.7

Solve the equations in exercises 1–15, and check your answers.

1. $\dfrac{1}{4} + \dfrac{9}{x} = 1$

2. $\dfrac{2}{y} + \dfrac{1}{2} = \dfrac{7}{2y}$

3. $\dfrac{p}{p + 3} = \dfrac{3}{5}$

4. $\dfrac{3}{t + 2} - \dfrac{2}{t^2 - 4} = \dfrac{2}{t - 2}$

Answers:

1. _____

2. _____

3. _____

4. _____

5. _____

6. _____

7. _____

8. _____

9. _____

10. _____

11. _____

12. _____

13. _____

14. _____

15. _____

16. _____

17. _____

18. _____

5. $\dfrac{x+4}{9} = \dfrac{2+5x}{27}$

6. $\dfrac{t-5}{3} = \dfrac{7}{5} - \dfrac{t+2}{5}$

7. $\dfrac{2}{x-1} + \dfrac{x-2}{3} = \dfrac{4}{x-1}$

8. $\dfrac{y+4}{y+7} - \dfrac{3}{8} = \dfrac{y}{y+3}$

9. $\dfrac{4}{t} - \dfrac{1}{t+3} = \dfrac{3t+2}{t^2+2t-3}$

10. $\dfrac{5}{a-2} + \dfrac{10}{a+2} = 7$

11. $\dfrac{x}{x-2} + 4 = \dfrac{2}{x-2}$

12. $\dfrac{t-1}{t} - \dfrac{t+1}{t} = 0$

13. $\dfrac{a-3}{a-1} = \dfrac{2a-4}{a-1}$

14. $\dfrac{2}{x-3} - \dfrac{3}{x+3} = \dfrac{12}{x^2-9}$

15. $\dfrac{x-4}{x-3} + \dfrac{x-2}{x-3} = x - 3$

In exercises 16–18, solve for the specified variable.

16. $T = \dfrac{VP}{k}$; for P 17. $I = \dfrac{E}{R+r}$; for R 18. $\dfrac{3}{r} = \dfrac{1}{p} + \dfrac{1}{q}$; for p

5.8   APPLICATIONS OF RATIONAL EXPRESSIONS

Many applications, such as shared-work problems, distance-speed problems, and several other types of problems involving equations containing rational expressions. We shall discuss in this section how to convert these types of problems into mathematical models.

Upon completion of this section we will be able to solve more application problems.

A.   Application problems involving unknown numbers

B.   Application problems involving distances

C.   Application problems involving work

D.   Application problems involving variation

Recall the techniques of solving application problems discussed in chapter 2 on linear equations.

A. Application Problems Involving Numbers

Example 1:   If one fourth of a number is added to one fifth of the same number, the result is 18. Find the number.

Solution:

Let the required number be x.

Then $\dfrac{1}{4}x + \dfrac{1}{5}x = 18$ or $\dfrac{x}{4} + \dfrac{x}{5} = 18$

The l.c.d. of all fractions is **20.**

$$\frac{x}{4}\cdot\frac{5}{5} + \frac{x}{5}\cdot\frac{4}{4} = 18 \longrightarrow \frac{5x+4x}{20} = 18$$

$$\frac{9x}{20} = 18 \longrightarrow 9x = (18)(20) = 360$$

Therefore, $x = \dfrac{360}{9} = 40.$ Check: $\dfrac{1}{4}(\mathbf{40}) + \dfrac{1}{5}(\mathbf{40}) = 18.$

Example 2:   Three times a number is subtracted from four times its reciprocal. The result is 11. Find the number.

Solution:

Let the number be x. Then from the given condition we get:

$4\left(\dfrac{1}{x}\right) - 3x = 11$ or $\dfrac{4}{x} - 3x = 11$.   The l.c.d. $= x$

$$\left(\frac{4}{x} - 3x\right)x = 11x$$

$$\frac{4}{x}\cdot x - 3x^2 = 11x \longrightarrow 4 - 3x^2 = 11x$$

$$0 = 3x^2 + 11x - 4 \quad \text{or} \quad 3x^2 + 11x - 4 = 0$$

$(x+4)(3x-1) = 0 \longrightarrow x + 4 = 0$ or $3x - 1 = 0$

$$x = -4 \quad \text{or} \quad x = \frac{1}{3}$$

Check your solution for:

$x = -4:$ $\dfrac{4}{x} - 3x = 11 \longrightarrow \dfrac{4}{-4} - 3(-4) = 11$

$\longrightarrow -1 + 12 = 11$ True

$x = \dfrac{1}{3}:$ $\dfrac{4}{x} - 3x = 11 \longrightarrow \dfrac{4}{\frac{1}{3}} - 3\left(\dfrac{1}{3}\right) = 11$

$\longrightarrow 12 - 1 = 11$ True

Therefore the number is -4 or $\dfrac{1}{3}$.

Warm Up

1. If two-thirds of a number is added to one-half of the same number, the result is seven.

2. Three times the reciprocal of a certain number subtracted from two times that number is five.

Answers:

1. 6   2. 3 and $-\dfrac{1}{2}$

B. Application Problems Involving Distance

Warm Up

Warm Up

3. A boat moving downstream with the current travels 250 miles in the same time it can travel 200 miles against the current. If the current is 5 miles per hour, what is the speed of the boat in still water?

Example 3: An airplane flying against the wind travels 175 miles in the same time that it can travel 200 miles with the wind. If the wind speed is 10 miles per hour, what is the speed of the airplane in still air.

Solution:

Let the speed of the airplane in still air $= x$ miles per hour

Wind speed $= 10$ miles per hour

Formula for the distance traveled: **Distance = Speed · Time**

Flight	Speed x Time = Distance
With Wind	$(x + 10) \cdot t = 200$
Against Wind	$(x - 10) \cdot t = 175$

Therefore, while flying with wind: $\quad (x + 10)t = 200.$ $\qquad$ (1)

While flying against wind: $\qquad (x - 10)t = 175.$ $\qquad$ (2)

From equation (1): $\qquad t = \dfrac{200}{x + 10}$ $\qquad$ Solve for t

From equation (2): $\qquad t = \dfrac{175}{x - 10}$ $\qquad$ Solve for t

Equating the two values of t, we get: $\quad \dfrac{200}{x + 10} = \dfrac{175}{x - 10}.$ $\qquad$ (3)

We shall solve equation (3) for x. It is an equation containing rational expressions.

The l.c.d. of the fractions is $(x + 10)(x - 10)$.

Multiply both sides of (3) by $(x + 10)(x - 10)$ and simplify.

$$\frac{200}{x + 10}(x - 10)(x + 10) = \frac{175}{x - 10}(x - 10)(x + 10)$$

$$200(x - 10) = 175(x + 10) \longrightarrow 200x - 2000 = 175x + 1750$$

$$\longrightarrow -175x + 200x = 1750 + 2000$$

$$\longrightarrow 25x = 3750 \longrightarrow x = 150$$

Therefore, the speed of the airplane in still air is 150 miles per hour.

Answers:

3. 45 miles per hour

C. Application Problems Involving Work

The key to such problems is to *express the rate of work per unit time,* where the unit of time can be an hour, a day, a week, or something else.

For example, if a job can be completed in *n* days, then the rate at which the work is done equals "nth part of the job" per day.

Example 4:

A drain can empty a swimming pool in 4 days. A second drain can empty this pool in 2 days. In how much time will the two drains together empty the pool?

4. John can do a certain job in 4 hours. Peter can do the same job in 6 hours. How long does it take if both of them to do the job together?

Solution:

Find the rate of work for each drain and use the formula:

rate x time = work done.

Suppose the two drains together empty the pool in x days.

drain	time alone	rate	· time	= work done
First	4 days	$\frac{1}{4}$	x	$\frac{x}{4}$
Second	2 days	$\frac{1}{2}$	x	$\frac{x}{2}$

Now,

work done by first drain	+	Work done by second drain	= 1 (= whole work)
$\frac{x}{4}$	+	$\frac{x}{2}$	= 1

We solve the equation: $\dfrac{x}{4} + \dfrac{x}{2} = 1$.

The l.c.d. is 4. Multiply both sides of the equation by 4.

$$\left(\frac{x}{4}+\frac{x}{2}\right)(4) = 1\cdot 4 \longrightarrow \frac{x}{4}\cdot 4 + \frac{x}{2}\cdot 4 = 4 \longrightarrow x+2x=4$$

$$3x = 4 \longrightarrow x = \frac{4}{3}$$

Therefore, the two drains empty the pool together in $\dfrac{4}{3}$ days or 1 day and 8 hours.

Example 5:

A mechanic helped by his assistant can repair an engine in 4 hours. Working alone, the mechanic would have repaired the engine in 6 hours. How long will it take the assistant to repair the engine all by himself ?

5. A train operating with one engine covers a distance in 4 hours. If a second engine is added to the same train, it covers the same distance in 2.5 hours. How long will it take to cover the same distance if the second engine was to do it alone?

Solution:

Suppose that the assistant can repair the engine in x hours.

REPAIR	TIME	RATE
Mechanic	6 hours	1 / 6
Assistant	x hours	1 / x
Together	4 hours	1 / 4

work done by mechanic	+	Work done by assistant	=	Work done by two together
↓		↓		↓
$\dfrac{1}{6}$	+	$\dfrac{1}{x}$	=	$\dfrac{1}{4}$

Therefore, we must solve the equation: $\dfrac{1}{6} + \dfrac{1}{x} = \dfrac{1}{4}$, l.c.d. $= \mathbf{12x}$

$$\mathbf{12x}\left(\frac{1}{6} + \frac{1}{x}\right) = \mathbf{12x}\left(\frac{1}{4}\right) \longrightarrow 2x + 12 = 3x \longrightarrow 12 = x \text{ or } x = 12$$

Therefore, the assistant will take 12 hours to repair the engine working alone.

D. Applications Involving Variation

If we say that y varies directly as x, then it means that the ratio $\dfrac{y}{x}$ is a constant. If this constant

is k, we get $\dfrac{y}{x} = k$. Therefore, y *varies directly* as x results in the equation $y = kx$, where k

is the *constant of variation*. The constant of variation can be different from case to case. For example, John can walk *twice* as fast as Michael; Thomas can walk *three-halves times as fast as Michael.*

$$\frac{\text{Speed of John}}{\text{Speed of Michael}} = \frac{2x}{1x} = 2 \, (\text{constant})$$

$$\frac{\text{Speed of Thomas}}{\text{Speed of Michael}} = \frac{3/2x}{1x} = \frac{3}{2} = 1.5 \, (\text{constant})$$

A few more examples of variation:

VARIATION	RATIO	EQUATION
y varies directly as x	$\dfrac{y}{x}$	$y = kx$
y varies directly as square of x	y / x^2	$y = kx^2$
y varies inversely as x	$y / (\dfrac{1}{x})$	$y = \dfrac{k}{x}$
y varies inversely as square of x	$y / (\dfrac{1}{x^2})$	$y = \dfrac{k}{x^2}$

Warm Up

6. Suppose A varies directly as B. Given that $A = 5$ when $B = 20$. Find B, when A is 12.

Example 6: Suppose A varies directly as B. Given that $A = 4$ when B is 10, find B when A is 18.

Solution:

The relationship A varies *directly* as B, results in an equation $A = kB$ where k is the constant of variation. The given condition "$A = 4$ when $B = 10$" determines the constant of variation. Substitute $A = 4$ and $B = 10$ in $A = kB$.

$$4 = 10k \quad \text{or} \quad k = \frac{4}{10} = \frac{2}{5}.$$

Therefore, the equation of variation becomes $A = \frac{2}{5}B$.

Now to find the value of B, when $A = 18$, substitute 18 for A in the equation $A = \frac{2}{5}B$.

$$18 = \frac{2}{5}B \longrightarrow B = \frac{90}{2} = 45$$

Warm Up

6. (contd)

Example 7: The intensity of illumination I from a source of light varies inversely as the square of the distance d from the source. If the intensity is 150 candle power when the source is 4 feet away, find:

  a)   the intensity when the source is 5 feet away.

  b)   the distance of the source of light in order for the intensity to be 24 candle power.

7. The displacement of a car varies inversely with the force acting on the car. If the displacement of the car is 120 miles when the force is 40 lbs per hour,

Solutions:

I varies inversely as square of d. The resulting equation is $I = \dfrac{k}{d^2}$, where k is a constant of variation. It is given that $I = 150$ when $d = 4$.

a) Find the distance when the force of the car is one-half the initial force.

Substituting these values in $I = \dfrac{k}{d^2}$, we get $150 = \dfrac{k}{4^2}$

$$k = 150 \cdot (16) = 2400$$

Therefore, the equation that expresses variation for the problem is

$$I = \frac{2400}{d^2}. \qquad (1)$$

a)   To find the intensity when the source is 5 feet away, we substitute 5 for d in (1).

$$I = \frac{2400}{5^2} \longrightarrow I = \frac{2400}{25} = \mathbf{96}$$

b) Find the force when the displacement is doubled.

b)   To find the distance from the light source to create 24 candle power light we   substitute 24 for I in (1).

$$24 = \frac{2400}{d^2} \longrightarrow d^2 = \frac{2400}{24}$$
$$\longrightarrow d^2 = 100$$
$$\longrightarrow d = 10 \quad \text{or} \quad d = -10$$

Since the distance is always positive we reject the value $d = -10$. Hence the source of light should be 10 feet away to provide 24 candle power of illumination.

Warm Up

8. The force F required to pull a wagon varies jointly as square of the velocity v and square root of the weight W. Given $F = 120$ lbs, $v = 10$ miles/hr and $W = 144$ lbs, find the constant of variation.

6. 48   7. a) 240 b) 20 8. $\frac{1}{10}$

Example 8: Find the constant of variation if x varies jointly as y and the cube of z; given $x = 32$, $y = 5$, and $z = 2$.

Solution:

If k is a constant of variation, then $x = kyz^3$.

Substitute 32 for x, 5 for y and 2 for z.

$$32 = k(5)(2^3) \longrightarrow 32 = k(5)(8)$$

$$\text{or} \qquad 40k = 32$$

$$k = \frac{32}{40} = \frac{4}{5}$$

EXERCISE 5.8

Answers:

1. _____

2. _____

3. _____

4. _____

5. _____

6. _____

1. One-third of a number is 3 less than one-half of the number. Find the number.

2. The numerator of a fraction is 3 less than its denominator. If $\frac{1}{10}$ is added to the fraction the result is $\frac{1}{2}$. What is the fraction?

3. A certain number is twice another number. If the sum of their reciprocals is 4, find the numbers.

4. When three times a number is added to four times its reciprocal, the results is 13. Find the number.

5. A boat travels 20 miles upstream in the same time that it would take to travel 30 miles downstream. If the rate of the stream is 5 miles per hour, find the speed of the boat in still water.

6. John can drive a motor boat 45 miles downstream in the same amount of time that he takes to drive 27 miles upstream. The speed of the motorboat in still water is 12 miles per hour. What is the rate of the stream?

7. A train travels 220 miles and returns the same distance. The total time taken by the train is $9\frac{1}{2}$ hours. If the speed of the train averaged 15 miles per hour more while going back, how fast did the train travel in each direction.

7. _____

8. An airplane flying against the wind travels 360 miles in the same time that it would take the same plane to travel 480 miles with the wind. If the wind speed is 20 miles per hour, find the speed of the airplane in still air.

8. _____

9. Hoses A and B together can fill a swimming pool in 6 hours. If hose A alone takes 10 hours to fill the pool, how long would it take hose B to fill the pool?

9. _____

10. Computer A can do a data analysis job in 4 hours. Computer B can do the same job in 6 hours. How long should it take to complete the job if both the computers were put to work together?

10. _____

11. A certain copier can do a printing job in 7 hours. Another copier can do the job in 12 hours. How long would it take to do the job if the two copiers worked together?

11. _____

12. Kristy can clean the house in 5 hours, and her father can clean the house in 4 hours. Kristy's younger brother, Tom, can completely mess up the house in 10 hours. If Kristy and her father clean the house, and if Tom plays in the house, all at the same time, how long will it take to clean the house?

12. _____

13. _____

13. Cynthia can do a job in 5 hours. When Cynthia and her elder sister Cassandra work together, it takes them 3 hours to finish the same job. How long would it take Cassandra to complete the job alone?

14. _____

14. One half of the profits from a sale are to be given to two scholarships so that the value of one scholarship is $\frac{5}{4}$ times that of the other. If the profits from the sale amount is $1980 how much is the scholarship with lesser value?

305

15. _____

15. A 5 horse power snow blower and a 9 horse power snow blower can together clear a parking lot in 1 hour. The 5-horsepower alone can do this job in $3\frac{1}{2}$ hours. How long will it take the 9-horsepower to do this job all by itself?

16. _____

16. The variable x varies directly as y, and $x = 7$, when $y = 2$. Find x when y is 6.

17. _____

17. If v varies inversely as the cube of a and $v = 2$, when $a = 2$,
   a) find the constant of variation   **b)** find v, when $a = 4$.

18. _____

18. The variable z varies jointly as x and y, and $z = 36$, when $x = 3$ and $y = 4$. Find z when $x = 5$ and $y = 2$.

19. _____

19. When a particle is let go from above, the distance traveled by the particle varies as the square of time. If the distance traveled by the particle in 2 seconds is 64 feet, find the equation connecting the distance and the time.

20. _____

20. If x varies directly as the square of r and inversely as the square of s, and if when $r = 4$ and $s = 2$, then $x = 4$.

   a) Determine an equation connecting x, r, and s.

   b) Find x when $r = 6$ and $s = 5$.

5.9   CHAPTER SUMMARY

Examples

Rational Expressions

1. To determine the values of the variable for which a rational expression is not defined we proceed as follows:

1. Where is $\dfrac{3x^2 + 4x - 1}{x^2 - x - 2}$ not defined?

Step 1   Set the denominator of the rational expression to zero.

$x^2 - x - 2 = 0$

Step 2   Solve the equation obtained in Step 1.

$(x - 2)(x + 1) = 0$

$\rightarrow x = 2, \ x = -1$

Step 3   Solutions in Step 2 are the values the variable for which the expression is not defined.

Examples

2. To find the numerical value of an expression, substitute the value for the variable in the expression and simplify.

2. Evaluate: $\dfrac{x^2+2}{x^2+1}$ for $x=2$

$$\frac{(2)^2+2}{(2)^2+1}=\frac{6}{5}$$

Simplifying Rational Expressions

3. The steps to simplify a rational expression to lowest terms:

3. $\dfrac{x^3+x^2-2x}{x^2+2x}$

Step 1 Factor the numerator completely.

$x(x-1)(x+2)$

Step 2 Factor the denominator completely.

$x(x+2)$

Step 3 Determine the greatest common factor of the numerator and the denominator.

g.c.f. $= x(x+2)$

Step 4 Divide the numerator and the denominator by the greatest common factor.

$\dfrac{x(x-1)(x+2)}{x(x+2)}=x-1$

Multiplication and Division

4. The steps to multiply two rational expressions

4. $\dfrac{x^2+x}{x^2-x-2}\cdot\dfrac{x^2-1}{x^2-2x}$

Step 1 Multiply the numerators and the denominators.

$=\dfrac{\left(x^2+x\right)\left(x^2-1\right)}{\left(x^2-x-2\right)\left(x^2-2x\right)}$

Step 2 Factor the numerators and denominators.

$=\dfrac{x(x+1)(x-1)(x+1)}{(x-2)(x+1)x(x-2)}$ g.c.f. $= x(x+1)$

Step 3 Write in lowest terms by dividing with the g.c.d

$=\dfrac{(x-1)(x+1)}{(x-2)(x-2)}$

5. The steps to divide a rational expression $\dfrac{P}{Q}$ by $\dfrac{R}{S}$:

5. $\dfrac{x^2+x}{x^2-x-2}\div\dfrac{x^3-x}{x^2-4}$

$=\dfrac{x^2+x}{x^2-x-2}\cdot\dfrac{x^2-4}{x^3-x}$

Step 1 Multiply $\dfrac{P}{Q}$ and the reciprocal of $\dfrac{R}{S}$.

i.e., multiply $\dfrac{P}{Q}$ by $\dfrac{S}{R}$

$=\dfrac{x(x+1)\cdot(x-2)(x+2)}{(x-2)(x+1)\cdot x(x-1)(x+1)}$

$=\dfrac{x+2}{(x-1)(x+1)}$

Step 2 Write the product in lowest terms.

Examples

Least Common Denominator

6. The steps to find the least common multiples (l.c.m.) of the polynomial:

Step 1 Factor each polynomial completely.

Step 2 Determine the different factors and their maximum exponents.

Step 3 The l.c.m. of the polynomials is the product of different factors, each raised to its maximum exponent as determined in step 2.

7. The least common denominator of fractions is defined to be the least common multiple of the denominators of the fractions.

8. The steps for writing a rational expression with a given expression as the *new* denominator.

Step 1 Find the quotient:

$$\frac{\text{new denominator}}{\text{old denominator}} = k\,(\text{say})$$

Step 2 Multiply the given fraction by $\dfrac{k}{k}$

Step 3 Simplify and expand if necessary.

Addition and Subtraction

9. To add rational expressions with the same denominator we add the numerators and place the sum over the common denominator.

10. The steps for adding or subtracting rational expressions with different denominators.

Step 1 Find the l.c.d.

Step 2 Rewrite each rational expression with the l.c.d as the new denominator.

---

6. $x^2 - x, \; x^2 - 1$

$x(x-1), \qquad (x-1)(x+1)$

$x^1, \; (x-1)^1, \; (x+1)^1$

$x(x-1)(x+1)$

8. write $\dfrac{2x-1}{x^2-x}$ with $x(x-1)(x+1)$
as the new denominator.

$$\frac{x(x-1)(x+1)}{x^2-x} = \frac{x(x-1)(x+1)}{x(x-1)}$$
$$= x+1$$

$$\frac{2x-1}{x^2-x} = \frac{2x-1}{x(x-1)} \cdot \frac{x+1}{x+1}$$

$$= \frac{(2x-1)(x+1)}{x(x-1)(x+1)} = \frac{2x^2+x-1}{x^3-x}$$

9. $\dfrac{3x-1}{x-1} + \dfrac{5}{x-1}$

$$= \frac{3x-1+5}{x-1} = \frac{3x+4}{x-1}$$

10. $\dfrac{2x-1}{x^2-x} + \dfrac{x+2}{x^2-1}$

$x^2 - x = x(x-1)$
$x^2 - 1 = (x-1)(x+1)$
$\text{l.c.d} = x(x-1)(x+1)$

$$\frac{2x-1}{x^2-x} = \frac{2x-1}{x(x-1)} \cdot \frac{x+1}{x+1}$$

$$= \frac{(2x-1)(x+1)}{x(x-1)(x+1)}$$

Examples

$$\frac{(x+2)}{x^2-1} = \frac{x+2}{(x-1)(x+1)} \cdot \frac{x}{x}$$

$$= \frac{x(x+2)}{x(x-1)(x+1)}$$

Step 3 Add the new equivalent fractions with the same denominator.

$$\frac{2x-1}{x^2-x} + \frac{x+2}{x^2-1}$$

$$= \frac{(2x-1)(x+1)}{x(x-1)(x+1)} + \frac{x(x+2)}{x(x-1)(x+1)}$$

$$= \frac{(2x-1)(x+1) + x(x+2)}{x(x-1)(x+1)}$$

Step 4 Reduce the result to lowest terms.

$$= \frac{2x^2+x-1+x^2+2x}{x(x-1)(x+1)}$$

$$= \frac{3x^2+3x-1}{x(x-1)(x+1)}$$

Complex Fractions

11. Simplifying Complex Fractions

11. $\dfrac{1+\dfrac{2}{x}}{\dfrac{3}{x}-4}$

Method 1:

Step 1 Find the l.c.d. of all fractions appearing in the numerator and the denominator.

l.c.d. $= x$

Step 2 Multiply both the numerator and the denominator by the l.c.d. and simplify.

$$\frac{\left(1+\dfrac{2}{x}\right)x}{\left(\dfrac{3}{x}-4\right)x} = \frac{x+2}{3-4x}$$

Method 2:

$$\frac{1+\dfrac{2}{x}}{\dfrac{3}{x}-4}$$

Step 1 Simplify the numerator.

$$1+\frac{2}{x} = \frac{x}{x} + \frac{2}{x} = \frac{x+2}{x}$$

Step 2 Simplify the denominator.

$$\frac{3}{x}-4 = \frac{3}{x} - \frac{4x}{x} = \frac{3-4x}{x}$$

Examples

Step 3 Divide the numerator by the denominator, and simplify.

$$\frac{1 + \dfrac{2}{x}}{\dfrac{2}{x} - 4} = \frac{\dfrac{x+2}{x}}{\dfrac{3-4x}{x}}$$

$$= \frac{x+2}{x} \cdot \frac{x}{3-4x}$$

$$= \frac{x+2}{3-4x}$$

Equations With Rational Expressions

12. Solving equations with rational expressions

Step 1   Find the l.c.d. of all the rational expressions in the equation.

Step 2   Multiply both sides of the equation by the l.c.d and simplify.

Step 3   Solve the resulting equation.

Step 4   Verify the answer obtained in step 3 by substituting it into the original equation. Reject any solution that makes a denominator zero.

12. $\dfrac{2}{y} + \dfrac{1}{2} = \dfrac{7}{2y}$

l.c.d. $= 2y$

$2y\left(\dfrac{2}{y} + \dfrac{1}{2}\right) = 2y\left(\dfrac{7}{2y}\right)$

$\rightarrow 4 + y = 7$

$\rightarrow y = 3$

$\dfrac{2}{3} + \dfrac{1}{2} = \dfrac{7}{2(3)}$

$\rightarrow \dfrac{7}{6} = \dfrac{7}{6}$ **True**

Applications

13. The steps to solve problems involving numbers

Step 1   Identify the required number (unknown). Let the desired number be x.

Step 2   Determine other numbers in terms of the unknown.

Step 3   Use the given information to setup an equation.

Step 4   Solve the equation.

Step 5   Check the solution.

14. The steps to solve problems involving distances

Step 1   Identify the unknown as distance, time, or rate.

Step 2   Use a table to organize the information regarding distance, time, and rate.

Step 3   Use the formula $d = rt$ or $t = \dfrac{d}{r}$, or $r = \dfrac{d}{t}$

Step 4   Use the given information and setup an equation.

310

Step 5   Solve the equation.

Step 6   Check the solution.

15.   The steps to solve problems involving work

Step 1   Identify the unknown.

Step 2   Use a table to organize the given information.

Step 3   Use the formula: Rate x Time = Work Done.

Step 4   Use the given relationship to form an equation.

Step 5   Solve the equation.

Step 6   Verify the solution.

16.   Variation

y varies directly as x : $y = kx$

y varies directly as square of x : $y = kx^2$

y varies inversely as x : $y = \dfrac{k}{x}$

y varies inversely as square of x : $y = \dfrac{k}{x^2}$

z varies jointly as x and y : $z = kxy$

z varies jointly as square of x and inversely as cube of y: $z = \dfrac{kx^2}{y^3}$

5.10   REVIEW EXERCISE

In exercises 1–6, find the values for which the rational expression is not defined.

1. $\dfrac{4x - 1}{3x - 2}$ **2.** $\dfrac{2x^2 + 1}{x^2 - 4x + 4}$ **3.** $\dfrac{1}{6p^2 + p - 1}$

4. $\dfrac{x^2 - x + 1}{10x^3 + 4x^2 + 5x + 2}$ **5.** $\dfrac{4}{3x^2 + 1}$ **6.** $\dfrac{2x + 1}{x^3}$

In exercises 7–10, evaluate the expression for the indicated values.

7. $\dfrac{3x + 5}{4x - 3}; x = -2$ **8.** $\dfrac{4}{3x^2 + 1}; x = -1$ **9.** $\dfrac{3x^2 + 7x - 2}{4x^3 + 3x + 5}; x = \dfrac{1}{2}$

10. $\dfrac{x - 1}{x^2 - 2x + 2}; x = 2$

In exercises 11–17, write the rational expression in lowest terms.

11. $\dfrac{12p^3}{16p^5}$

12. $\dfrac{18x^2y^3}{27xy^4}$

13. $\dfrac{3x-4}{4-3x}$

14. $\dfrac{2(x^2-4)}{4(x-2)}$

15. $\dfrac{x^3-81x}{x^2-18x+81}$

16. $\dfrac{9a^2-16b^2}{9a^2+24ab+16b^2}$

17. $\dfrac{8p^2-14pq-15q^2}{2p^2-5pq+4p-10q}$

In exercises 18–28, perform the indicated operations.

18. $\dfrac{4x}{5y}\cdot\dfrac{3y^2}{2}$

19. $\dfrac{3x+2}{4x}\cdot\dfrac{5x^2}{2x+1}$

20. $\dfrac{2x-3}{3x+5}\cdot\dfrac{4x-1}{2x+1}$

21. $\dfrac{3x^3}{7}\div\dfrac{6x^2}{5}$

22. $\dfrac{3x^2}{5x+7}\div\dfrac{2x^2}{x+1}$

23. $\dfrac{2p-3}{3p+5}\div\dfrac{4p-6}{9p+15}$

24. $\dfrac{y^2-3y+2}{2y-1}\div\dfrac{y^2-6y+5}{2y^2+y-1}$

25. $\dfrac{x^3+8}{x-2}\cdot\dfrac{x^2-4x+4}{x^2-2x+4}\div\dfrac{x+2}{x-1}$

26. $\dfrac{x+2}{x-4}\div\dfrac{x-4}{x+3}\div\dfrac{x-4}{x+2}$

27. $\dfrac{ab-b^2}{a^2-ab}\cdot\dfrac{a^2+ab}{ab-b^2}\div\dfrac{ab+a^2}{a^2-ab}$

28. $\dfrac{p+3}{p-7}\div\dfrac{p-7}{p+5}\cdot\dfrac{p+5}{p+3}$

In exercises 29–31, find the least common denominator.

29. $\dfrac{1}{x},\dfrac{3}{y}$

30. $\dfrac{3}{4-x},\dfrac{2}{x-4}$

31. $\dfrac{3x+1}{x^2-2x+1},\dfrac{4-5x}{2x^2-3x+1}$

In exercises 32–36, find the least common denominator of the rational expressions. In each case rewrite the expression with the l.c.d. as the new denominator.

32. $\dfrac{x+1}{6x^2},\dfrac{3x-1}{4x^3}$

33. $\dfrac{3x}{(x+1)^2},\dfrac{5}{2(x+1)}$

34. $\dfrac{2x}{x^2-9},\dfrac{3x+1}{x^2-5x+6}$

35. $\dfrac{x}{x^3-8},\dfrac{2}{(x-2)^2}$

36. $\dfrac{y}{8y^3+1},\dfrac{4y}{4y^2-2y+1}$

In exercises 37–44, perform the indicated operations.

37. $\dfrac{4}{x}+\dfrac{5}{x}$

38. $\dfrac{x-2}{4x}-\dfrac{3-x}{4x}$

39. $\dfrac{2a}{a-3}+\dfrac{3a}{3-a}$

40. $\dfrac{p+5}{p^2+2p-15}+\dfrac{2}{p-3}$

41. $\dfrac{1}{y-x}+\dfrac{x}{(x-y)^2}$

42. $\dfrac{x-1}{x^3-1}-\dfrac{x+1}{x^2+x+1}$

43. $\dfrac{4}{x^2 - x} - \dfrac{1}{x^2 + x - 2} + \dfrac{6}{x^2 + 2x}$ **44.** $\dfrac{4x - 1}{2x^2 + 5x - 3} - \dfrac{x + 3}{6x^2 + x - 2}$

In exercises 45–48, simplify the complex fraction.

45. $\dfrac{\dfrac{3xy}{z}}{\dfrac{6x^3}{z^2}}$ **46.** $\dfrac{\dfrac{x - y}{x + y}}{\dfrac{1}{x^2} - \dfrac{1}{y^2}}$ **47.** $\dfrac{\dfrac{2}{x^2 y} - \dfrac{3}{xy^2}}{\dfrac{3}{x^2 y^2} + \dfrac{1}{xy}}$ **48.** $\dfrac{\dfrac{1}{1 + y}}{1 - \dfrac{1}{1 + y}}$

In exercises 49–52, solve the equation and check your answers.

49. $x + \dfrac{x}{x - 2} = \dfrac{2}{x - 2}$ **50.** $\dfrac{x}{x - 2} + \dfrac{2}{x + 3} = \dfrac{10}{x^2 + x - 6}$

51. $\dfrac{3}{x - 3} + \dfrac{4}{x - 4} = \dfrac{25}{x^2 - 7x + 12}$ **52.** $\dfrac{2x - 4}{x + 2} = 5 - \dfrac{3x + 2}{x - 1}$

In exercises 53–54, solve for the specified variable.

53. $\dfrac{1}{x} = \dfrac{1}{y} + \dfrac{1}{z}$; for y **54.** $\dfrac{a}{b} = \dfrac{3b - c}{a + c}$; for c

55. The sum of the numerator and denominator of a fraction is 68. When 12 is added to the numerator and subtracted from the denominator, the result is $\dfrac{11}{6}$. Find the fraction.

56. A number is twice another number. If the sum of their reciprocals is $\dfrac{5}{2}$, find the numbers.

57. An airplane flying against the wind travels 250 miles in the same time that it would travel 300 miles with the wind. The wind speed is 10 miles per hour. Find the speed of the airplane in still air.

58. A boat travels 20 miles upstream in the same time that it would take to travel 30 miles downstream. If the rate of the stream is 5 miles per hour, find the speed of the boat in still water.

59. Two photographers can together complete an assignment in 4 hours. Working alone one of the photographers can complete the job in 6 hours. How long would it take the other photographer to complete the job?

60. A printing press can print a magazine in 5 hours. After the press has been in operation for 2 hours, a second printing press joins the first one. If the job is finished in two more hours, how long will it take the second press to print the same magazine alone?

61. The amount of garbage produced in a given location varies directly with the number of people living in the area. It is known that 25 tons of garbage is produced by 100 people in one year. If there is an influx of 5,000 people in a state, find the amount of additional garbage that will have to be picked up in one year in that state.

62. The volume of a sphere varies directly as the cube of its radius. The volume is 36π cubic inches when the radius is 3 inches. What is the volume of the sphere when the radius is 6 centimeters?

63. Newton's law of gravitation states that the gravitational attraction between two objects varies jointly as the product of their masses and inversely as the square of the distance between their center of mass. What will be the change in attraction between the two objects if both masses are doubled, and the distance between their centers is cut in half?

5.11   SELF TEST

1. Find the values of x for which $\dfrac{3x - 1}{2x^2 + 3x - 2}$ is not defined.

2. Evaluate $\dfrac{4t - 1}{3t^2 + 5t - 1}$ at $t = -2$

3. Which of the expressions are in lowest terms?

    a) $\dfrac{3x^2}{4xy}$ **b)** $\dfrac{3x^2 z}{4xy}$ **c)** $\dfrac{2r^3 - s^3}{2r - s}$

In exercises 4–7, perform the indicated operations

4. $\dfrac{14a}{10b} \div \dfrac{35a}{15b}$ **5.** $\dfrac{(x - 1)^2}{(x + 2)^2} \cdot \dfrac{x^2 - 4}{x^2 - 1}$ **6.** $\dfrac{p^2 + p - 2}{p - 3} \div (p + 2)$

7. $\dfrac{x^3 - y^3}{(x - y)^3} \div \dfrac{x^2 + xy + y^2}{x^2 - 2xy + y^2}$

In exercises 8–9, find the least common denominator.

8. $\dfrac{4}{5x^3}, \dfrac{5}{12x^2}, -\dfrac{9}{20x}$ **9.** $\dfrac{5}{4x - 5}, \dfrac{1}{25 - 16x^2}, \dfrac{3x + 7}{(4x + 5)^2}$

10. Identify the missing numerator $\dfrac{32}{9x^2} = \dfrac{}{18x^3 - 9x^2}$

11. Rewrite $\dfrac{2x^2 - 7x + 6}{x^2 - x - 6}$ and $\dfrac{x}{x^2 - 4}$ with the least common denominator as the new denominator.

In exercises 12–15, perform the indicated operations.

12. $\dfrac{2}{3x} + \dfrac{5}{4x}$ **13.** $\dfrac{2}{x^3} - \dfrac{3}{x^2} + \dfrac{5}{x}$ **14.** $\dfrac{3}{2x - 3} - \dfrac{2}{9 - 4x^2}$

15. $\dfrac{b}{b - a} - \dfrac{a}{a + b} + \dfrac{a^2 + b^2}{a^2 - b^2}$

In exercises 16–17, simplify the complex fraction.

16. $\dfrac{2-\dfrac{1}{x}}{1+\dfrac{5}{x}}$

17. $\dfrac{\dfrac{x^2}{x-3}+\dfrac{x}{x-3}}{\dfrac{2x}{x-3}-\dfrac{x}{x+3}}$

In exercises 18–20, solve the equation and check your solution.

18. $x+\dfrac{2x}{x-1}=\dfrac{3-x}{x-1}$

19. $\dfrac{x}{x-2}-\dfrac{2}{x+4}=\dfrac{12}{x^2+2x-8}$

20. $\dfrac{x}{x-2}-\dfrac{2}{x+4}=\dfrac{13x^2+26x-62}{7(x-2)(x+4)}$

21. Five times a number is added to three times the reciprocal of the number. The result is $\dfrac{17}{2}$. Find the number.

22. A boat goes 8 miles per hour in still water. It takes as long to go 40 miles downstream as to go 24 miles upstream. Find the speed of the current.

23. Using a small mower, a student can finish a job in 9 hours. After he had been working for one hour, another student joined him with a tractor. Together they complete the remaining job in 2 hours. How many hours would it take to do the job using the tractor only?

24. Suppose that y varies inversely as the cube of x.

    a)   Write an equation expressing this variation.

    b) $y=448$ when $x=4$; calculate the value of the constant of variation.

    c)   Calculate y when x is 8.

CHAPTER 6

LINEAR EQUATIONS/INEQUALITIES IN TWO VARIABLES

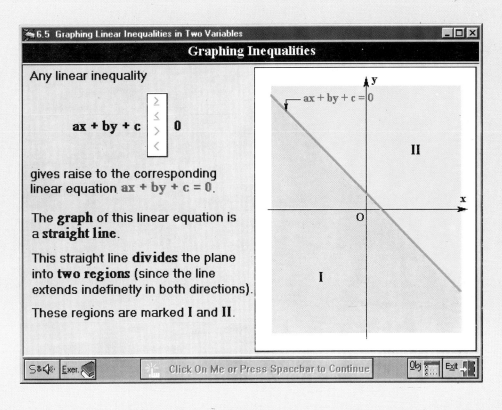

CHAPTER 6

LINEAR EQUATIONS/INEQUALITIES IN TWO VARIABLES

This chapter is divided into the following sections.

6.1 LINEAR EQUATIONS IN TWO VARIABLES

Equations of the form $3x + 4 = 0$ are called *linear equations in one variable*. Equations of the type: $y = 2x^2 - 3x$, $y = 3x + 4$, and $4x + 5y = 1$ are examples of equations in two variables.

An equation in two variables, say x and y, is called linear if it can be written in the form $ax + by = c$, where a, b and c are real numbers, and at least one of a or b is non–zero. Thus, for example, $2x - 7y = 1$ is a linear equation in x and y, and $3q = p - 5$ is a linear equation in p and q.

Upon completion of this section we will be able to:

A. Write a solution of a linear equation.
B. Complete a table of values, as solutions.
C. Plot ordered pairs.

A. Solution of a Linear Equation

A **solution** of a linear equation in two variables is a pair of numbers, one for each variable, which when substituted for the respective variables makes the equation true.

For example, $2x + 3y = 1$ is satisfied by $x = 2$ and $y = -1$.

$x = 2$, $y = -1$: $2(2) + 3(-1) = 1 \longrightarrow 4 - 3 = 1$ True

Thus, the pair $x = 2$ and $y = -1$ is a solution of $2x + 3y = 1$.

This is also expressed by saying that the *ordered pair* $(x, y) = (2, -1)$ is a solution of $2x + 3y = 1$.

We may check whether or not the ordered pair is a solution of the given equation by using calculator. See example 1 on page 519 in Appendix B.

An ordered pair is a pair (a, b) of numbers for which the order of occurrence of the two numbers a and b is important. Thus $(2, -1)$ is not the same as $(-1, 2)$. For an ordered pair (a, b), **a** is called the **first component** and b is called the **second component.** In general, letters representing components of an ordered pair are in alphabetical order.

A linear equation in two variables has infinitely many solutions.

Warm Up

1. Verify that $x = 2$, $y = 2$, and $x = 4$, $y = -1$, are solutions of the equation $3x + 2y = 10$

Example 1: Verify that $x = 2$, $y = 3$ and $y = -1$, $x = 4$ are solutions of the equation $2x + y = 7$. Write these solutions as ordered pairs of numbers.

Solution:

Verify: $x = 2$, $y = 3$: Substitute these values in $2x + y = 7$

$$2 \cdot 2 + 1 \cdot 3 = 7 \longrightarrow 7 = 7 \qquad \text{True}$$

Therefore, $x = 2, y = 3$ is a solution of $2x + y = 7$. This solution is written as $(2, 3)$.

Again, substitute $y = -1$ and $x = 4$ in the equation.

$$2x + y = 7$$
$$2 \cdot 4 + 1 \cdot (-1) = 7 \longrightarrow 7 = 7 \qquad \text{True}$$

Therefore, $y = -1$ and $x = 4$ is also a solution of $2x + y = 7$. This solution is written as $(4, -1)$, and not as $(-1, 4)$, since the value of x is always the first component in the ordered pair.

2. Identify whether the given ordered pair is a solution of the indicated equation

a) $(3, 1)$; $2x - y = 4$

b) $(1, 2)$; $x - y = -1$

c) $(2, 5)$; $3x - y = 1$

Example 2: Identify whether the given ordered pair is a solution of the indicated equation.

a) $(-4, 5)$; $2x - y = 10$
b) $(1, 1)$; $x - y = 0$
c) $(1, 3)$; $2y - x = 5$

Solutions:

a) $(-4, 5)$; $2x - y = 10$ Substitute -4 for x and 5 for y.

$$2(-4) - 5 = 10 \longrightarrow -8 - 5 = 10$$
$$\longrightarrow -13 = 10 \qquad \text{False}$$

Therefore $(-4, 5)$ **is not a solution** of $2x - y = 10$.

b) $(1, 1)$; $x - y = 0$ Substitute 1 for x and 1 for y.

$$1 - 1 = 0 \longrightarrow 0 = 0 \qquad \text{True}$$

Therefore $(1, 1)$ **is a solution** of $x - y = 0$.

318

c)   **(1,3)**; $2y - x = 5$ Substitute
1 for x and 3 for y.

$$2 \cdot 3 - 1 = 5 \longrightarrow 5 = 5 \qquad \text{True}$$

Therefore $(1, 3)$ **is a solution** of $2y - x = 5$.

B. Completing a Table of Values

In order to graph an equation in two variables we shall construct a table of values. This can be done by substituting the value of one variable into the equation and solving for the other.

Example 3:   For the equation $2x + 5y - 3 = 0$, find the missing component of the ordered pairs in order for these pairs to be the solutions.

a) $(-3, ?)$ **b)** $(?, 5)$

Solutions:

a) $(-3, ?)$; $2x + 5y - 3 = 0,$ First component is -3

$2(-3) + 5y - 3 = 0,$ Substitute -3 for x

$-6 + 5y - 3 = 0$

$$5y = 9 \longrightarrow y = \frac{9}{5}$$

Thus, the completed ordered pair is $\left(-3, \dfrac{9}{5}\right)$.

b) $(?, 5)$; $2x + 5y - 3 = 0,$ Second component is 5

$2x + 5 \cdot 5 - 3 = 0$ Substitute 5 for y

$2x + 22 = 0$

$$2x = -22 \longrightarrow x = -11$$

Thus, the completed ordered pair is $(-11, 5)$.

In order to complete the table of values, we must complete the ordered pairs as shown in the following examples.

Example 4:   Complete the given table of values for the equation $2x + y = 7$.

x	-1	2	5		
y				3	-2

Solution:

When   **x is -1**; $2(-1) + y = 7 \longrightarrow -2 + y = 7 \longrightarrow y = 9$

When   **x is 2**; $2 \cdot 2 + y = 7 \longrightarrow 4 + y = 7 \longrightarrow y = 3$

When   **x is 5**; $2 \cdot 5 + y = 7 \longrightarrow 10 + y = 7 \longrightarrow y = -3$

Warm Up

When **y is 3**; $2x + 3 = 7 \longrightarrow 2x = 4 \longrightarrow x = 2$

When **y is −2**; $2x + (-2) = 7 \longrightarrow 2x = 9 \longrightarrow x = 4.5$

Therefore, the completed table of values is:

x	-1	2	5	2	4.5
y	9	3	-3	3	-2

5. Complete the following table of values for the equation $x = -2$

x				
y	4	-4	0	5

Example 5: Complete the following table of values for the equation $x = 3$.

x			
y	-3	0	5

Solution:

Since the given equation $x = 3$ does not contain y, the value of x remains 3 for all values of y. Therefore, the completed table of values is

x	3	3	3
y	-3	0	5

Answers:

3. a) $\frac{3}{2}$ b) -6

4.
x	2	-3	4	2	$\frac{11}{4}$
y	1	$\frac{23}{3}$	$-\frac{5}{3}$	1	0

5.
x	-2	-2	-2	-2
y	4	-4	0	5

C. Plotting Ordered Pairs

When two intersecting lines, one horizontal and another vertical, are drawn in the plane, the plane is divided into four regions. [See the figure below.] Each of these regions is called a **quadrant.** A coordinate system can be set up, such that:

    i)   the point of intersection of these lines represents the number zero.

    ii)   numbers to the right of zero on the horizontal number line are positive.

    iii)   numbers above zero on the vertical line are positive.

- the point of intersection is called the **origin.**
- the horizontal number line is called the **x-axis.**
- the vertical line is called the **y-axis .**
- the x-axis and y-axis together constitute the **rectangular coordinate system.**
- the quadrants are numbered as shown in the figure below.

Notes: 1. Ordinarily, it is desirable to use the same unit of measurement on the x-axis and the y-axis.

2. Quadrants are numbered with Roman numerals in the counter-clockwise direction.

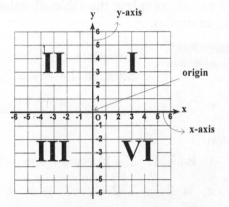

Figure 6.1

Every ordered pair of real numbers represents a point on the plane. The point represented by (a, b) is said to have a as its **x-coordinate** and b as its **y-coordinate**. In general, a and b are called the **coordinates** of the point.

A point with coordinates (a, b) is plotted as follows:

1. Mark a on the x-axis.

2. Go $|b|$ units vertically *up* from a if b is *positive* , and $|b|$ units vertically *down* if b is *negative*. If b is zero, then the point a on the x - axis is the required point.

Warm Up

Example 6:	Plot the following points on a coordinate plane.

a) $(2, 4)$ **b)** $(-2, 5)$ **c)** $(-5, -7)$

d) $\left(\dfrac{5}{2}, -1\right)$ **e)** $(3, 0)$ **f)** $(0, -2)$

Solutions:

a) $(2, 4)$ Locate the point representing 2 on the x-axis. Move *vertically upwards* $|4|$ units from this point. The point A in Figure 6.2 is the plot of $(2, 4)$.

b) $(-2, 5)$ Locate the point representing -2 on the x-axis. Then move $|5| = 5$ units *vertically upwards*. The point B in Figure 6.2 is the plot of $(-2, 5)$.

c) $(-5, -7)$ Locate the point representing -5 on the x-axis. Move *vertically downwards* $|-7|$ units from this point. The point C is Figure 6.2 is of the plot of $(-5, -7)$.

d) $\left(\dfrac{5}{2}, -1\right)$ Locate the point representing $\dfrac{5}{2}$ on the x-axis.

Move *vertically downwards* $|-1|$ unit from this point. The point D in Figure 6.2 is the plot of $(5/2, 1)$.

e) $(3, 0)$ Locate the point representing 3 on the x-axis. This is the point whose coordinates are $(3, 0)$. The point E in Figure 6.2 is the plot of $(3, 0)$.

f) $(0, -2)$ Locate the point representing zero on x-axis. Move vertically downwards $|-2|$ units from this point. The point F in Figure 6.2 is the plot of the point $(0, -2)$.

6. Plot the following points:

a) $(3 , 3)$

b) $(2 , -2)$

c) $(0 , 5)$

d) $(-3 , 0)$

e) $(-4 , 2)$

f) $(-2 , -5)$

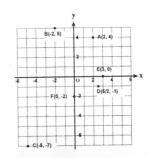

Figure 6.2

321

Warm Up

7. Find the coordinates of the points shown in the following figure.

Answers:

6.

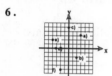

7. a) $(4,1)$ **b)** $(2,5)$ **c)** $(-2,3)$
   d) $(-5,0)$ **e)** $(-3,-5)$ **f)** $(6,-3)$

We can plot points using calculators. See example 3 on page 520 in Appendix B.

Notes: **1.** Any point whose y-coordinate is zero lies on the x-axis.

2. Any point whose x-coordinate is zero lies on the y-axis.

3. The coordinates of the origin are $(0,0)$.

 Example 7: Find the coordinates of the point shown in figure 6.3.

Solution:

A:	$(3,2)$	B:	$(-2,6)$
C:	$(-4,-4)$	D:	$(6,-2)$
E:	$(2,0)$	F:	$(-3,0)$
G:	$(0,3)$	H:	$(0,-3)$

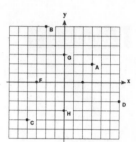

Figure 6.3

EXERCISE 6.1

Answers:

1. _____
2. _____
3. _____
4. _____
5. _____
6. _____
7. _____
8. _____
9. _____
10. _____
11. _____
12. _____

In exercises 1–8,   determine whether the given ordered pair is a solution of the given equation.

1. $x + 3y = 5;\ (1,2)$ **2.** $2x - 5y = 7;\ (6,1)$

3. $2x + 5y + 10 = 0;\ (-5,0)$ **4.** $3x - 2y = 12;\ (0,6)$

5. $x = 5;\ (7,0)$ **6.** $x + 3 = 0;\ (-3,2)$

7. $2x = 3y;\ (6,4)$ **8.** $y = 1;\ (3,1)$

In exercises 9–15,   complete the ordered pairs for the given equations.

9. $(4,\ ?);\ x - 3y = 2$ **10.** $(-3,\ ?);\ 2x + y = 5$

11. $(?,2);\ x = 8$ **12.** $(?,\ -4);\ 2x + 3y = 8$

13. $(0, ?)$; $3x + 5y = 10$ **14.** $(?, 0)$; $2x + 7y + 10 = 0$

15. $(-2, ?)$; $2x + 7y = 10$

In exercises 16–20, complete the table of values for the given equation.

16. $3x - 5y = 15$;

x	0		4
y		0	3

17. $x - 2y = 3$;

x	-1	3		
y			2	-1

18. $y + 3 = 4x$;

x	-2	0	5	
y				

19. $x = 5$;

x				
y	-3	4	7	

20. $y + 4 = 0$;

x	0	-1	4	
y				

21. **Plot the ordered pairs on the same coordinate system.**
   a) $(2, -3)$ **b)** $(-4, 7)$ **c)** $(3, 5)$
   d) $(6, 2)$ **e)** $(-6, 2)$ **f)** $(0, 0)$

22. **Plot the ordered pairs on the same coordinate system.**
   a) $(-4, 0)$ **b)** $(0, 5)$ **c)** $(-2, -2)$ **d)** $(3, 0)$
   e) $(0, -5)$ **f)** $(-3, -5)$

23. **Without plotting the points, determine the quadrant in which the point lies.**
   a) $(4, 5)$ **b)** $(-3, -7)$ **c)** $(4, -2)$ **d)** $(-3, 2)$

.13. _____

14. _____

15. _____

16. _____

17. _____

18. _____

19. _____

20. _____

21.

22.

23.

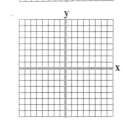

24. Determine whether the following points lie on *x*-axis or *y*-axis, or neither.

a) $(-3,0)$ b) $(0,-1)$ c) $(5,0)$

d) $(2,-3)$ e) $(0,4)$ f) $(1,4)$

24.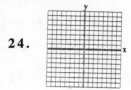

25. Determine the coordinates of each of the points shown in the figure.

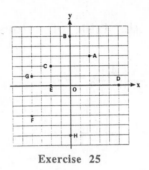

Exercise 25

25. _____

6.2   GRAPHING LINEAR EQUATIONS IN TWO VARIABLES

In this section we shall learn how to graph a linear equation. Upon completion of this section we will be able to:

    A.   Graph linear equations.

    B.   Use the intercepts to graph the linear equation.

A. Graphing a Linear Equation

The **graph** of an equation is a curve such that the ordered pairs representing points on the curve are the solutions of the equation.

A general strategy for graphing an equation in *x* and *y* consists of three steps:

    Step 1   Construct a table of several *x*- and *y*-values for the equation and obtain the corresponding ordered pairs (x, y).

    Step 2   Plot the ordered pairs obtained in step 1 on a coordinate system.

    Step 3   Draw a smooth curve passing through the points plotted in step 2.

In Section 6.4 we shall see that the equation of a straight line is linear in *x* and *y*. Conversely, it can be shown that the graph of any linear equation in two variables is a straight line. Since a straight line is determined once two points on it are known, it is enough to make a table consisting of two *x*- and *y*-values for graphing a linear equation. However, in practice, it is recommended to make a table of *three* values. This will ensure a check on the graph.

A general procedure to graph a **linear equation** in *x* and *y* consists of the following steps:

Step 1	Construct a table of *three* ordered pairs.
Step 2	Plot the three points.
Step 3	Draw a straight line passing through the three points.

Notes: 1.   Since plotting a point with fractional coordinates is not convenient unless you use a suitable scale, it is advisable (for practical convenience) that the tables of values should avoid fractions as far as possible.

2   As far as possible, the *x* or *y* values should be chosen in order that the resulting points are not too close to each other.

Example 1:

Graph the line $2x - 3y = 0$.

Solution:

Step 1   Construct a table of *three* x- and y-values for the equation $2x - 3y = 0$.

x	0	3	−3
y	0	2	−2

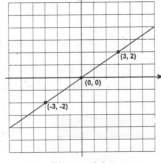

Step 2   Plot the points: $(0,0)$, $(3,2)$, $(-3,-2)$.

Figure 6.4

Step 3   Draw the straight line passing through the three points.

Note: Observe that the graph of $2x - 3y = 0$ is a line passing through the origin.

We may graph a line using calculator. See example 2 on page 521 in Appendix B.

For all real numbers **a, b** (both not zero), the graph of the linear equation with no constant term ($ax + by = 0$) is a straight line passing through the origin.

Example 2:

Graph the equation $2x + 3y = 6$.

Solution:

Step 1   Construct a table of x- and y-values for the equation $2x + 3y = 6$.

x	0	3	6
y	2	0	−2

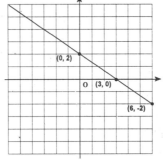

Step 2   Plot the points: $(0,2)$, $(3,0)$, $(6,-2)$.

Figure 6.5

Step 3   Draw the line passing through the three points.

Warm Up

1. Graph the line $3x - 2y = 0$

2. Graph the equation
   $y = 2x + 2$

325

Warm Up

3. Graph the equation $x = -4$

Example 3:   Graph the equation $x = 4$.

Solution:

Step 1   Construct a table of three x- and y-values for the equation $x = 4$.

x	4	4	4
y	0	2	-2

Step 2   Plot the points: $(4, 0)$, $(4, 2)$, $(4, -2)$.

Step 3   Draw the line through the three points.

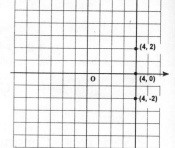

Figure 6.6

Note: Observe that the graph of x = 4 is a vertical line passing through (4,0).

The graph of the linear equation $x = k$ is a **vertical** line through the point $(k, 0)$. In particular, the graph of $x = 0$ is the y-axis.

4. Graph the equation $y - 3 = 0$

Example 4:   Graph the equation $y + 4 = 0$.

Solution:

Observe that $y + 4 = 0$ can be rewritten as $y = -4$.

Step 1   Construct a table of *three* x- and y-values for the equation $y = -4$.

x	0	3	5
y	-4	-4	-4

Step 2   Plot the points: $(0, -4)$, $(3, -4)$, $(5, -4)$.

Step 3   Draw the straight line passing through the three points.

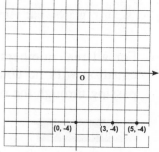

Figure 6.7

Answers:

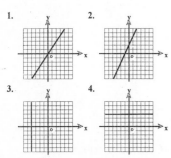

Note: Observe that the graph of $y = -4$ is a horizontal line through (0,- 4).

The graph of the linear equation $y = k$ is a **horizontal** line through the point $(0, k)$. In particular, the graph of $y = 0$ is the x-axis.

Intercepts

Consider the graph in example 2 (Figure 6.5). Notice that the graph crosses the x-axis at $(3, 0)$ and the y-axis at $(0, 2)$. Then $(3, 0)$ is called the **x-intercept** of the graph. Sometimes we say that the x-intercept is 3. Similarly, $(0, 2)$ is called the **y-intercept** of the graph. Sometimes we say that the y-intercept is 2.

- To find the x-intercept, substitute 0 for y in the given equation and solve for x.

- To find the y-intercept, substitute 0 for x in the given equation and solve for y.

Observations:

1. The graph of a linear equation of the form $x = k$ (no y – term) has only one x-intercept, which is $(k, 0)$, and no y-intercept. For example, the x-intercept of $x + 2 = 0$ is $(-2, 0)$.

2. The graph of a linear equation of the form $y = k$ (no x – term) has only one y-intercept, namely, $(0, k)$, and no x intercept. For example, the y-intercept of $y = 3$ is $(0, 3)$.

3. The graph of a linear equation of the form $ax + by = 0$ (no constant term) has an x intercept $(0, 0)$ and a y-intercept $(0, 0)$.

B. Using Intercepts for the Graph of a Linear Equation

For an equation of the form $ax + by + c = 0$ with a, b and c all non-zero, we can use the intercepts to draw the graph.

Step 1	Find the x -intercept.
Step 2	Find the y -intercept.
Step 3	Find another point for a check.
Step 4	Plot the three points and draw a straight line through them.

Warm Up

Example 5: Find the intercepts for the graph of $x - 2y = 6$. Draw the graph.

5. Find the intercepts for the graph of $2x - y = 6$.

Solution:

Step 1 **x–intercept:** Substitute 0 for y.
$x - 2 \cdot 0 = 6 \longrightarrow x = 6$
The x -intercept is $(6, 0)$.

Step 2 **y–intercept:** Substitute 0 for x.
$0 - 2y = 6 \longrightarrow y = -3$
The y -intercept is $(0, -3)$.

Step 3 Check point:
If $x = 2$, then $2 - 2y = 6$
$-2y = 4 \longrightarrow y = -2$

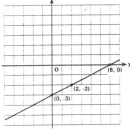

Figure 6.8

Then $(2, -2)$ is another point on the graph.

Step 4 Plot the points $(6, 0)$, $(0, -3)$, $(2, -2)$, and draw a straight line through them. (Figure 6.8).

Note: The method of using intercepts to graph a linear equation consists essentially of determining three points.

Warm Up

6. Graph the linear equations

using intercepts: $y = \dfrac{x}{2} - 1$.

Answers:

5. $(3, 0)$ and $(0, -6)$

6. $(0, -1)$ and $(2, 0)$

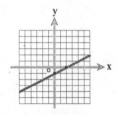

Example 6:   Graph the linear equation $3y = 5x - 2$.

Solution:

Rewrite this equation as $5x - 3y = 2$.

x-intercept: $5x - 3 \cdot \mathbf{0} = 2 \ (y = 0)$

Solve for x : $x = \dfrac{2}{5}$

Therefore, the x-intercept is $\left(\dfrac{2}{5}, 0\right)$

y-intercept: $5 \cdot \mathbf{0} - 3y = 2 \ (x = 0)$

Solve for y : $y = -\dfrac{2}{3}$

Therefore, the y-intercept is $\left(0, -\dfrac{2}{3}\right)$.

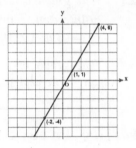

Figure 6.9

Since the x-intercept and the y-intercept are fractional numbers, which are usually difficult to plot exactly, we construct a table of *three* x- and y-values.

x	1	4	-2
y	1	6	-4

We plot the points $(1, 1)$, $(4, 6)$, $(-2, -4)$ and draw a straight line through them **(Fig. 6.9)**.

EXERCISE 6.2

In exercises 1–8, complete the table of x- and y-values. Draw the graph of the equation by plotting these points.

1. $x = 3$:

x			
y	0	2	5
(x, y)			

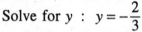

2. $y = 5$:

x	-4	0	2
y			
(x, y)			

3. $x + 2 = 0$:

x			
y	3	-1	4
(x, y)			

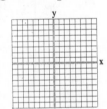

4. $2y + 6 = 0$:

x	-3	1	3
y			
(x, y)			

5. $2x + y = 0$:

x	-3	1	3
y			
(x, y)			

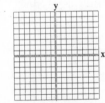

6. $3x = 5y$:

x	0	5	
y			-3
(x, y)			

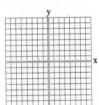

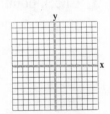

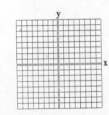

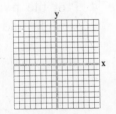

7. $2x + 3y = 2$:

x		4	
y	2		0
(x,y)			

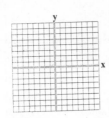

8. $3x = 1 + 4y$:

x		3	-5
y	-1		
(x,y)			

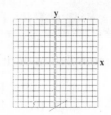

In exercises 9–14, find the intercepts for each equation.

9. $3x + 5y = 15$

10. $-4x + 3y = 12$

11. $x - 7y = 3$

12. $4x - y = 0$

13. $2x + 3 = 0$

14. $3y = 5$

In exercises 15–24, graph the linear equations. Use the intercepts wherever convenient.

15. $x + 2y = 4$

16. $2x - 3y = 6$

17. $2x + 3y = 5$

18. $x = 3y + 2$

19. $x = -3$

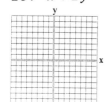 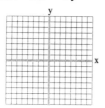 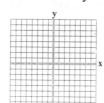 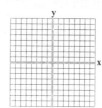 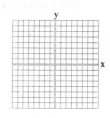

20. $y + 1 = 0$

21. $x + y + 4 = 0$

22. $3x - y = 4$

23. $x = 0$

24. $y = 0$

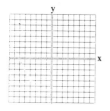 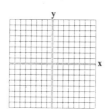 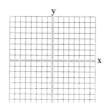 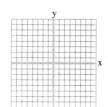 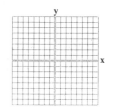

In exercises 25–26, complete the table of x- and y-values. Plot these points and draw the graph.

25. $y = -x^2$

x	0	1	2	3	-1	-2	-3
y							
(x,y)							

26. $y = x^2 + 2x + 2$

x	0	1	2	-1	-2	-3	-4
y							
(x,y)							

 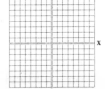

6.3   SLOPE OF A LINE

Upon completion of this section we will be able to:

        A.   Find the slope of a line given two points.

        B.   Find the slope from the equation of a line.

        C.   Use the slope to determine whether two lines are parallel or perpendicular.

A.   Definition of Slope

In the Figure 6.10 there are three points P, Q, R with coordinates $(x_1, y_1), (x_2, y_2), (x_3, y_3)$, respectively, on the line L. For two points on the line, we want to measure the ratio of the change in the y-coordinates to the change in their x-coordinates. Construct the point $S(x_2, y_1)$ as shown in figure 6.10 and observe that

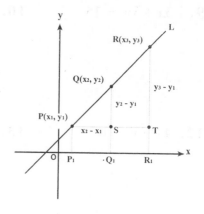

$QS = QQ_1 - SQ_1 = QQ_1 - PP_1 = y_2 - y_1 =$ the change in y-coordinates

$SP = P_1Q_1 = OQ_1 - OP_1 = x_2 - x_1 =$ the change in x-coordinates.

Figure 6.10

Therefore, $\dfrac{\text{change in y - coordinates from } P \text{ to } Q}{\text{change in x - coordinates from } P \text{ to } Q} = \dfrac{y_2 - y_1}{x_2 - x_1}$

Similarly, construct the point $T(x_3, y_1)$ and observe that

$$\frac{\text{change in y - coordinates from } P \text{ to } R}{\text{change in x - coordinates from } P \text{ to } R} = \frac{y_3 - y_1}{x_3 - x_1}.$$

The triangles PQS and PRT are similar triangles [notice $\overleftrightarrow{QS}$ and $\overleftrightarrow{RT}$ are parallel, and parallel to the y-axis]. Therefore,

$$\frac{QS}{SP} = \frac{RT}{TP} \quad \text{or} \quad \frac{y_2 - y_1}{x_2 - x_1} = \frac{y_3 - y_1}{x_3 - x_1}.$$

Thus, this ratio does not depend on the choice of two points on a line. Actually, this *measures the inclination or steepness* of a line, and is called the **slope** of the line.

The **slope** of a line passing through the points (x_1, y_1) and (x_2, y_2) is:

$$\text{Slope} = \frac{y_2 - y_1}{x_2 - x_1}, \quad \text{if } x_1 \neq x_2.$$

A slope is determined by two points on a line. If the x-coordinates of two points on a line are equal, then the line must be vertical (parallel to y-axis). Vertical lines have equations of the form $x = k$. **The slope is not defined for a vertical line.**(Why?) Because all points on a vertical line have the same x-coordinate, therefore the denominator of the ratio for the slope of the vertical line is zero.

If two points on a line have equal y - coordinates, the line must be horizontal (parallel to the x–axis). Horizontal lines have equations of the form $y = k$. **The slope of a horizontal line is 0.** (Why?) Because all points in a horizontal line have the same y–coordinate, therefore the numerator of the ratio for the slope is zero.

Example 1:   Find the slope of the following lines. Draw the graph of these lines.

a)   The line through $(3,5)$ and $(2,-1)$.

b)   The line through $(2,-3)$ and $(-1,2)$.

Solutions:

To draw these lines, plot the two given points and join them by a straight line.

a) Slope $= \dfrac{-1-5}{2-3} = \dfrac{-6}{-1} = 6$ **b)** Slope $= \dfrac{2-(-3)}{-1-2} = \dfrac{5}{-3} = -\dfrac{5}{3}$

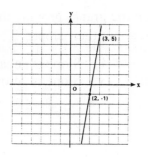

Figure 6.11

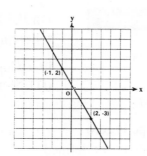

Figure 6.12

Warm Up

1. Find the slope of line through following pair of points:
   a) $(2, 4)$ and $(-1 , 1)$

   b) $(1, 5)$ and $(-1, -1)$

Observation:

In Example 1(a), the slope is positive and the line rises from left to right. In Example 1 (b), the slope is negative, and the line falls from left to right.

• If the slope of a line is *positive,* then it *rises* from left to right.
• If the slope of a line is *negative,* then it *falls* from left to right.

Example 2:   Find the slopes of the lines through the points.

a) $(3,5),(6,7)$ **b)** $(1,4),(3,4)$

c) $(2,-1),(2,0)$

Solutions:

a) $(3,5),(6,7)$:   Slope $= \dfrac{7-5}{6-3} = \dfrac{2}{3}$

b) $(1,4),(3,4)$:   Slope $= \dfrac{4-4}{3-1} = \dfrac{0}{2} = 0$ Horizontal line

c) $(2,-1),(2,0)$:   Slope $= \dfrac{0-(-1)}{2-2} = \dfrac{1}{0}$ Undefined vertical line

2. Find the slopes of the lines through the given points.

   a) $(3, 8)$ and $(4, 5)$

   b) $(3, -1)$ and $(1, -1)$

   c) $(3, 6)$ and $(3, 13)$

Warm Up

3. Given four lines who slopes

are: **a)** 0 **b)** $\dfrac{1}{2}$ **c)** −3

d) not defined

determine which of these lines :

i) fall from left to right

ii) vertical

iii) rising from left to right

iv) horizontal

4. Describe the slope of the following lines:
a) horizontal line
b) line rises from left to right
c) line falls from left to right
d) vertical line

Answers:

1. a) 1 **b)** 3

2. a) −3 **b)** 0 **c)** undefined

3. a) IV **b)** III **c)** I **d)** II

4. a) 0 **b)** positive **c)** negative
d) undefined

Example 3: Given four lines whose slopes are:

a) 4 **b)** not defined **c)** $-\dfrac{1}{3}$ **d)** 0,

determine which of these lines is:

i)   Rising from the left to right
ii)   Falling from left to right
iii)   Vertical
iv)   Horizontal.

Solutions:

a) Since the slope is a positive, line is rising from left to right.
b) Since the slope is not defined, the line is vertical.
c) Since the slope is negative, the graph is falling from left to right.
d) Since the slope is zero, the graph is a horizontal line.

Example 4: For the lines shown on the graph, provide the following information about their slopes.

i) Slope is positive.   **ii)** Slope is negative.
iii) Slope is not defined. **iv)** Slope is zero.

Solutions:

I: Slope is zero   [horizontal line]
J: Slope is not defined   [vertical line]
K: Slope is negative   [falls from left to right]
L: Slope is zero   [horizontal line]
M: Slope is positive   [rising from left to right]
N: Slope is not defined   [vertical line]

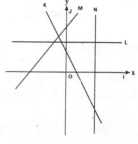

Figure 6.13

B.   Finding the slope of a line from the equation of the line

We know that the graph of a linear equation is a line. Linear equations can be written in one of the two forms: i) $x = a$ (if the y term is absent) ii) $y = mx + b$ (if the **y** term is present).

The slope of a line can be determined directly from its equation.

-   The slope of the line with equation $x = a$ is **undefined**.
-   The slope of the line with equation $y = mx + b$ is **m**.

The following examples provide verification of the above statements.

332

Example 5: For each of the following equations, take any two points on the line and calculate the slope.

   a) $x = -2$ **b)** $y = 3x + 1$

Solutions:

a) $x = -2$: $(-2, 1)$, $(-2, 0)$ are two points on the graph of $x = -2$.

Slope $= \dfrac{0-1}{-2-(-2)} = \dfrac{-1}{0}$.   Undefined

Therefore, the slope of $x = -2$ is undefined.

Notice that graph of $x = -2$ is a vertical line.

b) $y = 3x + 1$: $(1, 4)$ and $(0, 1)$ are two points on the graph of $y = 3x + 1$.

Slope $= \dfrac{1-4}{0-1} = \dfrac{-3}{-1} = 3$

Thus slope = coefficient of x in the equation $y = 3x + 1$.

Example 6: Determine the slopes of the following lines.

   a) $y = 4x - 2$ **b)** $3y + 5x = 0$

   c) $\dfrac{x}{3} - \dfrac{y}{4} = 4$ **d)** $3x - 2y + 6 = 0$

   e) $3x + 5 = 0$

Solutions:

a) $y = 4x - 2$

  Step 1   Solve the equation for y. $y = 4x - 2$

  Step 2   Slope = coefficient of x = **4**.

b) $3y + 5x = 0$

  Step 1 $3y = -5x$ Solve for y

       $y = \dfrac{-5}{3}x$

  Step 2   Slope = coefficient of x.

       $= -\dfrac{5}{3}$

c) $\dfrac{x}{3} - \dfrac{y}{5} = 4$

  Step 1   Solve for y.

       $5x - 3y = 60 \longrightarrow -3y = 60 - 5x$

       $\longrightarrow -3y = -5x + 60$

       $\longrightarrow y = \dfrac{5}{3}x - 20$

  Step 2   Slope = coefficient of x.

       $= \dfrac{5}{3}$

d) $3x - 2y - 6 = 0$

d) $3x - 2y + 6 = 0$

Step 1 $-2y = -3x - 6$ Solve for y

$$y = \frac{3}{2}x + 3$$

Step 2   Slope = coefficient of x.

$$= \frac{3}{2}.$$

e) $2y - 5 = 0$

e) $3x + 5 = 0$

$3x + 5 = 0$ cannot be solved for y since it does not contain a y - term. The equation $3x + 5 = 0$ can be written in the form $x = -\dfrac{5}{3}$,   which is a vertical line. Hence, the slope is undefined.

Answers:

5. a) 0 b) 2

6. a) 3 b) $\frac{5}{2}$ c) $\frac{3}{4}$ d) $\frac{3}{2}$ e) 0

C. Slope of Parallel and Perpendicular Lines

Recall that two lines are said to be **parallel** if they do not intersect.   The lines $y = 3x - 5$ and $y = 3x + 1$ have the same slope. The graphs of these lines are shown on the same coordinate system in Figure 6.14. The two lines are parallel. **Any two non-vertical lines are parallel if and only if they have the same slope.**

Next consider the graphs of $-2y = x + 1$ and $y = 2x$. Notice that their slopes are respectively $-1/2$ and 2. The product of their slopes is $= (-2)\left(\dfrac{1}{2}\right) = -1$. The two lines are shown in Figure 6.15 and are perpendicular.

Any two lines, neither of which is horizontal or vertical, are perpendicular if and only if the *product of their slopes is –1.*

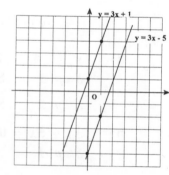

Figure 6.14

- Two *non-vertical* lines are parallel if and only if they have the same slope.

- Two lines, *neither of which is vertical nor horizontal,* are perpendicular if and only if the product of their slopes is –1. We also say that the two slopes are negative reciprocals of each other.

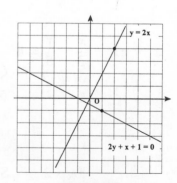

Figure 6.15

334

Example 7: Determine whether each of the following pairs of lines is parallel, perpendicular or neither.

a) $3x + 2y = 4$
$4x + 6y = 3$

b) $2x + 3y = 3$
$2y = 3x - 4$

c) $4x + 6y = 3$
$6x + 9y = 7$

Solutions:

a) Slope of $3x + 2y = 4$
$2y = -3x + 4$
$y = -\dfrac{3}{2}x + 2$
Slope $= -\dfrac{3}{2}$

Slope of $2y = 3x - 4$
$y = \dfrac{3}{2}x - 2$
Slope $= \dfrac{3}{2}$

The slopes are not equal, and their product is not equal to -1. Therefore, $3x + 2y = 4$ and $2y = 3x - 4$ are neither parallel nor perpendicular.

b) Slope of $2x + 3y = 3$
$3y = -2x + 3$
$y = -\dfrac{2}{3}x + 1$
Slope $= -\dfrac{2}{3}$

Slope of $2y = 3x - 4$
$y = \dfrac{3}{2}x - 2$
Slope $= \dfrac{3}{2}$

The product of the slopes of the two lines $= \left(-\dfrac{2}{3}\right) \cdot \left(\dfrac{3}{2}\right) = -1$.

Therefore, the two lines are perpendicular.

c) Slope of $4x + 6y = 3$
$6y = 3 - 4x$
$y = \dfrac{3}{6} - \dfrac{4}{6}x$
$y = \dfrac{1}{2} - \dfrac{2}{3}x$
Slope $= -\dfrac{2}{3}$

Slope of $6x + 9y = 7$
$y = \dfrac{7}{9} - \dfrac{6}{9}x$
$y = \dfrac{7}{9} - \dfrac{2}{3}x$
Slope $= -\dfrac{2}{3}$

The slopes of $4x + 6y = 3$ and $6x + 9y = 7$ are equal. Therefore, the two lines are parallel.

Warm Up

7. Determine whether the following pair of lines is parallel, perpendicular or neither.

a) $5x + 3y = 8$
$3x + 4y = 5$

b) $5x + 3y = 8$
$3x - 5y = 5$

c) $5x + 3y = 8$
$10x + 6y = 11$

Answers:

7. **a)** neither parallel nor perpendicular

b) perpendicular

c) parallel

EXERCISE 6.3

In exercises 1–8, find the slope of the line passing through the given pair of points.

1. $(3,2), (-2,4)$ **2.** $(1,-1), (-1,1)$ **3.** $(-2,3), (-2,5)$

Answers:

1. _____

2. _____

3. _____

4. _____

5. _____

6. _____

7. _____

8. _____

9. _____

10. _____

11. _____

12. _____

13. _____

14. _____

15. _____

4. $(4,1), (-5,1)$ **5.** $(3,0), (0,4)$ **6.** $(3,0), (3,-3),$

7. $(1,4), (5,-3)$ **8.** $(3,-1), (1,-2)$

In exercises 9–15, find the slope of the line.

9. $y = 4x - 1$ **10.** $3x + 5y = 1$ **11.** $2x = y + 1$

12. $-2x + 4y = 7$ **13.** $3x - y = 2$ **14.** $3x + 3y = 1$

15. $2x - 3y + 4 = 0$

16. **Consider the lines A, B, C, D, and E in the figure. For each line, which of the following is true.**

   I.   The slope is positive

   II.   The slope is negative.

   III. The slope is zero

   IV. The slope is not defined.

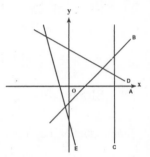

Exercise 16

17. _____

18. _____

19. _____

20. _____

In exercises 17–20, without drawing the graph of the line, determine whether the line is rising from left to right or falling from left to right.

17. $3x = 4y - 7$ **18.** $2x + 3y = 9$

19. $5y - 4x + 1 = 0$ **20.** $x + 7y - 2 = 0$

In exercises 21–24, given two points on each line, use these points to find the slopes and verify that: (1) the slopes of parallel lines are equal, and (2) the product of the slopes of perpendicular lines is –1.

21.

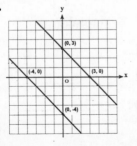

22.

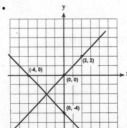

23.

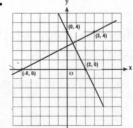

24.

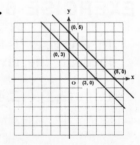

In exercises 25–30, determine whether the pair of lines is parallel, perpendicular or neither.

25. $y = 3x + 7$
      $y = 3x - 5$

26. $y = 2x + 1$
      $2y = -1$

27. $3y + 5x = 1$
       $5y - 3x + 4 = 0$

28. $2y = 4x + 7$
      $4y + 2x = 0$

29. $2x + 3y = 4$
      $6y = 5 - 4x$

30. $7y + 2x = 4$
      $7y = 1 + 2x$

25. _____

26. _____

27. _____

28. _____

29. _____

30. _____

6.4   EQUATION OF A LINE

In this section we shall investigate how to find the equation of a line and its graph under some given conditions. Specifically, we will learn to:

     A.   Write the equation of a line given its slope and y-intercept.
     B.   Graph a line given the slope and y-intercept.
     C.   Write the equation of a line given its slope and a point on the line.
     D.   Write the equation of a line given two points on the line.

A. Slope-Intercept Form of a Line

From the last section we know that for the equation $y = mx + b$, m (the coefficient of x) is the slope of the line $y = mx + b$. What does b represent? Notice that $y = m \cdot 0 + b$ implies that $(0, b)$ is the y-intercept of the line. Recall that the y-intercept of a line is obtained by substituting zero for x and solving for y.

The equation $y = mx + b$ is called the **slope-intercept** form of the equation of a line. Here the slope is m, and the y-intercept is $(0, b)$.

Example 1:   Find the equation of a line given that:

     a)   slope $= -2$, y-intercept is $(0, 4)$.

     b)   slope $= \dfrac{5}{3}$, y-intercept is $(0, -3)$.

Solutions:

     Since, we are given the slope and y-intercept, we shall use the slope-intercept form to find the equation of the lines.

     a)   Let the equation of the line be: $y = mx + b$
        Here, slope $= m = -2$ <small>Given</small>
        y-intercept $= (0, b) = (0, 4)$ <small>Given</small>
        Therefore, $b = 4$.

        Hence, the equation of the line is: $y = -2x + 4.$

Warm Up

1. Find the equation of a line given that:

   a) Slope $= -3$, y-intercept is $(0, 2)$

337

Warm Up

b) Slope $= \dfrac{3}{5}$, y-intercept is $(0, 3)$

Answers:

1. **a)** $y = -3x + 2$ **b)** $y = \dfrac{3}{5}x + 3$

b)   Let the equation of the line be: $y = mx + b$

Here, slope $= m = \dfrac{5}{3}$,   Given

y-intercept $= (0, b) = (0, -3)$.   Given

Therefore, $b = -3$

Hence, the equation of the line is $y = \dfrac{5}{3}x - 3$ or $3y = 5x - 9$.

B.   Graphing a Line in the Slope - Intercept Form

Recall that the general method to graph a line, whose equation (in any form) is given is to first find three points on the line, plot them, and join them by a straight line. However, when the equation is given in the slope-intercept form, we can use the slope and the intercept directly to draw the graph. We demonstrate this with the help of two examples.

Warm Up

2. Graph the line $y = 3x + 4$

Example 2:   Graph the line $y = 2x - 3$.

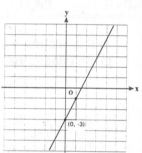

Step 1   Find the y-intercept and slope.
The y-intercept is $(0, -3)$.
Slope $= 2$

Step 2   Plot the point $(0, -3)$.

Step 3   Slope $= \dfrac{2}{1} = \dfrac{\text{change in } y - \text{coordinates}}{\text{change in } x - \text{coordinates}}$

Figure 6.16

Therefore, starting from the point $(0, -3)$ move 1 unit horizontally to the *right* and 2 units vertically *upwards*. Recall that the movement to right (horizontally) and upwards (vertically) signifies positive changes in both directions

Step 4   Join $(0, -3)$ and the new point by a straight line.

3. Graph the line $y = -2x + 5$

Example 3:   Graph the line
$$y = -\frac{2}{5}x + 1.$$

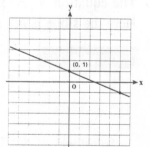

Step 1   Slope of the line: $-\dfrac{2}{5}$
The y-intercept is : $(0, 1)$

Step 2   Plot the point $(0, 1)$.

Figure 6.17

Step 3   Slope $= \dfrac{-2}{5} = \dfrac{\text{change in } y - \text{coordinates}}{\text{change in } x - \text{coordinates}}$

Therefore, starting from the point $(0, 1)$ move 5 units horizontally to the *right* and 2 units vertically *downwards*.

Step 4   Join $(0, 1)$ and the resulting point by a straight line.

338

Note: We may also interpret $-\dfrac{2}{5}$ as $\dfrac{2}{-5}$. In this case starting from $(0,1)$ we shall move 5 units horizontally to the *left* and 2 units vertically *upwards.* This will also result in the same straight line.

Example 4: Graph the line with slope -3 and passing through $(2, 2)$.

Solution:

Plot the point $(2,2)$.

Slope $= -3 = \dfrac{-3}{1}$. Starting from the point $(2,2)$ move 1 unit horizontally to the right and 3 units vertically downwards. Join the two points.

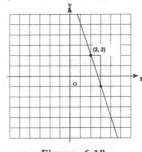

Figure 6.18

Warm Up

4. Graph the line with slope 1.5 and passing through $(2, 1)$.

Answers:

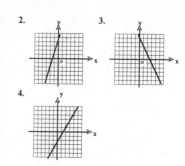

2.   3.

4.

C. Equation of a Line in "Point - slope" Form

The equation of a line is said to be in **point-slope** form if the equation involves the slope of the line and the coordinates of a given point on the line. Suppose a line passes through a point (x_1, y_1) and has slope **m.** Now take any other point (x, y) on the line.

Therefore, the slope $= \dfrac{y - y_1}{x - x_1} = m$ or $y - y_1 = m(x - x_1)$. This is known as the point-slope form of the equation of a line.

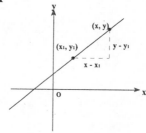

Figure 6.19

> The point-slope form of the equation of a line with slope m and passing through (x_1, y_1) is $y - y_1 = m(x - x_1)$

We took "any other point" as (x, y). Since it is not a specific point, (x, y) is used to represent variable numbers. The point (x, y) is also called a general point on the line.

Example 5: Find the equation of the line with slope $-1/2$ and passing through $(3, -1)$.

Solution:

Since the slope of the line and a point on it are given, the point–slope form is used. The point-slope form of an equation is $y - y_1 = m(x - x_1)$.

Here $m = -\dfrac{1}{2}$, $x_1 = 3$, and $y_1 = -1$. Substitute these values in the equation and we have the following:

$$y - (\mathbf{-1}) = -\frac{\mathbf{1}}{\mathbf{2}}(x - 3) \longrightarrow y + \mathbf{1} = -\frac{1}{2}(x - 3)$$

$$\mathbf{2}(y + 1) = -(x - 3) \qquad \text{Use the distributive property}$$

$$2y + 2 = -x + 3 \longrightarrow 2y + x = 1$$

Verify that the point $(3, -1)$ satisfies this equation.

Warm Up

5. Find the equation of the line with slope $\left(-\dfrac{3}{2}\right)$ and passing through $(6, 1)$.

Warm Up

6. Find the equation of a line:

a) passing through $(2, -3)$ and parallel to $x + 3y = 6$

Example 6:   Find the equation of a line:

    a) passing through $(4,5)$ and *parallel* to $2x - 3y = 4$.

    b) passing through $(-2,1)$ and *perpendicular* to $4x + 7y + 3 = 0$.

Solutions:

a) $2x - 3y = 4 \longrightarrow 3y = 2x - 4 \longrightarrow y = \dfrac{2}{3}x - \dfrac{4}{3}$

The slope of $2x - 3y = 4$ is $\dfrac{2}{3}$.

Since the line in question is parallel to $2x - 3y = 4$, its slope is also $\dfrac{2}{3}$.

Therefore, find the equation of the line with slope $\dfrac{2}{3}$, and passing through $(4,5)$.

    Here, $m = \dfrac{2}{3}$, $x_1 = 4$ and $y_1 = 5$.

Substitute these values in the point-slope form.

$$y - y_1 = m(x - x_1)$$

$$y - 5 = \dfrac{2}{3}(x - 4) \longrightarrow 3(y - 5) = 2(x - 4)$$

$$\longrightarrow 3y - 15 = 2x - 8$$

$$\longrightarrow 3y = 2x + 7$$

Verify that the point $(4,5)$ satisfies this equation.

---

b) passing through $(3, 5)$ and perpendicular to $2x + 5y = 7$

---

b) $4x + 7y + 3 = 0$ Solve for y.

$$7y = -4x - 3$$

$$y = -\dfrac{4}{7}x - \dfrac{3}{7}$$

The slope of $4x + 7y + 3 = 0$ is $-\dfrac{4}{7}$. Let the slope of the desired line be m. Since the two lines are perpendicular,

$$-\dfrac{4}{7} \cdot m = -1$$

or $m = \dfrac{7}{4}$, the negative reciprocal of $-\dfrac{4}{7}$.

We now find the equation of the line with the slope $\dfrac{7}{4}$ and passing through the point $(-2, 1)$.

Here $m = \dfrac{7}{4}$, $x_1 = -2$ and $y_1 = 1$. Substitute these values in the point-slope form.

$$y - y_1 = m(x - x_1)$$

$$y - \mathbf{1} = \frac{7}{4}(x - (\mathbf{-2})) \longrightarrow y - 1 = \frac{7}{4}(x + 2)$$

$$\longrightarrow 4(y - 1) = 7(x + 2)$$

$$\longrightarrow 4y - 4 = 7x + 14$$

$$\longrightarrow 4y = 7x + 18$$

Verify that the point $(-2, 1)$ satisfies this equation

D.   Equation of a Line in Two–point Form

We know that a line is completely determined by any two points on it. We use the point-slope form to find the equation of a line when two points on it are known.

Suppose (x_1, y_1) and (x_2, y_2) are two points on a line. Assume that the line is not vertical, so that its slope can be determined.

$$\text{The slope of the line} = \frac{y_2 - y_1}{x_2 - x_1}.$$

Thus, the line has the slope $= \dfrac{y_2 - y_1}{x_2 - x_1}$ and passes through (x_1, y_1).

Substituting these values in the point slope form $y - y_1 = m(x - x_1)$

We get : $\quad y - y_1 = \dfrac{y_2 - y_1}{x_2 - x_1}(x - x_1)$

which is the required equation of a line in two point form.

Note: We could use the slope $\dfrac{y_2 - y_1}{x_2 - x_1}$ and the point (x_2, y_2) "instead of" the slope $= \dfrac{y_2 - y_1}{x_2 - x_1}$ and the point (x_1, y_1). The resulting equation will be the same as the original equation.

The equation of the line passing through the points (x_1, y_1) and (x_2, y_2) is

$$(y - y_1)(x_2 - x_1) = (x - x_1)(y_2 - y_1) \quad \text{or} \quad (y - y_2)(x_2 - x_1) = (x - x_2)(y_2 - y_1).$$

This is called the **two-point** form equation of a line.

Note: If the x-coordinate of two points on a line are equal, then the line must be vertical. The slope of such a line is not defined. The point-slope and slope intercept forms cannot be used in such cases. However, the two-point form of the equation: $(y - y_1)(y_2 - y_1) = (x - x_1)(x_2 - x_1)$ can still be used to find the equation of a vertical line.

Example 7:   Find the equation of a line passing through $(-2, 5)$ and $(3, 4)$.

Since two points on the line are known, use the two-point form

$$(y - y_1)(x_2 - x_1) = (x - x_1)(y_2 - y_1).$$

Here, $x_1 = -2$, $y_1 = 5$, $x_2 = 3$, and $y_2 = 4$.

Therefore, the equation of the line is:

$$(y - 5)(3 - (-2)) = (x - (-2))(4 - 5) \qquad \text{Simplify}$$

$$5(y - 5) = -1(x + 2)$$

$$5y - 25 = -x - 2$$

$$5y + x = 23.$$

EXERCISE 6.4

Answers:

1. _____

2. _____

3. _____

4. _____

5. _____

6. _____

7. _____

8. _____

9. _____

10. _____

11. _____

In exercises 1–5,   find the equation of a line.

1. Slope $= 2$,   y - intercept $(0, 3)$

2. Slope $= -3$,   y - intercept $(0, -2)$

3. Slope $= -1$,   y - intercept $\left(0, \dfrac{2}{3}\right)$

4. Slope $= \dfrac{3}{5}$,   y - intercept $(0, 4)$

5. Slope $= 0$,   y - intercept $\left(0, -\dfrac{1}{2}\right)$

In exercises 6–11,   graph the line for which the slope m and one of its points are given.

6. $m = \dfrac{3}{2}$; $(-4, 2)$ 7. $m = -\dfrac{5}{2}$; $(1, 1)$

8. $m = 0$; $(2, 1)$ 9. $m = $ undefined; $(3, -1)$

10. $m = 4$; $(2, 5)$ 11. $m = -2$; $(-2, -1)$

In exercises 12–14, rewrite the equations in slope-intercept form.

12. $x - y = 3$ **13.** $3x - 5y = 4$ **14.** $2x + 7y - 9 = 0$

In exercises 15–21, find the equation of the line with a given slope and passing through a given point.

15. $m = 4;\ (-1, 2)$ **16.** $m = -3;\ (2, 5)$ **17.** $m = -\dfrac{4}{5};\ (-1, 0)$

18. $m = 0;\ \left(\dfrac{5}{3}, -\dfrac{3}{7}\right)$ **19.** $m = \dfrac{5}{2};\ (2, 5)$ **20.** $m = -\dfrac{2}{3};\ \left(\dfrac{1}{2}, \dfrac{3}{4}\right)$

21. $m = -\dfrac{7}{9};\ x - \text{intercept } (4, 0)$

In exercises 22–26, find the equation of the line with the given two points.

22. $(-1, 2), (2, 3)$ **23.** $(1, 0), (0, 5)$ **24.** $(-4, 3), (3, -4)$

25. $\left(\dfrac{1}{3}, 1\right), \left(\dfrac{2}{3}, \dfrac{4}{3}\right)$ **26.** $\left(-\dfrac{1}{5}, \dfrac{2}{3}\right), \left(\dfrac{3}{5}, 4\right)$

In exercises 27–30, find the equation of the line with the given conditions.

27. passes through $(2, 1)$, and is parallel to the line $4x - 3y = 1$.

28. passes through $(-3, 2)$, and is perpendicular to the line $2x + y = 3$.

29. passes through $(4, 3)$, and is perpendicular to $3x - 2y + 4 = 0$.

30. passes through $(4, 3)$, and is parallel to $3x - 2y + 4 = 0$.

12. _____

13. _____

14. _____

15. _____

16. _____

17. _____

18. _____

19. _____

20. _____

21. _____

22. _____

23. _____

24. _____

25. _____

26. _____

27. _____

28. _____

29. _____

30. _____

6.5   GRAPHING LINEAR INEQUALITIES IN TWO VARIABLES

In Chapter 2 we learned how to solve linear inequalities in one variable. In this chapter we shall learn to solve linear inequalities in two variables. Recall that the solving and graphing of linear inequalities in one variable make use of the solution of the *corresponding linear equation*. In just the same way, the solving and graphing of linear inequalities in two variables uses the graphing of the *corresponding equation*. We shall refer to ≤ (less than or **equal to**) and ≥   (greater than or **equal to**) types of inequalities as **non-strict** inequalities, and < and > types of inequalities as **strict** inequalities.

Upon completion of this section we will be able to:

> A .   Graph strict and non-strict inequalities.

A.   Graphing Inequalities

Any linear inequality $ax + by + c \begin{array}{|c|} \geq \\ \leq \\ > \\ < \end{array} 0$ gives rise to the corresponding linear equation

$ax + by + c = 0$. The graph of this linear equation is a straight line. This straight line divides the plane into two regions (since the line extends indefinitely in both directions). These regions are marked I and II. [See Figure 6.20]

Basic Principles

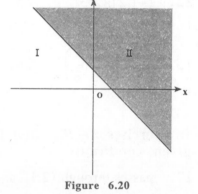

- All points in one of the two regions satisfy $ax + by + c < 0$.

- All points in the other region of the plane satisfy $ax + by + c > 0$.

To graph an inequality in two variables we use the following steps.

Figure 6.20

Step 1	Replace the inequality by an equality and graph the resulting equation. This graph is a line which will be called the **boundary**. Draw a solid boundary line if the inequality is non-strict, and a dotted/dashed line if the inequality is strict.
Step 2	Choose a **test point not on the boundary**. Substitute the coordinates of the point in the inequality.
Step 3	If the resulting statement is *true*, then the region of the plane *containing* the *test point* should be shaded for the graph of solutions of the inequality. If the resulting statement is *false*, shade the region *not containing* the test point for the graph of the inequality. If the inequality is non-strict, then the boundary line is a part of the graph (solution). The graph of an inequality is the set of all possible solutions of that inequality.

344

Example 1:   Graph the inequality $2x - y > 3$.

Step 1   Graph the line $2x - y = 3$ as a *dotted* line since the inequality is *strict*.

Step 2   Choose a test point. Let us choose $(0,0)$.
$2 \cdot 0 - 0 > 3$ or $0 > 3$ FALSE

Step 3   Shade the region *not containing* $(0,0)$ for the graph of the inequality

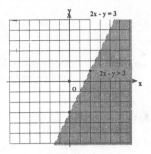

Figure 6.21

Note: If the boundary *does not* pass through the origin, then it is convenient to use the origin, i.e. $(0,0)$, as a test point.

We can graph the solution of an inequality using calculator. See example 1 on page 522 in Appendix B.

Example 2:   Graph the inequality $y \le 3x$.

Step 1   Graph the line $y = 3x$ as a *solid line* since the inequality is *non strict*.

Step 2   Choose a test point. Let us choose $(1,0)$. Notice that we cannot choose $(0,0)$ as a test point since the boundary passes through $(0,0)$.
$0 \le 3 \cdot 1$ or $0 \le 3$ TRUE

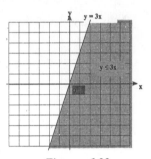

Figure 6.22

Step 3   Shade the region of the plane which contains the test point $(1,0)$ for the graph of the inequality.

Example 3:   Graph the inequality $2y < 5$.

Step 1   Graph the line $2y = 5$ as a *dotted line* since the inequality is *strict*.

Step 2   Choose a test point. Let the test point be $(0,0)$.   Notice that $2y = 5$ does not contain $(0,0)$.
$2 \cdot 0 < 5$ or $0 < 5$ TRUE

Step 3   Shade the region of the plane containing $(0, 0)$ for the graph of the inequality.

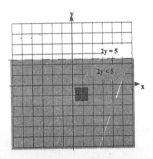

Figure 6.23

Warm Up

1. Graph the inequality
$3x - 2y > 5$

2. Graph the inequality $y \le \dfrac{3}{2} x$

3. Graph the inequality $3y < 7$

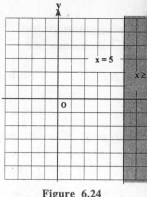

Figure 6.24

Warm Up

4. Graph the inequality $x \geq 3$

Answers:

1.

points on the line not included

2.

3.

4.

points on the line not included

Example 4:   Graph the inequality $x \geq 5$.

Step 1   Graph the line $x = 5$ as a *solid line,* since the inequality is *not strict.*

Step 2   Choose a test point, say $(0,0)$.
  $0 \geq 5$ **FALSE**

Step 3   Shade the region of the plane that does not contain the test point for the graph of the inequality.

Note: Compare the graph of the inequality $x \geq 5$ when considered in only one variable (Figure 6.25) with the graph $x \geq 5$ when it is considered to be in two variables (Figure 6.24). Notice that in two variables $x \geq 5 \longrightarrow x + 0 \cdot y \geq 5$.

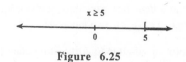

Figure 6.25

EXERCISE 6.5

In exercises 1–6, complete the graphs by shading the appropriate region.

1. $x + y > 3$

2. $2y - x \leq 5$

3. $3x - 4y \geq 12$

4. $3x + y < 0$

5. $x > -2$

6. $y \leq 0$

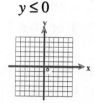

In exercises 7–16, graph the linear inequalities.

7. $x + 2y \leq 4$

8. $3x - 2y > 2$

9. $2x - y \leq -3$

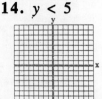

10. $x + 4y \geq 5$

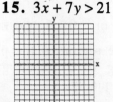

11. $x < y$

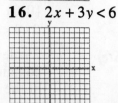

12. $3x \geq y$

13. $2x \geq -5$

14. $y < 5$

15. $3x + 7y > 21$

16. $2x + 3y < 6$

6.6   FUNCTIONS AND RELATIONS

The concept of a function is very important in mathematics. A function can be viewed as a rule that assigns *exactly one* element y in a set Y to each element x in set X.   For example the equation $y = 3x + 5$ is a rule which assigns to each real number x exactly one real number, namely "five more than three times x ." A function can be compared to an input/output machine.

Figure 6.26

A more general concept is that of a relation. In this section we study relations and functions.

Upon completion of this section we will be able to:

        A.   Understand the definition of a relation.
        B.   Understand the definition of a function.
        C.   Understand vertical line test.
        D.   Use the *f(x)* notation.

Definition of a Relation

Consider the following examples:

(i)   When a ball is thrown upwards, with a certain velocity, the position of the ball above the ground varies with the time the ball has been in air. Suppose distance of the ball from the ground, measured in feet, is given in terms of time t, measured in seconds, by the formula:

$$d = 100t - 16t^2.$$

For each value of t, we can get a value of d.   For example, when $t = 2$,

$$d = 100 \cdot 2 - 16 \cdot 2^2 = 136.$$

This can be expressed in the form of the ordered pair (2,136). The set of all such ordered pairs expresses a relationship between the position of the particle above the ground and the time taken to get to that position.

(ii)   Let X be the set of all whole numbers between 25 and 200, and Y the set of all persons living in a town. To a number n in X we associate all those persons " p " who are n years of age and write this as *(n, p)*.   The set of all such ordered pairs expresses the relationship between age and persons. This relation gives information about the number of people of a certain age in the town.

Any set of ordered pairs is called a **relation**. The set of all *first components* in the ordered pairs of a relation is called its **domain**, and the set of all *second components* is called its **range**.

Example 1: Find the domain and range of the relation
$\{(-3,1),\ (0,2),\ (-3,2),\ (1,1),\ (2,3),\ (4,-1)\}$.

Solution:

Domain = the set of all first components
= $\{-3, 0, 1, 2, 4\}$

Range = the set of all second components = $\{-1, 1, 2, 3\}$

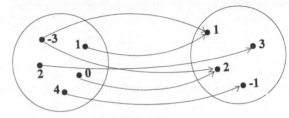

Figure 6.27

Note: Sometimes it is convenient to represent a relation graphically. For example, the relation in Example 1 above can be graphed as in Figure 6.27.

B. Definition of a Function

A function is a special type of relation. Notice that in example 1, the number -3 was associated with *two* elements, namely, 1 and 2. Such a situation is not permissible if a relation is to qualify as a function.

A **function** is a set of ordered pairs in which each distinct first component has exactly one second component.

Note: By definition every function is a relation. However some relations may not be functions. The relation in example 1 is not a function.

Most functions have an infinite number of ordered pairs and are defined by an equation which provides the rule for associating second components with first components. As a matter of convention, we shall use equations in x and y, where x represents the first component, and y represents the second component.

Examples of functions:

1. $y = |x|$ is a function. Some of the ordered pairs are:

$(0,0), (-1,1), (1,1), (-4,4), (5,5), (-5,5)$.

2. The equation $y = \dfrac{9}{5}x + 32$ expresses a relationship between the Fahrenheit scale of temperature *(y)* and the Celsius scale of temperature *(x)*. Thus, for example $(10,50)$ is an element of the function defined by $y = \dfrac{9}{5}x + 32$. This expresses the fact that $10°\,C$ corresponds to exactly one value $y = 50°\,F$.

C. Vertical Line Test

It is not necessary that all equations represent a function. For example, consider the equation $y^2 = x$. This equation defines a relation which is not a function because $(1,1)$ and $(1,-1)$, are both ordered pairs of this relation. The graph of an equation can be used to test whether the equation represents a function. This can be done with the help of the **vertical line test**. The vertical line test is based on the defining property of the function that *no element in the domain corresponds to more that one element in the range.*

Vertical Line Test: If any vertical line cuts or meets the graph of an equation in at most one point, then the equation defines a function.

Example 2:   The graphs of some equations are given below. Determine whether the relation defined by each of these graphs is a function or not.

Warm Up

2. The graphs of some equations are given below. Determine whether the relation is a function or not.

Solutions:

a)

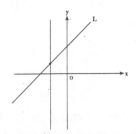

Figure 6.28

a)

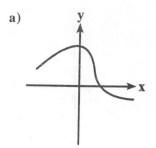

Function: A vertical line cannot intersect a non-vertical line (L) in more than one point.

b)

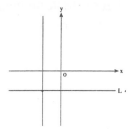

Figure 6.29

b)

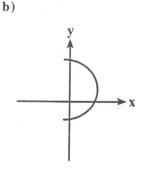

Function: A vertical line cannot intersect a horizontal line (L) in more than one point.

c)

Figure 6.30

c)

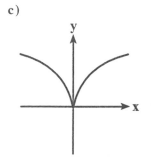

Not a function: The graph is a vertical line. This line meets itself at infinitely many points.

Warm Up

d)

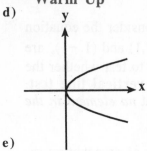

e)

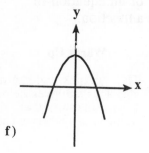

f)

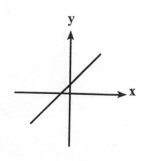

3. Which of the following are equations of functions?

a) $y = 4x + 7$

b) $y = 6$

c) $y = 3x^2$

d) $2y^2 = x$

e) $x = -4$

(d)

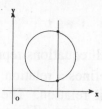

Figure 6.31

Not a function: There are vertical lines which cut the circle in two points.

(e)

Figure 6.32

Function: No vertical line meets the graph in more than one point.

(f)

Figure 6.33

Not a function: There are vertical lines which intersect the graph in more than one point.

Note: Any linear equation in x and y, which does not represent a vertical line, defines a function.

Example 3: Which of the following are functions?
a) $y = 3x - 5$ b) $y = 3$
c) $y = x^2$ d) $y^2 = x$
e) $x = 4$ f) $x^2 + y^2 = 4$

Solutions:

a) *Function:* since the graph of $y = 3x - 5$ is a non-vertical line. Also, notice that the relation $y = 3x - 5$ gives exactly one component of y for *each* value of x.

b) *Function:* same reason as for (a).

c) *Function:* the equation $y = x^2$ gives *exactly one* value of y for *each* value of x.

d) *Not a function:* the equation $y^2 = x$ does not give exactly one value of y for each value of x. For example, $(-2)^2 = 4$ and $2^2 = 4$ imply that $(4, -2)$ and $(4, 2)$ are both on the graph of $y^2 = x$. Therefore, two second components correspond to a single first component.

e) *Not a function:* graph of $x = 4$ is a vertical line.

350

f) *Not a function:* since $(0,-2)$ and $(0,2)$ are two points on the graph of $x^2 + y^2 = 4$. Therefore, two second components correspond to a single first component.

Example 4: Find the domain and range of the following functions.

    a) $y = 2x + 1$ **b)** $y = \dfrac{2}{1-x}$ **c)** $y = x^2$

Solutions:

a) $y = 2x + 1$

Any real number may be used for x. Therefore, the domain of $y = 2x + 1$ is the set of all real numbers. Also, any real number can be obtained by substituting a suitable value of x. Therefore, the range of $y = 2x + 1$ is also the set of all real numbers.

b) $y = \dfrac{2}{1-x}$

Any real number *other than 1* may be used for x. Notice when $x = 1$: $\dfrac{2}{1-x} = \dfrac{2}{1-1} = \dfrac{2}{0}$, which is not defined. Therefore, the domain of $y = \dfrac{2}{1-x}$ is the set of all real numbers *different from 1*. Also, any real number except $y = 0$ can be obtained by substituting a suitable value of x. Therefore, the range of $y = \dfrac{2}{1-x}$ is the set of all real numbers except 0.

c) $y = x^2$

Any real number can be used for x. Therefore, the domain of $y = x^2$ is the set of all real numbers. The relation $y = x^2$ means y cannot be negative since the square of a real number is never negative. Try different values of x to verify this statement. Therefore, the range of $y = x^2$ is the set of all non-negative real numbers.

4. Find the domain and range of the following.

    a) $y = 3x + 2$

    b) $y = \dfrac{2}{x-2}$

    c) $y = 4x^2$

Answers:

2. a) Function **b)** Not a function
    c) Function **d)** Not a function
    e) Function **f)** Function

3. a) Function **b)** Function
    c) Function   **d)** Not a function
    e) Not a function

4. a) All real numbers **b)** Domain: all real numbers except $x = 2$, Range: all real numbers except 0 **c)** Domain: All real numbers Range: All non-negative real numbers

D. Functional Notation

It is customary to name functions by letters like f, g, h, etc. Thus, the function $y = 3x - 1$ may be written as $f(x) = 3x - 1$. $f(x)$ is read as "f of x". In this notation:

(i) f is the name of the function.

(ii) x is a domain value.

(iii) $f(x)$ is the unique range value corresponding to x in the domain.

Since $f(x)$ is defined by an algebraic expression, the range value $f(4)$ is found by substituting 4 for x in the expression.

In this notation $f(4)$ means the range value corresponding to the domain value 4.

Therefore, $f(4) = 3 \cdot 4 - 1 = 11$ Thus "f at 4 equals 11".

Warm Up

5. For the function
$f(x) = 5x^2 + 6x - 2$ find
a) $f(-2)$ b) $f(0)$, c) $f(2)$

Answers:

5. a) 6   b) –2   c) 30

Example 5:   For the function $f(x) = 3x^2 + 4x - 1$, find

a) $f(-3)$ b) $f(0)$ c) $f(5)$

Solutions:

$$f(x) = 3x^2 + 4x - 1$$

a) $f(-3) = 3(-3)^2 + 4(-3) - 1 = 3 \cdot 9 + 4 \cdot (-3) - 1 = 14$

b) $f(0) = 3 \cdot 0^2 + 4 \cdot 0 - 1 = -1$

c) $f(5) = 3(5)^2 + 4(5) - 1 = 3(25) + 20 - 1 = 75 + 20 - 1 = 94$

EXERCISE 6.6

Answers:

1. _____

2. _____

3. _____

4. _____

5. _____

In exercises 1–5, determine which of the relations are functions? Find the domain and the range in each case.

1. $\{(-2,2),(-1,0),(-3,0),(-1,5)(0,0)\}$

2. $\{(3,1),(2,0),(-2,-4,)(4,2)\}$

3. $\{(-1,1),(-2,2),(0,0),(1,1)(2,2)\}$

4. $\{(-1,1),(-2,4),(0,0),(1,1),(2,4)\}$

5. $\{(4,2),(1,-1),(0,0)(9,-3),(9,3)\}$

In exercises 6–13, identify, the graphs of a functions.

6.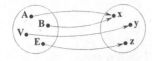

7.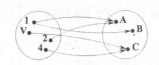

8.

9.

10.

11.

12.

13.

In exercises 14–21, determine which of the equations define functions?

14. $y = -2x + 1$

15. $y = 3x + \dfrac{1}{2}$

16. $4x + 3y - 7 = 0$

17. $x = -3$

18. $2x + 5y \geq 4$

19. $y = x^2$

20. $y = \dfrac{1}{3x + 1}$

21. $y = \dfrac{4x}{x^2 + 2}$

In exercises 22–27, find the indicated values.

22. $f(x) = 3x^2 - x + 2;$ $f(2),\ f(0)$

23. $g(x) = -3|x|;$ $g(-2),\ g(0),\ g(3)$

24. $h(x) = 4x + 5;$ $h(5),\ h(-3)$

25. $F(x) = -3x^2 + 5x;$ $F(4),\ F(-4)$

26. $P(x) = \dfrac{3}{x^2 + 1};$ $P(-2),\ P(0),\ P(-1)$

27. $Q(x) = -(x - 3)^2;$ $Q(3),\ Q(-3),\ Q(0)$

14. _____

15. _____

16. _____

17. _____

18. _____

19. _____

20. _____

21. _____

22. _____

23. _____

24. _____

25. _____

26. _____

27. _____

6.7   CHAPTER SUMMARY

Linear equations in two variables

1.   An ordered pair is a solution of an equation in two variables if it satisfies the equation.

2.   A linear equation has infinitely many solutions.

Graphing Equations

3.   The graph of $x = k$ is a vertical line through $(k, 0)$.

4.   The graph of $y = k$ is a horizontal line through $(0, k)$.

5.   To graph a linear equation in two variables x and y.

- Find three ordered pairs satisfying the linear equation.

- Plot the corresponding points.

- Draw a straight line through three points.

Slope of a line

6. The slope of a *vertical* line is **not defined.**

7.   The slope of a non-vertical line passing through (x_1, y_1) and (x_2, y_2) is given by:

$$\frac{y_2 - y_1}{x_2 - x_1} \qquad (x_1 \neq x_2)$$

8.   The slope of a *horizontal* line is 0. $\left[\text{Here } y_1 = y_2\right]$

9.   To find the slope of a line from its equation:

- Solve the equation for y.

- The slope is the coefficient of x in the new equation.

1. (2,1) is a solution of $x + 2y = 4$ since $2 + 2(\mathbf{1}) = 4$ is **true.**

2. (1,3) , (2,5) , (3,7) ... are all solutions of $2x - y + 1 = 0$.

3. The graph of $x = 2$ is a line joining points (2,0), (2,1) , (2,2)... These points are on vertical line.

4. The graph of $y = 3$ is a line joining points (0,3) , (1,3), (2,3)... These points are on a horizontal line.

5. Graph the equation $2x + y = 2$

x	0	1	2
y	2	0	−2
(x, y)	(0,2)	(1,0)	(2,−2)

6. Slope of $x = 4$ is not defined. Here $x_1 = x_2$ or denominator of slope ratio is zero.

7. Slope of a line passing through (2,1), and (1,3) is:

$$\text{Slope} = \frac{3 - 1}{1 - 2} = \frac{2}{-1} = -2$$

8. Slope of $y = 3$ is zero. Here $y_1 = y_2$ or the numerator of slope ratio is zero.

9. Find the slope of $2x + y = 3$

$$2x + y = 3 \rightarrow y = -2x + 3$$

$$\text{Slope} = -2$$

354

Examples

10. Two non-vertical lines are parallel if and only if they have the same slope.

10. Two lines $y = 2x + 3$ and $y = 2x - 5$ are parallel because slope of each line $= 2$.

11. The slopes of two perpendicular lines are the negative reciprocals of each other.

11. Two lines $y = 2x + 3$ and $y = -\dfrac{1}{2}x + 3$ are perpendicular because $(2)\left(-\dfrac{1}{2}\right) = -1$.

Slopes of perpendicular lines:

12. Two non-vertical lines are perpendicular if and only if the product of their slopes is –1.

12. The lines $y = 2x$ and $y = -\dfrac{1}{2}$ are perpendicular, because product of slopes $= (2)\left(-\dfrac{1}{2}\right) = -1$

Equations of a line

13. **Slope-Intercept Form:**
If m is the slope and $(0, b)$ the y-intercept of a line, then its equation is $y = mx + b$.

13. The equation of a line with slope $= 3$ and intercept $(0,2)$ is $y = 3x + 2$.

Point-Slope Form
If m is the slope of a line which passes through (x_1, y_1), then its equation is
$y - y_1 = m(x - x_1)$.

- The equation of a line with slope $= 2$ and passing through $(1,3)$ is: $y - 3 = 2(x - 1)$.

Two-Point Form

The equation of a line passing through (x_1, y_1) and (x_2, y_2) is:

$$y - y_1 = \frac{y_2 - y_1}{x_2 - x_1}(x - x_1)$$

- The equation of a line passing through $(1, -2)$ and $(4, 2)$ is:
$$y - (-2) = \frac{2 - (-2)}{4 - 1}(x - 1)$$
$$\rightarrow \quad y + 2 = \frac{4}{3}(x - 1)$$
$$\rightarrow \quad 3y + 6 = 4x - 4$$
$$\rightarrow \quad 4x - 3y = 10$$

Graphing linear inequalities

14. Solve $2x - y \le 1$

14. The steps to solve a linear inequality in two variables.

- Change the inequality symbol to an equality symbol and draw the graph of the resulting line. Draw a solid line if the inequality is non strict ($\le$ or $\ge$) and dotted line if the inequality is strict ($<$ or $>$).

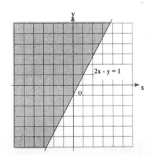

355

Examples

• Choose a test point on either side of the line, but not on the line. If the line does not pass through the origin then (0, 0) is the best choice as a test point.

Let (0,0) be a test point and it satisfies the inequality. Therefore the shaded side of the test point is the solution.

• If the test point satisfies the given inequality then the part of the plane on the side of the test point is the solution, or else the other side is the solution. For a non-strict inequality, the solid line is part of the solution.

Functions and Relations

15. A *function* is a set of ordered pairs in which each first component has exactly one second component.

15. $\{(2,3),(3,4),(4,5),(-1,0)\}$
represents a function because for each x there is a unique y.

$\{(1,2),(1,-2),(3,1)\}$
is not a function because for $x = 1$ there are two distinct values of y.

16. The set of first components of the ordered pairs of a relation is called its *domain*.

16. The domain of $\{(2,3),(3,4),(4,5),(-1,0)\}$ is: $\{2,3,4,-1\}$

17. The set of second components of the ordered pairs of a relation is called its *range*.

17. The range of $\{(2,3),(3,4),(4,5),(-1,0)\}$ is: $\{3,4,5,0\}$

18. Vertical Line Test: If all vertical lines cut or meet the graph of an equation in at most one point, then the equation defines a function.

18.

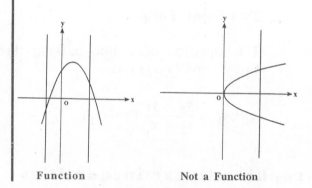

Function   Not a Function

6.8   REVIEW EXERCISE

In exercises 1–3, determine whether the indicated ordered pair is a solution of the given equation.

1. $-3x + 4y = 10$; $(-2, 1)$ **2.** $5x + 7y = 2$; $(1, -1)$

3. $2x = 5y$; $(10, 4)$

In exercises 4–5, complete the ordered pair so that it is a solution of the indicated equation.

4. $x + 3y = 5$; $(?, -2)$ **5.** $2x - 3y = 7$; $(-4, ?)$

In exercises 6–7, complete the table of values for the indicated equation.

6. $2x - y = 4$,

x	1	-3		
y			3	2

7. $x = -2$,

x			
y	-1	2	0

8. Plot the following ordered pairs on the same coordinate system.

   a) $(-1, 3)$ **b)** $(2, 5)$

   c) $(3, -7)$ **d)** $(-4, -1)$

   e) $(3, 0)$ **f)** $(0, -2)$

   g) $(0, 0)$

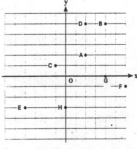

9. Determine the coordinates of each of the points shown on the figure.

Exercise 9

In exercises 10–13, complete the tables of x- and y-values for the given equation. Draw the graph by plotting these points.

10. $x = 4$

x			
y	-3	1	2

11. $y = -5$

x	-2	0	3
y			

12. $2x = 3y$

x	-3		
y		0	2

13. $3x + 4y = 1$

x	-1	3	-5
y			

In exercises 14–15, find the x- and y-intercepts. Use intercepts to graph the equations.

14. $\dfrac{x}{2} + \dfrac{y}{3} = 1$ **15.** $4x - 5y = 20$

In exercises 16–17, complete the table of x- and y-values for the given equations. Plot these points and sketch the graph.

16. $y = x^2$:

x	0	-1	-2	1	2
y					

17. $y = x^2 - 2x + 2$:

x	0	-1	1	2	-2	3	4
y							

In exercises 18–19, find the slope of the line passing through the pairs of points.

18. $(-2, 4)$, $(3, 9)$ **19.** $(3, 5)$, $(6, 1)$

In exercises 20–21, find the slope of the lines and the y-intercept.

20. $3x = 4y + 1$ **21.** $2x + 5y + 3 = 0$

Which pair of lines in exercises 22–25, are parallel and which are perpendicular?

22. $y = 3x + 7$
$3y = x - 7$

23. $2y - 5x = 1$
$6y = 15x + 11$

24. $x + 3y = 5$
$3x = y + 1$

25. $2x - y = 0$
$x + 2y + 1 = 0$

In exercises 26–35, find an equation of the line using the given information.

26. Slope $= -3$, y – intercept $(0,0)$. **27.** Slope $= \dfrac{5}{7}$, y – intercept $(0,-3)$.

28. Slope $= 0$, passes through $(3,5)$. **29.** Slope $= \dfrac{2}{3}$, passes through $(-2,3)$.

30. Passes through the points $(2,5)$ and $(3,3)$.

31. Passes through $(3,-1)$ and is parallel to the line $2y + 6x = 9$.

32. Passes through $(-1,1)$ and is perpendicular to $4y = 3x + 5$.

33. Slope $= \dfrac{1}{3}$, passes through $(-2,4)$.

34. Slope $=$ undefined, passes through $(0,0)$.

35. Passes through $(-2,-3)$ and $(1,-4)$.

In exercises 36 – 40, graph the linear inequality.

36. $2x - y \leq 1$ **37.** $x + 2y \geq 5$ **38.** $\dfrac{x}{3} + \dfrac{y}{2} < 1$

39. $y > 3x$ **40.** $y < -4$

In exercises 41 – 42, identify any relation which is a function? Also determine the domain and the range in each case.

41. $\{(2,1),(3,1),(4,-1),(2,2)\}$ **42.** $\{(0,0),(1,1),(2,1),(-1,0),(-2,3)\}$

In exercises 43 – 45, the use vertical line test to determine whether the relations are functions.

43.

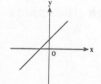

44.

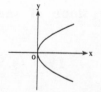

45.

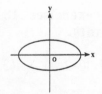

358

6.9   SELF TEST

1.   **Complete the ordered pairs for the given equation.**

$3x - 2y = 11;$ $(-1, ?\ ),\ (2, ?\ ),\ (\ ?, 2),\ (\ ?, -1).$

2.   **Which of the following ordered pairs are solutions of the equation** $2x + 3y = 7$?

$(2,1),\ (-2,4),\ \left(0, \dfrac{7}{3}\right),\ (-1,3),\ (7,0).$

In exercises 3–6,   graph the linear equation.   Find the y-intercept   where indicated.

3. $3x = y;$ $y-$intercept   4. $5x + 2y = 1$

5. $x + 2 = 0;$ y-intercept   6. $y = -3;$ y-intercept

In exercises 7–10,   find the slope of the lines.   Also determine the y-intercept where indicated.

7.   Passing through (-1,5) and (4,7)   8. $2y + 3 = 0;$ y-intercept
9. $3x - 5 = 0;$ y-intercept   10. $2y + 3x = 7;$ y-intercept

Graph the lines in exercises 11–13.

11. $2y = x + 6$ 12.   Slope $= -2,$ passing through $(1,2)$

13.   Passing through $(-1, 3),$ and $(2, 4)$

In exercises 14–15,   graph the linear inequality in two variables:

14. $2x - y \le 4$ 15. $x + y > 7$

In exercises 16–17,   identify the relation which is a function?   Also find the domain and range in each case?

16. $\{(-3,-2),\ (-1,-3),\ (-2,-3),\ (0,-1),\ (0,4)\ \}$ 17. $\{(2,3),\ (4,3),\ (6,-3),\ (7,0)\ \}.$

In exercises 18–20,   identify graphs as functions or not functions

18.   19.   20.

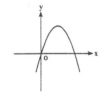   

In exercises 21 and 22   identify which of the equation is of a straight line.

21. $3xy = 1$ 22. $\dfrac{2}{3}x = 4 - 5y$

CHAPTER 7

SYSTEMS OF LINEAR EQUATIONS AND INEQUALITIES

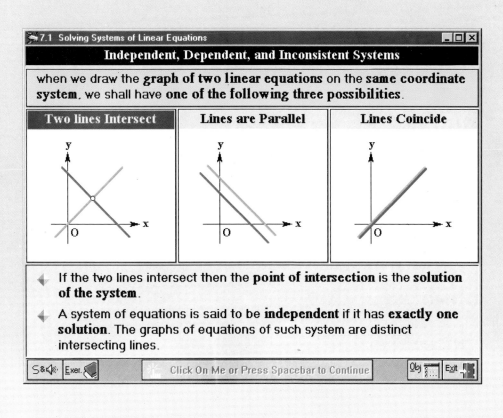

7.1 Solving Systems of Linear Equations

Independent, Dependent, and Inconsistent Systems

when we draw the **graph of two linear equations** on the **same coordinate system**, we shall have **one of the following three possibilities**.

| Two lines Intersect | Lines are Parallel | Lines Coincide |

- If the two lines intersect then the **point of intersection** is the **solution of the system**.

- A system of equations is said to be **independent** if it has **exactly one solution**. The graphs of equations of such system are distinct intersecting lines.

S&◁» Exer. Click On Me or Press Spacebar to Continue Obj Exit

CHAPTER 7

SYSTEMS OF LINEAR EQUATIONS AND INEQUALITIES

A number of equations in several variables considered simultaneously is said to form a **system of equations.** When all the equations in a system are linear, the system is called a *system of linear equations* or a **linear system.** Linear systems of equations and inequalities occur frequently in the solutions of problems related to science, social sciences, and business. In this chapter we shall consider a system of two linear equations or inequalities in two variables and study different methods of solving such systems. In real life situations, however, the number of variables and equations can be very large, and can be easily solved with the help of computers. Computer methods are based on algorithms which have their roots in some of the methods that will be investigated in this chapter.

This chapter is divided into the following sections.

7.1   SOLVING BY GRAPHING

Consider a system of linear equations in x and y, for example

$$3x + 5y = 2$$
$$4x - 2y = -6.$$

We have seen in chapter 6 that a single equation has infinitely many solutions. In fact, for any value of x, a value of y can be obtained from a linear equation so that (x, y) is a solution of the linear equation. An ordered pair of numbers may be a solution to both linear equations in the system. For example, $(-1, 1)$ is a solution of both equations in the above system.

$$3(-1) + 5(1) = 2 \qquad \text{TRUE}$$
$$4(-1) - 2(1) = -6 \qquad \text{TRUE}$$

Such an ordered pair of numbers is called a solution of the system.

The **solution of a system** of linear equations in two variables is the set of all ordered pairs which are solutions of every linear equation in the system.

In this chapter, *we shall consider a system of two equations in two variables only.*

Upon completion of this section we will be able to:

A. Identify solutions of a system of linear equations.
B. Solve linear systems by graphing.
C. Identify independent, dependent or inconsistent systems.

A. Identifying a Solution of a System of Linear Equations

As pointed out above, an ordered pair (a, b) is a solution of a system of linear equations in two variables if $x = a$ and $y = b$ satisfy each linear equation of the system.

Warm Up

1. Identify whether the indicated ordered pair is a solution of the given system.

   a) $4x - 3y = 6$ $(3, 2)$
   $3x + y = 11$

Example 1: Identify whether the indicated ordered pair is solution of the given system.

a) $3x - 4y = 11$ $(1, -2)$
$3x + y = 1$

b) $3x - 2y = 0$ $(2, 3)$
$4x - 3y = 1$

c) $2x + y = 3$ $(1, -1)$
$x - y = 0$

Solutions:

To decide whether an ordered pair is a solution of a system of linear equations, substitute the values for the unknowns.

a) Substitute 1 for x and -2 for y.

$$3x - 4y = 11 \qquad\qquad 3x + y = 1$$
$$3(\mathbf{1}) - 4(-\mathbf{2}) = 11 \qquad 3(\mathbf{1}) + (-\mathbf{2}) = 1$$
$$3 + 8 = 11 \qquad\qquad 3 - 2 = 1$$
$$11 = 11 \quad \text{TRUE} \qquad\qquad 1 = 1 \quad \text{TRUE}$$

$(1, -2)$ *satisfies both* equations.
Therefore, $(1, -2)$ is a *solution* of the system.

b) $2x - 3y = 1$ $(-4, -3)$
$3x - 4y = 0$

b) Substitute 2 for x and 3 for y.

$$3x - 2y = 0 \qquad\qquad 4x - 3y = 1$$
$$3 \cdot 2 - 2 \cdot 3 = 0 \qquad 4 \cdot 2 - 3 \cdot 3 = 1$$
$$6 - 6 = 0 \qquad\qquad 8 - 9 = 1$$
$$0 = 0 \quad \text{TRUE} \qquad\qquad -1 = 1 \quad \text{FALSE}$$

$(2, 3)$ *does not satisfy both* equations.
Therefore, it is *not a solution* of the system.

c) Substitute 1 for x and -1 for y.

$$2x + y = 3 \qquad\qquad x - y = 0$$
$$2(\mathbf{1}) + (-\mathbf{1}) = 3 \qquad\qquad 1(\mathbf{1}) - (-\mathbf{1}) = 0$$
$$2 - 1 = 3 \qquad\qquad\qquad 1 + 1 = 0$$
$$1 = 3 \quad \text{FALSE} \qquad\qquad 2 = 0 \quad \text{FALSE}$$

$(1, -1)$ *does not satisfy either* equations.
Therefore, it is *not a solution* of the system.

Warm Up

c) $x + 2y = 0;\ (6, 3)$

$x + y = 3$

Answers:

1. a) True **b)** True **c)** False

B. Solving by Graphing

There are several methods which can be used to solve a system of linear equations. We shall study three of these methods in this chapter. In this section, we shall learn how to solve a system of linear equations by graphing both equations on the same coordinate system. A solution of the system must be a point on the graph of each line because it satisfies each equation. Since two distinct lines can intersect in at most one point, we have the following conclusion.

> A system of linear equations *cannot have more than one solution* if the graphs of the equations are distinct non parallel lines.

Example 2:   Solve the following systems of equations by graphing.

a) $x + 3y = 4$ b) $3x - y = 7$

        $2x - y = 1$ $x + y = 1$

Solutions:

We shall graph each of the equations in a system on the same coordinate system. The coordinates of the point of intersection, if any, form the solution of the system.

To draw the graph, we make table of three x - and y - values for each equation.

Warm Up

2. Solve

a) $3x + y = -2$

$x - 2y = 4$

b) $x + 3y = -5$

$x - y = 7$

Answers:

2. a) $(0, -2)$ **b)** $(4, -3)$

a)   Table for $x + 3y = 4$

x	0	1	4
y	4/3	1	0
(x, y)	$(0, 4/3)$	$(1, 1)$	$(4, 0)$

Table for $2x - y = 1$

x	0	1	1 / 2
y	−1	1	0
(x, y)	$(0, -1)$	$(1, 1)$	$(1/2, 0$

The graphs are shown in Fig. 7.1. They intersect at $(1, 1)$. Therefore, $(1, 1)$ is a solution of the system. Verify by substituting 1 for x and 1 for y in the two equations that both equations are satisfied.

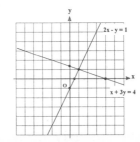

Figure 7.1

See examples 1-4 on pages 524-525 for solving systems of equations using calculator.

b)   Table for $3x - y = 7$

x	0	3	1
y	−7	2	−4
(x, y)	$(0, -7)$	$(3, 2)$	$(1, -4)$

Table for $x + y = 1$

x	0	1	− 1
y	1	0	2
(x, y)	$(0, 1)$	$(1, 0)$	$(-1, 2)$

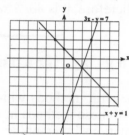

The graphs are shown in Figure 7.2. They intersect in $(2, -1)$. Therefore, $(2, -1)$ is a solution of the system.   Verify by substituting 2 for x and -1 for y in the two equations, that $(2, -1)$ is a solution of both.

Figure 7.2

Note: When finding a solution by graphing, it is very important to verify the solution. In most cases, it may not be possible to determine the exact coordinates of the point of intersection from the graph . In such cases the solution obtained from the graph will only be an *approximation* of the actual solution.

C.   Independent, Dependent, and Inconsistent Systems

When we draw the graph of two linear equations on the same coordinate system, we shall have one of the following three possibilities

(i) **two lines intersect,** or (ii) **the lines are parallel,** or (iii) **the lines coincide**

(i)   If the two lines intersect then the **point of intersection is the solution of the system.**

A system of equations is said to be **independent** if it has *exactly one solution.*
The graphs of the equations of such a system are distinct intersecting lines (Figure 7.3).

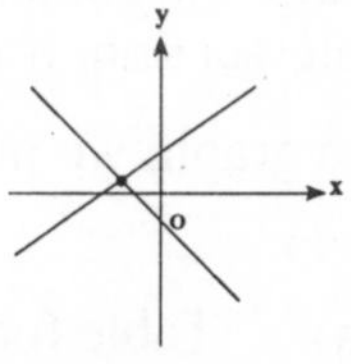

Figure 7.3

(ii) If the two lines are parallel, then the **lines do not intersect and the system has** *no solution.*

A system of equations is said to be **inconsistent** if it has *n o solution.*
The graphs of the equations of such a system are a pair of distinct and parallel lines (Figure 7.4).

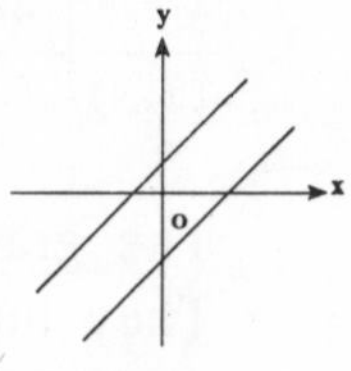

Figure 7.4

(iii) If the two lines coincide then **every point on the line is a solution of the system.**

A system of equations is said. to be **dependent** if the system of equations has infinitely many solutions. The graphs of the equations of such a system are the same line (Figure 7.5).

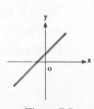

Figure 7.5

Note: Two equations will represent the same line if one equation can be obtained from the other by multiplying it by a suitable number, for example, $4x - 6y = 8$ and $2x - 3y = 4$. Notice $4x - 6y = 8$ can be obtained by multiplying both sides of $2x - 3y = 4$ by 2.

Example 3: Graph each of the following systems of equations. Determine whether the system is independent, dependent or inconsistent.

a) $2x + 3y = 6$
   $4x + 6y = 24$

b) $2x + y = 1$
   $x - 2y = 7$

c) $3x - 2y = 5$
   $6x = 4y + 10$

Solutions:

a) Table for $2x + 3y = 6$

x	0	3	-3
y	2	0	4
(x, y)	$(0, 2)$	$(3, 0)$	$(-3, 4)$

Table for $4x + 6y = 24$

x	0	6	3
y	4	0	2
(x, y)	$(0, 4)$	$(6, 0)$	$(3, 2)$

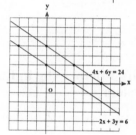

Figure 7.6

The two lines are parallel. The system is *inconsistent* and has no solution.

b) Table for $2x + y = 1$

x	0	-1	1
y	1	3	-1
(x, y)	$(0, 1)$	$(-1, 3)$	$(1, -1)$

Table for $x - 2y = 7$

x	1	-1	1
y	-3	-4	-3
(x, y)	$(1, -3)$	$(-1, -4)$	$(1, -3)$

The two lines intersect. Therefore, the system is independent and has only one solution. The solution is $x \approx 2$ and $y \approx -2.6$

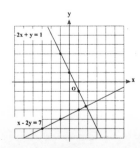

Figure 7.7

Warm Up

3. Describe the graph of each of the following systems of equations. Determine whether the system is independent, dependent or inconsistent.

a) $3x + 2y = 16$
   $6x + 4y = 25$

b) $x - 3y = 9$
   $3x + y = 2$

c) $4x - 5y = 7$

$8x = 10y + 14$

Answers:

3. a) Two lines are parallel, the system is inconsistent and has no solution.

b) Two lines are perpendicular and intersect. The system has only one solution.

c) Two lines are identical and the system is dependent.

c) Table for $3x - 2y = 5$

x	3	1	-1
y	2	-1	-4
(x, y)	$(3, 2)$	$(1, -1)$	$(-1, -4)$

Table for $6x = 4y + 10$

x	2	1	-3
y	$1/2$	-1	-7
(x, y)	$(2, 1/2)$	$(1, -1)$	$(-3, -7)$

The two lines are identical. Therefore, the system is dependent. In fact, every point on this line is a solution of the system. Observe that equations $6x = 4y + 10$ and $3x - 2y = 5$ are identical.

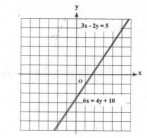

Figure 7.8

EXERCISE 7.1

Answers:

1. _____

2. _____

3. _____

4. _____

5. _____

6. _____

7. _____

8. _____

9. _____

10. _____

11. _____

12. _____

In exercises 1–6, identify whether the indicated ordered pair is a solution of the given system.

1. $4x - 3y = 6$
$x + 2y = 7$ $(3, 2)$

2. $3x - y + 4 = 0$
$2x + 5y = 3$ $(-1, 1)$

3. $-2x + 5y = 1$
$x - y = 3$ $(2, -1)$

4. $3x + 2y = 0$
$2x = 3y - 5$ $(-2, -3)$

5. $4x + 3y = 15$
$x - y + 5 = 0$ $(0, 5)$

6. $3x + y = 5$
$2y = 10 - 6x$ $(1, 2)$

In exercises 7–12, solve the systems of equations by graphing. Identify whether the system is inconsistent or dependent.

7. $x - 2y = 2$
$x + 2y = 6$

8. $4x + y = 5$
$3x = 2y + 12$

9. $2x + y = 5$
$y = 3$

10. $x - 2y = 5$
$2x = 4y - 2$

11. $3x + 5y = 8$
$6x = 16 - 10y$

12. $\frac{2}{3}x + \frac{4}{3}y = 4$
$\frac{1}{2}x - \frac{2}{5}y = 3$

In exercises 13–18, calculate the slope of each line of the system. Using this information, decide whether the system is inconsistent, dependent or independent solution.

13. $3x = 4y + 7$

$y = x + 7$

14. $2y + 5x = 8$

$5y - 2x = 1$

15. $2x = 3y + 2$

$-6x + 9y = 5$

16. $2x - y = 4$

$y = 2x + 9$

17. $2x + 3y = 7$

$4x = 14 - 6y$

18. $\dfrac{3}{5}x + \dfrac{7}{3}y = 10$

$\dfrac{4}{7}x + \dfrac{2}{3}y = -5$

13. _____

14. _____

15. _____

16. _____

17. _____

18. _____

7.2   SOLVING BY SUBSTITUTION

The graphing method is good in as much as it provides visualization of the process of solving systems of equations. However, it has its limitations. One limitation was pointed out in the last section , i.e. many times it may be difficult to read the exact values of the coordinates of the point of intersection from the graph. The visualization is difficult if there are three variables, and it is not possible to draw the graphs when the number of variables is four or more. In such cases, we use algebraic methods. In this section we study the **substitution method.**

Upon completion of this section we will be able to:

      A.   Solve linear systems by the method of substitution.

      B.   Identify dependent and inconsistent systems.

A.   Solving by Substitution

The method of substitution is particularly useful when one equation can be easily solved for one of the variables. We can solve for one variable in terms of another from one equation, and then substitute the result in the second equation. The following steps may be used in solving a system by the method of substitution.

Step 1	Solve one of the equations for either variable.
Step 2	Substitute the solution for this variable in the second equation. This results in an equation in one variable.
Step 3	Solve the equation obtained in step 2.
Step 4	Substitute the value obtained in step 3 into the equation in step 1, and solve for the second variable.
Step 5	Check your solution by substituting it in the given equations. You may use the calculator.

Note: In Step 4, substitution can be made in either of the two given equations.

Warm Up

1. Solve

$$5x + 3y = 10$$
$$3x - y = 6$$

Example 1:   Solve the system. $3x - 5y = -6$
$$x + 3y = 2$$

Solution:

Step 1   Solve the second equation for x.
$$x + 3y = 2 \longrightarrow x = 2 - 3y \qquad \textbf{(1)}$$

Step 2   Substitute $2 - 3y$ for x in the first equation.
$$3x - 5y = -6 \longrightarrow 3(2 - 3y) - 5y = -6$$

Step 3 $6 - 9y - 5y = -6 \longrightarrow 6 - 14y = -6$
$$\longrightarrow -14y = -12$$
$$\longrightarrow y = \frac{-12}{-14} \longrightarrow y = \frac{6}{7}$$

Step 4   Substitute $\dfrac{6}{7}$ for y in equation (1): $x = 2 - 3y$.
$$x = 2 - 3\left(\frac{6}{7}\right) = 2 - \frac{18}{7} = -\frac{4}{7}$$

Therefore, $\left(-\dfrac{4}{7}, \dfrac{6}{7}\right)$ is a solution of the system.

Step 5   Check:

Substitute $-\dfrac{4}{7}$ for x and $\dfrac{6}{7}$ for y in the given equations, and verify that both equations are satisfied. You may use a calculator or proceed as follows.

$$
\begin{array}{ll}
3x - 5x = -6 & x + 3y = 2 \\[4pt]
3\left(-\dfrac{4}{7}\right) - 5\left(\dfrac{6}{7}\right) = -6 & \dfrac{4}{7} + 3\left(\dfrac{6}{7}\right) = 2 \\[8pt]
\dfrac{-12}{7} - \dfrac{30}{7} = -6 & \dfrac{-4}{7} + \dfrac{18}{7} = 2 \\[8pt]
\dfrac{-42}{7} = -6 & \dfrac{14}{7} = 2 \\[8pt]
-6 = -6 \quad \text{TRUE} & 2 = 2 \quad \text{TRUE}
\end{array}
$$

Notes: 1. This example shows that the substitution method can be employed where the graphic method may be inaccurate, since it is hard to read $-\dfrac{4}{7}$ or $\dfrac{6}{7}$ from a graph.

2. In Step 1, it is preferable to choose an equation which contains a variable with its coefficient equal to 1 or -1, if possible.

2. Solve
$$x + 2y = 4$$
$$3x + 4y = 6$$

Example 2:   Solve $2x - y = 5$ $4x + 3y = 4$.

Solution:

Step 1   Solve the first equation for y:
$$2x - y = 5 \longrightarrow y = 2x - 5 \qquad \textbf{(1)}$$

Step 2   Substitute this y in the second equation

$$4x + 3y = 4 \longrightarrow 4x + 3(2x - 5) = 4$$

Step 3   Solve the equation in step 2 for x.

$$4x + 6x - 15 = 4 \quad \text{or} \quad 10x = 19 \longrightarrow x = \frac{19}{10}$$

Step 4   Substitute $\frac{19}{10}$ for x in equation (1): $y = 2x - 5$

$$y = 2x - 5 \qquad y = 2\left(\frac{19}{10}\right) - 5 \qquad \left[\text{Substitute } x \text{ - value}\right]$$

$$y = \frac{19}{5} - 5 \longrightarrow y = -\frac{6}{5}$$

Therefore, the solution is $\left(\dfrac{19}{10}, -\dfrac{6}{5}\right)$.

Step 5   Check:

Substitute $x = \dfrac{19}{10}$ and $y = -\dfrac{6}{5}$ in both equations.

$2x - y = 5$	$4x + 3y = 4$
$2\left(\dfrac{19}{10}\right) - \left(-\dfrac{6}{5}\right) = 5$	$4\left(\dfrac{19}{10}\right) + 3\left(\dfrac{-6}{5}\right) = 4$
$\dfrac{19}{5} + \dfrac{6}{5} = 5$	$\dfrac{38}{5} - \dfrac{18}{5} = 4$
$\dfrac{25}{5} = 5$	$\dfrac{20}{5} = 4$
$5 = 5$ TRUE	$4 = 4$ TRUE

In the following questions we shall leave step 5 (checking the solution) to the reader.

Example 3:   Solve: $3x - 2y = -6$
$$-5x + 4y = 16.$$

Solution:

Step 1 $3x - 2y = -6 \longrightarrow 2y = 3x + 6$

$$\longrightarrow y = \frac{3}{2}x + 3 \qquad\qquad (1)$$

Step 2 $-5x + 4y = 16 \longrightarrow -5x + 4\left(\frac{3}{2}x + 3\right) = 16$

Step 3 $-5x + 6x + 12 = 16$ or $x + 12 = 16 \longrightarrow x = 4$

Step 4   Substitute $x = 4$ in equation (1):

$$y = \frac{3}{2}x + 3 \longrightarrow y = \frac{3}{2}(4) + 3 \longrightarrow y = 6 + 3 \longrightarrow y = 9$$

Step 5   Check the solution $(4, 9)$ by substituting it into the *original* system of equations.

Warm Up

3.   Solve
$$2x + 3y = -16$$
$$4x - 5y = 12$$

Warm Up

4. Solve

$$\frac{1}{2}x + \frac{3}{4}y = 18$$

$$\frac{2}{3}x - \frac{3}{5}y = 8$$

Example 4:   Solve: $\frac{3}{4}x + \frac{2}{3}y = 7$

$$\frac{3}{5}x - \frac{1}{2}y = 18.$$

Solution:

First, we eliminate fractions. To do this multiply each equation by the least common denominator of the fractions.

First Equation:

$$\frac{3}{4}x + \frac{2}{3}y = 7 \quad \xrightarrow{\text{l.c.d} = 12} \quad 12\left(\frac{3}{4}x + \frac{2}{3}y\right) = 12(7)$$

$$\longrightarrow \quad 12\left(\frac{3}{4}\right)x + 12\left(\frac{2}{3}\right)y = 84$$

$$\longrightarrow \quad 9x + 8y = 84$$

Second Equation:

$$\frac{3}{5}x - \frac{1}{2}y = 18 \quad \xrightarrow{\text{. l.c.d} = 10} \quad 10\left(\frac{3}{5}x - \frac{1}{2}y\right) = 10(18)$$

$$\longrightarrow \quad 6x - 5y = 180$$

The given system is now simplified to: $9x + 8y = 84$ **(1)**

$$6x - 5y = 180 \quad \textbf{(2)}$$

We shall solve this system by substitution.

Step 1   Solve the equation (2) for x

$$6x - 5y = 180 \quad \longrightarrow \quad 6x = 180 + 5y$$

$$\longrightarrow \quad x = 30 + \frac{5}{6}y$$

Step 2   Substitute x in the equation (1)

$$9x + 8y = 84 \longrightarrow \quad 9\left(30 + \frac{5}{6}y\right) + 8y = 84$$

Step 3 $270 + \dfrac{45}{6}y + 8y = 84 \quad \longrightarrow \quad 270 + \dfrac{15}{2}y + 8y = 84$

$$\longrightarrow \quad 270 + \frac{31}{2}y = 84$$

$$\longrightarrow \quad \frac{31}{2}y = 84 - 270$$

$$\longrightarrow \quad \frac{31}{2}y = -186$$

$$\longrightarrow \quad y = -\frac{186 \cdot 2}{31} \quad \longrightarrow \quad y = -12$$

Step 4   Substitute for y in: $x = 30 + \dfrac{5}{6}y$

$$x = 30 + \dfrac{5}{6}(-12)$$
$$x = 30 - 10$$
$$x = 20$$

Step 5   Check the solution $(20, -12)$ by substituting it into the *original* system.

Answers:

1. $(2, 0)$ 2. $(-2, 3)$ 3. $(-2, -4)$
4. $(21, 10)$

B.   Dependent and Inconsistent Systems

Example 5:   Solve the following system of linear equations.
$$x - 5y = 7$$
$$10y = 2x + 5$$

Solution:

Step 1 $x - 5y = 7 \longrightarrow x = 5y + 7$

Step 2   Substitute for x in the second equation:
$$10y = 2x + 5 \longrightarrow 10y = 2(5y + 7) + 5$$

Step 3 $$10y = 10y + 14 + 5$$
$$\mathbf{0 = 19}$$

This is a **FALSE** statement. Hence the system has no solution, i.e. the system is **inconsistent.**

Recall graphs of these equations will be parallel lines. We may verify this by comparing their slopes.

5.   Solve
$$x - 5y = 7$$
$$15y = 3x - 9$$

Example 6:   Solve the system $2x + 3y = 6$
$$9y = 18 - 6x.$$

Solution:

Step 1 $9y = 18 - 6x \longrightarrow y = \dfrac{18 - 6x}{9}$

Step 2   Substitute for y in the first equation
$$2x + 3y = 6 \longrightarrow 2x + 3\left(\dfrac{18 - 6x}{9}\right) = 6$$

Step 3 $2x + \dfrac{54}{9} - \dfrac{18x}{9} = 6 \longrightarrow 2x + 6 - 2x = 6$
$$\longrightarrow 6 = 6 \quad \text{TRUE}$$

This is a true statement but contains no variable for which to solve. This means that the system is **dependent.**

A conclusion leading to an *identity* $(6 = 6)$ implies that the system is dependent.

6.   Solve
$$3x + 4y = 13$$
$$16y = 52 - 12x$$

Answers:

5. inconsistent system
6. Dependent system $0 = 0$

Recall in this case, the graphs of both equations coincide. We may verify by writing both equations in the slope-intercept form.

EXERCISE 7.2

Answers:

1. _____
2. _____
3. _____
4. _____
5. _____
6. _____
7. _____
8. _____
9. _____
10. _____
11. _____
12. _____
13. _____
14. _____
15. _____
16. _____
17. _____
18. _____
19. _____
20. _____

Solve each of the following systems of equations by the substitution method. Identify whether the system is dependent or inconsistent.

1. $x + y = 5$
$x - y = 1$

2. $x - y = 5$
$3x + 2y = 10$

3. $x - y = 3$
$3y = x$

4. $2x + y = -4$
$x - 2y = -7$

5. $4x + y = 5$
$x - 3 = 0$

6. $3x + 5y = 10$
$y = 2$

7. $4y + x = 13$
$3x - 2y = -6$

8. $2x + 3y = 0$
$\dfrac{1}{3}x = \dfrac{1}{2}y - \dfrac{2}{3}$

9. $4x + 3y - 1 = 0$
$3x = 2y - 12$

10. $3x - 2y = 0$
$2x - 5y = -11$

11. $8x + 3y = 4$
$-4x + 3y = 1$

12. $6x + 5y = 13$
$3x + 2y = 4$

13. $9x + 7y = 4$
$3x + 2y = 1$

14. $2x - 7y + 2y + 2 = 5y + 16$
$6x - 2y = 2x + 28$

15. $\dfrac{2}{3}x - \dfrac{1}{4}y + 8 = 0$
$\dfrac{1}{2}x - \dfrac{3}{8}y + 9 = 0$

16. $\dfrac{5}{6}x + \dfrac{2}{3}y = \dfrac{7}{6}$
$\dfrac{10}{7}x - \dfrac{4}{9}y = \dfrac{17}{21}$

17. $3x - 2y = 2$
$6x = 4y + 7$

18. $2x + y = 6$
$3y = 18 - 6x$

19. $\dfrac{3}{5}x + \dfrac{2}{3}y = \dfrac{1}{3}$
$18x + 20y = 10$

20. $\dfrac{2}{3}x - \dfrac{1}{2}y = 1$
$2x - \dfrac{3}{2}y = 2$

7.3   SOLVING BY ADDITION

Upon completion of this section, we will be able to

    A.   Solve linear systems by addition.

    B.   Identify dependent and inconsistent systems by the addition method.

A.   Addition Method

The strategy of the **addition method** is to replace the original system of equations by an equivalent, and possibly a simpler system, in such a way that the coefficients of one of the variables in the two equations are negatives of each other. Adding the respective sides of the equations of the equivalent system eliminates this variable. This facilitates the solution of the other variable. The following steps may be used to solve a linear system of equations by the addition method.

Step 1	Write both equations in the form $ax + by = c$. It is important that a variable occupies the same position in both equations.
Step 2	Multiply both sides of one or both equations by suitable numbers so that the coefficients of x (or y) in the resulting equations are negatives of each other.
Step 3	Add the two equations. This will result in an equation in only one variable.
Step 4	Solve the equation obtained in step 3.
Step 5	Substitute the value obtained in step 4 in either of the original equations and find the value of the *other variable*.
Step 6	Check your answer.

Note: In some cases, it may be more convenient to repeat steps 2-4 for the other variable instead of step 5.

Example 1:

Solve $4x - 3y = 15$
$-2x + 3y = -9$

Solution:

    Step 1   Not needed

    Step 2   Not needed since the coefficients of y are -3 and 3.

    Step 3   Add the two equations.

$$\begin{array}{r} 4x - 3y = 15 \\ -2x + 3y = -9 \\ \hline 2x = 6 \end{array}$$

    Step 4   Solve $2x = 6 \longrightarrow x = 3$

Warm Up

1.   Solve

$$5x - 4y = 12$$
$$-5x + 2y = 4$$

373

Warm Up

2. Solve

$3x + 7y - 62 = 0$
$y = 2x + 4$

3. Solve

$x - 4y = -3$
$4x + 5y = 2$

Step 5 Substitute $x = 3$ in either one of the (original) equations to find the value of y. Let us substitute 3 for x in the second equation.

$$-2x + 3y = -9$$
$$-2(3) + 3y = -9$$
$$3y = -3 \longrightarrow y = -1$$

Step 6 We may verify that $(3, -1)$ satisfies both equations. Therefore, the solution is $(3, -1)$.

Note: The substitution method for the above example will involve fractions.

Example 2:   Solve $2x + 5y + 5 = 0$
                                     $2y = 3x + 17$

Solution:

Step 1 Rewrite both equations in the form $ax + by = c$.

$$2x + 5y + 5 = 0 \longrightarrow 2x + 5y = -5 \qquad \textbf{(1)}$$
$$2y = 3x + 17 \longrightarrow -3x + 2y = 17 \qquad \textbf{(2)}$$

Step 2 Let us eliminate x.. Multiply equation (1) by 3 and equation (2) by 2.

$$3(2x + 5y) = 3(-5) \longrightarrow 6x + 15y = -15$$
$$2(-3x + 2y) = 2(17) \longrightarrow -6x + 4y = 34$$

Step 3 Add the two equations.

$$\begin{array}{r} 6x + 15y = -15 \\ -6x + 4y = 34 \\ \hline 19y = 19 \end{array}$$

Step 4 Solve $19y = 19$ for y. $y = \dfrac{19}{19}, \quad y = 1$

Step 5 Substitute 1 for y in either of the original equations, say the first equation 1.

$$2x + 5(\textbf{1}) + 5 = 0$$
$$2x = -10$$
$$x = -5$$

Step 6 Verify that $(-5, 1)$ is a solution of the *original* system.

Example 3:   Solve $5x = 11y + 2$
                             $3x + 7y = 5.$

Solution:

Step 1 Rewrite the first equation in the form $ax + by = c$.

$$5x = 11y + 2 \longrightarrow 5x - 11y = 2$$

We shall solve the system: $5x - 11y = 2 \qquad \textbf{(1)}$
                                       $3x + 7y = 5. \qquad \textbf{(2)}$

Step 2   Let us eliminate x. Multiply equation 1 by –3 and equation 2 by 5

$$-3(5x - 11y) = -3(2) \longrightarrow -15x + 33y = -6$$
$$5(3x + 7y) = 5(5) \longrightarrow 15x + 35y = 25$$

Step 3   Add the two equations.

$$-15x + 33y = -6$$
$$\underline{15x + 35y = 25}$$
$$68y = 19$$

Step 4   Solve $68y = 19$ for y. $y = \dfrac{19}{68}$

If we substitute $\dfrac{19}{68}$ for y in either one of the equations as required by Step 5, the resulting calculations will be somewhat complicated. In such a case, we repeat the Steps 2 - 4, and this time eliminate the (other) variable y. We multiply equation (1) by 7 and equation (2) by 11 and add.

$$7(5x - 11y) = 7(2) \quad \text{Multiply by 7} \quad \textbf{or} \quad 35x - 77y = 14$$
$$11(3x + 7y) = 11(5) \quad \text{Multiply by 11} \quad \underline{33x + 77y = 55}$$
$$68x = 69$$

$$\textbf{or} \quad x = \dfrac{69}{68}$$

Step 5   We may verify that $\left(\dfrac{69}{68}, \dfrac{19}{68}\right)$ is the solution of the *original* system.

Example 4:   Solve $\dfrac{3}{2}x - \dfrac{3}{4}y = \dfrac{15}{4}$

$$\dfrac{5}{3}y - \dfrac{4}{3}x = \dfrac{-19}{3}$$

4. Solve $\dfrac{2}{3}x - \dfrac{4}{5}y = -\dfrac{28}{15}$

$$\dfrac{5}{4}y - \dfrac{5}{4}x = \dfrac{15}{4}$$

Solution:

First multiply both sides of each equation by the l.c.d. of the fractions in that equation. This is done to eliminate fractions.

$$\dfrac{3}{2}x - \dfrac{3}{4}y = \dfrac{15}{4} \xrightarrow{\text{l.c.d} = 4} 4\left(\dfrac{3}{2}x - \dfrac{3}{4}y\right) = 4\left(\dfrac{15}{4}\right)$$
$$\longrightarrow 6x - 3y = 15$$

Again,

$$\dfrac{5}{3}y - \dfrac{4}{3}x = \dfrac{-19}{3} \xrightarrow{\text{l.c.d} = 3} 3\left(\dfrac{5}{3}y - \dfrac{4}{3}x\right) = 3\left(\dfrac{-19}{3}\right)$$
$$\longrightarrow 5y - 4x = -19$$

Warm Up

We shall now solve the system: $6x - 3y = 15$
$$5y - 4x = -19.$$

Step 1 $6x - 3y = 15 \longrightarrow 6x - 3y = 15$ **(1)**
$5y - 4x = -19 \longrightarrow -4x + 5y = -19$ **(2)**

Step 2 $4(6x - 3y) = 4(15)$ **or** $24x - 12y = 60$
$6(-4x + 5y) = 6(-19)$ $\underline{-24x + 30y = -114}$

Step 3   Add the two equations $18y = -54$

Step 4 $18y = -54 \longrightarrow y = \dfrac{-54}{18} = -3$

Step 5   Substitute -3 for y in say the equation (1).
$$6x - 3(-3) = 15 \longrightarrow 6x + 9 = 15 \longrightarrow 6x = 6$$
$$\longrightarrow x = 1$$

Step 6   Verify that $(1, -3)$ satisfies the *original* system.

Answers:

1. $(-4, -8)$ 2. $(2, 8)$

3. $\left(-\dfrac{1}{3}, \dfrac{2}{3}\right)$ 4. $(-4, -1)$

B.   Identify Dependent and Inconsistent Systems

Warm Up

5. Solve the system
$$4x - 5y = 21$$
$$10y - 8x + 42 = 0$$

Example 5:   Solve the system. $3x - 4y = 5$
$$8y - 6x + 10 = 0.$$

Solution:

$$3x - 4y = 5 \longrightarrow 3x - 4y = 5$$

$$8y - 6x + 10 = 0 \longrightarrow -6x + 8y = -10$$

Let us eliminate x.

$2(3x - 4y) = 2(5)$ multiply by 2   **or** $6x - 8y = 10$

$1(-6x + 8y) = 1(-10)$ multiply by 1   **or** $\underline{-6x + 8y = -10}$
$$0 = 0 \quad \text{True}$$

This results in a true statement which does not contain x or y. Thus, the system is dependent and has infinite number of solutions. Recall the graphs of the equations in this system are **coincident lines**.

Example 6:   Solve the system $2x - 5y = 3$
$4x - 10y = 2.$

Solution:

Let us eliminate x.

$4(2x - 5y) = 4(3)$ Multiply by 4   **or** $8x - 20y = 12$
$-2(4x - 10y) = -2(2)$ Multiply by -2 **or** $\underline{-8x + 20y = -4}$
$0 = 8$ False

This results in a false statement. This means that the system does not have a solution, or the system is inconsistent. Recall that the graphs of the equations in this system are **parallel lines.**

Warm Up

6. Solve the system
$3x - 2y = 4$
$9x - 6y = 13$

Answers:

5. $0 = 0$ True coincident lines
6. $0 = 1$ False parallel lines

EXERCISE 7.3

Answers:

Solve the following systems of equations by the addition method. Identify whether the system is dependent or inconsistent.

1. $x - y = 7$
$x + y = 3$

2. $x + y = 5$
$x - y = 2$

3. $3x + y = -8$
$5x - y = -16$

4. $x + 5y = 8$
$x - 3y = -4$

5. $2x + 3y = 8$
$3x - 2y = -1$

6. $4x + 9y = 8$
$6y - 2x = 3$

7. $3x + 7y = 5$
$14y = 10 - 6x$

8. $3x + 5y = -19$
$6x + 7y = -23$

9. $3x - 2y = -13$
$9x + 5y = 16$

10. $4x + 8y = -5$
$x + 2y = 1$

11. $3y + 11 = -2x$
$5x + 2y = 22$

12. $9x + 21y = 10$
$4x - 2y = \dfrac{2}{3}$

1. _____

2. _____

3. _____

4. _____

5. _____

6. _____

7. _____

8. _____

9. _____

10. _____

11. _____

12. _____

Answers:

13. _____

14. _____

15. _____

16. _____

17. _____

18. _____

19. _____

20. _____

13. $x = \dfrac{5}{2}y + 1$

$2x - 5y = 2$

14. $x = \dfrac{5}{2}y + 1$

$2x - 5y = 3$

15. $\dfrac{x}{2} + \dfrac{y}{2} = 3$

$\dfrac{x}{2} - \dfrac{y}{2} = -1$

16. $\dfrac{x}{2} - \dfrac{y}{3} + 4 = 0$

$\dfrac{x}{2} + \dfrac{y}{9} = 0$

17. $\dfrac{5}{2}x + y = \dfrac{-11}{2}$

$\dfrac{3}{4}x - \dfrac{3}{4}y = -\dfrac{15}{4}$

18. $\dfrac{4}{3}x + \dfrac{1}{3}y = \dfrac{5}{3}$

$-\dfrac{8}{7}x - \dfrac{2}{7}y = -\dfrac{10}{7}$

19. $\dfrac{5}{6}x + \dfrac{2}{3}y = \dfrac{7}{6}$

$\dfrac{10}{7}x - \dfrac{4}{9}y = \dfrac{17}{21}$

20. $7x - 2y = 3$

$5x + 4y = 5$

7.4   SYSTEMS OF LINEAR INEQUALITIES

Graphing the solution of a linear inequality was discussed in section 6.5. In this section we shall study how to solve systems of linear inequalities in two variables. A **system of linear inequalities** consists of two or more linear inequalities considered together.

Upon completion of this section you will be able to graph solutions of a system of linear inequalities.

Graphing a System of Linear Inequalities

The solution of a system of linear inequalities is the set of all points that make *each* inequality in the system true.

We shall solve a system of linear inequalities by graphing each inequality on the same coordinate plane. We shall use the following two steps.

Step 1   Graph *each* linear inequality using the same coordinate system.
Step 2   Indicate the solution by shading the common region *distinctly*.

378

Example 1:

Graph the solution of the linear system.

$$x + y \leq 2$$
$$2x - y > 3$$

Solution:

Step 1   Graph $x + y \leq 2$ and $2x - y > 3$ in the same coordinate plane.

The graph of $x + y \leq 2$:

(i)   Draw the graph of $x + y = 2$ as a solid line.

(ii)   Choose $(0,0)$ as a test point.

(iii) $0 + 0 \leq 2$ is *true*.
Therefore, shade the region *containing* $(0,0)$.

The graph of $2x - y > 3$:

(i)   Draw the graph of $2x - y = 3$ as a dotted line.
(ii)   Choose $(0,0)$ as a test point.
(iii) $2 \cdot 0 - 0 > 3$ is false.

Therefore, shade the region *not containing* $(0,0)$.

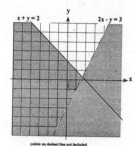

points on dashed line not included

Figure 7.9

Step 2   The solution of the system is given by the common or overlapping region. The solution is shaded in the darkest shade (Figure 7.9).

We can solve systems of linear inequalities using calculator. See example 1-3 on pages 526-527.

Example 2:

Graph the solution of the system.

$$x \geq 1$$
$$y \geq x$$
$$3x + 4y < 12$$

Solution:

Step 1   Graph $x \geq 1$, $y \geq x$, and $3x + 4y < 12$ in the same coordinate plane. The regions indicated by arrows in Figure 7.10 are the solutions of these three inequalities.

Step 2   The solution of the system is given by the common or the overlapping region. The solution is the shaded portion.

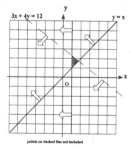

points on dashed line not included

Figure 7.10

EXERCISE 7.4

Find the graph of the solution of the following system in inequalities.

1. $x + y \geq 4$
$x - y < 1$

2. $x \geq 1$
$2x + y \leq 5$

3. $2x - y \geq 4$
$x + 2y \leq 1$

4. $4x + 3y > 6$
$x - 2y < 4$

5. $y < 3x + 2$
$y < -2x + 3$

6. $y + 2 > x$
$y \geq 2x - 1$

7. $x + 2y < 3$
$2x + 4y < 12$

8. $x + 2y < 3$
$x + y < 1$

9. $2x + y \leq 4$
$y > 2x$
$x \geq 0$

10. $x - y < 4$
$y \leq 0$
$x \geq 0$

7.5   APPLICATIONS

Upon completion of this section we will be able to set up a system of linear equations for solving word problems.

As emphasized earlier, the strategy for solving word or applied problems consists essentially of the following steps.

Step 1	Read the problem carefully and identify the unknowns.
Step 2	Formulate the problem and write two equations. [A figure is helpful.]
Step 3	Solve the system of equations.
Step 4	Answer the question asked in the problem.
Step 5	Verify your solution.

Example 1:   The sum of two numbers is 85. Two times the smaller number exceeds the greater number by 26. Find the number.

Solution:

Step 1   Suppose x is the smaller number and y is the larger number.

Step 2   The sum of x and y $= x + y = 85$
2 times smaller number - greater number $= 26$ or
$2x - y = 26$

Step 3   Solve the system of equations.

$$
\begin{aligned}
x + y &= 85 & \textbf{(1)} \\
2x - y &= 26 & \textbf{(2)} \\
\hline
3x &= 111 & \text{Add the equations}
\end{aligned}
$$

$$x = \frac{111}{3} \quad \text{or} \quad x = 37$$

Substitute 37 for x in equation (1).

$$x + y = 85 \longrightarrow 37 + y = 85 \longrightarrow y = 85 - 37 \longrightarrow y = 48$$

Step 4   Therefore, the two numbers are 37 and 48.

Step 5   Verify the solutions: The sum $(37 + 48) = 85$
and $2(37) - 48 = 26$

Example 2:   The sum of a two-digit number and its tens digit is 51. The sum of the number and its units digit is 54. Find the number.

Solution:

Recall the following:

"If the units digit of a number is n, and its tens digit is m, then the number is equal to $10m + n$." For example, $34 = 10 \cdot 3 + 4$.

Step 1   Suppose that the units digit of the required number is n, and the tens digit is m.

Step 2   Then the number $= 10m + n$

Now **the number + ten digits** $= 51$

$(10m + n) + m = 51$ or $\textbf{11}m + n = \textbf{51}$

Again, **the number + units digit** $= 54$

or $(10m + n) + n = 54$ or $\textbf{10}m + \textbf{2}n = \textbf{54}$.

Warm Up

1.   The sum of two numbers is 15. Twice the smaller number exceeds the greater by 6. Find the number.

2. The sum of a two-digit number and its tens digit is 63. The sum of the number and its unit digit is 66. Find the number.

Warm Up

Step 3   We must solve the system: $11m + n = 51$ **(1)**
$$10m + 2n = 54   \textbf{(2)}$$

From the equation (1) we have $n = \textbf{51} - \textbf{11}m$.   **(3)**

Substituting $51 - 11m$ for n in the equation (2):

$$10m + 2(\textbf{51} - \textbf{11}m) = 54 \longrightarrow 10m + 102 - 22m = 54$$
$$\longrightarrow -12m + 102 = 54$$
$$\longrightarrow -12m = -48 \longrightarrow m = \textbf{4}$$

Substitute 4 for m in equation 3.

$$n = 51 - 11m = 51 - 11 \cdot \textbf{4} = 51 - 44 = 7$$

Step 4   Hence, the number is $10 \cdot \textbf{4} + \textbf{7} = 47$.

Step 5   Verify the solution:
The number + ten's digit $= 47 + 4 = 51$ Given
The number + one's digit $= 47 + 7 = 54$ Given

3. A pile of 30 coins consists of nickels and dimes. The total value is $2.25. Find the number of coins of each type.

Example 3:   A pile of 40 coins consists of nickels and dimes. The total value of the coins is $3.35. Find the number of coins of each type.

Solution:

Step 1   Let number of nickels $= x$, and let number of dimes $= \textbf{y.}$

Step 2   Total number of coins $= x + y$ and $x + y = \textbf{40}$

Total value of nickels $=$ $5x$ **cents**

Total value of dimes $=$ $10y$ **cents**

Total value of the coins $=$ 3.35 $=$ 335 **cents**

Thus, $\textbf{5}x + \textbf{10}y = \textbf{335}$

Step 3   We must solve the system: $x + y = 40$ **(1)**
$$5x + 10y = 335.   \textbf{(2)}$$

From equation (1), we have $y = 40 - x$.

Substituting $40 - x$ for y in the equation (2):

$$5x + 10(\textbf{40} - \textbf{x}) = 335$$
$$5x + 400 - 10x = 335$$
$$-5x + 400 = 335 \longrightarrow -5x = 335 - 400$$
$$\longrightarrow -5x = -65 \longrightarrow x = \textbf{13}$$

Substituting 13 for x in equation (1).

$$x + y = 40 \longrightarrow \textbf{13} + y = 40 \longrightarrow y = 27$$

Step 4   Therefore, there are 13 nickels and 27 dimes.

Step 5   Verify the solution: 13 nickels + 27 dimes
$= (13 \times 5 + 27 \times 10)$ cents
$= (65 + 270)$ cents
$= 335$ cents
$= \$3.35 =$ the given total value

Warm Up

| **Example 4:** | A sporting goods store sells 3 fishing reels and 5 fishing rods for \$309, and 6 fishing reels and 2 fishing rods for \$282. Find the price of each item. |

Solution:

Step 1   Let price of fishing reel $= x$ dollars.

Let price of fishing rod $= y$ dollars.

Step 2   **First sale:** 3 fishing reels + 5 fishing rods $= 309$

or $3x + 5y = 309$

Second sale: 6 fishing reels + 2 fishing rods $= 282$
or $6x + 2y = 282$

Step 3   We must solve the system: $3x + 5y = 309$ **(1)**

$6x + 2y = 282$ **(2)**

Now, multiply equation (1) by -2 and add it to equation (2).

$-2(3x + 5y) = -2(309)$ $-6x - 10y = -618$
$\quad 6x + 2y = 282$ or $\quad\underline{6x + 2y = 282}$

$\qquad\qquad -8y = -336$

$\longrightarrow \qquad y = \dfrac{-336}{-8} = 42$

Substitute 42 for y in equation (1).

$3x + 5y = 309$ or $3x + 5 \cdot \mathbf{42} = 309$ or $x = 33$

Step 4   Therefore the cost of a fishing reel is \$33 and the cost of a fishing rod is \$42.

Step 5   Verify the solution.

| **Example 5:** | A pharmacist has 30 % and 80% powder mixtures on hand. How many pounds of each powder will be required to produce 8 pounds of a 50% powder mixture? |

Solution:

Step 1   Let the number of pounds of 30% mixture $= x$

Let the number of pounds of 80% mixture $= y$

4. A sporting goods store sells 2 fishing reels and 13 fishing rods for \$280 and 1 fishing reel and 4 fishing rods for \$120. Find the price for each item.

5. A pharmacist has 40% and 60% powder mixtures on hand. How many pounds of each powder will be required to produce 6 pounds of a 50% powder mixture?

Warm Up

Step 2   The number of 1bs of 30% mixture + number of lbs of 80 mixture = 8

$$x + y = 8$$

The concentration of x lbs of 30% mixture + y lbs of 80% mixture = the concentration of 8 lbs of 50% mixture

$$0.3x + 0.8y = 0.5(8) \quad \text{or} \quad 3x + 8y = 40$$

Step 3   We must solve the linear system: $x + y = 8$ **(1)**

$$3x + 8y = 40. \quad \textbf{(2)}$$

From the first equation we have $x = 8 - y.$ Substitute this for x in the second equation.

$$3x + 8y = 40 \longrightarrow 3(8 - y) + 8y = 40$$

$$\longrightarrow 24 - 3y + 8y = 40$$

$$\longrightarrow 24 + 5y = 40 \longrightarrow y = \frac{16}{5} = 3.2 \text{ lbs.}$$

$$x + y = 8 \longrightarrow x + 3.2 = 8 \longrightarrow x = 8 - 3.2 = 4.8 \text{ lbs}$$

Step 4   Therefore the pharmacist would require 4.8 pounds of 30% mixture and 3.2 pounds of 80% mixture to get 8 lbs of 50% mixture.

Step 5   Verify the solution: $4.8 \times 0.30 + 3.2 \times .80 = 8 \times 0.50$
$$1.44 + 2.56 = 4.00 \quad \text{TRUE}$$

6. Swimming downstream, a swimmer can cover 4 miles in 20 minutes. It takes the swimmer 30 minutes to swim back. Find the speed of the current.

Example 6:   Swimming downstream, a swimmer can cover 2 miles in 15 minutes. It takes the swimmer 20 minutes to swim back. Find the speed of the swimmer in still water and the speed of the current.

Solution:

Step 1   Let speed of the swimmer in still water = x miles per hour. Let the speed of the current = y miles per hour

Step 2   Swimming downstream, the speed of the swimmer = $x + y$. Swimming upstream, the speed of the swimmer = $x - y$. Since the unit of time in the speed is hours, convert 15 minutes and 20 minutes in terms of hours.

$$15 \text{ minutes} = \frac{15}{60} \text{ hour} = \frac{1}{4} \text{ hour.}$$

$$20 \text{ minutes} = \frac{20}{60} \text{ hour} = \frac{1}{3} \text{ hour.}$$

Recall   (Time taken) $\cdot$ (Speed)   = Distance

Therefore

for going downstream $\dfrac{1}{4} \cdot (x + y) = 2$

for going upstream $\dfrac{1}{3} \cdot (x - y) = 2$

or $x + y = 8$ **(1)**

  $x - y = 6$ **(2)**

Step 3   To solve this system we add the two equations.

$$x + y = 8$$
$$x - y = 6$$
$$\overline{2x \quad = 14} \longrightarrow x = 7$$

Substitute 7 for x in equation (1).

$$x + y = 8 \longrightarrow 7 + y = 8 \longrightarrow y = 1$$

Step 4   Therefore, the speed of the swimmer is 7 miles per hour, and the current speed is 1 mile per hour.

Step 5   Verify the solution:

Going downstream, $(x + y) \cdot 15$ mts. = 2 miles

or $(7 + 1) \cdot \dfrac{15}{60}$ hours = 2

or $8 \cdot \dfrac{1}{4} = 2$

Going upstream, $(7 - 1) \cdot 20$ min = 2

$$6 \cdot \dfrac{20}{60} = 2 \longrightarrow 6 \cdot \dfrac{1}{3} = 2$$

Example 7:   Two cars start from towns 400 miles apart and travel toward each other. They pass each other after 4 hours. Find the speed of each car if the difference between their speeds is 20 miles per hour.

Solution:

Step 1   Let the speed of the faster car $= x$ miles per hour.
Let the speed of the slower car $= y$ miles per hour.

7.   Two cars start from two towns 200 miles apart and travel towards each other. They pass each other in 2 hours. Find the speed of each car if the difference between their speeds is 10 miles per hour.

Warm Up

Step 2   The distance traveled by first car $= 4x$
The distance traveled by second car $= 4y$

Car	Rate	· Time	= Distance
Faster	x	4	$4x$
Slower	y	4	$4y$

At the point of crossing, the distance traveled by two cars
$= 4x + 4y$. Therefore, $\mathbf{4x + 4y = 400}$ or $x + y = 100$
We also know the difference in speeds $x - y = 20$

Step 3   To solve this system of equations, we add the two
equations.

$$x + y = 100 \qquad \mathbf{(1)}$$
$$x - y = 20 \qquad \mathbf{(2)}$$
$$2x \quad = 120 \longrightarrow x = 60 \text{ miles / hr}$$

Substitute 60 for x in the equation (1).

$$\mathbf{x} + y = 100 \longrightarrow \mathbf{40} + y = 100 \longrightarrow y = 60 \text{ miles / hr}$$

Step 4   The two cars travel at 60 miles per hour and 40 miles
per hour respectively.

Step 5   Verify the solution:

Distance traveled by the first car $= 60 \times 4 = 240$ miles
Distance traveled by the second car $= 40 \times 4 = 160$ miles

Total distance $= 240 + 160 = 400$ True

Answers:

1. The two numbers are 7 and 8
2. 58   **3.** 15 nickels , 15 dimes
4. fish reels is $88 , fishing rod is $8
5. The pharmacist would require 3 lbs
   of each mixture
6. speed of swimmer in still water is
   10 mi/hr , speed of current is 2 mi/h
7. speed of faster car is 55 mi/h and
   slower car is 45 mi/h.

EXERCISE   7.5

Answers:

1. _____

2. _____

1. The sum of two integers is 6. Twice the smaller integer is 24
   less that the larger integer. Find the integers.

2. The sum of two numbers is 63. Their difference is 9. Find
   the numbers.

3. The perimeter of a rectangle is 72 cm. The sum of twice the length and three times the width is 88 *cm*. Find the dimensions of the rectangle.

3. _____

4. In a certain right triangle one acute angle is $15°$ less than two times the other acute angle. Find the difference between the two acute angles. [Hint: The sum of the angles in a triangle is $180°$]

4. _____

5. A theater sold $520 worth of tickets. An adult ticket costs $3.00 each and children's ticket cost $2.00 each. If 190 tickets were sold, how many tickets of each kind did the theater sell?

5. _____

6. Two pounds of rib steak and six pounds of hamburger meat cost $12.30, and three pounds of rib steak and two pounds of hamburger meat costs $9.70. Find the cost per pound of each type of meat.

6. _____

7. Connie invested all of her $3000 savings, part at an annual rate of 6%, and the rest at an annual rate of 9%. Her annual income from both the investments was 8% of her total investment. How much did she invest at 6%?

7. _____

8. A hospital purchased a total of 185 bottles of glucose solution. Small bottles cost $2 each, and large ones cost $3 each. The total cost was $480. How many bottles of each size were purchased?

8. _____

9. An automatic vending machine in Country Store provides a packet of 28 stamps worth 10 cents and 20 cents. The cost of the packet is $4. If the stamps are priced at their face value, how many stamps of each type are there?

9. _____

10. A textbook author receives $2 royalty for each of his algebra books sold and a $3 royalty for each of his trigonometry books sold. During one royalty period, a total of 11,500 copies of the two books were sold. The author received a total of $27,800 in royalties. How many books of each kind were sold?

10. _____

Answers:

11. _____

12. _____

13. _____

14. _____

15. _____

16. _____

17. _____

11. Rollins invested a part of $6,000 at 10% and the rest at 8%. His annual income from these investments is $556. How much did he invest at each rate?

12. A pharmacist wants 1000 oz of 12.2% alcohol solution. He has 8% and 15% alcohol solutions to mix. How many ounces of the 8% solution will be required?

13. A 30% dye solution is to be mixed with an 80% dye solution to make 60 liters of 50% solution. How many liters of each kind of solution is needed?

14. A lab technician has 15% and 40% concentrations of nitric acid. A class is conducting an experiment that requires 300 milliliters of a 25% concentration of nitric acid. How many milliliters of each concentration should be mixed to make the desired concentration?

15. A supermarket mixes coffee that sells for $1.50 per pound with coffee that sells $2 per pound to obtain 25 pounds of coffee selling for $1.68 per pound. How many pounds of each kind of coffee are required?

16. An airplane can fly 360 miles into the wind are 3 hours. If the plane reverses the direction and the wind conditions remain the same, the return trip takes only two hours. Find the speed of the plane in still air.

17. A boat can travel 60 miles downstream in 3 hours. If the boat can travel 30 miles upstream in 2 hours, find the speed of the current and the speed of the boat in still water.

Answers:

18.   Two cars leave a common place at the same time and travel in opposite directions. The difference in their speeds is 10 miles per hour. After two hours the cars are 200 miles apart. Find the speed of each car.

18. _____

19.   A car travels 50 miles in the same time that a plane travels 180 miles. The difference between their speeds is 143 miles per hour. Find the speed of the airplane.

19. _____

20.   Two trains start from stations 1050 miles apart and travel toward each other. They pass each other after 6 hours. Find the speed of each train if one of the trains travels 25 miles slower than the other.

20. _____

7.6   CHAPTER SUMMARY

Examples

Solving a System of Linear Equations by Graphing

1. The solution of a system of linear equations in two variables is the set of all ordered pairs which satisfy all equations of the system.

2. To solve a system of linear equations in two variables graphically, we graph both equations of the system in the same coordinate plane. The point of intersection, if any, is a solution of the system.

Solving Systems of Linear Equations by Substitution

3. To solve a system of two linear equations in two variables by substitution, we use the following steps:

   Step 1   Solve one of the equations for either variable.

   Step 2   Substitute the expression for this variable in the second equation.

   Step 3   Solve the equation obtained in Step 2.

1. Solve the system by graphing
   $$2x + y = 7$$
   $$x + 3y = 6$$
   Graph the two lines

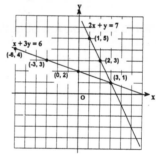

The solution is (3, 1), the point of intersection.

3. Solve: $2x - y = 0$
             $x + y = 3$

$$2x - y = 0 \rightarrow y = 2x$$

$$x + y = 3 \rightarrow x + 2x = 3$$

$$\rightarrow 3x = 3$$

$$\rightarrow x = 1$$

Examples

Step 4	Substitute the value obtained in Step 3 in the equation determined in Step 1.

$$2x - y = 0 \quad \rightarrow \quad 2(1) - y = 0$$
$$\rightarrow \quad 2 - y = 0$$
$$\rightarrow \quad y = 2$$

Step 5	Check your solution by substituting it into the original equations.

Solution is: (1,2)

$$2x - y = 0 \quad \rightarrow \quad 2(1) - 2 = 0 \text{ True}$$
$$x + y = 3 \quad \rightarrow \quad (1) + (2) = 3 \quad \text{True}$$

Solving Systems of Linear Equations by Addition

4. To solve a system of two linear equations in two variables by addition, we use the following steps:

4. $3x + 4y = -2$ **(1)**

      $2x - 3y = 4$ **(2)**

Step 1	Write both equations in the form $ax + by = c$. When writing the two equations in this form, align the variables.

Not needed

Step 2	Multiply one or both equations by suitable numbers, so that the coefficients of x (or y) in the resulting equations are negatives of each other.

Multiply equation (1) by -2 and (2) by 3.

$$(-2)(3x + 4y) = (-2)(-2) \text{ or}$$
$$-6x - 8y = 4 \quad \textbf{(1)}$$
$$3(2x - 3y) = 3 \cdot 4 \text{ or}$$
$$6x - 9y = 12 \quad \textbf{(2)}$$

Step 3	Add the two equations.

$$\begin{array}{r} -6x - 8y = 4 \\ 6x - 9y = 12 \\ \hline -17y = 16 \end{array}$$

Step 4	Solve the equation obtained in Step 3.

$$17y = -16 \rightarrow y = -\frac{16}{17}$$

Step 5	Substitute the value obtained in step 4 in either of the original equations and solve for the other variable. If this involves fractions then repeat step 2 to 4 to eliminate the other variables.

Multiply equation (1) by 3 and (2) and 4.

$$3(3x + 4y) = 3(-2) \rightarrow 9x = 12y = -6$$
$$4(2x - 3y) = 4(4) \rightarrow \underline{8x - 12y = 16}$$
$$17x = 10$$
$$x = \frac{17}{10}$$

Step 6	Check your answers.

Solving Systems of Linear Inequalities

5. To solve a system of linear inequalities in two variables, we use the following two steps.

Step 1	Graph each linear inequality on the same coordinate system.

Step 2	The solution of the system is the region common to the solutions of individual inequalities. Indicate each region by shading distinctly. Finally, shade distinctly the common region for the solution of the system.

5. Solve graphically: $x - y \geq 0$

                        $2x - y \leq 2$

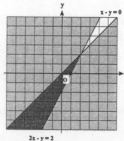

Applications of Linear System of Equations

6. We use the following five steps approach to solve application problems.

Step 1   Read the problem carefully and identify the unknown.

Step 2   Formulate the problem and write two equations.

Step 3   Solve the system of equations.

Step 4   Answer the question asked in the problem.

Step 5   Check your solution.

7.7 REVIEW EXERCISE

1. **Check whether the given ordered pair is a solution of the system or not.**

a) $2x + 3y = 4$ $\left(\dfrac{1}{2}, 1\right)$ b) $4x - y = 1$ $(3, 2)$

     $4x + 5y = 6$ $2x + 3y = 4$

In exercises 2–6, solve the systems of equations by graphing. Identify whether the system is inconsistent or dependent.

2. $2x = 3y$
     $2x + y = 8$

3. $2x - 3y = 8$
     $3x - y = -2$

4. $y - 3x + 4 = 0$
     $6x - 2y = 5$

5. $x - y = 4$
     $3x = 3y + 12$

6. $2x + 3y + 10 = 0$
     $3x - 4y = 19$

In exercises 7–12, solve the system of equations by the method of addition. Identify whether the systems are inconsistent or dependent.

7. $3x + 2y = 8$
     $6x + 4y = 13$

8. $3x - y = 2$
     $2x + y = 3$

9. $4x + 3y = 10$
     $5y + 3x = 14$

10. $3x - 5y = 2$
      $6x = 10y + 4$

11. $11x - 9y = 15$
      $4x - 10y = -8$

12. $\dfrac{2}{3}x + \dfrac{1}{2}y = 3$
      $\dfrac{2}{5}x - \dfrac{3}{2}y = -1$

In exercises 13–18, solve the system of equations by the method of substitution. Identify whether the system is inconsistent or dependent.

13. $y = 3x + 1$
      $y = \dfrac{1}{2}x - 1$

14. $y = 3x + 3$
      $y = 3x + 1$

15. $x - 3y = 10$
      $2x - y = 6$

16. $x - 2y + 2 = 0$ **17.** $y = 4x + 9$ **18.** $2x + 3y = 3$

$3x + 10y + 2 = 0$ $4x - y = 1$ $10x + 15y = 15$

In exercise 19–25, the systems of inequalities graphically.

19. $x + y < 3$ **20.** $y + 2x \le 5$ **21.** $x - y \le 5$

$3x - y > 6$ $y + 1 > 4x$ $x + y \ge -1$

22. $12x + 2y > 6$ **23.** $y \ge 3x - 2$ **24.** $3x - 2y \le 6,\ y \le 2,\ x \ge 1$

$6x + y \le 8$ $y + 2x < 4$

25. $x + y > 4,\ 2x + 2y < 1$

26. Find two numbers such that their sum is 101 and their difference is 37.

27. The sum of the digits of a two-digit number is 11. Twice the tens digit exceeds the digit in the units place by 1. Find the number.

28. An airplane flies with the wind at a velocity of 550 miles per hour. When flying against the wind, the plane's speed is 470 miles per hour. Find the speed of the airplane if the wind were calm.

29. How many liters of 30% acid solution and how many liters of 90% acid solution must be mixed to produce 300 liters of 80% acid solution?

30. Shirley invests $10,000 in stocks and bonds. The stocks return is 15% a year, and the bonds return is 10% a year. If the total return on the investment after one year is $1100, how much did Shirley invest in stocks and bonds each?

7.8   SELF TEST

In exercises 1–2, solve the systems by graphing. Identify the system is inconsistent or dependent.

1. $x - y = 3$ **2.** $2x + y = 1$

$2x + y = 3$ $4x + 2y = 10$

In exercises 3–5, solve the system by substitution method.

3. $2x + y = 5$ **4.** $3x - 5y = 7$ **5.** $4x + 3y = 8$

$x - 2y = 10$ $9x = 15y + 21$ $6x - 5y + 7 = 0$

In exercises 6–9, solve the system by the method of addition.

6. $5x + 4y = 3$ **7.** $5x - 7 + 2y = 5y + 4$ **8.** $2x + 3y = 7$ **9.** $\dfrac{3}{5}x + \dfrac{2}{3}y = 1$

$7x + 5y = 3$ $3y + 4 = x + y$ $4x + 6y = 15$ $18x + 20y = 30$

In exercises 10–12, graph the solution of the systems of inequalities:

10. $3x - 2y \le 6$ **11.** $2x + y > 5$ **12.** $x - y \le 5$

$y > 1$ $x - y < 1$ $-x - 2y \ge 4$

13. The sum of two numbers is 67, and their difference is 29. Find the numbers.

14. The Goodies Club recently ran a bake sale to raise charity. Donuts were sold for $0.50 a piece and the coffee for $0.70 per person. It is known that 120 items were sold and $68 collected. How many cups of coffee were sold?

CHAPTER 8

ROOTS AND RADICALS

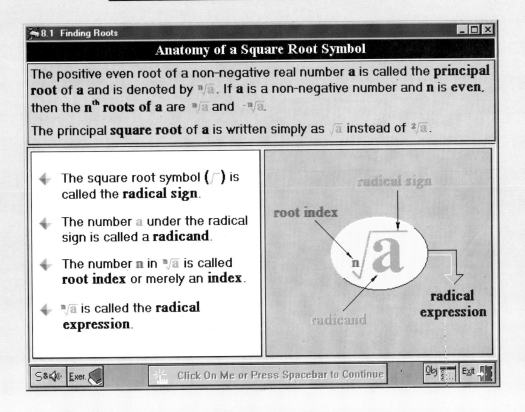

8.1 Finding Roots

Anatomy of a Square Root Symbol

The positive even root of a non-negative real number **a** is called the **principal root** of **a** and is denoted by $\sqrt[n]{a}$. If **a** is a non-negative number and **n** is **even**, then the **n**th **roots of a** are $\sqrt[n]{a}$ and $-\sqrt[n]{a}$.

The principal **square root** of **a** is written simply as $\sqrt{a}$ instead of $\sqrt[2]{a}$.

- The square root symbol ($\sqrt{\ }$) is called the **radical sign**.
- The number a under the radical sign is called a **radicand**.
- The number **n** in $\sqrt[n]{a}$ is called **root index** or merely an **index**.
- $\sqrt[n]{a}$ is called the **radical expression**.

radical sign

root index

radicand

radical expression

S&◁ Exer. ※ Click On Me or Press Spacebar to Continue Obj Exit

CHAPTER 8

ROOTS AND RADICALS

In Chapter 3 we defined integer exponents. Here we shall consider the situations when the exponents are rational numbers. We shall define different terms associated with such expressions, establish rules for writing such expressions in different forms, and revisit laws of exponents.

This chapter is divided into the following sections.

8.1   FINDING ROOTS

Consider the equation $a^2 = 4$.
We know that the only possible values for a are -2 and 2.
Recall these values $(-2$ and $2)$ are called **square roots** of 4.

Again what is b if $b^3 = -\dfrac{1}{8}$?

Clearly $b = -\dfrac{1}{2}$ since $\left(-\dfrac{1}{2}\right)^3 = \left(-\dfrac{1}{2}\right)\left(-\dfrac{1}{2}\right)\left(-\dfrac{1}{2}\right) = -\dfrac{1}{8}$.

$-\dfrac{1}{2}$ is called the *cube root* of $-\dfrac{1}{8}$.

In general if r is a real number and n is a *positive integer* then,

$$a \text{ is the } n^{th} \text{ root of } r \qquad \text{and} \qquad r = a^n.$$

1.   When $n = 2$, the nth root is called the square root.
2.   When $n = 3$, the nth root is called the cube root.
3.   The nth root of 0 is always 0 since $0^n = 0$ for any positive integer n.

Upon completion of this section we will be able to:

A.   Find roots.
B.   Determine whether a root is a rational number, irrational number, or not a real number.
C.   Find decimal approximations for irrational square roots.
D.   Use the Pythagorean formula.

A. Finding Square Roots and Higher Roots

Warm Up

1. Find the square root of the following numbers:

   a) 81

   b) 121

   c) −144

Example 1:   Find the square roots of the following numbers

a)   36   b)   49   c)   − 81

Solutions:

a)   Since $(6)^2 = 36$ and $(-6)^2 = 36$, therefore **6 and − 6 are square roots of 36.**

b)   We know $7^2 = 49$ and $(-7)^2 = 49$. Therefore **7 and −7 are square roots of 49.**

c)   Since the square of any real number is never negative, there is no real number whose square is − 81. Therefore, the **square root of − 81 *is not a real number.***

---

2. Find the cube roots of the following numbers:

   a) 64

   b) $-\dfrac{1}{8}$

   c) 125

Example 2:   Find cube roots of the following numbers:

a)   27   b)   − 8   c) $\dfrac{1}{64}$

Solutions:

a)   We know that 3 is the *only* number whose cube is 27. Therefore, **the cube root of 27 is 3.**

b)   − 2 is the *only* real number whose cube is − 8. Therefore, **the cube root of − 8 is − 2.**

c) $\dfrac{1}{4}$ is the *only* real number whose cube is $\dfrac{1}{64}$ since $\left(\dfrac{1}{4}\right)^3 = \left(\dfrac{1}{4}\right)\left(\dfrac{1}{4}\right)\left(\dfrac{1}{4}\right) = \dfrac{1}{64}$. Therefore, **the cube root of $\dfrac{1}{64}$ is $\dfrac{1}{4}$.**

---

3. Find the fourth root of the following numbers;

   a) 81

   b) −256

Example 3:   Find the fourth roots of the following numbers

a)   16   b)   − 16

Solutions:

a)   Notice that $2^4 = 2 \cdot 2 \cdot 2 \cdot 2 = 16$ and $(-2)^4 = (-2)(-2)(-2)(-2) = 16$.
The fourth power of no other real number equals 16.
Therefore, the **fourth roots of 16 are 2 and − 2.**

b)   Since the fourth power of no real number can be negative, **the fourth root of − 16 is not a real number.**

We may observe that *when n is odd,* we can define the nth root of any real number. However, *when n is even,* the nth root can be defined for only non-negative real numbers. As seen in the above examples, there is only one odd root of a real number. But there are *two* even roots of a non-negative real number, since a number and its negative give the same result when raised to an even power $\left[2^2 = 4, (-2)^2 = 4; \quad 3^4 = 81, (-3)^4 = 81, \text{etc.}\right]$.

The *positive even root* of a non-negative real number a is called the **principal root** of a and is denoted by $\sqrt[n]{a}$. If a is a non-negative real number and n is even, then the nth roots of a are $\sqrt[n]{a}$ and $-\sqrt[n]{a}$.

The principal **square root** of a is written simply as $\sqrt{a}$ and *not* as $\sqrt[2]{a}$.

If n *is odd*, then for *any* real number a there is only one real nth root, which is denoted by $\sqrt[n]{a}$.

Anatomy of a square root symbol.

n is called the **index**.

$\sqrt{\ }$ is called a **radical sign**.

a is called the **radicand**.

$\sqrt[n]{a}$ is called the **radical expression.**

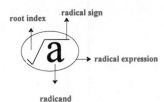

| radical sign
| root index
| radical expression
| radicand

| **Example 4:** | Simplify the following radical expressions. |

a) $\sqrt{121}$ b) $\sqrt{-36}$ c) $\sqrt{\dfrac{1}{81}}$

d) $\sqrt[5]{0}$ e) $\sqrt[3]{64}$ f) $\sqrt[3]{-729}$

g) $\sqrt[4]{16}$ h) $\sqrt[4]{-81}$

Solutions:

a) $\sqrt{121} = 11$, since $11^2 = 121$. $\sqrt{121}$ is a positive root.

b) $\sqrt{-36}$ does not exist in real numbers.   The radicand is negative.

c) $\sqrt{\dfrac{1}{81}} = \dfrac{1}{9}$, since $\left(\dfrac{1}{9}\right)^2 = \left(\dfrac{1}{9}\right)\left(\dfrac{1}{9}\right) = \dfrac{1}{81}$.

d) $\sqrt[5]{0} = 0$, since $(0)^5 = 0$.

e) $\sqrt[3]{64} = 4$ since $(4)^3 = 4 \cdot 4 \cdot 4 = 64$.

f) $\sqrt[3]{-729} = -9$, since $(-9)^3 = (-9)(-9)(-9) = -729$.

g) $\sqrt[4]{16} = 2$, since $2^4 = 2 \cdot 2 \cdot 2 \cdot 2 = 16$.

h) $\sqrt[4]{-81}$ is not a real number since the fourth power of every real number is positive.

Warm Up

4.   Simplify the following radical expressions:

a) $\sqrt{144}$

b) $\sqrt{-49}$

c) $\sqrt{\dfrac{1}{4}}$

d) $\sqrt[7]{0}$

e) $\sqrt[3]{216}$

f) $\sqrt[3]{8}$

g) $\sqrt[4]{81}$

h) $\sqrt[4]{-81}$

5. Simplify the following expressions:

a) $\left(\sqrt[2]{15}\right)^2$

b) $-\left(-\sqrt[3]{-8}\right)^3$

Answers:

1. a) 9 b) 11 c) no real solution
2. a) 4 b) $-\dfrac{1}{2}$ c) 5
3. a) 3 b) no real solution
4. a) 12 b) no real solution c) $\dfrac{1}{2}$ d) 0
   e) 6 f) 2 g) 3 h) no real solution
5. a) 15 b) –8

Example 5: Simplify the following expressions.

a) $\left(\sqrt{13}\right)^2$ b) $\left(-\sqrt{15}\right)^2$ c) $\left(\sqrt[3]{7}\right)^3$

d) $\left(-\sqrt[3]{-9}\right)^3$ e) $\left(\sqrt{8x^2+5}\right)^2$

Solutions:

a) $\left(\sqrt{13}\right)^2 = 13$

b) $\left(-\sqrt{15}\right)^2 = \left(-\sqrt{15}\right)\left(-\sqrt{15}\right) = \left(\sqrt{15}\right)^2 = 15$

c) $\left(\sqrt[3]{7}\right)^3 = 7$ If $a^3 = r$ then $a = \sqrt[3]{r}$.

d) $\left(-\sqrt[3]{-9}\right)^3 = \left(-\sqrt[3]{-9}\right)\left(-\sqrt[3]{-9}\right)\left(-\sqrt[3]{-9}\right)$

$= -\left(\sqrt[3]{-9}\right)^3 = -(-9) = 9$

e) $\left(\sqrt{8x^2+5}\right)^2 = 8x^2 + 5$

B. Rational, Irrational and Real Numbers

Recall that numbers of the type   4,   9, $\dfrac{4}{9}$, $\dfrac{9}{25}$ ...

are all perfect squares of rational numbers:

$4 = (2)^2$, $9 = (3)^2$, $\dfrac{4}{9} = \left(\dfrac{2}{3}\right)^2$, $\dfrac{9}{25} = \left(\dfrac{3}{5}\right)^2$...

Therefore the square roots of **perfect squares**

$\sqrt{4} = 2$, $\sqrt{9} = 3$, $\sqrt{\dfrac{4}{9}} = \dfrac{2}{3}$, $\sqrt{\dfrac{9}{25}} = \dfrac{3}{5}$...

are also rational numbers.

What about **square roots** of rational numbers that are **not perfect squares**?

For example : $\sqrt{2}$, $\sqrt{3}$, $\sqrt{7}$ ...   We define such numbers as **irrational numbers.**

Similarly, cube roots of **perfect cubes** 8,   27,   125,   –8, ...
are rational numbers $\sqrt[3]{8} = 2$ $\sqrt[3]{27} = 3$ $\sqrt[3]{125} = 5$ $\sqrt[3]{-8} = -2$...

What about **cube roots** of rational numbers that are **not perfect cubes** ?

For example : $\sqrt[3]{7}$, $\sqrt[3]{2}$, $\sqrt[3]{10}$...   We define such numbers as **irrational numbers**.

We know that there is no real number whose square is negative. Later in chapter 9, we shall define new types of numbers to deal with square roots of negative numbers. At this time we want to emphasize that **if a is a negative number, then $\sqrt{a}$ is not a real number.**

Example 6:   Which of the following are rational, irrational, or not real?

a) $\sqrt{16}$ b) $\sqrt{17}$ c) $\sqrt{-4}$

d) $\sqrt{\dfrac{4}{9}}$ e) $\sqrt{\dfrac{4}{27}}$ f) $\sqrt{-\dfrac{1}{5}}$

Solutions:

a) $\sqrt{16}$ is *rational*   because $16 = 4^2$ is a perfect square.

b) $\sqrt{17}$ is *irrational* because 17 is not a perfect square.

c) $\sqrt{-4}$ is *not real*   because -4 is negative.

d) $\sqrt{\dfrac{4}{9}}$ is *rational*   because $\dfrac{4}{9} = \left(\dfrac{2}{3}\right)^2$ is a perfect square.

e) $\sqrt{\dfrac{4}{27}}$ is *irrational* because $\dfrac{4}{27}$ is not a perfect square.

f) $\sqrt{-\dfrac{1}{5}}$ is *not real*   because $-\dfrac{1}{5}$ is negative.

C.   Remark on Irrational Numbers

It is always possible to approximate irrational numbers by numbers in decimal form. This can be done by using calculators. Scientific calculators have an exponential key which can be used to approximate any root of a number, when it is defined. Most other calculators have a square root key which can be used to approximate square roots.

Use a calculator to approximate the value of π, $\sqrt{2}$, and $\sqrt[3]{5}$.

$\pi \approx 3.142$ $\sqrt{2} \approx 1.414$ $\sqrt[3]{5} \approx 1.710$

D.   Pythagorean Formula and Square Roots

Recall the Pythagorean formula:

If a right triangle with legs a and b has hypotenuse c,

then $c^2 = a^2 + b^2.$

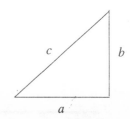

In other words **Hypotenuse = $\sqrt{(Base)^2 + (Height)^2}$**

Warm Up

7. A right triangle has its legs equal to 4 cm and 6 cm. Find the hypotenuse.

8. The hypotenuse of a right triangle is 5. If one leg of the triangle is 3, find the other leg.

9. Use the Illustration in Example 9. Elizabeth is flying a kite on a 30 foot string. The vertical distance between the kite and the ground is 15 feet. What is the horizontal distance between Elizabeth and the kite.

Answers:

7. $2\sqrt{13}$ cm   **8.** 4

9. 25.98 feet

Example 7:   A right triangle has its legs equal to 6 cm and 8 cm. Find the hypotenuse.

Solution:

Use the Pythagorean formula.

$$(hypotenuse)^2 = (6)^2 + (8)^2 = 36 + 64 = 100$$

Therefore, $hypotenuse = \sqrt{100} = 10$ cm.

Example 8:   The hypotenuse of a right triangle is 12 cm. If one leg of the triangle is 5 cm, find the other leg. Approximate your answer to three decimal places (thousandth place).

Solution:

Suppose the second leg is x cm. Then

$$12^2 = 5^2 + x^2 \qquad \text{Pythagorean formula}$$
$$144 = 25 + x^2$$
$$x^2 = 144 - 25 = 119.$$

Therefore $x = \sqrt{119}$

$= 10.9087121$ Use the square root key on calculator.

$\approx 10.909.$ Round off to the third decimal place.

Example 9:   Elizabeth is flying a kite on a 60 foot string. The horizontal distance between Elizabeth and the kite is 25 feet. How high is the kite above Elizabeth's hand? Round off your answer to two decimal places.

Solution: Suppose the height of the kite above Elizabeth's hand is x feet.

By Pythagorean formula:

$$60^2 = 25^2 + x^2$$
$$\rightarrow \quad x^2 = 60^2 - 25^2$$
$$= 3600 - 625$$
$$= 2975$$

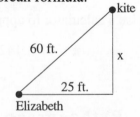

Therefore $x = \sqrt{2975}$

≈ 54.5435605 Use the square root key on the calculator.

≈ 54.54 feet.   Round off to hundredths place.

EXERCISE 8.1

In exercises 1–5, find the principal square root of each number.

1. 4   **2.** 81   **3.** $\dfrac{1}{25}$ **4.** 0   **5.** -16

In exercises 6–11, find the indicated roots.

6. 8; cube root   **7.** -32; fifth root

8. 81; fourth root   **9.** -626; fourth root

10. 729; sixth root   **11.** $\dfrac{8}{125}$; cube root

In exercises 12–18, find the value of the radicals.

12. $\sqrt{36}$ **13.** $\sqrt{144}$ **14.** $\sqrt[3]{-64}$ **15.** $\sqrt[3]{\dfrac{1}{27}}$

16. $\sqrt[5]{\dfrac{32}{243}}$ **17.** $\sqrt[4]{625}$ **18.** $\sqrt{-121}$

Evaluate the expressions in exercises 19–25.

19. $\left(\sqrt{17}\right)^2$ **20.** $\left(\sqrt{-17}\right)^2$ **21.** $\left(-\sqrt{17}\right)^2$

22. $\left(\sqrt[3]{-47}\right)^3$ **23.** $\left(\dfrac{1}{\sqrt[4]{47}}\right)^4$

24. $\left(\sqrt{3x^2 - 1}\right)^2$ $\left[\text{Assume } x^2 \geq \tfrac{1}{3}\right]$ **25.** $\left(\sqrt[3]{\dfrac{x^2 + x}{4}}\right)^3$

In exercises 26–30, identify numbers as rational, irrational, or non-real.

26. $\sqrt{4}$ **27.** $\sqrt{18}$ **28.** $\sqrt{-25}$ **29.** $\sqrt{\dfrac{4}{49}}$ **30.** $-\sqrt{\dfrac{1}{16}}$

1. _____
2. _____
3. _____
4. _____
5. _____
6. _____
7. _____
8. _____
9. _____
10. _____
11. _____
12. _____
13. _____
14. _____
15. _____
16. _____
17. _____
18. _____
19. _____
20. _____
21. _____
22. _____
23. _____
24. _____
25. _____
25. _____
27. _____
28. _____
29. _____
30. _____

In exercises 31–33, determine the third side of a right triangle ABC, whose hypotenuse is AC. Approximate the value to three decimal places where necessary.

31. _____

31. AB = 3 in, BC = 4 in, AC = ?

32. _____

32. AB = 5 in, AC = 8 in, BC = ?

33. _____

33. AC = 9 cm, BC = 4 cm, AB = ?

34. _____

34. Mario is flying a kite on 80 feet of string. The horizontal distance between Mario and the kite is 35 feet. How high is the kite above the ground if Mario's hands are 4 feet above the ground? Approximate your answer to thousandth place.

35. _____

35. A ladder is 10 feet long, and leans against a wall. The foot of the ladder is 5 feet from the wall. Approximate to two decimal places how high the top of the ladder would rest against the wall?

8.2   MULTIPLICATION AND DIVISION OF RADICALS

Upon completion of this section we will be able to:

A. Multiply radicals.

B. Simplify radicals with the product rule.

C. Simplify quotients of radicals with the quotient rule.

A. Product Rule of Radicals

Two radicals $\sqrt[m]{a}$ and $\sqrt[n]{b}$ are said to be of the **same index** if $m = n$.

$$\sqrt{3}, \quad \sqrt{4} \text{ are of the same index } \mathbf{2}.$$

$$\sqrt[3]{5}, \quad \sqrt[3]{-7} \text{ are of the same index } \mathbf{3}.$$

The radicals $\sqrt{3}$, $\sqrt[3]{5}$ are not of the same index.

We can multiply radicals of the same index using the following product rule:

> **Product Rule of Radicals**
>
> If **a** and **b** are any two non-negative real numbers then
>
> $$\sqrt[n]{a} \cdot \sqrt[n]{b} = \sqrt[n]{ab} \qquad \text{where } n \text{ is an integer and } n \geq 2.$$

Example 1:   Use the product rule for radicals to find each of the following products.

a) $\sqrt{2} \cdot \sqrt{5}$ b) $\sqrt[3]{4} \cdot \sqrt[3]{16}$

c) $\sqrt[5]{3} \cdot \sqrt[5]{7}$ d) $\sqrt{13} \cdot \sqrt{x}$

Solutions:

a) $\sqrt{2} \cdot \sqrt{5} = \sqrt{2 \cdot 5} = \sqrt{10}$

b) $\sqrt[3]{4} \cdot \sqrt[3]{16} = \sqrt[3]{4 \cdot 16} = \sqrt[3]{64} = 4$

c) $\sqrt[5]{3} \cdot \sqrt[5]{7} = \sqrt[5]{3 \cdot 7} = \sqrt[5]{21}$

d) $\sqrt{13} \cdot \sqrt{x} = \sqrt{13x}$

B.   Simplifying Radicals

We use the following steps to simplify radicals.

> *Step 1*   Write the prime factorization of the radicand.
>
> *Step 2*   Apply the product rule $\sqrt[n]{xy} = \sqrt[n]{x} \cdot \sqrt[n]{y}$.
>
> *Step 3*   Use the fact that: $\sqrt[n]{a^n} = a$ if n is odd, and
>
> $$\sqrt[n]{a^n} = |a| \quad \text{if } n \text{ is even,}$$
>
> and simplify.

Example 2:   Simplify each of the following.

a) $\sqrt{50}$ b) $\sqrt{96}$ c) $\sqrt[3]{243}$ d) $\sqrt[5]{480}$

Solutions:

a) $\sqrt{50}$:

Step 1	$50 = 2 \cdot 5 \cdot 5$	Prime factorization of radicand
Step 2	$\sqrt{50} = \sqrt{2 \cdot 5^2}$	
	$= \sqrt{2} \cdot \sqrt{5^2}$	Product rule
Step 3	$= (\sqrt{2})5 = 5\sqrt{2}$	Square root of 5^2 is 5

Warm Up

b) $\sqrt{108}$

c) $\sqrt[3]{81}$

d) $\sqrt[5]{16}$

3. Find each of the following products and simplify.

a) $\sqrt{32} \cdot \sqrt{20}$

b) $\sqrt{5} \cdot \sqrt{35}$

c) $\sqrt[3]{25} \cdot \sqrt[3]{160}$

Answers:

2. a) $4\sqrt{3}$ **b)** $6\sqrt{3}$ **c)** $3\sqrt{3}$ **d)** $\sqrt[5]{16}$

3. a) $8\sqrt{10}$ **b)** $5\sqrt{7}$ **c)** $10\sqrt[3]{4}$

---

b) $\sqrt{96}$:

Step 1 $96 = 2 \cdot 2 \cdot 2 \cdot 2 \cdot 2 \cdot 3$ Prime factorization of radicand

$= 2^2 \cdot 2^2 \cdot 2 \cdot 3$

Step 2 $\sqrt{96} = \sqrt{2^2 \cdot 2^2 \cdot 2 \cdot 3}$

$= \sqrt{2^2} \cdot \sqrt{2^2} \cdot \sqrt{2} \cdot \sqrt{3}$ Product rule

Step 3 $= 2 \cdot 2 \cdot \sqrt{2} \cdot \sqrt{3}$ $\sqrt{a^2} = a$

$= 4\sqrt{2} \cdot \sqrt{3} = 4\sqrt{2 \cdot 3} = \mathbf{4\sqrt{6}}$ Product rule

c) $\sqrt[3]{243}$:

Step 1 $243 = 3 \cdot 3 \cdot 3 \cdot 3 \cdot 3 = 3^3 \cdot 3 \cdot 3$

Step 2 $\sqrt[3]{243} = \sqrt[3]{3^3 \cdot 3 \cdot 3}$

$= \sqrt[3]{3^3}\, \sqrt[3]{3 \cdot 3}$ Product rule

Step 3 $= 3 \cdot \sqrt[3]{3 \cdot 3} = 3\sqrt[3]{9}$ $\sqrt[3]{a^3} = a$

d) $\sqrt[5]{480}$:

$480 = 2 \cdot 2 \cdot 2 \cdot 2 \cdot 2 \cdot 3 \cdot 5$ Prime factorization

$\sqrt[5]{480} = \sqrt[5]{2^5 \cdot 3 \cdot 5} = \sqrt[5]{2^5}\, \sqrt[5]{3 \cdot 5} = \mathbf{2\sqrt[5]{15}}$

Example 3:   Find each of the following products and simplify.

a) $\sqrt{8} \cdot \sqrt{98}$ **b)** $\sqrt{6} \cdot \sqrt{90}$ **c)** $\sqrt[3]{45} \cdot \sqrt[3]{150}$

Solutions:

a) $\sqrt{8} \cdot \sqrt{98} = \sqrt{8 \cdot 98}$ Product rule

$= \sqrt{(2 \cdot 2 \cdot 2)(2 \cdot 7 \cdot 7)}$ Prime factorization

$= \sqrt{2 \cdot 2 \cdot 2 \cdot 2 \cdot 7 \cdot 7}$

$= \sqrt{2^2 \cdot 2^2 \cdot 7^2} = \sqrt{2^2} \cdot \sqrt{2^2} \cdot \sqrt{7^2} = 2 \cdot 2 \cdot 7 = \mathbf{28}$

b) $\sqrt{6} \cdot \sqrt{90} = \sqrt{6 \cdot 90}$

$= \sqrt{(2 \cdot 3)(2 \cdot 3 \cdot 3 \cdot 5)} = \sqrt{2^2 \cdot 3^2 \cdot 3 \cdot 5}$

$= \sqrt{2^2} \cdot \sqrt{3^2} \cdot \sqrt{3 \cdot 5} = 2 \cdot 3 \cdot \sqrt{3 \cdot 5} = \mathbf{6\sqrt{15}}$

c) $\sqrt[3]{45} \cdot \sqrt[3]{150} = \sqrt[3]{45 \cdot 150}$

$= \sqrt[3]{(3 \cdot 3 \cdot 5)(2 \cdot 3 \cdot 5 \cdot 5)}$

$= \sqrt[3]{3^3 \cdot 5^3 \cdot 2} = \sqrt[3]{3^3} \cdot \sqrt[3]{5^3} \cdot \sqrt[3]{2} = 3 \cdot 5 \cdot \sqrt[3]{2} = \mathbf{15\sqrt[3]{2}}$

C. Quotient Rule of Radicals

If a and b are non-negative real numbers, and $b \neq 0$ then for any integer $n \geq 2$.

$$\frac{\sqrt[n]{a}}{\sqrt[n]{b}} = \sqrt[n]{\frac{a}{b}}.$$

In particular, for $n = 2$, $\dfrac{\sqrt{a}}{\sqrt{b}} = \sqrt{\dfrac{a}{b}}$.

Example 4: Find the quotients.

a) $\dfrac{\sqrt{20}}{\sqrt{5}}$ b) $\dfrac{\sqrt[4]{45}}{\sqrt[4]{5}}$ c) $\dfrac{\sqrt{x}}{\sqrt{4}}$ d) $\dfrac{\sqrt[3]{81}}{\sqrt[3]{3x}}$

Solutions:

a) $\dfrac{\sqrt{20}}{\sqrt{5}} = \sqrt{\dfrac{20}{5}} = \sqrt{4} = 2$

b) $\dfrac{\sqrt[4]{45}}{\sqrt[4]{5}} = \sqrt[4]{\dfrac{45}{5}} = \sqrt[4]{9}$

c) $\dfrac{\sqrt{5a^2b}}{\sqrt{125b^3}} = \sqrt{\dfrac{5a^2b}{125b^3}} = \sqrt{\dfrac{a^2}{25b^2}} = \sqrt{\left(\dfrac{a}{5b}\right)^2} = \dfrac{a}{5b}$

d) $\dfrac{\sqrt[3]{81}}{\sqrt[3]{3x}} = \sqrt[3]{\dfrac{81}{3x}} = \sqrt[3]{\dfrac{27}{x}} = \dfrac{\sqrt[3]{27}}{\sqrt[3]{x}} = \dfrac{\sqrt[3]{3^3}}{\sqrt[3]{x}} = \dfrac{3}{\sqrt[3]{x}}$

Example 5: Simplify each of the following radicals.

a) $\dfrac{\sqrt{216}}{\sqrt{6}}$ b) $\dfrac{\sqrt[4]{729}}{\sqrt[4]{9}}$ c) $\dfrac{\sqrt[3]{405}}{\sqrt[3]{5}}$

d) $\sqrt{\dfrac{25x}{x^3}}$ e) $\sqrt{\dfrac{4}{7}} \cdot \sqrt{\dfrac{2}{35}}$

Solutions:

a) $\dfrac{\sqrt{216}}{\sqrt{6}} = \sqrt{\dfrac{216}{6}} = \sqrt{36} = \sqrt{6^2} = 6$

b) $\dfrac{\sqrt[4]{729}}{\sqrt[4]{9}} = \sqrt[4]{\dfrac{729}{9}} = \sqrt[4]{81} = \sqrt[4]{3^4} = 3$

c) $\dfrac{\sqrt[3]{405}}{\sqrt[3]{15}} = \sqrt[3]{\dfrac{405}{15}} = \sqrt[3]{\dfrac{3 \cdot 3 \cdot 3 \cdot 3 \cdot 5}{3 \cdot 5}} = \sqrt[3]{3^3} = 3$

Warm Up

4. Find the quotients.

a) $\dfrac{\sqrt{20}}{\sqrt{5}}$

b) $\dfrac{\sqrt[3]{21}}{\sqrt[3]{7}}$

c) $\dfrac{\sqrt{3a^2b^2}}{\sqrt{9a^3b}}$

d) $\dfrac{\sqrt[3]{16}}{\sqrt[3]{4x}}$

5. Simplify each of the following radicals.

a) $\dfrac{\sqrt{450}}{\sqrt{2}}$

b) $\dfrac{\sqrt[4]{162}}{\sqrt[4]{2}}$

c) $\dfrac{\sqrt[3]{320}}{\sqrt[3]{5}}$

Warm Up

d) $\sqrt{\dfrac{49x^2}{x^6}}$

6. Simplify the following:

a) $\sqrt[3]{81y^6z^7}$

b) $\sqrt{\dfrac{60x^5}{y^3}}$

c) $\dfrac{3a^3b^4}{\sqrt[3]{64a^3b^6}}$

d) $\sqrt{8x}\left(\dfrac{\sqrt{9x^4}}{\sqrt{16x}}\right)$

d) $\sqrt{\dfrac{25x}{x^3}} = \sqrt{\dfrac{25}{x^2}} = \dfrac{\sqrt{25}}{\sqrt{x^2}} = \dfrac{5}{|x|}$

e) $\sqrt{\dfrac{4}{7}} \cdot \sqrt{\dfrac{2}{35}} = \sqrt{\dfrac{4}{7} \cdot \dfrac{2}{35}} = \sqrt{\dfrac{2 \cdot 2 \cdot 2}{7 \cdot 7 \cdot 5}} = \dfrac{\sqrt{2^2} \cdot \sqrt{2}}{\sqrt{7^2} \cdot \sqrt{5}} = \dfrac{2\sqrt{2}}{7\sqrt{5}}$

Example 6:   Simplify the following.

a) $\sqrt[3]{72y^8z^9}$ **b)** $\sqrt{\dfrac{20x^3}{y^2}}$

c) $\dfrac{5a^2b^3}{\sqrt[3]{8a^3b^3}}$ **d)** $\sqrt{20x}\left(\dfrac{\sqrt{4x^2}}{\sqrt{81x}}\right)$

Solutions:

a) $\sqrt[3]{72y^8z^9}$

$= \sqrt[3]{2 \cdot 2 \cdot 2 \cdot 3 \cdot 3 \cdot y^3 \cdot y^3 \cdot y^2 \cdot z^3 \cdot z^3 \cdot z^3}$ Factorization

$= \sqrt[3]{2^3 \cdot 3^2 \cdot y^3 \cdot y^3 \cdot y^2 \cdot z^3 \cdot z^3 \cdot z^3}$

$= \sqrt[3]{2^3} \cdot \sqrt[3]{3^2} \cdot \sqrt[3]{y^3} \cdot \sqrt[3]{y^3} \cdot \sqrt[3]{y^2} \cdot \sqrt[3]{z^3} \cdot \sqrt[3]{z^3} \cdot \sqrt[3]{z^3}$ Product rule

$= 2 \cdot \sqrt[3]{3^2} \cdot y \cdot y \cdot \sqrt[3]{y^2} \cdot z \cdot z \cdot z$

$= 2\sqrt[3]{9}\ y^2z^3\ \sqrt[3]{y^2} = 2y^2z^3\sqrt[3]{9}\sqrt[3]{y^2} = 2y^2z^3\ \sqrt[3]{9y^2}$

b) $\sqrt{\dfrac{20x^3}{y^2}} = \dfrac{\sqrt{20x^3}}{\sqrt{y^2}} = \dfrac{\sqrt{20}\sqrt{x^3}}{\sqrt{y^2}} = \dfrac{\sqrt{2 \cdot 2 \cdot 5}\sqrt{x^2 \cdot x}}{\sqrt{y^2}}$

$= \dfrac{\sqrt{2^2 \cdot 5}\sqrt{x^2 \cdot x}}{\sqrt{y^2}} = \dfrac{\sqrt{2^2} \cdot \sqrt{5} \cdot \sqrt{x^2} \cdot \sqrt{x}}{\sqrt{y^2}}$

$= \dfrac{2 \cdot \sqrt{5} \cdot x \cdot \sqrt{x}}{y} = \dfrac{2x\sqrt{5x}}{y}$

c) $\dfrac{5a^2b^3}{\sqrt[3]{8a^3b^3}} = \dfrac{5a^2b^3}{2ab} = \dfrac{5ab^2}{2}$

d) $\sqrt{20x}\left(\dfrac{\sqrt{4x^2}}{\sqrt{81x}}\right)=\sqrt{20x}\ \sqrt{\dfrac{4x^2}{81x}}$

$$=\sqrt{\dfrac{80x^3}{81x}}=\sqrt{\dfrac{80x^2}{81}}=\sqrt{\dfrac{2\cdot2\cdot2\cdot2\cdot5x^2}{3\cdot3\cdot3\cdot3}}$$

$$=\sqrt{\dfrac{2^2\cdot2^2\cdot5\cdot x^2}{3^2\cdot3^2}}=\dfrac{\sqrt{2^2\cdot2^2\cdot5\cdot x^2}}{\sqrt{3^2\cdot3^2}}$$

$$=\dfrac{\sqrt{2^2}\cdot\sqrt{2^2}\cdot\sqrt{5}\cdot\sqrt{x^2}}{\sqrt{3^2}\cdot\sqrt{3^2}}=\dfrac{2\cdot2\cdot\sqrt{5}\cdot x}{3\cdot3}$$

$$=\dfrac{4x\sqrt{5}}{9}$$

4. a) 2   **b)** $\sqrt[3]{3}$ **c)** $\sqrt{\dfrac{b}{3a}}$ **d)** $\dfrac{\sqrt[3]{4}}{\sqrt[3]{x}}$

5. a) 15   **b)** 3   **c)** 4   **d)** $\dfrac{7}{x^2}$

6. a) $3y^2z^2\sqrt[3]{3z}$ **b)** $\dfrac{2x^2}{y}\sqrt{\dfrac{15x}{y}}$

   c) $\dfrac{3a^2b^2}{4}$ **d)** $\dfrac{3x^2}{\sqrt{2}}$

EXERCISE 8.2

Answers:

In exercises 1–7, use the product rule to write the expression under one radical.

1. $\sqrt{4}\cdot\sqrt{7}$ **2.** $\sqrt{5}\cdot\sqrt{8}$ **3.** $\sqrt[4]{2}\cdot\sqrt[4]{9}$ **4.** $\sqrt[3]{-25}\cdot\sqrt[3]{35}$

5. $\sqrt[5]{7}\cdot\sqrt[5]{9}$ **6.** $\sqrt{13}\cdot\sqrt{x^3}$ **7.** $\sqrt[3]{x}\cdot\sqrt[3]{y^2}$

In exercises 8–11, use the quotient rule and simplify.

8. $\sqrt{7}\div\sqrt{20}$ **9.** $\sqrt[3]{25}\div\sqrt[3]{8}$

10. $\sqrt{x^2y}\div\sqrt{y},\ y>0$ **11.** $\dfrac{\sqrt[5]{p^2q}}{\sqrt[5]{r^3}},\quad r\neq0$

Simplify radicals in exercises 12–20.

12. $\sqrt{48}$ **13.** $\sqrt{128}$ **14.** $\sqrt{54}$ **15.** $\sqrt{120}$

16. $\sqrt[3]{1080}$ **17.** $\sqrt[4]{240}$ **18.** $\sqrt[5]{-288}$

19. $\sqrt[3]{-3125}$ **20.** $\sqrt[3]{3125}$

1. _____

2. _____

3. _____

4. _____

5. _____

6. _____

7. _____

8. _____

9. _____

10. _____

11. _____

12. _____

13. _____

14. _____

15. _____

16. _____

17. _____

18. _____

19. _____

20. _____

21. _____

22. _____

23. _____

24. _____

25. _____

26. _____

27. _____

28. _____

29. _____

30. _____

In exercises 21–30, perform the indicated operations and simplify (variables represent positive numbers).

21. $\sqrt{32p^5}$

22. $\sqrt{a^2b^5}$

23. $\sqrt[3]{a^5b^4}$

24. $\sqrt{\dfrac{2000}{81}}$

25. $\sqrt[3]{-\dfrac{216}{125}}$

26. $\dfrac{\sqrt[4]{3x^2y}}{\sqrt[4]{48x^7y^3}}$

27. $-\dfrac{\sqrt[3]{5x^4y^5}}{\sqrt[3]{-x^2y^4}}$

28. $\sqrt[3]{8x^3y} \cdot \sqrt[3]{9xy^4}$

29. $\dfrac{\left(\sqrt[3]{2a^2b^3}\right)\left(\sqrt[3]{-4a^5b^9}\right)}{\sqrt[3]{64a^2b^3}}$

30. $\dfrac{\sqrt{20x^2y^3} \cdot \sqrt{5xy}}{\sqrt{36xy^2}}$

8.3   ADDITION AND SUBTRACTION OF RADICALS

Two radical expressions which have the *same radicand* and the *same index* are called *like or similar* radicals. In this section we will learn how to:

    A.   Add and subtract like radicals.
    B.   Simplify radical sums and differences.

A. Adding and Subtracting Like Radicals

Like radicals are added or subtracted using the distributive property.

Warm Up

1. Perform the indicated operations.

a) $3\sqrt{5} + 6\sqrt{5}$

b) $7\sqrt[3]{7} - 3\sqrt[3]{7}$

c) $2\sqrt[4]{9} - 5\sqrt[4]{9}$

Answers:

1. a) $9\sqrt{5}$ **b)** $4\sqrt[3]{7}$ **c)** $-3\sqrt[4]{9}$

Example 1:   Perform the indicated operation.

a) $2\sqrt{5} + 7\sqrt{5}$ b) $6\sqrt[3]{12} - 4\sqrt[3]{12}$

c) $\sqrt[4]{7} - 5\sqrt[4]{7}$

Solutions:

a) $2\sqrt{5} + 7\sqrt{5} = (2+7)\sqrt{5}$ Distributive property

$= 9\sqrt{5}$

b) $6\sqrt[3]{12} - 4\sqrt[3]{12} = (6-4)\sqrt[3]{12}$ Distributive property

$= 2\sqrt[3]{12}$

c) $\sqrt[4]{7} - 5\sqrt[4]{7} = 1 \cdot \sqrt[4]{7} - 5\sqrt[4]{7}$ Distributive property

$= (1-5)\sqrt[4]{7} = -4\sqrt[4]{7}$

408

B.   Simplifying Radical Sums and Differences

The radicals of the type $\sqrt{2}$ and $\sqrt{5}$ cannot be added together. However, some radical expressions can be simplified so that their radical parts are alike. For example $\sqrt{8}$ and $\sqrt{18}$ can be simplified as;

$$\sqrt{8} = \sqrt{4 \cdot 2} = \sqrt{4} \cdot \sqrt{2} = 2\sqrt{2} \text{ and}$$
$$\sqrt{18} = \sqrt{9 \cdot 2} = \sqrt{9} \cdot \sqrt{2} = 3\sqrt{2} .$$

Such radicals expressions can be added or subtracted after simplification.

Example 2:   Simplify

a) $4\sqrt{3} - 6\sqrt{27}$ **b)** $5\sqrt{15} + \sqrt{60}$

c) $\sqrt[3]{81} + 4\sqrt[4]{375}$

Solutions:

We shall simplify each of the radicals by using the prime factorization of the radicands.

a) $4\sqrt{3} - 6\sqrt{27} = 4\sqrt{3} - 6\sqrt{3 \cdot 3 \cdot 3}$ Prime factorization

$= 4\sqrt{3} - 6\sqrt{3^2 \cdot 3}$ Product rule

$= 4\sqrt{3} - 6\sqrt{3^2} \cdot \sqrt{3}$

$= 4\sqrt{3} - 6 \cdot 3 \cdot \sqrt{3}$ $\sqrt[n]{a^n} = a$

$= 4\sqrt{3} - 18\sqrt{3} = -14\sqrt{3}$ Add

b) $5\sqrt{15} + \sqrt{60} = 5\sqrt{3 \cdot 5} + \sqrt{2 \cdot 2 \cdot 3 \cdot 5}$ Prime factorization

$= 5\sqrt{3 \cdot 5} + \sqrt{2^2 \cdot 3 \cdot 5}$

$= 5\sqrt{3} \cdot \sqrt{5} + \sqrt{2^2} \cdot \sqrt{3} \cdot \sqrt{5}$ Product rule

$= 5\sqrt{3} \cdot \sqrt{5} + 2\sqrt{3} \cdot \sqrt{5}$ $\sqrt[n]{a^n} = a$

$= 5\sqrt{3 \cdot 5} + 2\sqrt{3 \cdot 5}$ Product rule

$= 5\sqrt{15} + 2\sqrt{15} = 7\sqrt{15}$ Add

c) $\sqrt[3]{81} + 4\sqrt[3]{375} = \sqrt[3]{3 \cdot 3 \cdot 3 \cdot 3} + 4\sqrt[3]{5 \cdot 5 \cdot 5 \cdot 3}$ Prime Fact

$= \sqrt[3]{3^3 \cdot 3} + 4\sqrt[3]{5^3 \cdot 3}$

$= \sqrt[3]{3^3} \cdot \sqrt[3]{3} + 4\sqrt[3]{5^3} \cdot \sqrt[3]{3}$ Product rule

$= 3\sqrt[3]{3} + 4 \cdot 5 \cdot \sqrt[3]{3}$ $\sqrt[n]{a^n} = a$

$= 3\sqrt[3]{3} + 20\sqrt[3]{3}$

$= 23\sqrt[3]{3}$ Add

Warm Up

2.   Simplify

a) $3\sqrt{2} + 3\sqrt{8}$

b) $12\sqrt{12} - 3\sqrt{48}$

c) $13\sqrt[3]{320} + 2\sqrt[3]{40}$

Warm Up

3. Simplify

a) $\sqrt{36} + \sqrt{1}$

b) $4\sqrt{60} - 2\sqrt{15}$

c) $11 + 3\sqrt{16} + 5\sqrt{8} - 6\sqrt{2}$

d) $\sqrt{32} - \sqrt{98} + \sqrt{242}$

4. Simplify the following expressions:

a) $2\sqrt{3}\left(2\sqrt{5} - 4\sqrt{6}\right)$

b) $\left(\sqrt{4} - \sqrt{2}\right)\left(\sqrt{4} + \sqrt{2}\right)$

Example 3:   Simplify.

a) $\sqrt{25} + \sqrt{4}$ b) $4\sqrt{3} - 2\sqrt{75}$

c) $3 + 2\sqrt{4} + 5\sqrt{6} - 3\sqrt{24}$

d) $\sqrt{80} - \sqrt{128} + \sqrt{288}$

Solutions:

a) $\sqrt{25} + \sqrt{4} = \sqrt{5^2} + \sqrt{2^2} = 5 + 2 = \mathbf{7}$

b) $4\sqrt{3} - 2\sqrt{75} = 4\sqrt{3} - 2\sqrt{5 \cdot 5 \cdot 3}$ Prime factorization

$= 4\sqrt{3} - 2\sqrt{5^2 \cdot 3}$

$= 4\sqrt{3} - 2\sqrt{5^2} \cdot \sqrt{3}$ Product rule

$= 4\sqrt{3} - 2 \cdot 5 \cdot \sqrt{3}$ $\sqrt{5^2} = 5$

$= 4\sqrt{3} - 10\sqrt{3} = -\mathbf{6\sqrt{3}}$ Combine like radicals

c) $3 + 2\sqrt{4} + 5\sqrt{6} - 3\sqrt{24}$

$= 3 + 2\sqrt{2^2} + 5\sqrt{2 \cdot 3} - 3\sqrt{2 \cdot 2 \cdot 2 \cdot 3}$

$= 3 + 2\sqrt{2^2} + 5\sqrt{2 \cdot 3} - 3\sqrt{2^2 \cdot 2 \cdot 3}$

$= 3 + 2\sqrt{2^2} + 5\sqrt{2 \cdot 3} - 3\sqrt{2^2} \cdot \sqrt{2 \cdot 3}$

$= 3 + 2 \cdot 2 + 5\sqrt{2 \cdot 3} - 3 \cdot 2 \cdot \sqrt{2 \cdot 3}$

$= 3 + 4 + 5\sqrt{6} - 6\sqrt{6} = \mathbf{7 - \sqrt{6}}$

d) $\sqrt{80} - \sqrt{128} + \sqrt{288}$

$= \sqrt{2 \cdot 2 \cdot 2 \cdot 2 \cdot 5} - \sqrt{2 \cdot 2 \cdot 2 \cdot 2 \cdot 2 \cdot 2 \cdot 2}$
$\quad + \sqrt{2 \cdot 2 \cdot 2 \cdot 2 \cdot 2 \cdot 3 \cdot 3}$

$= \sqrt{2^2 \cdot 2^2 \cdot 5} - \sqrt{2^2 \cdot 2^2 \cdot 2^2 \cdot 2} + \sqrt{2^2 \cdot 2^2 \cdot 2 \cdot 3^2}$

$= \sqrt{2^2} \cdot \sqrt{2^2} \cdot \sqrt{5} - \sqrt{2^2} \cdot \sqrt{2^2} \cdot \sqrt{2^2} \cdot \sqrt{2}$
$\quad + \sqrt{2^2} \cdot \sqrt{2^2} \cdot \sqrt{2} \cdot \sqrt{3^2}$

$= 2 \cdot 2 \cdot \sqrt{5} - 2 \cdot 2 \cdot 2 \cdot \sqrt{2} + 2 \cdot 2 \cdot \sqrt{2} \cdot 3$

$= 4\sqrt{5} - 8\sqrt{2} + 12\sqrt{2} = \mathbf{4\sqrt{5} + 4\sqrt{2}}$

Example 4:   Simplify the following expressions.

a) $3\sqrt{3}\left(4\sqrt{8} - 5\sqrt{27}\right)$ b) $\left(\sqrt{5} + \sqrt{2}\right)\left(\sqrt{5} - \sqrt{2}\right)$

c) $4\sqrt{15} \cdot \sqrt{5} - 3\sqrt{3}$

d) $\left(2\sqrt{a} - 4\sqrt{b}\right)^2$, $a \geq 0$, $b \geq 0$

e) $\left(\sqrt{x} + 2\sqrt{y}\right)\left(2\sqrt{x} - 3\sqrt{y}\right)$, $x \geq 0$, $y \geq 0$

f) $\sqrt[3]{2} \; \sqrt[3]{8x^2} - \sqrt[3]{54x^6}$ $x \geq 0$

Solutions:

a) $3\sqrt{3}\left(4\sqrt{8}-5\sqrt{27}\right)$

$\quad = \left(3\sqrt{3}\right)\left(4\sqrt{8}\right)-\left(3\sqrt{3}\right)\left(5\sqrt{27}\right)$ Distributive property

$\quad = 12\sqrt{3\cdot 8}-15\sqrt{3\cdot 27}$ Product rule

$\quad = 12\sqrt{3\cdot 2\cdot 2\cdot 2}-15\sqrt{3\cdot 3\cdot 3\cdot 3}$ Prime factorization

$\quad = 12\sqrt{2^2\cdot 2\cdot 3}-15\sqrt{3^2\cdot 3^2}$

$\quad = 12\ \sqrt{2^2}\cdot\sqrt{2\cdot 3}-15\ \sqrt{3^2}\cdot\sqrt{3^2}$ Product rule

$\quad = 12\left(2\sqrt{6}\right)-15(9)$ $\sqrt[n]{a^n}=a$

$\quad = \mathbf{24\sqrt{6}-135}$

c) $3\sqrt{12}\cdot\sqrt{4}-2\sqrt{12}$

b) $\left(\sqrt{5}+\sqrt{2}\right)\left(\sqrt{5}-\sqrt{2}\right)=\left(\sqrt{5}\right)^2-\left(\sqrt{2}\right)^2$ $\begin{array}{l}(a+b)(a-b)\\ =a^2-b^2\end{array}$

$\quad\quad\quad\quad\quad\quad\quad\quad\quad = 5-2=\mathbf{3}$

d) $\left(3\sqrt{a}-2\sqrt{b}\right)^2$

c) $4\sqrt{15}\cdot\sqrt{5}-3\sqrt{3}=4\sqrt{75}-3\sqrt{3}$

$\quad\quad\quad\quad\quad\quad = 4\sqrt{3\cdot 25}-3\sqrt{3}$

$\quad\quad\quad\quad\quad\quad = 4\sqrt{3\cdot 5^2}-3\sqrt{3}$

$\quad\quad\quad\quad\quad\quad = 4\sqrt{3}\cdot\sqrt{5^2}-3\sqrt{3}$

$\quad\quad\quad\quad\quad\quad = \left(4\sqrt{3}\right)(5)-3\sqrt{3}$

$\quad\quad\quad\quad\quad\quad = 20\sqrt{3}-3\sqrt{3}=\mathbf{17\sqrt{3}}$

d) $\left(2\sqrt{a}-4\sqrt{b}\right)^2=\left(2\sqrt{a}\right)^2-2\left(2\sqrt{a}\right)\left(4\sqrt{b}\right)+\left(4\sqrt{b}\right)^2$

$\quad\quad\quad\quad\quad = 4\left(\sqrt{a}\right)^2-16\sqrt{a}\sqrt{b}+16\left(\sqrt{b}\right)^2$

$\quad\quad\quad\quad\quad = 4a-16\sqrt{a}\sqrt{b}+16b$

$\quad\quad\quad\quad\quad = 4a-16\sqrt{ab}+16b$

$\quad\quad\quad\quad\quad = 4a+16b-16\sqrt{ab}$

e) $\left(\sqrt{x}-2\sqrt{y}\right)\left(3\sqrt{x}+\sqrt{y}\right)$

e) $\left(\sqrt{x}+2\sqrt{y}\right)\left(2\sqrt{x}-3\sqrt{y}\right)$

$\quad = \left(\sqrt{x}\right)\left(2\sqrt{x}\right)+\sqrt{x}\left(-3\sqrt{y}\right)+\left(2\sqrt{y}\right)\left(2\sqrt{x}\right)+\left(2\sqrt{y}\left(-3\sqrt{y}\right)\right)$

$\quad = 2\left(\sqrt{x}\right)^2-3\sqrt{x}\sqrt{y}+4\sqrt{y}\cdot\sqrt{x}-6\left(\sqrt{y}\right)^2$

$\quad = 2x-3\sqrt{x}\sqrt{y}+4\sqrt{y}\cdot\sqrt{x}-6y$

$\quad = 2x-6y-3\sqrt{x}\cdot\sqrt{y}+4\sqrt{x}\cdot\sqrt{y}$

$\quad = 2x-6y-3\sqrt{xy}+4\sqrt{xy}$

$\quad = 2x-6y+\sqrt{xy}$

f) $\sqrt[3]{4}\,\sqrt[3]{16}-\sqrt[3]{81x^5}$

Warm Up

Answers:

2. a) $9\sqrt{2}$ b) $12\sqrt{3}$ c) $56\sqrt[3]{5}$

3. a) 7 b) $6\sqrt{15}$ c) $23+4\sqrt{2}$ d) $8\sqrt{2}$

4. a) $4\sqrt{15}-24\sqrt{2}$ b) 2 c) $8\sqrt{3}$

   d) $9a-12\sqrt{ab}+4b$

   e) $3x-5\sqrt{xy}-2y$

   f) $4-3x\sqrt[3]{3x^2}$

f) $\sqrt[3]{2}\ \sqrt[3]{8x^3}-\sqrt[3]{54x^6} = \sqrt[3]{2\cdot 8x^3}-\sqrt[3]{54x^6}$

$= \sqrt[3]{2\cdot 2\cdot 2\cdot 2\cdot x^3}-\sqrt[3]{2\cdot 3\cdot 3\cdot 3\cdot x^3\cdot x}$

$= \sqrt[3]{2^3\cdot 2\cdot x^3}-\sqrt[3]{2\cdot 3^3\cdot x^3\cdot x^3}$

$= \sqrt[3]{2^3}\cdot\sqrt[3]{2}\cdot\sqrt[3]{x^3}-\sqrt[3]{2}\cdot\sqrt[3]{3^3}\cdot\sqrt[3]{x^3}\cdot\sqrt[3]{x^3}$

$= 2\cdot\sqrt[3]{2}\cdot x-\sqrt[3]{2}\cdot 3\cdot x\cdot x$

$= 2x\sqrt[3]{2}-3x^2\sqrt[3]{2}$

$= \left(2x-3x^2\right)\sqrt[3]{2}$

EXERCISE 8.3

Answers:

1. _____

2. _____

3. _____

4. _____

5. _____

6. _____

7. _____

8. _____

9. _____

10. _____

11. _____

12. _____

13. _____

14. _____

15. _____

16. _____

In exercises 1–10, perform the indicated operations.

1. $3\sqrt{2}-4\sqrt{2}$

2. $5\sqrt{7}-2\sqrt{7}$

3. $-\sqrt[3]{4}+4\sqrt[3]{4}$

4. $-\sqrt[4]{2}-3\sqrt[4]{2}$

5. $2\sqrt[5]{3}-3\sqrt[5]{3}+7\sqrt[5]{3}$

6. $4\sqrt[3]{-5}+7\sqrt[3]{-5}-15\sqrt[3]{-5}$

7. $\dfrac{7}{8}\sqrt{15}-\dfrac{4}{5}\sqrt{15}$

8. $\dfrac{5}{6}\sqrt[4]{11}+\dfrac{4}{9}\sqrt[4]{11}$

9. $\sqrt{8}\cdot\sqrt{3}-2\sqrt{6}$

10. $\sqrt[3]{-9}\ \sqrt[3]{72}-2\sqrt[3]{6}\cdot\sqrt[3]{4}$

In exercises 11–20, perform the indicated operations and simplify. Assume that the variables represent non-negative real numbers.

11. $2\sqrt{3}\left(4\sqrt{27}-5\sqrt{32}\right)$

12. $\left(2\sqrt{3}-\sqrt{5}\right)\left(2\sqrt{3}+\sqrt{5}\right)$

13. $\left(3\sqrt{x}+5\sqrt{y}\right)^2$

14. $\left(\sqrt{p}+3\sqrt{q^3}\right)\left(4\sqrt{p}-2\sqrt{q}\right)$

15. $\left(\sqrt[3]{x}-2\sqrt[3]{y}\right)^3$

16. $4\sqrt{x^3}-7x\sqrt{xy^2}$

17. $\left(2\sqrt{x} - 3\sqrt{y}\right)\left(2\sqrt{x} + 3\sqrt{y}\right)$ $\left(\text{Recall factors of } a^2 - b^2\right)$

18. $\left(\sqrt[3]{p^4} + \sqrt[3]{q^2}\right)\left(\sqrt[3]{p^2} - 2\sqrt[3]{q^4}\right)$

19. $\left(\sqrt[3]{3x} - \sqrt[3]{2y}\right)\left(\sqrt[3]{9x^2} + \sqrt[3]{6xy} + \sqrt[3]{4y^2}\right)$ $\left(\text{Recall factors of } a^3 - b^3\right)$

20. $\sqrt{3}\left(4\sqrt{3r} - 5\sqrt{2}\right)^2$

17. _____

18. _____

19. _____

20. _____

8.4   RATIONALIZING THE DENOMINATOR

Rationalizing means changing the given radical expression so that the denominator is free of radicals. This process is called *rationalizing the denominator*.

Upon completion of this section, we will be able to:

      A.   Rationalize denominators

      B.   Write radicals in simplified form.

      C.   Rationalize some other denominators.

A.   Rationalizing Denominators

To rationalize the denominator of $\dfrac{5}{\sqrt[3]{xy}}$, we need to rewrite this expression so that the denominator

becomes $\sqrt[3]{x^3 y^3}$ which is a rational expression xy. How do we rewrite the given expression?

We explain that through the examples.

      For rationalizing the denominator the basic idea is to be able to rewrite the denominator in the form $\sqrt[n]{a^n}$.

Warm Up

1. Rationalize the denominators.

a) $\dfrac{4}{\sqrt{3}}$

b) $\dfrac{3}{\sqrt{6}}$

c) $\dfrac{2}{3\sqrt{8}}$

2. Rationalize the denominators.

a) $\dfrac{4}{\sqrt[3]{4}}$

b) $\dfrac{3}{\sqrt[3]{3}}$

c) $\dfrac{2}{\sqrt[4]{4}}$

Example 1:   Rationalize the denominators:

a) $\dfrac{3}{\sqrt{7}}$ b) $\dfrac{4}{\sqrt{8}}$ c) $\dfrac{5}{4\sqrt{3}}$

Solutions:

a)
$$\frac{3}{\sqrt{7}} = \frac{3}{\sqrt{7}} \cdot \frac{\sqrt{7}}{\sqrt{7}}$$

Multiply numerator and denominator by $\dfrac{\sqrt{7^2}}{\sqrt{7}} = \sqrt{\dfrac{7^2}{7}} = \sqrt{7}$

$$= \frac{3\sqrt{7}}{\sqrt{7} \cdot \sqrt{7}}$$

Multiply fractions

$$= \frac{3\sqrt{7}}{\sqrt{7^2}}$$

Product rule of radicals

$$= \frac{3\sqrt{7}}{7}$$

b)
$$\frac{4}{\sqrt{8}} = \frac{4}{\sqrt{8}} \cdot \frac{\sqrt{8}}{\sqrt{8}} = \frac{4\sqrt{8}}{\sqrt{8} \cdot \sqrt{8}} = \frac{4\sqrt{8}}{8} = \frac{\sqrt{8}}{2}.$$

$\dfrac{\sqrt{8}}{2}$ can be further simplified.   **STOP and THINK.**

c)
$$\frac{5}{4\sqrt{3}} = \frac{5}{4\sqrt{3}} \cdot \frac{\sqrt{3}}{\sqrt{3}} = \frac{5\sqrt{3}}{4\sqrt{3^2}} = \frac{5\sqrt{3}}{4 \cdot 3} = \frac{5\sqrt{3}}{12}$$

Example 2:   Rationalize the following denominators.

a) $\dfrac{4}{\sqrt[3]{2}}$ b) $\dfrac{5}{\sqrt[3]{4}}$ c) $\dfrac{1}{\sqrt[4]{9}}$

Solutions:

a)
$$\frac{4}{\sqrt[3]{2}} = \frac{4}{\sqrt[3]{2}} \cdot \frac{\sqrt[3]{2^2}}{\sqrt[3]{2^2}}$$

Multiply and divide by $\dfrac{\sqrt[3]{2^3}}{\sqrt[3]{2}} = \sqrt[3]{\dfrac{2^3}{2}} = \sqrt[3]{2^2}$

$$= \frac{4\sqrt[3]{2^2}}{\sqrt[3]{2} \cdot \sqrt[3]{2^2}} = \frac{4\sqrt[3]{2^2}}{\sqrt[3]{2 \cdot 2^2}} = \frac{4\sqrt[3]{2^2}}{\sqrt[3]{2^3}} = \frac{4\sqrt[3]{4}}{2}$$

$$= 2\sqrt[3]{4}$$

b)
$$\frac{5}{\sqrt[3]{4}} = \frac{5}{\sqrt[3]{4}} \cdot \frac{\sqrt[3]{4^2}}{\sqrt[3]{4^2}}$$

$\dfrac{\sqrt[3]{4^3}}{\sqrt[3]{4}} = \sqrt[3]{\dfrac{4^3}{4}} = \sqrt[3]{4^2}$

$$= \frac{5\sqrt[3]{4^2}}{\sqrt[3]{4} \cdot \sqrt[3]{4^2}} = \frac{5\sqrt[3]{4^2}}{\sqrt[3]{4^3}} = \frac{5\sqrt[3]{4^2}}{4} = \frac{5\sqrt[3]{16}}{4}.$$

$\dfrac{5\sqrt[3]{16}}{4}$ can be further simplified. **STOP** and **THINK.**

c)

$$\frac{1}{\sqrt[4]{9}} = \frac{1}{\sqrt[4]{9}} \cdot \frac{\sqrt[4]{9^3}}{\sqrt[4]{9^3}}$$

$$= \frac{\sqrt[4]{9^3}}{\sqrt[4]{9^4}} = \frac{\sqrt[4]{9^3}}{9} \qquad \frac{\sqrt[4]{9^4}}{\sqrt[4]{9}} = \sqrt[4]{\frac{9^4}{9}} = \sqrt[4]{9^3}$$

$\dfrac{\sqrt[4]{9^3}}{9}$ can be further simplified. **STOP** and **THINK.**

B. Writing Square Roots in Simplified Form

A *square root* radical is said to be in simplified form if:

- The radicand does not contain any factor, different from 1, which is a perfect square.
- The radicand does not contain fractions.
- No denominator contains a radical.

The third condition above means that, if needed, the denominator must be rationalized.

Example 3:   Simplify the following.

a) $\sqrt{\dfrac{8}{3}}$ b) $\sqrt{\dfrac{5}{6}} \cdot \sqrt{\dfrac{3}{8}}$ c) $\sqrt{\dfrac{3x^2}{y}}$ $(y > 0)$

Solutions:

a) $\sqrt{\dfrac{8}{3}} = \dfrac{\sqrt{8}}{\sqrt{3}} = \dfrac{\sqrt{8}}{\sqrt{3}} \cdot \dfrac{\sqrt{3}}{\sqrt{3}} = \dfrac{\sqrt{8} \cdot \sqrt{3}}{\sqrt{3} \cdot \sqrt{3}} = \dfrac{\sqrt{8} \cdot \sqrt{3}}{3}$

$$= \dfrac{\sqrt{2 \cdot 2 \cdot 2} \cdot \sqrt{3}}{3} = \dfrac{\sqrt{2^2} \cdot \sqrt{2} \cdot \sqrt{3}}{3}$$

$$= \dfrac{2 \cdot \sqrt{2 \cdot 3}}{3} = \dfrac{2\sqrt{6}}{3}$$

b) $\sqrt{\dfrac{5}{6}} \cdot \sqrt{\dfrac{3}{8}} = \sqrt{\dfrac{5}{6} \cdot \dfrac{3}{8}} = \sqrt{\dfrac{3 \cdot 5}{48}} = \sqrt{\dfrac{3 \cdot 5}{3 \cdot 16}} = \sqrt{\dfrac{5}{16}} = \dfrac{\sqrt{5}}{4}$

c) $\sqrt{\dfrac{3x^2}{y}} = \dfrac{\sqrt{3x^2}}{\sqrt{y}} = \dfrac{\sqrt{3}\sqrt{x^2}}{\sqrt{y}} = \dfrac{\sqrt{3} \cdot x}{\sqrt{y}} = \dfrac{x\sqrt{3}}{\sqrt{y}} \cdot \dfrac{\sqrt{y}}{\sqrt{y}}$

$$= \dfrac{x\sqrt{3} \cdot \sqrt{y}}{\sqrt{y} \cdot \sqrt{y}} = \dfrac{x\sqrt{3} \cdot \sqrt{y}}{y} = \dfrac{x\sqrt{3y}}{y}$$

C.   Rationalizing other Denominators

We shall see how the formula $(a+b)(a-b)=a^2-b^2$ learned earlier in chapter 3 can be used to rationalize some other denominators.

> Two binomials which differ only in the sign between the two terms are called **conjugate binomials**. Thus $a+\sqrt{b}$ and $a-\sqrt{b}$ are conjugates of each other.

Warm Up

4. Write down the conjugate.

a) $\sqrt{5}-\sqrt{2}$

b) $2\sqrt{8}-\sqrt{5}$

c) $8-6\sqrt{2}$

d) $-13\sqrt{5}+\sqrt{7}$

5. Rationalize the denominators.

a) $\dfrac{1}{4-\sqrt{2}}$

Example 4:   Write down a conjugate of the following.

a) $\sqrt{3}+\sqrt{5}$ b) $2\sqrt{7}-\sqrt{6}$
c) $3-5\sqrt{2}$ d) $-4\sqrt{6}+2\sqrt{8}$

Solutions:

a) The conjugate of $\sqrt{3}+\sqrt{5}$ is $\sqrt{3}-\sqrt{5}$.

b) The conjugate of $2\sqrt{7}-\sqrt{6}$ is $2\sqrt{7}+\sqrt{6}$.

c) The conjugate of $3-5\sqrt{2}$ is $3+5\sqrt{2}$.

d) The conjugate of $-4\sqrt{6}+2\sqrt{8}$ is $-4\sqrt{6}-2\sqrt{8}$.

Example 5:   Rationalize the denominators.

a) $\dfrac{1}{3-\sqrt{5}}$ b) $\dfrac{\sqrt{2}+3}{2\sqrt{2}+5}$

Solutions:

a) $\dfrac{1}{3-\sqrt{5}}$:

Step 1   Multiply both the numerator and denominator by the conjugate of the denominator. The conjugate of $3-\sqrt{5}$ is $3+\sqrt{5}$.

$$\frac{1}{3-\sqrt{5}}=\frac{1}{3-\sqrt{5}}\cdot\frac{3+\sqrt{5}}{3+\sqrt{5}}=\frac{1(3+\sqrt{5})}{(3-\sqrt{5})(3+\sqrt{5})}$$

$$=\frac{(3+\sqrt{5})}{(3)^2-(\sqrt{5})^2}$$

Step 2   Simplify. $\dfrac{3+\sqrt{5}}{(3)^2-(\sqrt{5})^2}=\dfrac{3+\sqrt{5}}{9-5}=\dfrac{3+\sqrt{5}}{4}$

416

b) $\dfrac{\sqrt{2}+3}{2\sqrt{2}+5}:$ The conjugate of $2\sqrt{2}+\sqrt{5}$ is $2\sqrt{2}-\sqrt{5}$.

$$\frac{\sqrt{2}+3}{2\sqrt{2}+5}=\frac{\left(\sqrt{2}\right)+3}{\left(2\sqrt{2}\right)+5}\cdot\frac{2\sqrt{2}-\sqrt{5}}{2\sqrt{2}-\sqrt{5}}$$

$$=\frac{\left(\sqrt{2}+3\right)\left(2\sqrt{2}-\sqrt{5}\right)}{\left(2\sqrt{2}\right)^2-\left(\sqrt{5}\right)^2}$$

$$=\frac{\left(\sqrt{2}\right)\left(2\sqrt{2}\right)+\sqrt{2}\left(-\sqrt{5}\right)+\left(3\cdot2\sqrt{2}\right)+3\left(-\sqrt{5}\right)}{\left(2\sqrt{2}\right)^2-\left(\sqrt{5}\right)^2}$$

$$=\frac{2\cdot2-\sqrt{10}+6\sqrt{2}-3\sqrt{5}}{8-5}$$

$$=\frac{4-\sqrt{10}+6\sqrt{2}-3\sqrt{5}}{3}$$

Warm Up

b) $\dfrac{\sqrt{5}+6}{3\sqrt{3}-5}$

Answers:

4. a) $\sqrt{5}+\sqrt{2}$ **b)** $2\sqrt{8}+\sqrt{5}$

 c) $8+6\sqrt{2}$ **d)** $-13\sqrt{5}-\sqrt{7}$

5. a) $\dfrac{4+\sqrt{2}}{14}$

 b) $\dfrac{3\sqrt{15}+5\sqrt{5}+18\sqrt{3}+30}{2}$

EXERCISE 8.4

In exercises 1–8, rationalize the denominator and simplify.

1. $\dfrac{3}{\sqrt{2}}$ **2.** $\dfrac{4}{\sqrt{5}}$ **3.** $\dfrac{4}{\sqrt{6}}$ **4.** $\dfrac{3}{2\sqrt{18}}$

5. $\dfrac{4}{\sqrt[3]{10}}$ **6.** $\dfrac{5}{2\sqrt[4]{4}}$ **7.** $\dfrac{\sqrt[4]{3}}{2\sqrt[4]{4}}$ **8.** $\dfrac{3\sqrt{15}}{5\sqrt{6}}$

In exercises 9–13 , simplify as far as possible.

9. $\sqrt{\dfrac{16}{7}}$ **10.** $\sqrt{\dfrac{40}{3}}$ **11.** $\sqrt{\dfrac{2}{5}}\cdot\sqrt{\dfrac{3}{10}}$ **12.** $\sqrt{\dfrac{1}{13}}\cdot\sqrt{\dfrac{39}{10}}$

13. $\sqrt{\dfrac{1}{10}}\cdot\sqrt{\dfrac{20}{3}}$

Answers:

1. _____
2. _____
3. _____
4. _____
5. _____
6. _____
7. _____
8. _____
9. _____
10. _____
11. _____
12. _____
13. _____

14. _____

15. _____

16. _____

17. _____

18. _____

19. _____

20. _____

21. _____

22. _____

23. _____

24. _____

25. _____

In exercises 14–18, rationalize the denominator and write in the simplified form.

14. $\sqrt{\dfrac{4}{x}}$ **15.** $\sqrt{\dfrac{6x^3}{4y}}$ **16.** $\sqrt[3]{\dfrac{5p^4q}{q^2}}$ **17.** $\sqrt{\dfrac{4r^2s}{3}}$ **18.** $\sqrt[3]{\dfrac{11a^3}{b}}$

In exercises 19–25, rationalize the denominator and simplify.

19. $\dfrac{2}{\sqrt{3}-\sqrt{2}}$ **20.** $\dfrac{3}{\sqrt{5}+1}$ **21.** $\dfrac{\sqrt{7}-\sqrt{2}}{\sqrt{2}+\sqrt{7}}$ **22.** $\dfrac{\sqrt{3}-1}{\sqrt{3}+1}$

23. $\dfrac{\sqrt{x}+\sqrt{y}}{\sqrt{x}-\sqrt{y}}$ **24.** $\dfrac{3x}{\sqrt{3x}\left(\sqrt{2}-1\right)}$ **25.** $\dfrac{9x^3}{\sqrt{5x}\left(\sqrt{11}-\sqrt{2}\right)}$

8.5   FRACTIONAL EXPONENTS

In chapter 3 we discussed *integer* exponents and the laws governing them.   Upon completion of this section, we will be able to:

   A.   Define and use $a^{1/n}$.

   B.   Define and use $a^{m/n}$.

   C.   Properties of Radicals.

A. Definition of $a^{1/n}$

For any *non-negative* number a and a positive integer n, $a^{1/n} = \sqrt[n]{a}$.

The denominator of the fractional exponents becomes the index of the radical.

$$a^{1/2} = \sqrt[2]{a} = \sqrt{a} \qquad\qquad a^{1/5} = \sqrt[5]{a}$$

(If there is no index in the radical then it is understood that the index is 2.)

Warm Up

1. Simplify

  a) $196^{1/2}$

  b) $729^{1/3}$

Example 1:   Simplify.   **a)** $9^{1/2}$ **b)** $8^{1/3}$

  c) $256^{1/4}$ **d)** $243^{1/5}$

Solutions:

  a) $9^{1/2} = \sqrt{9} = 3$ $9 = 3\cdot 3 = 3^2$

  b) $8^{1/3} = \sqrt[3]{8} = 2$ $8 = 2^3$

418

c) $256^{1/4} = \sqrt[4]{256} = 4$ $\qquad$ $256 = 4^4$

d) $243^{1/5} = \sqrt[5]{243} = 3$ $\qquad$ $243 = 3^5$

Warm Up

c) $81^{1/4}$

d) $1024^{1/5}$

*For a real number **a**, and a positive integer **n***

- $a^{1/n} = \sqrt[n]{a}$ $\qquad$ If $a > 0$

- $a^{1/n} = 0$ $\qquad$ If $a = 0$

- $a^{1/n}$ is not a real number if $a < 0$ and n is even.

Example 2: $\qquad$ Simplify each of the following expressions.

$\qquad$ **a)** $\quad 125^{1/3}$ $\qquad$ **b)** $\quad (-125)^{1/3}$

$\qquad$ **c)** $\quad -125^{1/3}$ $\qquad$ **d)** $\quad 0^{1/10}$

$\qquad$ **e)** $\quad (-256)^{1/4}$ $\quad$ **f)** $\quad -256^{1/4}$

Solutions:

a) $\quad 125^{1/3} = \sqrt[3]{125} = 5$ $\qquad$ $125 = 5^3$

b) $\quad (-125)^{1/3} = \sqrt[3]{-125} = -5$ $\qquad$ $-125 = (-5)^3$

c) $\quad -125^{1/3} = -\left(\sqrt[3]{125}\right) = -5$ $\qquad$ $125 = (5)^3$

d) $\quad 0^{1/10} = 0$

e) $\quad (-256)^{1/4}$ is not a real number since -256 is negative and $n = 4$ is even.

f) $\quad -256^{1/4} = -\left(\sqrt[4]{256}\right) = -4$ $\qquad$ $256 = 4^4$

Note that $\qquad$ $-256^{1/4} \neq (-256)^{1/4}$

$\qquad\qquad\qquad\qquad \downarrow \qquad\qquad\quad \downarrow$

$\qquad\qquad\qquad$ The base of the $\quad$ The base of the
$\qquad\qquad\qquad$ exponent is 256 $\quad$ exponent is -256

Warm Up

2. Simplify the following expressions.

a) $(-729)^{1/3}$

b) $(216)^{1/3}$

c) $-216^{1/3}$

d) $(-625)^{1/4}$

e) $(625)^{1/4}$

Answers:

1. **a)** 14 **b)** 9 **c)** 3 **d)** 4

2. **a)** −9 **b)** 6 **c)** −6

$\quad$ **d)** no real solution **e)** 5

B. Definition of $a^{m/n}$

$a^{m/n}$ is defined so as to follow the general power rule of exponents.

$$a^{m/n} = \left(a^m\right)^{1/n} = \left(a^{1/n}\right)^m, \text{ for all real } a \text{ and nonzero integers } m, n, \text{ except when } a < 0 \text{ and } n \text{ is even.}$$

Warm Up

3. Simplify

a) $27^{2/3}$

b) $9^{3/2}$

c) $(-64)^{4/3}$

d) $a^{2/3} \cdot a^{4/3}$

e) $\left(b^{3/6}\right)^2$

f) $\left(3x^{4/6}y^{-1/3}\right)^6$

Example 3:   Simplify.

a) $8^{2/3}$ b) $4^{3/2}$ c) $(-27)^{4/3}$

d) $a^{1/2} \cdot a^{2/3}$ e) $\left(a^{3/4}\right)^2$ f) $\left(2x^{4/3}y^{-2/3}\right)^3$

Solutions:

a) $8^{2/3} = \left(8^2\right)^{1/3} = (64)^{1/3} = (2 \cdot 2 \cdot 2 \cdot 2 \cdot 2 \cdot 2)^{1/3}$

$$= \left(4^3\right)^{1/3} = \sqrt[3]{4^3} = 4$$

Alternatively, $8^{2/3} = \left(8^{1/3}\right)^2 = \left(\sqrt[3]{8}\right)^2 = 2^2 = 4$.

b) $4^{3/2} = \left(4^3\right)^{1/2} = 64^{1/2} = \sqrt{64} = 8$

Alternatively, $4^{3/2} = \left(4^{1/2}\right)^3 = \left(\sqrt{4}\right)^3 = 2^3 = 8$.

c) $(-27)^{4/3} = \left[(-27)^4\right]^{1/3}$

$$= \left[(-27)(-27)(-27)(-27)\right]^{1/3}$$

$$= (27 \cdot 27 \cdot 27 \cdot 27)^{1/3}$$

$$= \sqrt[3]{3^3 \cdot 3^3 \cdot 3^3 \cdot 3^3}$$

$$= \sqrt[3]{3^3} \cdot \sqrt[3]{3^3} \cdot \sqrt[3]{3^3} \cdot \sqrt[3]{3^3}$$

$$= 3 \cdot 3 \cdot 3 \cdot 3 = 81.$$

Alternatively, $(-27)^{4/3} = \left[(-27)^{1/3}\right]^4 = \left(\sqrt[3]{-27}\right)^4$

$$= (-3)^4 = 81$$

d) $a^{1/2} \cdot a^{2/3} = a^{1/2 + 2/3}$ $a^m \cdot a^n = a^{m+n}$

$$= a^{5/6}$$

e) $\left(a^{3/4}\right)^2 = a^{3/4 \cdot 2}$ $\left(a^m\right)^n = a^{m \cdot n}$

$$= a^{3/2}$$

f) $\left(2x^{4/3}y^{-2/3}\right)^3 = 2^3\left(x^{4/3}\right)^3\left(y^{-2/3}\right)^3$ $(ab)^m = a^m b^m$

$$= 2^3 \cdot x^{\left(\frac{4}{3} \cdot 3\right)} \cdot y^{\left(-\frac{2}{3} \cdot 3\right)} \quad \left(a^m\right)^n = a^{mn}$$

$$= 8 \cdot x^4 \cdot y^{-2}$$

$$= \frac{8x^4}{y^2} \qquad\qquad a^{-n} = \frac{1}{a^n}$$

Example 4:   Simplify.

a) $\dfrac{6^{-2/7}}{6^{1/7} \cdot 6^{-5/7}}$ b) $\left(-\dfrac{8}{27} \cdot \dfrac{p^6}{q^{-4}}\right)^{-2/3}$

c) $\dfrac{\left(4x^2y\right)^{1/3}\left(2xy^2\right)^{1/3}}{\left(xy^2\right)^{2/3}}$

4.   Simplify

Solutions:

a) $\dfrac{6^{-2/7}}{6^{1/7} \cdot 6^{-5/7}} = \dfrac{6^{-2/7}}{6^{1/7+(-5/7)}}$ $a^m \cdot a^n = a^{m+n}$

$= \dfrac{6^{-2/7}}{6^{-4/7}} = 6^{-2/7-(-4/7)} = 6^{2/7}$ $\dfrac{a^m}{a^n} = a^{m-n}$

a) $\dfrac{7^{-4/7}}{7^{2/7} \cdot 7^{-1/7}}$

b) $= \left[\left(-\dfrac{8p^6}{27q^{-4}}\right)^{1/3}\right]^{-2} = \left[-\left(\dfrac{8p^6}{27q^{-4}}\right)^{1/3}\right]^{-2}$

$= \left[-\dfrac{\left(8p^6\right)^{1/3}}{\left(27q^{-4}\right)^{1/3}}\right]^{-2} = \left[-\left(\dfrac{8^{1/3}\left(p^6\right)^{1/3}}{27^{1/3}\left(q^{-4}\right)^{1/3}}\right)\right]^{-2}$

b) $\left(-\dfrac{1}{64} \cdot \dfrac{p^{1/3}}{q^{-1/3}}\right)$

$= \left[-\dfrac{2p^2}{3q^{-4/3}}\right]^{-2} = \left[-\dfrac{3q^{-4/3}}{2p^2}\right]^{2}$ $\left(\dfrac{a}{b}\right)^{-n} = \left(\dfrac{b}{a}\right)^{n}$

$= \dfrac{3^2\left(q^{-4/3}\right)^2}{2^2\left(p^2\right)^2} = \dfrac{9q^{-8/3}}{4p^4} = \dfrac{9}{4p^4q^{8/3}}$

c) $\dfrac{\left(4x^2y\right)^{1/3}\left(2xy^2\right)^{1/3}}{\left(xy^2\right)^{2/3}}$

$= \dfrac{\left[4^{1/3}\left(x^2\right)^{1/3}y^{1/3}\right]\left[2^{1/3}x^{1/3}\left(y^2\right)^{1/3}\right]}{x^{2/3}\left(y^2\right)^{2/3}}$

$= \dfrac{\left(4^{1/3} \cdot 2^{1/3}\right)\left(x^{2/3} \cdot x^{1/3}\right)\left(y^{1/3} \cdot y^{2/3}\right)}{x^{2/3} \cdot y^{4/3}}$

$= \dfrac{(4 \cdot 2)^{1/3}\left(x^{2/3} \cdot x^{1/3}\right)\left(y^{1/3} \cdot y^{2/3}\right)}{x^{2/3} \cdot y^{4/3}}$

$= \dfrac{8^{1/3} \cdot x^{2/3+1/3} \cdot y^{1/3+2/3}}{x^{2/3} \cdot y^{4/3}} = \dfrac{2xy}{x^{2/3} \cdot y^{4/3}} = \dfrac{2x \cdot x^{-2/3}}{y^{4/3} \cdot y^{-1}}$ $\dfrac{1}{x^{2/3}} = x^{-2/3}$

$= \dfrac{2x^{1-2/3}}{y^{4/3-1}} = \dfrac{2x^{1/3}}{y^{1/3}}$

c) $\dfrac{\left(5x^3y^2\right)^{1/3}\left(3xy\right)^{1/3}}{\left(x^2y^2\right)^{4/3}}$

Answers:

3. a) 9 **b)** 27 **c)** 256 **d)** a^2
 e) b **f)** $729x^4y^{-2}$

4. a) $\dfrac{1}{7^{5/7}}$ **b)** $-\dfrac{p^{1/3}q^{1/3}}{64}$ **c)** $\dfrac{5^{1/3} \cdot 3^{1/3}}{x^{4/3}y^{5/3}}$

C. Properties of Radicals

If $a > 0$ and $b > 0$ then:
- $\left(\sqrt[n]{a} \right)^n = \sqrt[n]{a^n}$.
- $\sqrt[n]{ab} = \sqrt[n]{a}\ \sqrt[n]{b}$.
- $\sqrt[n]{\dfrac{a}{b}} = \dfrac{\sqrt[n]{a}}{\sqrt[n]{b}}$.

Warm Up

5. Simplify

a) $\dfrac{\sqrt{100}}{\sqrt{25}}$

b) $\sqrt[3]{\dfrac{9}{2}}$

c) $\sqrt[3]{16x^7}$

d) $\dfrac{\sqrt{54x^2y^2}}{\sqrt{6x^4y^4}}$

Answers:

5. a) 2 b) $\dfrac{\sqrt[3]{36}}{2}$ c) $2x^2\sqrt[3]{2x}$

d) $\dfrac{3}{xy}$

Example 5:   Simplify.

a) $\dfrac{\sqrt{50}}{\sqrt{2}}$ b) $\sqrt[3]{\dfrac{9}{8}}$ c) $\sqrt[3]{24x^5}$

d) $\dfrac{\sqrt{45xy^2}}{\sqrt{5x}}, \quad y > 0$

Solutions:

a) $\dfrac{\sqrt{50}}{\sqrt{2}} = \sqrt{\dfrac{50}{2}}$ $\sqrt[n]{\dfrac{a}{b}} = \dfrac{\sqrt[n]{a}}{\sqrt[n]{b}}$

$= \sqrt{25} = 5$ $25 = 5^2$

b) $\sqrt[3]{\dfrac{9}{8}} = \dfrac{\sqrt[3]{9}}{\sqrt[3]{8}} = \dfrac{\sqrt[3]{9}}{2}$

c) $\sqrt[3]{24x^5} = \sqrt[3]{8x^3 \cdot 3x^2}$ $\sqrt[n]{ab} = \sqrt[n]{a}\ \sqrt[n]{b}$

$= \sqrt[3]{8x^3}\ \sqrt[3]{3x^2}$

$= \sqrt[3]{(2x)^3}\ \sqrt[3]{3x^2} = 2x\ \sqrt[3]{3x^2}$

d) $\dfrac{\sqrt{45xy^2}}{\sqrt{5x}} = \sqrt{\dfrac{45xy^2}{5x}} = \sqrt{9y^2} = \sqrt{(3y)^2} = 3y$

EXERCISE 8.5

Answers:

1. _____
2. _____
3. _____
4. _____
5. _____
6. _____

In exercises 1–10, write the expression in radical form and simplify.

1. $16^{1/2}$ 2. $36^{1/2}$ 3. $8^{1/3}$ 4. $-8^{1/3}$

5. $(-8)^{1/3}$ 6. $4^{5/2}$ 7. $27^{-2/3}$ 8. $121^{3/2}$

9. $-81^{1/4}$ 10. $(243)^{2/5}$

Simplify the expression in exercises 11–20.

11. $(8x)^{1/3}$

12. $\left(8x^2y^{-1}\right)^{-1/3}$

13. $\dfrac{\left(27x^3y\right)^{1/3}}{\left(xy^2\right)^{2/3}}$

14. $\left(\dfrac{4p^3q}{9pq}\right)^{1/2}$

15. $\sqrt{\left(2x^{-4}y^3\right)^7}$

16. $\left(x^3y^3\right)^{1/6}$

17. $\left(\dfrac{p^{2/3}}{q^{3/4}}\right)^{1/2}$

18. $\dfrac{y^{3/4} \cdot y^{7/4}}{2y^{5/4}}$

19. $\left(\left(x^{2/3}y^{4/3}\right)^{1/2} z^2\right)^{1/3}$

20. $\dfrac{\left(8xy^2\right)^{1/2}\left(2xy\right)^{1/2}}{\left(xy\right)^{1/2}}$; $x>0,\ y>0$

Simplify each of the following.

21. $\sqrt[3]{\dfrac{2}{3}}$

22. $\sqrt[3]{\dfrac{125}{49}}$

23. $\dfrac{\sqrt{10xy^2}}{\sqrt{2xy^3}}$

24. $\dfrac{\sqrt[3]{9x}}{\sqrt[3]{3xy}}$

7. _____
8. _____
9. _____
10. _____
11. _____
12. _____
13. _____
14. _____
15. _____
16. _____
17. _____
18. _____
19. _____
20. _____
21. _____
22. _____
23. _____
24. _____

8.6 EQUATIONS WITH RADICALS

To solve equations involving radicals we use the following *power rule*.

$$\text{If } a = b \text{ then } a^n = b^n.$$

Upon completion of this section we will learn to:

- Solve equations with radicals.
- Identify equations with no solutions.

Solving Equations with Radicals

We solve equations with radicals using the following steps.

Step 1	Apply properties of numbers and transfer terms so that at least one side of the equation contains only one radical.
Step 2	Raise both sides to a suitable power to remove this radical. Use $\left(\sqrt[n]{a}\right)^n = a$.
Step 3	Combine like terms.
Step 4	If the resulting equation still has a radical, repeat steps 1-3.
Step 5	Solve the equation obtained above.
Step 6	Check all solutions obtained in step 5 by substituting the values in the *original equation*. For radical equations, checking is required. A solution obtained in step 5 which does not satisfy the original equation is called an **extraneous solution.**

Warm Up

1. Solve the equation $\sqrt{5x} = 5$

Example 1:   Solve the equation $\sqrt{2x} = 5$.

Solution:

Step 1	Not needed.
Step 2	Square both sides $\left(\sqrt{2x}\right)^2 = 5^2 \longrightarrow 2x = 25$
Steps 3,4	Not needed.
Step 5	Solve the equation $x = \dfrac{25}{2}$
Step 6	Check the solution. $\sqrt{2x} = 5$

$$\sqrt{2 \cdot \frac{25}{2}} = 5 \quad \text{or} \quad \sqrt{25} = 5 \qquad \textbf{True}$$

Therefore, $x = \dfrac{25}{2}$ is a solution.

2. Solve the equation $\sqrt{x+4} = 3$

Example 2:   Solve the equation $\sqrt{x-3} = 4$.

Solution:

Step 1	Not needed.	*Step 2*	Square both sides.

$$\left(\sqrt{x-3}\right)^2 = 4^2$$
$$x - 3 = 16$$

Step 3	$x = 16 + 3$		
Step 4	Not needed.	*Step 5*	$x = 19$
Step 6	Check the solution. $\sqrt{x-3} = 4$		

$$\longrightarrow \sqrt{19-3} = 4$$
$$\longrightarrow \sqrt{16} = 4 \qquad \textbf{True}$$

Therefore, $x = \textbf{19}$ is a solution.

We can solve equations with radicals using calculator. See example 1 on page 530 in Appendix B.

Example 3:   Solve the equation $\sqrt[3]{4x-1} = 2$.

Solution:

Step 1   Not needed.   **Step 2**   Cube both sides.

$$\left(\sqrt[3]{4x-1}\right)^3 = 2^3$$

$$4x - 1 = 8$$

Step 3 $4x = 8 + 1$ **Step 4**   Not needed.
$4x = 9$

Step 5 $x = \dfrac{9}{4}$

Step 6   Check the solution.

$$\sqrt[3]{4x-1} = 2$$

$$\sqrt[3]{4\left(\dfrac{9}{4}\right) - 1} = 2$$

$$\longrightarrow \quad \sqrt[3]{9 - 1} = 2$$

$$\longrightarrow \quad \sqrt[3]{8} = 2 \quad \text{True}$$

Therefore, $x = \dfrac{9}{4}$ is a solution.

Example 4:   Solve the equation $\sqrt[4]{12x+4} + 2 = 0$.

Solution:

Step 1 $\sqrt[4]{12x+4} = -2$

Step 2   Raise both sides to the fourth power.

$$\left(\sqrt[4]{12x+4}\right)^4 = (-2)^4 \quad \longrightarrow \quad 12x + 4 = 16$$

Step 3 $12x = 16 - 4 \qquad \longrightarrow \qquad 12x = 12$

Step 4   Not needed.

Step 5 $x = \dfrac{12}{12} \qquad \longrightarrow \qquad x = 1$

Step 6   Check the solution .

$$\sqrt[4]{12x+4} + 2 = 0$$

$$\sqrt[4]{12(1)+4} + 2 = 0$$

$$\longrightarrow \quad \sqrt[4]{16} + 2 = 0$$

$$\longrightarrow \quad 2 + 2 = 0 \qquad \text{Not True}$$

Therefore, $x = 1$ is an ***extraneous solution.***

Warm Up

3.   Solve the equation
$\sqrt[3]{3x-2} = 2$

4.   Solve the equation
$\sqrt[4]{6x+9} + 3 = 0$

5. Solve the equation

$$q - \sqrt{q - 2} = 2$$

Example 5:   Solve the equation $p - \sqrt{p - 2} = 4$.

Solution:

Step 1 $p - 4 = \sqrt{p - 2}$

Step 2   Square both sides.

$$\left(\sqrt{p - 2}\right)^2 = (p - 4)^2$$
$$p - 2 = p^2 - 8p + 16 \qquad (a - b)^2 = a^2 - 2ab + b^2$$

Step 3 $0 = p^2 - 8p - p + 16 + 2$
$$\longrightarrow p^2 - 9p + 18 = 0$$

Step 4   Not needed.

Step 5 $(p - 6)(p - 3) = 0$

$$p - 6 = 0 \quad \text{or} \quad p - 3 = 0$$
$$p = 6 \quad \text{or} \quad p = 3$$

Step 6   Check the solution:

(i) For $p = 6$: $p - \sqrt{p - 2} = 4$
$$6 - \sqrt{6 - 2} = 4 \longrightarrow 6 - \sqrt{4} = 4$$
$$\longrightarrow 6 - 2 = 4 \text{ True}$$

Therefore, **$p = 6$ is a solution.**

(ii) For $p = 3$:
$$p - \sqrt{p - 2} = 4$$
$$3 - \sqrt{3 - 2} = 4 \longrightarrow 3 - \sqrt{1} = 4$$
$$\longrightarrow 3 - 1 = 4 \qquad \text{Not true}$$

Therefore, **$p = 3$** is an ***extraneous solution.***

6. Solve the equation

$$\sqrt{4x - 7} = 1 + \sqrt{2x}$$

Example 6:   Solve the equation $\sqrt{5x - 1} - \sqrt{x + 2} = 1$.

Solution:

Step 1 $\sqrt{5x - 1} = 1 + \sqrt{x + 2}$

Step 2   Square both sides.

$$\left(\sqrt{5x - 1}\right)^2 = \left(1 + \sqrt{x + 2}\right)^2 \qquad (a+b)^2 = a^2 + 2ab + b^2$$
$$5x - 1 = 1 + 2\sqrt{x + 2} + \left(\sqrt{x + 2}\right)^2$$
$$5x - 1 = 1 + 2\sqrt{x + 2} + x + 2$$

Step 3 $5x - 1 = x + 3 + 2\sqrt{x + 2} \longrightarrow 4x - 4 = 2\sqrt{x + 2}$

Step 4   The equation still contains a radical, so we repeat steps 1 - 3.

$$2\sqrt{x + 2} = 4x - 4 \qquad \text{Step 1}$$

$$\left(2\sqrt{x+2}\right)^2 = (4x-4)^2 \qquad \text{Step 2}$$

$$4(x+2) = 16x^2 - 32x + 16$$

$$16x^2 - 32x - 4x + 16 - 8 = 0$$

$$16x^2 - 36x + 8 = 0 \qquad \text{Step 3}$$

$$\text{or } 4\left(4x^2 - 9x + 2\right) = 0$$

Step 5 $$4\left(4x^2 - 9x + 2\right) = 0 \longrightarrow 4(x-2)(4x-1)=0$$

$$\longrightarrow \quad x - 2 = 0 \quad \text{or} \quad 4x - 1 = 0$$

$$\longrightarrow \quad x = 2 \quad \text{or} \quad x = \frac{1}{4}$$

Step 6 Check the solution. $\sqrt{5x-1} - \sqrt{x+2} = 1$
x = 2:
$$\sqrt{5(2)-1} - \sqrt{2+2} = 1 \longrightarrow \sqrt{9} - \sqrt{4} = 1 \quad \text{True}$$

Therefore, $x = 2$ is a solution.

$$x = \frac{1}{4}: \quad \sqrt{5\left(\frac{1}{4}\right)-1} - \sqrt{\frac{1}{4}+2} = 1$$

$$\longrightarrow \quad \sqrt{\frac{1}{4}} - \sqrt{\frac{9}{4}} = 1$$

$$\longrightarrow \quad \frac{1}{2} - \frac{3}{2} = 1 \quad \text{Not True}$$

Therefore, $x = \dfrac{1}{4}$ is an extraneous solution.

Example 7:   Solve the equation: $\sqrt[3]{y^3 - 7} + 1 = y$.

Solution:

Step 1 $\sqrt[3]{y^3 - 7} = y - 1$

Step 2 Cube both sides.
$y^3 - 7 = y^3 - 3y^2 + 3y - 1 \quad {\scriptstyle (a-b)^3 = a^3 - 3a^2b + 3ab^2 - b^3}$

Step 3 $y^3 - 7 - y^3 + 3y^2 - 3y + 1 = 0$
$3y^2 - 3y - 6 = 0$

Step 4 Not needed.

Step 5 $3\left(y^2 - y - 2\right) = 0 \longrightarrow 3(y-2)(y+1) = 0$
$y - 2 = 0 \quad \text{or} \quad y + 1 = 0$
$y = 2 \quad \text{or} \quad y = -1$

7. Solve the equation
$$\sqrt[3]{p^3 - 63} + 3 = p$$

Warm Up

Answers:

1. 5   2. 5   3. $\frac{10}{3}$
4. $x = 12$ is an extraneous solution
5. 3, 2
6. 8, $x = 2$ is an extraneous solution
7. 4, −1

Step 6   Check the solutions: $\sqrt[3]{y^3 - 7} + 1 = y$

$y = 2$:

$\sqrt[3]{2^3 - 7} + 1 = 2 \longrightarrow \sqrt[3]{1} + 1 = 2$ **True**

Therefore, $y = 2$ is a solution.

$y = -1$:

$\sqrt[3]{(-1)^3 - 7} + 1 = -1 \longrightarrow \sqrt[3]{-8} + 1 = -1$

$\longrightarrow -2 + 1 = -1$ **True**

Therefore, $y = -1$ is a solution.

EXERCISE 8.6

Answers:

1. _____
2. _____
3. _____
4. _____
5. _____
6. _____
7. _____
8. _____
9. _____
10. _____
11. _____
12. _____
13. _____
14. _____
15. _____
16. _____
17. _____
18. _____
19. _____
20. _____

Solve the following equations.

1. $\sqrt{x} = 3$

2. $\sqrt{x} = 4$

3. $\sqrt{y - 5} = 0$

4. $\sqrt{t + 5} = -2$

5. $\sqrt{z} + 3 = 7$

6. $\sqrt{x} - 4 = 5$

7. $\sqrt{t} + 8 = 5$

8. $x = \dfrac{\sqrt{16x - 12}}{2}$

9. $\sqrt{24 - 5t} = 6 - t$

10. $\sqrt{p + 2} = p$

11. $\sqrt{x + 7} = \sqrt{x + 4} - 3$

12. $\sqrt{x - 1} = 3 - \sqrt{x + 2}$

13. $\sqrt{x - 5} = 4 + \sqrt{x + 3}$

14. $\sqrt{4t - 1} = \sqrt{t - 1} + \sqrt{t + 2}$

15. $\sqrt{8x + 20} - \sqrt{7x + 11} = 1$

16. $\sqrt{2x - 1} = 4 - \sqrt{x - 4}$

17. $\sqrt{3x + 4} = \sqrt{2x + 1} + 1$

18. $\sqrt{4a^2 + 5a - 30} = 2a$

19. $\sqrt{p^2 - 3p - 12} = p$

20. $\sqrt{x + 2} + \sqrt{2x - 3} = \sqrt{11 - x}$

8.7   CHAPTER SUMMARY

Finding Roots

Examples

1.   If r is a real number and n is a positive integer such that $r = a^n$, then a is called the **nth root** of r.

   1.   • $81 = (-3)^4 \longrightarrow -3$ is a fourth root of 81.
       • $32 = 2^5 \longrightarrow 2$ is a fifth root of 32.

2.   No real number can be an even root of a negative real number.

   2.   •   There is no real number a such that $a^4 = -16$.
       • $\sqrt{-16}$ is not a real number.

3.   For a positive rational number r :

    • $\sqrt{r}$ is rational if r is a perfect square.

    • $\sqrt{r}$ is irrational if r is not a perfect square.

   3.   • $\sqrt{16} = 4$, $\sqrt{\dfrac{9}{16}} = \dfrac{3}{4}$ are rational numbers.
       • $\sqrt{17}$, $\sqrt{\dfrac{5}{9}}$, are irrational numbers.

4.   Each real number has exactly one cube root.

   4.   • $\sqrt[3]{8} = 2$ $\sqrt[3]{-27} = -3$

5.   For a positive rational number r:

    • $\sqrt[3]{r}$ is rational if r is a perfect cube.

    • $\sqrt[3]{r}$ is irrational if r is not a perfect cube.

   5.   • $\sqrt[3]{-8} = -2$, $\sqrt[3]{\dfrac{27}{64}} = \dfrac{3}{4}$ are rational numbers
       • $\sqrt[3]{7}$, $\sqrt[3]{\dfrac{5}{11}}$ are irrational numbers.

Multiplication and Division of Radicals

Product rule for Radicals

6.   If x and y are non - negative real numbers, then $\sqrt{x} \cdot \sqrt{y} = \sqrt{xy}$.

   6.   • $\sqrt{2} \cdot \sqrt{3} = \sqrt{6}$
       • $\sqrt{2} \cdot \sqrt{18} = \sqrt{36} = 6$

7.   If $\sqrt[n]{x}$ and $\sqrt[n]{y}$ are real, then $\sqrt[n]{x} \cdot \sqrt[n]{y} = \sqrt[n]{xy}$.

   7.   • $\sqrt[3]{5} \cdot \sqrt[3]{4} = \sqrt[3]{20}$,
       • $\sqrt[5]{8} \cdot \sqrt[5]{-4} = \sqrt[5]{-32} = -2$

Quotient Rule for Radicals

8.   If x and y are non - negative real numbers and y is **non-zero** then $\dfrac{\sqrt{x}}{\sqrt{y}} = \sqrt{\dfrac{x}{y}}$.

   8.   • $\dfrac{\sqrt{18}}{\sqrt{2}} = \sqrt{\dfrac{18}{2}} = \sqrt{9} = 3$,
       • $\sqrt{\dfrac{9}{16}} = \dfrac{\sqrt{9}}{\sqrt{16}} = \dfrac{3}{4}$

9.   If $\sqrt[n]{x}$ and $\sqrt[n]{y}$ are real and y is non-zero then $\dfrac{\sqrt[n]{x}}{\sqrt[n]{y}} = \sqrt[n]{\dfrac{x}{y}}$.

   9.   • $\dfrac{\sqrt[5]{12}}{\sqrt[5]{3}} = \sqrt[5]{\dfrac{12}{3}} = \sqrt[5]{4}$

429

Examples

Simplifying Radicals

10.   Steps to simplify radicals

   Step 1   Write the prime factorization of the radicand.
   Step 2   Apply the product rule.
   Step 3   Use $\sqrt[n]{a^n} = a$ and simplify.

10.   Simplify $\sqrt[3]{120}$

   • $120 = 2 \cdot 2 \cdot 2 \cdot 3 \cdot 5$

   • $\sqrt[3]{120} = \sqrt[3]{2^3} \cdot \sqrt[3]{3} \cdot \sqrt[3]{5}$
   $= 2\sqrt[3]{3} \cdot \sqrt[3]{5}$
   $= 2\sqrt[3]{15}$

Addition and Subtraction of Radicals

11.   **Addition of Radicals**

   We add *like* radicals by using the distributive property.

11.   • $3\sqrt{5} + 4\sqrt{5} = (3+4)\sqrt{5} = 7\sqrt{5}$
   • $3\sqrt{5} + 4\sqrt{5} = (3+4)\sqrt{5} = 7\sqrt{5}$
   • $2\sqrt{27} + 5\sqrt{3} = 2(3\sqrt{3}) + 5\sqrt{3}$
   $= 6\sqrt{3} + 5\sqrt{3}$
   $= (6+5)\sqrt{3} = 11\sqrt{3}$

12.   **Subtraction of Radicals**

   We subtract *like* radicals by using the distributive property.

12.   • $5\sqrt{3} - 7\sqrt{3} = (5-7)\sqrt{3}$
   $= -2\sqrt{3}$
   • $\sqrt{18} - \sqrt{8} = 3\sqrt{2} - 2\sqrt{2} = \sqrt{2}$

13.   Unlike radicals cannot be combined.

13.   • $\sqrt{2} + \sqrt{3}$ or $3\sqrt{5} - 2\sqrt{7}$ cannot be combined.

Rationalizing the Denominator

14.   A radical expression is said to be rationalized when its denominator contains no radicals.

14.   • $\dfrac{3}{\sqrt{5}} = \dfrac{3}{\sqrt{5}} \cdot \dfrac{\sqrt{5}}{\sqrt{5}} = \dfrac{3\sqrt{5}}{5}$

   • $\dfrac{5x}{\sqrt[3]{y}} = \dfrac{5x \cdot \sqrt[3]{y^2}}{\sqrt[3]{y} \cdot \sqrt[3]{y^2}} = \dfrac{5x\sqrt[3]{y^2}}{y}$

15.   Two binomials $a + \sqrt{b}$ and $a - \sqrt{b}$, which differ only in the sign of the radical term, are called conjugates of each other.

15.   •   The conjugate of $2 + 5\sqrt{3}$ is $2 - 5\sqrt{3}$
   •   The conjugate of $1 - \sqrt{2}$ is $1 + \sqrt{2}$

16.   To rationalize an expression whose denominator is of the form $a + c\sqrt{d}$ or $a\sqrt{b} + c\sqrt{d}$, we multiply the numerator and the denominator by the conjugate of the denominator and simplify.

16.   Rationalize $\dfrac{4 + 2\sqrt{3}}{3 - \sqrt{5}}$.

   The conjugate of $3 - \sqrt{5} = 3 + \sqrt{5}$.

   $\dfrac{4 + 2\sqrt{3}}{3 - \sqrt{5}} = \dfrac{4 + 2\sqrt{3}}{3 - \sqrt{5}} \cdot \dfrac{3 + \sqrt{5}}{3 + \sqrt{5}}$

   $= \dfrac{(4 + 2\sqrt{3})(3 + \sqrt{5})}{(3 - \sqrt{5})(3 + \sqrt{5})}$

   $= \dfrac{12 + 4\sqrt{5} + 6\sqrt{3} + (2\sqrt{3})\sqrt{5}}{(3)^2 - (\sqrt{5})^2}$

   $= \dfrac{12 + 4\sqrt{5} + 6\sqrt{3} + 2\sqrt{15}}{3 - 5}$

   $= -6 - 2\sqrt{5} - 3\sqrt{3} - \sqrt{15}$

Fractional Exponents

17. For any non-negative real number a and positive integer n, the principal root of $\sqrt[n]{a}$ **is written as** $a^{1/n}$.

17.   • $\sqrt[3]{5} = 5^{\frac{1}{3}}$ • $\sqrt{7} = 7^{\frac{1}{2}}$

18. $a^{\frac{m}{n}} = \sqrt[n]{a^m} = \left(\sqrt[n]{a}\right)^m$ for a, m, and n except when n is even and $a < 0$.

18.   • $(27)^{2/3} = \left(\sqrt[3]{27}\right)^2 = 3^2 = 9$

Equations with Radicals

19. **To solve an equation with radicals, we use the following steps:**

19.   Solve $\sqrt{x+8} - x = 2$

Step 1   Apply the properties of numbers and transfer terms so that **at least one side** of the equation contains **only one radical**.

$\sqrt{x+8} - x = 2 \longrightarrow \sqrt{x+8} = 2 + x$

Step 2   Raise both sides to a suitable power to remove this radical. Use $\left(\sqrt[n]{a}\right)^n = a$.

Since the left hand side is a square root, we square both sides.
$\left(\sqrt{x+8}\right)^2 = (2+x)^2 \longrightarrow x+8 = 4 + 4x + x^2$

Step 3   Combine like terms.

$x^2 + 3x - 4 = 0$

Step 4   If the resulting equation still has a radical term, repeat steps 1 - 3.

NA

Step 5   Solve the equation obtained above.

$x^2 + 3x - 4 = 0 \rightarrow (x+4)(x-1) = 0$
$\rightarrow x = -4 \text{ or } x = 1$

Step 6   Check all solutions obtained in Step 5 by substituting the values into the original equation. A solution which does not satisfy the original equation is called an **extraneous solution.**

Verify that $x = 1$ is a solution of the original equation but $x = -4$ is not a solution.

8.8 REVIEW EXERCISE

Simplify the expressions in exercises 1–5.

1. $\sqrt{25}$

2. $\sqrt{-\dfrac{1}{16}}$

3. $\sqrt[3]{729}$

4. $\sqrt[5]{-\dfrac{243}{3125}}$

5. $\left(\sqrt[3]{\dfrac{t^2+2t-1}{2t-1}}\right)^3$

In exercises 6–8, identify numbers as rational, irrational or non-real?

6. $\sqrt{\dfrac{48}{81}}$

7. $\sqrt{-49}$

8. $\sqrt{36}$

9. Find the square roots. a) 144 b) $\dfrac{81}{16}$

10. Find the cube roots. a) $\dfrac{125}{64}$ b) $-\dfrac{8}{343}$

11. One of the legs of a right triangle is 9 cm and its hypotenuse is 11 cm. Find the length of the third side.

12. A boat is being pulled into a dock with a rope attached to its front. When the boat is 6 feet from the dock, the height of the end of the rope is 3 feet. Approximate the length of the extended rope to the hundredths place.

Simplify the expressions in exercises 13–23.

13. $\sqrt{5}\cdot\sqrt{6}$

14. $\sqrt[3]{16}\cdot\sqrt[3]{-4}$

15. $\sqrt[3]{x^2y}\cdot\sqrt[3]{xy^2}$

16. $\sqrt[3]{3r^2s}\cdot\sqrt[3]{9r^3s^4}$

17. $-6\sqrt[5]{p^3q}\cdot\sqrt[5]{p^4q^2}$

18. $\dfrac{\sqrt[3]{48}}{\sqrt[3]{-6}}$

19. $\dfrac{\sqrt[4]{6x^2y}}{\sqrt[4]{96x^6y^9}}$

20. $\sqrt{3ab}\,\sqrt{6a};\ a>0,\ b>0$

21. $\dfrac{\sqrt{3ab^2}}{\sqrt{12a}};\ a>0$

22. $\dfrac{\sqrt{8x^3y^2}\cdot\sqrt{4xy^3}}{\sqrt{2x^2y}};\ x,y>0$

23. $\dfrac{\sqrt[3]{4a^3b^2}\cdot\sqrt[3]{-2a^4b^2}}{\sqrt[3]{27ab}}$

In exercises 24–32, perform the indicated operations.

24. $3\sqrt{2}+5\sqrt{3}-4\sqrt{18}$

25. $\sqrt[3]{40}+2\sqrt{80}+\sqrt{45}-\sqrt[3]{135}$

26. $\sqrt{81x^5}-\sqrt{16x^3}-\sqrt[3]{27x^4}$

27. $\left(2\sqrt{2}-\sqrt{3}\right)\left(2\sqrt{2}+\sqrt{3}\right)$

28. $\left(x-\sqrt{2}y\right)^2$

29. $\left(\sqrt{x}+2\sqrt{y}\right)^2$

30. $\left(\sqrt{x}-\sqrt{3}\right)\left(2\sqrt{x}+\sqrt{7}\right)$

31. $\left(\sqrt[3]{y}-1\right)\left(\sqrt[3]{y^2}+1\right)$

32. $\left(\sqrt[3]{4} - \sqrt[3]{3}\right)\left(\sqrt[3]{16} + \sqrt[3]{12} + \sqrt[3]{9}\right)$

In exercises 33–44, rationalize the denominators and simplify.

33. $\dfrac{7}{\sqrt{6}}$

34. $\dfrac{3x}{4\sqrt{x}}$

35. $\dfrac{5}{\sqrt[3]{4}}$

36. $\dfrac{5}{3 + \sqrt{5}}$

37. $\dfrac{2 + \sqrt{5}}{4 - \sqrt{3}}$

38. $\dfrac{\sqrt{5} - \sqrt{3}}{\sqrt{5} + \sqrt{3}}$

39. $\dfrac{2\sqrt{a} + \sqrt{b}}{\sqrt{a} - \sqrt{b}}; \quad a \neq b$

40. $\sqrt{\dfrac{5p^3}{4q^5}}$

41. $\dfrac{\sqrt{3a}}{\sqrt{a} + \sqrt{3}}; \quad a \neq -3$

42. $\dfrac{\sqrt{2p} - \sqrt{5q}}{\sqrt{5q} + \sqrt{2p}}; \quad 5q \neq 2p$

43. $\dfrac{\sqrt{x} - 2}{\sqrt{x + 2}}; \quad x \neq -2$

44. $\dfrac{\sqrt{y} + 2}{\sqrt{y} + 3}$

In exercises 45–47, simplify the expressions.

45. $25^{1/2}$

46. $(-27)^{1/3}$

47. $(25)^{3/2}$

In exercises 48–52, simplify the expressions and write your answer in terms of positive exponents only.

48. $x^{\frac{5}{2}} \cdot \left(2x^{\frac{1}{2}}\right)^3$

49. $\left(8x^2\right)^{1/3}$

50. $\left(4a^{-2}b\right)^{-3/2}$

51. $\dfrac{\left(8p^3q^2\right)^{2/3}}{\left(-216p^{-2}q\right)^{1/3}}$

52. $\sqrt{\left(4x^{-2}y\right)^3}$

Solve the equations in exercises 53–56 .

53. $\sqrt{2y - 3} = 3$

54. $\sqrt{x - 2} + 4 = x$

55. $\sqrt{p - 2} + 3 = \sqrt{p + 13}$

56. $\sqrt{x + 2} + 1 = \sqrt{x}$

57. The sum of two numbers is 11. The smaller number is the square root of one more than the greater number. Find the number.

58. The radius r of a circle is given by the formula $r = \sqrt{\dfrac{A}{\pi}}$, where A is the area measure of the circle. For a circle with radius 3 inches, find the area measure of the circle rounded to three places of decimal.

[π is an irrational number. The value of π approximated to three places of decimal is 3.142. Use your calculator to find the approximation of π to different number of decimal places.]

8.9   SELF TEST

Note: Assume that all variables represent positive real numbers.

Simplify

1. $\sqrt{169}$

2. $\sqrt[3]{-343}$

3. $\sqrt{27x^2}$

4. $\sqrt{\dfrac{25}{81}}$

5. $\sqrt[5]{-8}$ $\sqrt[5]{16}$

6. $\sqrt[4]{256x^5y^{11}} \cdot \sqrt[4]{48x^6y^2}$

7. $\dfrac{\sqrt[3]{24x^{18}y^4}}{\sqrt[3]{-3y}}$

8. $3\sqrt{3} + \sqrt{12} - \sqrt{27}$

9. $3\sqrt{27p} - 2\sqrt{48p} + 5\sqrt{75}$

10. $\left(\sqrt{5} - 2\sqrt{3}\right)\left(\sqrt{5} + 2\sqrt{3}\right)$

11. $\left(\sqrt{2y} + 7\right)\left(\sqrt{3y} - 7\right)$

Rationalize and simplify:

12. $\dfrac{\sqrt{2}}{3 - \sqrt{5}}$

13. $\dfrac{3\sqrt{2} + \sqrt{3}}{2\sqrt{2} - 3\sqrt{3}}$

14. $\dfrac{4x + \sqrt[3]{3}}{\sqrt[3]{x}}$

15. $\dfrac{5\sqrt{x} + 3\sqrt{y}}{5\sqrt{x} - 3\sqrt{y}}$

16. $\dfrac{\left(2^{5/3} \cdot 2^{-1/6}\right)^{1/2}}{2^{1/2}}$

17. $\dfrac{\left(8x^3y\right)^{1/2}\left(8xy^5\right)^{1/2}}{\left(x^3y^6\right)^{1/3}}$

Solve the equations:

18. $\sqrt{x - 3} = 1 - \sqrt{x}$

19. $6\sqrt{a} - 3 = a + 2$

20. $\sqrt{x + 2} + 1 = \sqrt{x}$

CHAPTER 9

QUADRATIC EQUATIONS

9.4 Quadratic Formula

Use the quadratic formula to solve the following quadratic equations:

Ex 1

- $x^2 - 4x - 5 = 0$
- $5x - 2x^2 = 0$
- $3x^2 - 5 = 0$
- $4x^2 + 4x + 1 = 0$

Step 1: The equation is already in **standard form** $ax^2 + bx + c = 0$.

Step 2: Here $a = 1$, $b = -4$, $c = -5$.

Step 3: $b^2 - 4ac = (-4)^2 - 4(1)(-5) = 16 + 20 = 36$.

Step 4: **Substituting** these values in the quadratic formula, we get:

Quadratic Formula → $x = \dfrac{-b \pm \sqrt{b^2 - 4ac}}{2a}$

$x = \dfrac{4 \pm 6}{2}$

Substitute the values → $x = \dfrac{-(-4) \pm \sqrt{36}}{2(1)}$

$x = \dfrac{4 + 6}{2}$ or $x = \dfrac{4 - 6}{2}$

$= \dfrac{4 \pm \sqrt{36}}{2}$

$x = 5$ or $x = -1$

The solutions are **5** and **-1**.

Observation

S&◁ Exer.   Click On Me or Press Spacebar to Continue   Obj   Exit

CHAPTER 9

QUADRATIC EQUATIONS

In Chapter 4 we learned how to solve quadratic equations by factoring. In this Chapter we shall learn how to solve a quadratic equation by some other methods. These methods are completing the square, the quadratic formula, and graphing. Basic to all these methods is the **square root property** of equations. We also introduce complex numbers in this section. Whereas an equation may not have real solutions, it always has complex solutions.

This section is divided into following sections.

9.1 SOLVING QUADRATIC EQUATIONS BY SQUARE ROOT PROPERTY

In this section we state the square root property of equations, and use it to solve certain quadratic equations. Recall that a quadratic equation can always be written in the form $ax^2 + bx + c = 0$, where a, b, c are real numbers, and $a \neq 0$.

Upon completion of this section we will be able to:

      A.   Use the square root property to solve equations of the type:

- Solve equations of the form $x^2 = k$, $k \geq 0$.
- Solve equations of the form $(ax + b)^2 = k$, $k \geq 0$.

A. Square Root Property

Recall that we studied the multiplication property of equality, which allowed us to multiply both sides of an equation by equal quantities. The **square root property** justifies taking the square roots of both sides of an equation.

Square Root Property of Equations:

If b is a *positive* number then $a^2 = b$ implies $a = \sqrt{b}$ or $a = -\sqrt{b}$.

Notes: **1.**   A positive number b has two square roots, $\sqrt{b}$ and $-\sqrt{b}$.

               2. $\sqrt{b}$ and $-\sqrt{b}$ are sometimes together written as $\pm \sqrt{b}$.

Warm Up

1. Use the square root property to solve the following equations.

a) $x^2 = 64$

b) $x^2 - 9 = 0$

c) $6x^2 = 54$

d) $x^2 = -6$

e) $4x^2 - 46 = 54$

2. Solve the following equations

a) $(x+2)^2 = 49$

b) $(2y+3)^2 = 1$

Example 1: Use the square root property to solve the following equations.

a) $x^2 = 9$ b) $x^2 - 27 = 0$
c) $4x^2 = 36$ d) $x^2 = -5$
e) $5x^2 - 34 = 26$

Solutions:

a) $x^2 = 9$ $x = \sqrt{9}$ or $-\sqrt{9}$ Square root property
$\longrightarrow x = 3$ or -3

Therefore, the solutions of the equation are ± 3.

b) $x^2 - 27 = 0 \longrightarrow x^2 = 27 \longrightarrow x = \sqrt{27}$ or $-\sqrt{27}$ Square root property
$\longrightarrow = 3\sqrt{3}$ or $-3\sqrt{3}$

Therefore, the solutions of the equation are $\pm 3\sqrt{3}$.

c) $9x^2 = 36 \longrightarrow x^2 = \dfrac{36}{9} \longrightarrow x^2 = 4$

Therefore by square root property $x = \sqrt{4}$ or $x = -\sqrt{4}$
Therefore, the solutions of the equation are ± 2.

d) $x^2 = -5$

Since -5 is a **negative number, the square root property cannot be applied.** In fact, we know that there is no real number whose square is negative. Therefore, $x^2 = -5$ has no real solution.

e) $5x^2 - 34 = 26 \longrightarrow 5x^2 = 26 + 34$

$5x^2 = 60 \longrightarrow x^2 = \dfrac{60}{5} = 12$

$x = \sqrt{12} = \mathbf{2\sqrt{3}}$ or $x = -\sqrt{12} = \mathbf{-2\sqrt{3}}$

$x = 2\sqrt{3}$ or $x = -2\sqrt{3}$

Therefore, the solutions of the equation are $\pm 2\sqrt{3}$.

Example 2: Solve the following equations.

a) $(x+1)^2 = 25$ b) $(2y-3)^2 = 45$
c) $(3x-1)^2 = -1$ d) $(3t-5)^2 + 6 = 8$

Solutions:

a) $(x+1)^2 = 25 \longrightarrow x+1 = 5$ or $x+1 = -5$ Square root property
$x = -1+5$ or $x = -1-5$
$x = 4$ or -6

Therefore the solutions are 4 and -6.

Check:

$$x = 4 \qquad\qquad x = -6$$
$$(4+1)^2 = 25 \qquad (-6+1)^2 = 25$$
$$5^2 = 25 \qquad\qquad (-5)^2 = 25$$
$$25 = 25 \qquad\qquad 25 = 25$$

TRUE   TRUE

Warm Up

c) $(3x+2)^2 = -9$

b) $(2y-3)^2 = 45$

$2y - 3 = +\sqrt{45}$ or $2y - 3 = -\sqrt{45}$ $(45 = 3\sqrt{5})$

$2y = 3 + 3\sqrt{5}$ or $2y = 3 - 3\sqrt{5}$

$y = \dfrac{3+3\sqrt{5}}{2}$ or $y = \dfrac{3-3\sqrt{5}}{2}$

Therefore, the solutions of the equation are $\dfrac{3 \pm 3\sqrt{5}}{2}$.

d) $(4t-7)^2 - 6 = 4$

c) $(3x-1)^2 = -1$

Since -1 is a negative number, the square root property cannot be applied. $(3x-1)^2 = -1$ has no real solution.

d) $(3t-5)^2 + 6 = 8 \longrightarrow (3t-5)^2 = 8 - 6 = 2$

$3t - 5 = \sqrt{2}$ or $3t - 5 = -\sqrt{2}$

$3t = 5 + \sqrt{2}$ or $3t = 5 - \sqrt{2}$

$t = \dfrac{5+\sqrt{2}}{3}$ or $\dfrac{5-\sqrt{2}}{3}$

Therefore, the solutions of the equation are $\dfrac{5 \pm \sqrt{2}}{3}$.

Answers:

1. a) 8 or ⁻8   b) 3 or ⁻3
   c) 3 or ⁻3   d) no solution
   e) ⁻5 or 5
2. a) ⁻9 or 5   b) ⁻1 or ⁻2
   c) no solution   d) $\dfrac{7+\sqrt{10}}{4}, \dfrac{7-\sqrt{10}}{4}$

EXERCISE   9.1

Solve the following equations.

1. $x^2 = 25$ 2. $x^2 = 81$ 3. $x^2 = 98$ 4. $y^2 = 44$

5. $3a^2 = 27$ 6. $-5x^2 = -25$ 7. $x^2 + 2 = 6$ 8. $p^2 - 10 = 17$

Answers:

1. _____
2. _____
3. _____
4. _____
5. _____
6. _____
7. _____
8. _____

9. _____

10. _____

11. _____

12. _____

13. _____

14. _____

15. _____

16. _____

17. _____

18. _____

19. _____

20. _____

9. $3t^2 - 5 = 10$ **10.** $4x^2 + 3 = 15$ **11.** $(3y-1)^2 = 4$

12. $(2m+5)^2 = 8$ **13.** $(3-5z)^2 = 18$ **14.** $(2x+1)^2 = -4$

15. $(3x+1)^2 = 0$ **16.** $3(2x-1)^2 = 24$ **17.** $(4p-1)^2 + 6 = 10$

18. $(2t+7)^2 - 6 = 6$ **19.** $(7-2x)^2 + 1 = 13$ **20.** $(4-2x)^2 + 6 = 4$

9.2   COMPLETING THE SQUARES

Recall that $(a+b)^2 = a^2 + 2ab + b^2$.   By using this formula we can change any second degree polynomial of the type $ax^2 + bx + c$ to a form that can help us solve quadratic equations using the square root property. Consider the following example.

To solve: $x^2 + 6x + 7 = 0$, we will first change the form of $x^2 + 6x + 7$ that can help us use square root property.

$$x^2 + 6x + 7 = \left(x^2 + 6x\right) + 7 \qquad \text{Group } x\text{-terms}$$
$$= \left(x^2 + 2\cdot 3x\right) + 7 \qquad \text{Rewrite coefficient of } x$$
$$= \left(x^2 + 2\cdot 3x + 3^2\right) + \underbrace{7 - 3^2}_{} = (x+3)^2 - 2 \qquad \text{Add and subtract } 3^2$$

$$\downarrow$$

[This is a perfect square: $(x+3)^2$]

Therefore, $x^2 + 6x + 7 = 0 \longrightarrow (x+3)^2 - 2 = 0 \longrightarrow (x+3)^2 = 2$

This equation is now similar to the equations discussed in the last section and can be solved by using square root property.   This is an example of completing the square.

Upon completion of this section we will be able to:

A.   Write a quadratic expression as a sum or difference of two squares.

B.   Solve equations of the $x^2 + bx + c = 0$ using the method of completing squares.

C.   Solve equations of the $ax^2 + bx + c = 0$ using the method of completing squares.

438

Completing the Square

First we shall explain how to complete the square of a quadratic **when the coefficient of the second degree term is 1**. Recall that a quadratic has three terms: a second degree term, a first degree term, and a constant term. Suppose the quadratic is $x^2 + bx + c$.

Step 1 $\qquad x^2 + bx + c = x^2 + 2 \cdot \dfrac{b}{2} \cdot x + c \qquad$ Notice $\dfrac{b}{2}$ is half the coefficient of x

Step 2 $\qquad x^2 + 2 \cdot \dfrac{b}{2} \cdot x + \left(\dfrac{b}{2}\right)^2 + c - \left(\dfrac{b}{2}\right)^2 \qquad$ Add and subtract $\left(\dfrac{b}{2}\right)^2$

Step 3 $\qquad$ The first three terms form a perfect square.

$$\left(x + \dfrac{b}{2}\right)^2 + c - \left(\dfrac{b}{2}\right)^2 \qquad \text{Complete the square}$$

Example 1: $\qquad$ Complete the square for the following.

$\qquad$ **a)** $\quad x^2 + 3x - 5 \qquad$ **b)** $\quad x^2 - 6x + 2$

Solutions:

a) $\quad x^2 + 3x - 5$

Step 1 $\quad x^2 + 3x - 5 = x^2 + 2 \cdot \dfrac{3}{2} \cdot x - 5$

Step 2 $\quad = x^2 + 2 \cdot \dfrac{3}{2} x + \left(\dfrac{3}{2}\right)^2 - 5 - \left(\dfrac{3}{2}\right)^2 \qquad$ Add and subtract $\left(\dfrac{3}{2}\right)^2$

Step 3 $\quad = \left(x + \dfrac{3}{2}\right)^2 - 5 - \left(\dfrac{3}{2}\right)^2 \qquad$ Complete the square

$\qquad\quad = \left(x + \dfrac{3}{2}\right)^2 - \dfrac{29}{4}$

b) $\quad x^2 - 6x + 2$

Step 1 $\quad x^2 - 6x + 2 = x^2 - 2 \cdot 3 \cdot x + 2$

Step 2 $\quad = x^2 - 2 \cdot 3 \cdot x + 3^2 + 2 - 3^2 \qquad$ Add and subtract 3^2

Step 3 $\quad = (x - 3)^2 - 7 \qquad$ Complete the square

Warm Up

1. Complete the square

$\qquad$ **a)** $x^2 + 5x + 3$

$\qquad$ **b)** $x^2 - 4x + 7$

Answers:

1. a) $\left(x + \dfrac{5}{2}\right)^2 - \dfrac{13}{4}$ **b)** $(x - 2)^2 + 3$

We will discuss the solution by completing squares in two parts.

$\qquad$ **Part A:** $\qquad$ When the equation is of the form $x^2 + bx + c = 0$ $\;(a = 1)$, and

$\qquad$ **Part B:** $\qquad$ When the equation is of the form $ax^2 + bx + c = 0$ $\;(a \neq 1)$.

B. Solving Quadratic Equations of the Form $x^2 + bx + c = 0$

The steps to solve a quadratic equation of the form $x^2 + bx + c = 0$ by **completing the square** are:

Step 1	Rewrite $x^2 + bx + c$ by completing the square.
Step 2	Write the equation in the form $(x + p)^2 = q$.
Step 3	If $q < 0$ then no real number can be a solution of the equation. If $q \geq 0$ then use square root property to solve $(x + p)^2 = q$.
Step 4	Check your solutions by substituting in the original equation or by using calculator.

Warm Up

2. Solve the following equations.

a) $x^2 - 4x + 3 = 0$

Example 2:   Solve the following equations.

    a) $x^2 - 6x + 7 = 0$ **b)** $x^2 + 7x = 4$

Solutions:

a) $x^2 - 6x + 7 = 0$

Step 1 $x^2 - 6x + 7 = \underbrace{x^2 - 2 \cdot 3 \cdot x + 3^2} + \underbrace{7 - 3^2}$

         $= (x - 3)^2 - 2 = 0$ Complete the square

Step 2 $x^2 - 6x + 7 = 0 \longrightarrow (x - 3)^2 - 2 = 0$

                 $\longrightarrow (x - 3)^2 = 2$

Step 3 $x - 3 = \pm\sqrt{2} \longrightarrow x = 3 \pm \sqrt{2}$

Therefore, the solutions are $3 \pm \sqrt{2}$.

Step 4   Check the solutions with a calculator.

b) $x^2 + 5x = 6$

b) $x^2 + 7x = 4 \longrightarrow x^2 + 7x - 4 = 0$

Step 1 $x^2 + 7x - 4 = 0$

        $= \underbrace{x^2 + 2 \cdot \frac{7}{2}x + \left(\frac{7}{2}\right)^2} \underbrace{- 4 - \left(\frac{7}{2}\right)^2}$ Complete the square

        $= \left(x + \frac{7}{2}\right)^2 - \frac{65}{4} = 0$ $-4 - \frac{49}{4} = -\frac{65}{4}$

Step 2 $x^2 + 7x - 4 = 0 \longrightarrow \left(x + \frac{7}{2}\right)^2 - \frac{65}{4} = 0$

                      $\longrightarrow \left(x + \frac{7}{2}\right)^2 = \frac{65}{4}$

440

Step 3 $\left(x+\dfrac{7}{2}\right)^2-\dfrac{65}{4} \longrightarrow x+\dfrac{7}{2}=\pm\sqrt{\dfrac{65}{4}}=\dfrac{\sqrt{65}}{2}=\pm\dfrac{\sqrt{65}}{2}$

$$x = -\dfrac{7}{2}\pm\dfrac{\sqrt{65}}{2}$$

Therefore, the solutions are $-\dfrac{7}{2}\pm\dfrac{\sqrt{65}}{2}$.

Step 4 Check the solutions with a calculator.

Example 3: Solve the equation $x^2+4x+4=0$

Solution:

Step 1 $x^2+2\cdot 2x+2^2=0$

$(x+2)^2=0 \longrightarrow (x+2)^2=0$

$x+2=0$ or $x=-2$

The solution is $x=-2$. Check the solution.

Answers:

2. a) 3 , 1 b) –6, 1 3. $x=-3$

Note: In cases where a quadratic equation has just one solution, as in Example 3, the equation is said to have repeated solutions.

C. Solving Quadratic Equation of the Form $ax^2+bx+c=0$

If the coefficient of the second degree term of an equation is different from 1, then we divide both sides of the equation by *this coefficient* to reduce the equation to the form $x^2+bx+c=0$ and the follow the same procedure as in part A.

For example:

(i) $3x^2+5x+9=0 \longrightarrow \dfrac{1}{3}\left(3x^2+5x+9\right)=\dfrac{1}{3}\cdot 0 \longrightarrow x^2+\dfrac{5}{3}x+3=0$

(ii) $-2x^2+7x=8 \longrightarrow \dfrac{1}{-2}\left(-2x^2+7x\right)=\dfrac{1}{-2}\cdot 8 \longrightarrow x^2-\dfrac{7}{2}x=-4$

$\longrightarrow x^2-\dfrac{7}{2}x+4=0$

Example 4: Solve the equations.
 a) $4p^2+8p=15$ b) $-3z^2-8z+1=0$

Solutions:

a) $4p^2+8p=15$

$\dfrac{1}{4}\left(4p^2+8p\right)=\dfrac{1}{4}\cdot 15$ — Divide by 4

$p^2+2p=\dfrac{15}{4} \longrightarrow p^2+2p-\dfrac{15}{4}=0$ — Simplify

441

Warm Up

$$\rightarrow \quad \underbrace{p^2 + 2\cdot 1 \cdot p + \mathbf{1}^2}_{} - \underbrace{\frac{15}{4} - \mathbf{1}^2}_{} = 0$$

$$\rightarrow \quad (p+1)^2 - \frac{19}{4} = 0$$

$$\rightarrow \quad (p+1)^2 = \frac{19}{4}$$

$$\rightarrow \quad p+1 = \pm \sqrt{\frac{19}{4}}$$

$$\rightarrow \quad p+1 = \pm \frac{\sqrt{19}}{2}$$

$$\rightarrow \quad p+1 = \pm \frac{\sqrt{19}}{2} \qquad p = -1 \pm \frac{\sqrt{19}}{2}$$

The solutions are $-1 \pm \dfrac{\sqrt{19}}{2}$.

b) $-4z^2 + 8z - 3 = 0$

b)

$$-3z^2 - 8z + 1 = 0$$

$$\rightarrow \quad \frac{1}{-3}\left(-3z^2 - 8z + 1\right) = \frac{1}{3}\cdot 0$$

$$\rightarrow \quad z^2 + \frac{8z}{3} - \frac{1}{3} = 0$$

$$\rightarrow \quad z^2 + 2\cdot\frac{4}{3}z + \left(\frac{4}{3}\right)^2 - \frac{1}{3} - \left(\frac{4}{3}\right)^2 = 0$$

$$\rightarrow \quad \left(z + \frac{4}{3}\right)^2 - \frac{19}{9} = 0$$

$$\rightarrow \quad \left(z + \frac{4}{3}\right)^2 = \frac{19}{9}$$

$$\rightarrow \quad z + \frac{4}{3} = \pm \sqrt{\frac{19}{9}}$$

$$\rightarrow \quad z = -\frac{4}{3} \pm \frac{\sqrt{19}}{3}$$

The solutions are $-\dfrac{4}{3} \pm \dfrac{\sqrt{19}}{3}$.

5. Solve $(3x+2)(x+5) = 16$

Example 5: Solve $(2x+1)(x-5) = 3$

Solution:

$$(2x+1)(x-5) = 3 \quad \rightarrow \quad 2x^2 - 9x - 5 = 3$$

$$\rightarrow \quad 2x^2 - 9x - 8 = 0$$

$$\rightarrow \quad \frac{1}{2}\left(2x^2 - 9x - 8\right) = \frac{1}{2}\cdot 0$$

$\longrightarrow \quad x^2 - \dfrac{9}{2}x - 4 = 0$

$\longrightarrow \quad x^2 - 2 \cdot \dfrac{9}{4}x + \left(\dfrac{9}{4}\right)^2 - 4 - \left(\dfrac{9}{4}\right)^2 = 0$

$\longrightarrow \quad \left(x - \dfrac{9}{4}\right)^2 - \dfrac{145}{16} = 0$

$\qquad\qquad\qquad\qquad\qquad -4 - \left(\dfrac{9}{4}\right)^2 = \dfrac{145}{16}$

$\longrightarrow \quad \left(x - \dfrac{9}{4}\right)^2 = \dfrac{145}{16}$

$\longrightarrow \quad x - \dfrac{9}{4} = \pm \dfrac{\sqrt{145}}{4}$

$\longrightarrow \quad x = \dfrac{9}{4} \pm \dfrac{\sqrt{145}}{4}$

The solutions are $\dfrac{9}{4} \pm \dfrac{\sqrt{145}}{4}$.

EXERCISE 9.2

Answers:

Find the number that should be added to each expression to make it a perfect square.

1. $x^2 + 4x$ **2.** $y^2 + 7y$ **3.** $p^2 - 6p$ **4.** $t^2 - t$

Complete the square.

5. $x^2 + 8x + 9$ **6.** $x^2 - 7x + 5$ **7.** $y^2 + y - 10$ **8.** $z^2 - 3z + 7$

Solve the following equations using the method of completing the square.

9. $x^2 + 4x + 2 = 0$ **10.** $z^2 + z - 10 = 0$ **11.** $y^2 - 3y - 9 = 0$

12. $x^2 + 7x = 7$ **13.** $t^2 + 6t = -8$ **14.** $a^2 - 5a = 3$

1. _____
2. _____
3. _____
4. _____
5. _____
6. _____
7. _____
8. _____
9. _____
10. _____
11. _____
12. _____
13. _____
14. _____ .

15. _____

16. _____

17. _____

18. _____

19. _____

20. _____

15. $2r^2 - 7r = 1$ **16.** $3x^2 = 2x + 1$

17. $-5y^2 + 4y + 3 = 0$ **18.** $4k^2 - 3k - 2 = 0$

19. $(x-2)(x+5) = 4$ **20.** $(3p+7)(p+4) = 5$

9.3   COMPLEX NUMBERS

We have seen that there are equations which do not have any real number for their solutions. For example, $x^2 = -2$ has no real number for its solution since square of no real number can be negative. Complex numbers were introduced essentially to be able to solve such equations. However, as it turned out later, complex numbers have found many more applications. In this section we shall define and study complex numbers.

Upon completion of this section we will be able to:

     A.   Write Square Roots of Negative Numbers as Multiples of i.
     B.   Add and Subtract Complex Numbers.
     C.   Multiply Complex Numbers.
     D.   Write Quotients of Complex Numbers in Standard Form.

A.   Write Square Roots of Negative Numbers as Multiplies of i

To be able to find the square root of any negative number we introduce a new symbol i for $\sqrt{-1}$ called imaginary unit.

> $\sqrt{-1}$ is called **imaginary unit** and is denoted by i.

Notice that squaring both sides of $i = \sqrt{-1}$ gives $i^2 = -1$.

The powers of the imaginary unit follow an interesting pattern:

$$i = \sqrt{-1} = i \qquad\qquad i^5 = i^4 \cdot i = 1 \cdot i = i$$

$$i^2 = \left(\sqrt{-1}\right)^2 = -1 \qquad\qquad i^6 = i^4 \cdot i^2 = 1(-1) = -1$$

$$i^3 = i^2 \cdot i = -1 \cdot i = -i \qquad\qquad i^7 = i^4 \cdot i^3 = 1(-i) = -i$$

$$i^4 = i^2 \cdot i^2 = (-1)(-1) = 1 \qquad i^8 = i^4 \cdot i^4 = 1 \cdot 1 = 1$$

It follows that: $i^n = +1$ if n is multiple of 4 ($n = 4, 8...etc.$)

$i^n = -1$ if n is a multiple of 2 and not 4 ($n = 2, 6, 10...etc.$).

and $i^n = i$ or $i^n = -i$ if n is odd.

Warm Up

Example 1: Simplify the following.

a) i^{12} b) i^{27} c) i^{-18} d) i^0

Solutions:

a) $i^{12} = \left(i^4\right)^3 = 1^3 = 1$

b) $i^{27} = i^{4 \cdot 6 + 3} = i^{4 \cdot 6} \cdot i^3 = (i^4)^6 \cdot i^3 = 1^6 \cdot i^3 = i^3 = -i$

c) $i^{-18} = i^{4(-5)+2} = \left(i^4\right)^{-5} \cdot i^2 = 1^{-5} \cdot i^2 = i^2 = -1$

d) $i^0 = 1$ $x^0 = 1$

1. Simplify

a) i^{14}

b) i^{31}

c) i^{-8}

d) i^{-0}

Example 2: Write the following as a multiple of i.

a) $\sqrt{-9}$ b) $\sqrt{-2}$ c) $\sqrt{-8}$

Solutions:

a) $\sqrt{-9} = \sqrt{-1}\sqrt{9} = i \cdot 3 = 3i$

b) $\sqrt{-2} = \sqrt{-1}\sqrt{2} = i\sqrt{2}$

c) $\sqrt{-8} = \sqrt{-1}\sqrt{8} = i2\sqrt{2} = 2\sqrt{2}\,i$

2. Write the following as a multiple of i.

a) $\sqrt{-4}$

b) $\sqrt{-81}$

c) $\sqrt{-18}$

Note: Multiplication by i is assumed to be commutative. One should be careful when writing a number like $\sqrt{2}\,i$ which is $\sqrt{2} \cdot i$ and not $\sqrt{2i}$. The radical bar must not be extended over i.

A number of the form ai is called an **imaginary number.**

Suppose we wish to solve the equation $(x + 2)^2 = -5$. Recall this equation has no solution in real numbers. However, with the introduction of the square root of a negative number as an imaginary number, we can find solutions to such equations.

$$(x + 2)^2 = -5$$
$$x + 2 = \pm\sqrt{-5}$$
$$x + 2 = \pm\sqrt{5}\,i$$
$$x = -2 \pm \sqrt{5}\,i$$

Real Number   Imaginary Number

If a and bi are real and imaginary numbers then $a + bi$ is the standard form of a **complex number.** Here a is called the **real part** and b is called the **imaginary part** of the **complex number.**

Complex Number = (Real Part) + (Imaginary Part) i

$(a + bi)$ a + bi

Warm Up

3. Write $\sqrt{-7} + 3$ in the standard form. Identify its real and imaginary parts.

Example 3: Write $\sqrt{-5} - 3$ in the standard form. Identify its real and imaginary parts.

Solution:

$$\sqrt{-5} - 3 = \sqrt{5}\sqrt{-1} - 3 = \sqrt{5}\ i - 3 = -3 + \sqrt{5}\ i$$

Real part $= -3$, and Imaginary part $= \sqrt{5}$

Observation:

(i) Every real number can be regarded as a complex number whose imaginary part is zero.

(ii) $a + bi$ is the same as $a + ib$

(iii) If $a + ib = 0$ then $a = 0$ and $b = 0$

Proof:

$$a + ib = 0 \implies a = -ib$$
$$\implies a^2 = i^2 b^2$$
$$\implies a^2 = -b^2$$
$$\implies a^2 + b^2 = 0$$
$$\implies a = 0 \text{ and } a = 0 \quad \text{Because the sum of squares of two real numbers is zero only if both the numbers are zero separately}$$

Thus, if a complex number is zero then its real part and imaginary part are zero separately.

(iv) If $a + ib = c + id \longrightarrow a = c$ and $b = d$

Proof:

$$a + ib = c + id$$
$$\implies (a - c) + i(b - d) = 0$$
$$\implies a - c = 0 \text{ and } b - d = 0 \quad \text{(Observation \#iii)}$$
$$\implies a = c \text{ and } b = d$$

If two complex numbers are equal then their real parts and imaginary parts are equal separately.

Warm Up

4. Decide which of the following are true.

a) $4 + 5i = \sqrt{16} + \dfrac{5}{3}i$

b) $4 + 5i = 5 + 4i$

Answers:

1. a) -1 b) $-i$ c) 1 d) 1
2. a) $2i$ b) $9i$ c) $3\sqrt{2}\ i$
3. $3 + \sqrt{7}\ i$, Real part $= 3$,
   Imaginary part $= \sqrt{7}$
4. a) false b) false

Example 4: Decide which of the following are true:

a) $3 + 5i = \sqrt{9} + \dfrac{10}{2}i$ b) $3 + 5i = 5 + 3i$

Solutions:

a) The real parts of the two complex numbers are equal, since $3 = \sqrt{9}$.
The imaginary parts of the two complex numbers are equal, since $5 = \dfrac{10}{2}$.

Hence, $3 + 5i = \sqrt{9} + \dfrac{10}{2}i$ is a true statement.

b) The real part of $3 + 5i = 3$.
The real part of $5 + 3i = 5$.
Therefore, the real part of $3 + 5i \neq$ the real part of $5 + 3i$.
Hence, $3 + 5i = 5 + 3i$ is false.

B. Addition and Subtraction of Complex Numbers

Complex numbers are **added and subtracted** as if they were binomials, where real parts can be considered as like terms and imaginary parts can be considered as like terms.

For example:

$$(a + bi) + (c + di) = (a + c) + (b + d)i$$

$$(a + bi) - (c + di) = (a - c) + (b - d)i$$

Example 5: Perform the indicated operations.

a) $(3 + 5i) + (-4 + 7i)$ b) $(4 - 9i) + (2 + 9i)$

c) $(-6 + 7i) - (-6 + 4i)$ d) $(5 + i) - (4 + 3i)$

Solutions:

a) $(3 + 5i) + (-4 + 7i) = (3 - 4) + (5 + 7)i$ Combine real and imaginery parts

$= -1 + 12i$

b) $(4 - 9i) + (2 + 9i) = (4 + 2) + (-9 + 9)i$ Combine real and imaginery parts

$= 6 + 0 \cdot i$

$= 6$

c) $(-6 + 7i) - (-6 + 4i) = [-6 - (-6)] + (7 - 4)i$

$= 0 + 3i = 3i$ Combine real and imaginery parts

d) $(5 + i) - (4 + 3i) = (5 - 4) + (1 - 3)i = 1 - 2i$

Warm Up

5. Perform the indicated operations.

a) $(4 + 6i) + (3 + 3i)$

b) $(14 - 6i) + (3 + 6i)$

c) $(8 + 3i) - (5i - 6)$

d) $(7 + 2i) - (3 + 4i)$

Answers:

5. a) $7 + 9i$ b) 17 c) $14 - 2i$
   d) $4 - 2i$

Notes: 1. To add two complex numbers, we add their real parts and add their imaginary parts.

2. To subtract two complex numbers, we subtract their real parts and subtract their imaginary parts.

C. Multiplication of Complex Numbers

Complex numbers are multiplied like binomials, where $i^2 = -1$. Thus,

$$(a + bi)(c + di) = ac + adi + bci + bdi^2$$
$$= ac + adi + bci - bd$$
$$= (ac - bd) + (ad + bc)i.$$

Foil Method

$i^2 = -1$

Combine like terms

Example 6: Multiply.

a) $(3 + 5i)(3 + 4i)$ b) $(2 - 3i)(-7 + 2i)$

c) $(-4 - 5i)(7 + i)$ d) $(3 + 4i)(3 - 4i)$

e) $4(3 + 5i)$ f) $(3i)(-5i)$

Warm Up

6. Multiply

a) $(3 + 6i)(2 + i)$

Warm Up	Solutions:

b) $(3-4i)(-2+3i)$

a) $(3+5i)(3+4i) = 9+12i+15i+20i^2$ Foil

$= 9+27i-20$ $i^2=-1$

$= -11+27i$

c) $(-6-3i)(7+2i)$

b) $(2-3i)(-7+2i) = -14+4i+21i-6i^2$ Foil

$= -14+25i+6$ $i^2=-1$

$= -8+25i$

d) $(4-5i)(4+5i)$

c) $(-4-5i)(7+i) = -28-4i-35i-5i^2$ Foil

$= -28-39i+5$ $i^2=-1$

$= -23-39i$

e) $3(8+5i)$

d) $(3+4i)(3-4i) = 9-12i+12i-16i^2$ Foil

$= 9+16 = 25$ $i^2=-1$

e) $4(3+5i) = (4+0\cdot i)(3+5i)$

$= 12+20i+0\cdot i+0\cdot i^2$ Foil

$= 12+20i$ $i^2=-1$

Note: $4(3+5i)=12+20i$ can also be obtained by applying distributive property. $4(3+5i)=12+20i = \mathbf{12+20i}$

f) $(6i)(-5i)$

f) $(3i)(-5i) = (0+3i)(0-5i)$

$= 0-0\cdot-5i+0\cdot 3i-15i^2$

$= -15i^2$ $i^2=-1$

Answers:

6. a) $15i$ **b)** $6+17i$

$= -15(-1)=15$

c) $-3(12+11i)$ **d)** 41

e) $24+15i$ **f)** 30

Note: $(3i)(-5i)=15$ is also obtained by applying associative and commutative properties of multiplication.
$(3i)(-5i) = (3(-5))(i\cdot i) = -15\cdot i^2 = -15(-1)=15$

D. Quotients of Complex Numbers

Next, we develop a procedure to simplify expressions of the type $\dfrac{a+bi}{c+di}$, i.e. rewrite this expression as follows.

$$\dfrac{a+bi}{c+di} = A + Bi$$

Real Part   Imaginary Part

This simplification will involve the use of the **conjugate** of a complex number.

The conjugate of a complex number is obtained by changing the sign of its imaginary part.

The conjugate of $a + bi = a - bi$

The conjugate of $a - bi = a + bi$

Notation: Conjugate of a complex number z is denoted by $\bar{z}$. Thus $\overline{a + bi} = a - bi$

Example 7:   Find the conjugate of

a) $3 + 4i$ b) $4 - 3i$ c) $-5 + 7i$
d) 4 e) $-5i$

Solutions:

Complex Number	Conjugate
a) $3 + 4i$	$3 - 4i$
b) $4 - 3i$	$4 + 3i$
c) $-5 + 7i$	$-5 - 7i$
d) 4	4
e) $-5i$	$5i$

Warm Up

7.   Find the conjugates of

a) $4 + 3i$

b) $3 - 4i$

c) $-5 + 9i$

d) 5

e) $-15i$

Notice that two complex numbers are conjugates of each other if they differ only in the sign of imaginary parts. Pairs of conjugate complex numbers have a very interesting property:

$$(a + ib)(a - ib) = a^2 - (ib)^2$$
$$= a^2 - i^2 b^2$$
$$= a^2 + b^2$$

Complex Conjugate   Real Numbers

$$(a + bi)(a - bi) = a^2 + b^2 = (\text{Real part})^2 + (\text{Imaginary part})^2$$

Example 8:   Determine $z\bar{z}$ where $\bar{z}$ denotes conjugate of the complex number z.

a) $z = 3 + 2i$ b) $z = -3 - 5i$

c) $z = 7i$ d) $z = 8$

Solutions:

a) $z = 3 + 2i, \quad \bar{z} = 3 - 2i$

$z\bar{z} = (3 + 2i)(3 - 2i) = (\text{real part})^2 + (\text{imaginary part})^2$

$= 3^2 + 2^2 = 13$

Warm Up

8.   Determine $z\bar{z}$ where $\bar{z}$ denotes conjugate of the complex number z.

a) $z = 2i + 3$

b) $z = -5 - 3i$

Warm Up

c) $z = -8i$

b) $z = -3 - 5i$, $\bar{z} = -3 + 5i$ $z\bar{z} = (-3)^2 + (-5)^2$
$= 9 + 25 = 34$

c) $z = 7i = 0 + 7i$, $\bar{z} = 0 - 7i$ $z\bar{z} = 0^2 + 7^2 = 49$

Alternatively, $z\bar{z} = (7i)(-7i) = -49i^2 = -49(-1) = 49$

d) $z = 14$

d) $z = 8 = 8 + 0i$, $\bar{z} = 8 = 8 - 0i$ $z\bar{z} = 8^2 + 0^2 = 64$

In Example 9 below, we list the steps for simplifying the quotient of two complex numbers.

Example 9: Simplify $\dfrac{3 + 4i}{-2 + 3i}$.

9. Simplify: $\dfrac{4i - 3}{-3 + 2i}$

Solution:

Step 1 Multiply the numerator and denominator by the conjugate of the denominator.

The conjugate of the denominator $(-2 + 3i)$ is $-2 - 3i$.

$$\frac{3 + 4i}{-2 + 3i} = \frac{(3 + 4i)(-2 - 3i)}{(-2 + 3i)(-2 - 3i)}$$

Step 2 Simplify the numerator and denominator.

$$= \frac{-6 - 9i - 8i - 12i^2}{(-2)^2 + (-3)^2} = \frac{-6 - 17i + 12}{13} \quad i^2 = -1$$

$$= \frac{6 - 17i}{13}$$

Step 3 Write the resulting complex number in standard form $= \dfrac{6}{13} - \dfrac{17}{13}i$

The real part $= \dfrac{6}{13}$ The imaginary part $= -\dfrac{17}{13}$

10. Rewrite the following quotients in the standard form

a) $\dfrac{2 + i}{-5i}$

Example 10: Re-write the following quotients in the standard form

a) $\dfrac{5 + i}{-2i}$ b) $\dfrac{i}{1 + 3i}$

Solutions:

a) $\dfrac{5 + i}{-2i} = \dfrac{(5 + i)(2i)}{(-2i)(2i)}$ Step 1; – conjugate of $-2i$ is $2i$

$$= \frac{10i + 2i^2}{-4i^2}$$ Step 2

$$= \frac{-2 + 10i}{4}$$

$$= \frac{-2}{4} + \frac{10}{4}i = -\frac{1}{2} + \frac{5}{2}i \qquad \text{Step 3}$$

b) $\quad \dfrac{i}{1+3i} = \dfrac{i(1-3i)}{(1+3i)(1-3i)} \qquad$ Step 1; Conjugate of 1+3i is 1–3i

$$= \frac{i - 3i^2}{1^2 + 3^2} = \frac{3 + i}{10} \qquad \text{Step 2}$$

$$= \frac{3}{10} + \frac{1}{10}i \qquad \text{Step 3}$$

Note: Addition and multiplication of complex numbers satisfy various properties of the system of real numbers. However, order is not defined for complex numbers. In other words, given two complex numbers, it cannot be said which one is greater or which one is smaller.

EXERCISE 9.3

Answers:

In exercises 1–5, simplify the imaginary number.

1. i^{13} **2.** i^{27} **3.** i^{-15} **4.** i^{-68} **5.** i^{82}

In exercises 6–8, write as multiplies of i .

6. $\sqrt{-4}$ **7.** $\sqrt{-15}$ **8.** $\sqrt{-45}$

Write the complex numbers in exercises 9–11, in standard form. Identify their real and imaginary parts.

9. $\sqrt{4} + \sqrt{-4}$ **10.** $\dfrac{6}{3} + \dfrac{\sqrt{-4}}{4}$ **11.** $5^2 + 4\sqrt{-3}$

Perform the indicated operations in exercises 12–25.

12. $(3 + 7i) + (4 - 3i)$ **13.** $(2 - 5i) + (-4 + 2i)$

14. $(8 + 5i) - (6 + 2i)$ **15.** $\left(4 + \sqrt{3}\,i\right) - (6 + i)$

16. $(3 + 5i) + (7 - 2i) - (-9 + 2i)$

17. $(4 - 7i) + [(3 + 5i) - (2 + 9i)]$

1. _____
2. _____
3. _____
4. _____
5. _____
6. _____
7. _____
8. _____
9. _____
10. _____
11. _____
12. _____
13. _____
14. _____
15. _____
16. _____
17. _____

18. _____

19. _____

20. _____

21. _____

22. _____

23. _____

24. _____

25. _____

26. _____

27. _____

28. _____

29. _____

30. _____

31. _____

32. _____

18. $(2-i)-[(1+7i)-(-3+i)]$ **19.** $(3+5i)(4-11i)$

20. $(-2+7i)(2+5i)$ **21.** $(9+4i)(9-4i)$

22. $(3+5i)(4-7i)(2+i)$ **23.** $(2+4i)(-3+8i)+(6-5i)$

24. $(2+4i)[(-3+8i)+(6-5i)]$ **25.** $(7i)[(2+3i)-(-4+5i)]$

In exercises 26–28, write down the conjugates, and verify that $(\text{complex numbers})(\text{conjugate})=(\text{real part})^2+(\text{imaginary part})^2$.

26. $2-5i$ **27.** $-2+9i$ **28.** $\sqrt{2}i$

Find the quotients in exercises 29-32. Write your answers in standard form.

29. $\dfrac{1}{2-5i}$ **30.** $\dfrac{-3}{3+4i}$ **31.** $\dfrac{7+2i}{1+i}$ **32.** $\dfrac{-4i}{-2+3i}$

9.4   QUADRATIC FORMULA

The method of solving quadratic equations by completing the square involved several steps. In this section we shall use this method to develop a formula that can be applied directly to solve any type of quadratic equations. This formula is called the **quadratic formula.**

Upon completion of this section you will be able to:

    A.   Develop the Quadratic Formula.

    B.   Use the Quadratic Formula for Solving Quadratic Equations.

    C.   Use the Quadratic Formula for Solving Applied Problems.

A. Quadratic Formula

We have seen that a quadratic equation can always be rewritten in the form $ax^2+bx+c=0$, with $a\neq0$. We shall apply the method of completing the square to $ax^2+bx+c=0$ to develop *quadratic formula.*

452

$$ax^2 + bx + c = 0 \qquad\qquad \text{Coefficient of } x^2 \text{ is } a$$

$$\frac{1}{a}\left(ax^2 + bx + c\right) = \frac{1}{a}\cdot 0 \qquad\qquad \text{Divide by } \frac{1}{a}$$

$$x^2 + \frac{b}{a}x + \frac{c}{a} = 0 \qquad\qquad \text{Simplify}$$

$$x^2 + 2\cdot\frac{b}{2a}\cdot x + \left(\frac{b}{2a}\right)^2 + \frac{c}{a} - \left(\frac{b}{2a}\right)^2 = 0 \qquad\qquad \text{Completing the Square}$$

$$\left(x + \frac{b}{2a}\right)^2 + \frac{c}{a} - \frac{b^2}{4a^2} = 0$$

$$\left(x + \frac{b}{2a}\right)^2 = \frac{b^2}{4a^2} - \frac{c}{a} = \frac{b^2}{4a^2} - \frac{4ac}{4a^2} = \frac{b^2 - 4ac}{4a^2}$$

$$x + \frac{b}{2a} = \pm\sqrt{\frac{b^2 - 4ac}{4a^2}} = \pm\frac{\sqrt{b^2 - 4ac}}{2a} \qquad\qquad \text{Square Root Property; } \sqrt{(2a)^2} = 2a$$

$$x = -\frac{b}{2a} \pm \frac{\sqrt{b^2 - 4ac}}{2a} = \frac{-b \pm \sqrt{b^2 - 4ac}}{2a}$$

The solutions of $ax^2 + bx + c = 0$, $a \neq 0$ are: $\quad x = \dfrac{-b \pm \sqrt{b^2 - 4ac}}{2a}$

This is generally referred to as the quadratic formula. The expression under the radical sign $b^2 - 4ac$ is called the **Discriminant.**

B. Using the Quadratic Formula for Solving Quadratic Equations

We use the following steps to apply the quadratic formula for solving quadratic equations.

Step 1   Write the quadratic equation in the form $ax^2 + bx + c = 0$.

Step 2   Identify the coefficient of x^2, the coefficient of x, and the constant.

$$ax^2 + bx + c$$

Coeff. of $x^2 = a$ Coeff. of $x = b$ Constant Term $= c$

Step 3   Compute the value of the discriminant $b^2 - 4ac$.

Step 4   Substitute the value of the discriminant in $x = \dfrac{-b \pm \sqrt{b^2 - 4ac}}{2a}$ and simplify.

Step 5   Check the solutions.

453

Warm Up

1. Use the quadratic formula to solve the following quadratic equations.

   a) $x^2 - 3x - 4 = 0$

Use the quadratic formula to solve the following quadratic equations.

a) $x^2 - 4x - 5 = 0$ b) $5x - 2x^2 = 2$

c) $3x^2 - 5 = 0$ d) $4x^2 + 4x + 1 = 0$

Solutions:

a) $x^2 - 4x - 5 = 0$

Step 1   The equation is already in the standard form $ax^2 + bx + c = 0$.

Step 2   Here $a = 1$, $b = -4$, $c = -5$.

Step 3 $b^2 - 4ac = (-4)^2 - 4(1)(-5) = 16 + 20 = 36$

Step 4   Substituting these values in the quadratic formula, we get

$$x = \frac{-b \pm \sqrt{b^2 - 4ac}}{2a} \qquad \text{Quadratic Formula}$$

$$= \frac{-(-4) \pm \sqrt{36}}{2(1)} \qquad \text{Substitute the Values}$$

$$= \frac{4 \pm \sqrt{36}}{2} \quad \longrightarrow \quad x = \frac{4 \pm 6}{2}$$

$$\longrightarrow \quad x = \frac{4+6}{2} \quad \text{or} \quad x = \frac{4-6}{2}$$

$$\longrightarrow \quad x = 5 \quad \text{or} \quad x = -1$$

The solutions are 5 and -1.

Step 5   Verify the solutions.

Check your solutions using calculator. See section 9.4 of Appendix B for illustration.

Observation:

The discriminant is a perfect square $(36 = 6^2)$, *and the solutions are rational numbers (5 and –1).*

b) $2x^2 + 3x - 5 = 0$

b) $5x - 2x^2 = 2$

Step 1   Rewrite the equation in the form $ax^2 + bx + c = 0$

$$-2x^2 + 5x - 2 = 0$$

Step 2   Here, $a = -2$, $b = 5$, $c = -2$.

Step 3 $b^2 - 4ac = (5)^2 - 4(-2)(-2) = 25 - 16 = 9$

Step 4 $x = \dfrac{-b \pm \sqrt{b^2 - 4ac}}{2a}$

$= \dfrac{-5 \pm \sqrt{9}}{2(-2)}$

$= \dfrac{-5 \pm 3}{-4}$

$\longrightarrow \quad x = \dfrac{-5+3}{-4} \quad$ or $\quad x = \dfrac{-5-3}{-4}$

$\longrightarrow \quad x = \dfrac{-2}{4} = \dfrac{-1}{2} \quad$ or $\quad x = \dfrac{-8}{-4} = 2$

The solutions are $\dfrac{1}{2}$ and 2.

Step 5 Verify the solutions.

Observation:

The discriminant is a perfect square $(9 = 3^2)$, and the solutions are rational numbers ($\dfrac{1}{2}$ and 2).

c) $3x^2 - 5 = 0$

c) $4x^2 - 7 = 0$

Step 1 Rewrite $3x^2 - 5 = 0$ in the form $ax^2 + bx + c = 0$

$3x^2 + 0 \cdot x - 5 = 0$

Step 2 $a = 3, \; b = 0, \; c = -5$

Step 3 $b^2 - 4ac = (0)^2 - 4(3)(-5) = 60$

Step 4 $x = \dfrac{-b \pm \sqrt{b^2 - 4ac}}{2a} = \dfrac{-0 \pm \sqrt{60}}{2(3)}$

$= \dfrac{\pm \sqrt{60}}{6}$

$= \pm \dfrac{2\sqrt{15}}{6} = \pm \dfrac{\sqrt{15}}{3}$

$x = \dfrac{\sqrt{15}}{3} \quad$ or $\quad x = \dfrac{-\sqrt{15}}{3}$

The solutions are $\dfrac{\sqrt{15}}{3}$ and $-\dfrac{\sqrt{15}}{3}$.

Step 5 Verify the solutions.

Observation:

The discriminant is a positive whole number but not a perfect square, and the solutions are irrational numbers.

Warm Up

d) $9x^2 + 6x + 1 = 0$

d) $4x^2 + 4x + 1 = 0$

Step 1   The equation is already in the standard form.

Step 2   Here $a = 4$, $b = 4$, $c = 1$.

Step 3 $b^2 - 4ac = (4)^2 - 4(4)(1) = 16 - 16 = 0$

Step 4 $x = \dfrac{-4 \pm \sqrt{0}}{2 \cdot 4} = \dfrac{-4 \pm 0}{8}$

$x = \dfrac{-4}{8}$ or $x = \dfrac{-4}{8}$

$x = -\dfrac{1}{2}$ or $x = -\dfrac{1}{2}$

The solution $-\dfrac{1}{2}$ is repeated.

Step 5   Verify the solutions using a calculator.

Observation:

The discriminant 0 and the equation has repeated solutions.

Example 2:   Solve the equations.

a) $3x^2 - 5x - 13 = 0$ **b)** $2x^2 + 4x + 1 = 0$

Solutions:

a) $3x^2 - 5x - 13 = 0$ Here, $a = 3$, $b = -5$, $c = -13$.

$b^2 - 4ac = (-5)^2 - 4(3)(-13) = 25 - 156 = 181$

$x = \dfrac{-b \pm \sqrt{b^2 - 4ac}}{2a}$ Quadratic Formula

$= \dfrac{-(-5) \pm \sqrt{181}}{2(3)} = \dfrac{5 \pm \sqrt{181}}{6}$

$x = \dfrac{5 + \sqrt{181}}{6}$ or $x = \dfrac{5 - \sqrt{181}}{6}$

The solutions are $\dfrac{5 + \sqrt{181}}{6}$ or $\dfrac{5 - \sqrt{181}}{6}$.

Observation:

The discriminant is positive non-zero number which is not a perfect square, and solutions are irrational numbers.

2.   a) $3x^2 - 9x + 5 = 0$

b) $2x^2 + 6x + 1 = 0$

b) $2x^2 + 4x + 1 = 0$ Here, $a = 2$, $b = 4$, $c = 1$

$b^2 - 4ac = (4)^2 - 4(2)(1) = 16 - 8 = 8$

$x = \dfrac{-b \pm \sqrt{b^2 - 4ac}}{2a}$ Quadratic Formula

$$= \frac{-4 \pm \sqrt{8}}{4} = \frac{-4 \pm 2\sqrt{2}}{4} = \frac{-2(2 \pm \sqrt{2})}{4} = \frac{-2 \pm \sqrt{2}}{2}$$

$$x = \frac{-2 + \sqrt{2}}{2} \quad \text{or} \quad x = \frac{-2 - \sqrt{2}}{2}$$

The solutions are $\dfrac{-2 + \sqrt{2}}{2}$ and $\dfrac{-2 - \sqrt{2}}{2}$.

The observation given in example **2(a)** also applies to this example.

Example 3:   Solve the equations.

   a) $7x^2 + 4x + 3 = 0$ **b)** $2x^2 = 3x - 6$

3. Solve the equation

   a) $5x^2 + 3x + 2 = 0$

Solutions:

a) $7x^2 + 4x + 3 = 0$ Here, $a = 7$, $b = 4$, $c = 3$.

$b^2 - 4ac = (4)^2 - 4(7)(3) = 16 - 84 = -68$

$$x = \frac{-b \pm \sqrt{b^2 - 4ac}}{2a}$$

$$= \frac{-4 \pm \sqrt{-68}}{14} = \frac{-4 \pm 2\sqrt{-17}}{4} = \frac{-2 \pm i\sqrt{17}}{7}$$

$$x = -\frac{2}{7} + \frac{\sqrt{17}}{7}i \quad \text{or} \quad x = -\frac{2}{7} - \frac{\sqrt{17}}{7}i$$

The solutions are $-\dfrac{2}{7} + \dfrac{\sqrt{17}}{7}i$ and $-\dfrac{2}{7} - \dfrac{\sqrt{17}}{7}i$.

Observation:
If the discriminant is a negative number then the solutions are complex conjugate numbers.

b) $2x^2 = 3x - 6$ Rewrite in the form $ax^2 + bx + c = 0$

$2x^2 - 3x + 6 = 0$ Here, $a = 2$, $b = -3$, $c = 6$.

$b^2 - 4ac = (-3)^2 - 4(2)(6) = 9 - 48 = -39$

$$x = \frac{-b \pm \sqrt{b^2 - 4ac}}{2a} \quad \text{Quadratic Formula}$$

$$= \frac{-(-3) \pm \sqrt{-39}}{4} = \frac{3 \pm \sqrt{39}\,i}{4}$$

b) $4x^2 = 3x - 5$

457

Warm Up

Answers:

1. a) $4, -1$ b) $-\frac{5}{2}, 1$

   c) $\frac{\sqrt{7}}{2}$ or $\frac{-\sqrt{7}}{2}$ d) $-\frac{1}{3}$

2. a) $\frac{9 \pm \sqrt{21}}{6}$ b) $\frac{-3 \pm \sqrt{7}}{2}$

3. a) $\frac{-3 \pm i\sqrt{31}}{10}$ b) $\frac{3 \pm \sqrt{71}\, i}{8}$

$$x = \frac{3}{4} + \frac{\sqrt{39}}{4}i \qquad \text{or} \qquad x = \frac{3}{4} - \frac{\sqrt{39}}{4}i$$

The solutions are $\frac{3}{4} + \frac{\sqrt{39}}{4}i$ *and* $\frac{3}{4} - \frac{\sqrt{39}}{4}i$.

The same observation as in **3(a)** also applies to this example.

The observations from the above three examples are summarized below.

1. If the discriminant is **positive**, the solutions are **real numbers and different**.
    - If the discriminate is a perfect square the solutions are rational numbers, otherwise the solutions are irrational numbers.

2. If the discriminant is **zero**, the solutions are **real and the same number.**

3. If the discriminant is **negative**, the solutions are **complex numbers**, which are conjugates of each other.

C. Applications

Recall the strategy for solving an applied problem:

- Read the problem carefully.
- Interpret the given information and prepare a mathematical model.
- Solve the equations involved in the model.
- Interpret the result.

Warm Up

4. The sum of squares of two consecutive positive integers is 61. Find the integers.

Example 4: The sum of squares of two consecutive positive integers is 145. Find the integers.

Solution:

We have to find **two consecutive positive integers**, the sum of whose squares is 145. Suppose the **smaller** of the two positive integers is x. The **next** positive integer is $x + 1$.

Now

$$x^2 + (x+1)^2 = 145 \qquad \text{Given condition}$$
$$x^2 + x^2 + 2x + 1 = 145 \qquad \text{Simplify}$$
$$2x^2 + 2x - 144 = 0$$

We divide both sides by 2 and get $x^2 + x - 72 = 0$

We use the quadratic formula to solve this quadratic equation.

$$a = 1, \; b = 1, \; and \; c = -72$$

$$b^2 - 4ac = (1)^2 - 4(1)(-72) = 1 = 288 = \textbf{289}$$

$$x = \frac{-b \pm \sqrt{b^2 - 4ac}}{2a}$$

$$= \frac{-1 \pm \sqrt{289}}{2} = \frac{-1 \pm 17}{2}$$

$$x = \frac{-1 + 17}{2} \quad \text{or} \quad x = \frac{-1 - 17}{2}$$

$$\longrightarrow \quad x = 8 \quad \text{or} \quad x = -9$$

Since the required integers are positive, the only possible solution is $x = 8$. Thus, the two integers are 8 and 9.

Check: The sum of the squares $= 8^2 + 9^2 = 64 + 81 = 145$ True

Example 5: Michael purchased certain number of shares of one stock for total of $1400. The second stock was selling for $6 less per share. Michael could have bought 3 shares more of the second stock for the same amount of money. How many shares did Michael purchase of the first stock? How much did each share cost?

Solution:

Suppose Michael purchased x shares of the first stock.

$$\text{Price per share} = \frac{\text{Total money invested}}{\text{Total number of shares purchased}} = \frac{1400}{x}$$

$$\text{Price of second share} = \frac{1400}{x} - 6 \qquad \text{Given}$$

Number of shares of second stock which could be purchased for $1400 = x + 3$.

The above information is summarized in the following model.

	Number	x Price	= Total Amount
First Stock	x	$\frac{1400}{x}$	1400
Second Stock	$x + 3$	$\frac{1400}{x} - 6$	$(x+3)\left(\frac{1400}{x} - 6\right)$

Thus, $(x+3)\left(\dfrac{1400}{x} - 6\right) = 1400$

$$x\left(\frac{1400}{x} - 6\right) + 3\left(\frac{1400}{x} - 6\right) = 1400$$

$$1400 - 6x + \frac{4200}{x} - 18 = 1400 \longrightarrow -6x + \frac{4200}{x} - 18 = 0$$

$$\longrightarrow -6x^2 - 18x + 4200 = 0$$

$$\longrightarrow x^2 + 3x - 700 = 0$$

5. Bob purchased a certain number of instruments for physics laboratory for a total of $600. Same instrument offered by a different manufacturer were selling for $5 less per instrument. Bob could have purchased 10 more instruments for the same amount of money. How many instruments did Bob purchase from the first vendor? How much did each instrument cost?

We can use quadratic formula to solve this equation.

Here, $a = 1, \ b = 3, \ c = -700$

$b^2 - 4ac = (3)^2 - 4(1)(-700) = 9 + 2800 = 2809$

$x = \dfrac{-b \pm \sqrt{b^2 - 4ac}}{2a} = \dfrac{-3 \pm \sqrt{2809}}{2} = \dfrac{-3 \pm 53}{2}$

$x = \dfrac{-3 + 53}{2}$ or $x = \dfrac{-3 - 53}{2}$

$x = 25$ or $x = -28$

The number of shares cannot be negative. Therefore, the acceptable solution is $x = 25$.

(i) Michael bought 25 shares of the first stock.

(ii) Price of each share $= \dfrac{1400}{25} = \$56$.

6. Harry and Patrick work together as a team and unload a truck in 2 hours. Harry is stronger and works faster than Patrick. If working alone, Harry would take 3 hours less than Patrick to unload the same truck. How long does it take for Patrick to unload the truck?

Example 6: Two cranes can together unload a ship in 4 hours. The faster crane takes 6 hours less than the slower crane, if each were to unload the same ship alone. How long does it take for each crane to unload this ship?

Solution:

Let the number of hours required by the faster crane to unload the ship $= x$.

Then the slower crane unloads the ship in $(x + 6)$ hours.

Crane	Rate x	Time =	Work Done
Faster Crane	$\dfrac{1}{x}$	4	$\dfrac{4}{x}$
Slower Crane	$\dfrac{1}{x + 6}$	4	$\dfrac{4}{x + 6}$

Since the ship is unloaded by the two cranes working together in 4 hours, we get:

$\dfrac{4}{x} + \dfrac{4}{x+6} = 1$ Multiply both sides by the l.c.d: $x \ (x+6)$

$x(x+6)\left[\dfrac{4}{x} + \dfrac{4}{x+6}\right] = x(x+6) \longrightarrow 4(x+6) + 4x = x(x+6)$

$\longrightarrow 4x + 24 + 4x = x^2 + 6x$ Simplify

$\longrightarrow x^2 - 2x - 24 = 0$

Now we solve $x^2 - 2x - 24 = 0$ $a = 1, \ b = -2, \ c = -24$

460

$$b^2 - 4ac = (-2)^2 - 4(1)(-24) = 4 + 96 = \mathbf{100}$$

$$x = \frac{-(-2) \pm \sqrt{100}}{2}$$

$$= \frac{2 \pm \sqrt{100}}{2}$$

$$= \frac{2 \pm 10}{2}$$

$$\longrightarrow \quad x = 6 \quad \text{or} \quad x = -4$$

Since -4 is not a feasible solution the faster crane unloads the ship in $x = 6$ hours, and the slower crane unloads the ship in $x + 6 = 12$ hours.

Answers:

4. $5, 6$

5. $\$30$ instruments at 20 each

6. 6 hours

EXERCISE 9.4

Answers:

In exercises 1–15, use quadratic formula to solve the following equations.

1. $x^2 - 3x + 2 = 0$

2. $2x^2 - 3x + 1 = 0$

3. $y^2 + 6y + 5 = 0$

4. $5x^2 + 6x + 1 = 0$

5. $6z - 3z^2 = 3$

6. $9x^2 + 12x + 4 = 0$

7. $t^2 + 5t = 4$

8. $p^2 - 7p + 2 = 0$

9. $3x^2 + 15x + 8 = 0$

10. $5x^2 + 7x - 2 = 0$

11. $2k^2 - 7k + 7 = 0$

12. $5r^2 = 3r - 2$

13. $s^2 + 4 = 3s$

14. $x^3 + 5x^2 + 8x = 0$ (Factor out x: Recall $x \cdot a \cdot b = 0 \ \rightarrow \ x = 0, a = 0, b = 0$)

15. $y^4 - 2y^2 - 8 = 0$ $\left[\text{Treat this as a quadratic in } y^2 \colon \left(y^2\right)^2 - 2\left(y^2\right) - 8 = 0. \right]$

16. Product of two consecutive positive even integers is 224. Find the integers.

Answers:

1. _____

2. _____

3. _____

4. _____

5. _____

6. _____

7. _____

8. _____

9. _____

10. _____

11. _____

12. _____

13. _____

14. _____

15. _____

16. _____

17. _____

17. The sum of the reciprocals of two consecutive odd integers is $\dfrac{8}{15}$. Find the numbers.

18. _____

18. The sum of an integer and its reciprocal is $\dfrac{37}{6}$. Find the integer.

19. _____

19. A ball is thrown upwards. The height h, measured in feet, attained by it after being in air for t seconds follows the rule: $h = -16t^2 + 32t + 50$

   (i)   From what height was the ball thrown upwards
   (ii) When will the ball be 30 feet above the ground?

20. _____

20. Diane invested $12000 for a certain number of shares of a stock. If the price of each share of stock were $20 more, Diane would get 20 shares less for the same amount of money. How many shares did Diane buy?

21. _____

21. A salesman worked for certain number of days to earn $240. If he had been paid $8 more per day he would have earned the same amount of money in 5 fewer days. How many days did he work?

22. _____

22. The area of a rectangular piece of cardboard is 48 square inches. If the piece is cut by one inch on each of the four sides, the area of the resulting piece would reduce by half. Find the dimensions of the original piece.

9.5   SOLVING QUADRATIC EQUATIONS GRAPHICALLY

In Chapter 6 we learned how to graph a linear equation. In this section we shall learn how to graph a quadratic equation $y = ax^2 + bx + c$, $a \neq 0$. The graph of $y = ax^2 + bx + c$ can be used to *approximate* the real roots of the equation $ax^2 + bx + c = 0$ by simply reading x-intercepts.

Upon completion of this section, we will be able to:

   A.   Graph the quadratic equation $y = ax^2 + bx + c$, a $\neq$ 0.
   B.   Find the vertex of a parabola.
   C.   Use the graph of $y = ax^2 + bx + c$ to approximate
        real solutions of the equation $ax^2 + bx + c = 0$.

A.   Graphing a Quadratic Equation

The simplest quadratic equation is $y = x^2$. The graph of $y = x^2$ is most fundamental, since graphs of all equations $y = ax^2 + bx + c$ can be derived from the graph of $y = x^2$. Our first example explains how to graph $y = x^2$.

Example 1:   Graph $y = x^2$.

Solution:

Make a table for several x- and y-values.

x	$y = x^2$	Point (x, y)
3	9	$(3, 9)$
2	4	$(2, 4)$
1	1	$(1, 1)$
0	0	$(0, 0)$
-1	1	$(-1, 1)$
-2	4	$(-2, 4)$
-3	9	$(3, 9)$

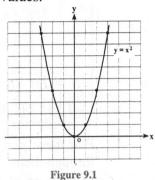

Figure 9.1

Plot these points on a graph paper, and draw a smooth curve through them. The graph is shown in Figure 9.1.

Example 2:   Graph $y = x^2 - 9$.

Solution:

Make a table for several x- and y-values.

x	$y = x^2 - 9$	(x, y)
4	7	$(4, 7)$
3	0	$(3, 0)$
2	-5	$(2, -5)$
1	-8	$(1, -8)$
0	-9	$(0, -9)$
-1	-8	$(-1, -8)$
-2	-5	$(-2, -5)$
-3	0	$(-3, 0)$
-4	7	$(-4, 7)$

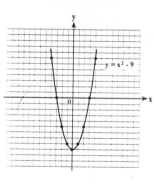

Figure 9.2

Plot these points on graph paper, and draw a smooth curve through them. The graph is shown in Fig. 9.2.   **Observe that the graph of $y = x^2 - 9$ is the same as the graph of $y = x^2$ shifted vertically down by 9 units.** Think about it and draw a general inference. Use your inference to determine how the graph of the following can be obtained from the graph of $y = x^2$.

(a) $y = x^2 - 1$ **(b)** $y = x^2 + 2$ **(c)** $y = x^2 - 4$

Warm Up

1. Graph $y = -x^2$

2. Graph $y = x^2 - 3$

Warm Up

3. Graph $y = (x-3)^2 + 5$

4. Graph $y = 3x^2$

Example 3:   Graph $y = (x-2)^2 + 6$.

Solution:

Make a table for several x- and y-values.

x	y	(x,y)
5	15	(5,15)
4	10	(4,10)
3	7	(3,7)
2	6	(2,6)
1	7	(1,7)
0	10	(0,10)
-1	15	$(-1,15)$

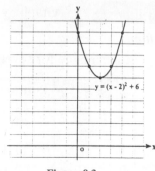

Figure 9.3

Plot these points on graph paper, and draw a smooth curve through them. The graph is shown as in Figure 9.3. **Observe that graph of $y = (x-2)^2 + 6$ is the same as the graph of $y = x^2$ shifted two units to the right and six units vertically up.** Think about and draw a general inference. Use your inference to determine how the graphs of a) $y = (x+1)^2 + 1$ b) $y = (x+3)^2 - 4$ can be obtained from the graph of $y = x^2$.

Example 4:   Graph $y = 2x^2$.

Solution:

Make a table for several x- and y-values.

x	y	(x,y)
-1.5	4.5	$(-1.5,4.5)$
-1	2	$(-1,2)$
$-.5$	.5	$(-.5,.5)$
0	0	(0,0)
.5	.5	(.5,.5)
1	2	(1,2)
1.5	4.5	(1.5,4.5)

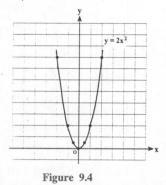

Figure 9.4

Plot these points, and draw a smooth curve through them. The graph is shown in Fig. 9.4 **Observe that the graph of $y = 2x^2$ is similar to the graph of $y = x^2$ but is narrower or closer to the y-axis.** Think about it and draw a general inference. Use your inference to determine how the graph of $y = \frac{1}{2}x^2$ is related to the graph of $y = x^2$.

Example 5:   Graph $y = -2x^2 + 5x - 2$

Solution:

Make a table for several x- and y- values.

x	y	(x, y)
-1	-9	$(-1, -9)$
0	-2	$(0, -2)$
1	1	$(1, 1)$
2	0	$(2, 0)$
3	-5	$(3, -5)$
4	-14	$(4, -14)$

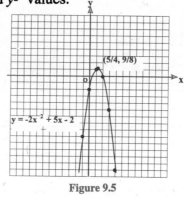

Figure 9.5

We may graph this equation using the calculator. See example 1 on page 469 for illustration.

Plot these points on graph paper, and draw a smooth curve joining them. The graph is shown in Fig. 9.5. Notice that the graph opens downwards. Observe that $y = -2x^2 + 5x - 2$ can also be graphed by completing the square for $-2x^2 + 5x - 2$ and using the inference that you may have drawn in examples 2 - 5.

$$y = -2x^2 + 5x - 2 = -2\left(x^2 - \frac{5}{2}x\right) - 2$$

$$= -2\left(x^2 - 2 \cdot \frac{5}{4}x + \frac{25}{16}\right) - 2 + \frac{25}{8} = -2\left(x - \frac{5}{4}\right)^2 + \frac{9}{8}$$

Now use observations from Examples 2, 3, and 4, with the additional information that if the coefficient of x^2 is negative, the graph opens downward.

In Examples 1 through 5, we have drawn graphs of different quadratic equations of the form $y = ax^2 + bx + c$. All these graphs are essentially of the same type. This graph is called a **parabola.**   Parabolas have many useful properties, and are important for solving real-life problems.

On reviewing the above examples, we can make the following observations.

The graph of $y = ax^2 + bx + c$:

1.   Opens upwards if a is **positive** (examples 1 - 4).

2.   Opens downwards if a is **negative** (example 5).

3.   There is a point on the graph which is the *lowest* if the graph opens *upwards,* and is the *highest* if the graph opens *down-wards.*   This point is called the **vertex** of the parabola.

4.   The graph is symmetrical about the vertical line through the vertex. This line is called the **axis** of the parabola.

Warm Up

5. Graph $y = 3x^2 + 7x - 6$

Answers:

1.   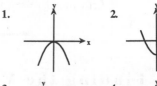   2.

3.   4.

5.

In Example 1, the vertex of the parabola is at the origin, and the axis is the y-axis. The following graphs are the graphs of Example 3 and Example 5, respectively. We have marked the vertex as V and the axis by a dotted line.

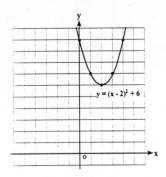

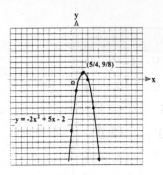

(Example 3)

Graph of $y = (x-2)^2 + 6$

(Example 5)

$y = -2x^2 + 5x - 2$

B. Finding the Vertex of a Parabola

The vertex of a parabola can be found by completing the square.

> *Step 1*   Complete the square for $ax^2 + bx + c$
>
> *Step 2*   Equate the square - term to zero and solve for x. This is the x- coordinate of the vertex.
>
> *Step 3*   Find the y- coordinate by substituting the x -coordinate in the equation.

Warm Up

6. Find the vertex and the axis of the parabola.

a) $y = (x-3)^2 - 4$

Example 6:   Find the vertex and the axis of the parabola.

a) $y = (x-2)^2 + 6$

b) $y = -2x^2 + 5x - 2$

Solutions:

a) $y = (x-2)^2 + 6$

Step 1   Not needed

Step 2 $x - 2 = 0 \longrightarrow x = 2$ Square Term = 0

Step 3 $y = (2-2)^2 + 6 = 6$ Substitute x –value

Therefore, the vertex is $(2, 6)$.

The line parallel to the y – axis through $(2, 6)$ is $x = 2$.

Therefore, the equation of the axis is $x = 2$.

b) $y = -2x^2 + 5x - 2$

Step 1 $-2x^2 + 5x - 2 = -2\left(x^2 - \dfrac{5}{2}x + 1\right)$

$\qquad\qquad = -2\left[x^2 - 2\cdot\dfrac{5}{4}x + \left(\dfrac{5}{4}\right)^2 + 1 - \left(\dfrac{5}{4}\right)^2\right]$

$\qquad\qquad = -2\left[\left(x - \dfrac{5}{4}\right)^2 - \dfrac{9}{16}\right] = -2\left(x - \dfrac{5}{4}\right)^2 + \dfrac{9}{8}$

Step 2 $x - \dfrac{5}{4} = 0 \longrightarrow x = \dfrac{5}{4}$ Square Term = 0

Step 3 $y = -2\left(\dfrac{5}{4} - \dfrac{5}{4}\right)^2 + \dfrac{9}{8} = \dfrac{9}{8}$ Substitute x –value

Therefore, the vertex is $\left(\dfrac{5}{4},\ \dfrac{9}{8}\right)$.

The line parallel to y-axis through $\left(\dfrac{5}{4},\ \dfrac{9}{8}\right)$ is $x = \dfrac{5}{4}$.

Therefore, the equation of the axis of the parabola is $x = \dfrac{5}{4}$.

Observation:

In example 6(b) the equation is $y = -2x^2 + 5x - 2$; $a = -2$, $b = 5$, $c = -2$. *The vertex is*
$\dfrac{5}{4} = \dfrac{-5}{2(-2)} = \dfrac{-b}{2a}$. *We can generalize this observation in the following statement.*

The x- coordinate of the vertex of the parabola $y = ax^2 + bx + c$ is $-\dfrac{b}{2a} = -\dfrac{\text{coeff. of } x}{2\left(\text{coeff. of } x^2\right)}$.

Notes:
1. In cases where the parabola intersects the x-axis, the x-coordinate of the vertex is the mean of the x-intercepts. Notice this fact in Examples 3 and 5. In fact, the axis of the parabola is a line parallel to y-axis and lying midway between the two x-intercepts.
2. It is always better to determine the coordinates of the vertex of a parabola before drawing its graph. This will give us better estimate of the graph.

The general method for drawing the graph of a parabola $\left(\text{equation: } y = ax^2 + bx + c\right)$ consists of the following steps.

    Step 1   Find the vertex of the parabola.

    Step 2   Find the points (x, y) on the parabola for at least three values of x less than the x-coordinate of the vertex, and at least three values of x greater than the x-coordinate of the vertex.

    Step 3   Plot the points and draw a smooth curve passing through these points.

Notes:
1. Steps 1 and 2 facilitate the choice of x values for making the table for x- and y- values.
2. For the parabola $y = ax^2 + bx + c$, the x-coordinate of the vertex is $-\dfrac{b}{2a}$, which is the mean of the two solutions of $ax^2 + bx + c = 0$.

C. Approximating Real Solutions of a Quadratic Equation Graphically

If a quadratic equation $ax^2 + bx + c = 0$ has real solutions, the graph of the parabola $y = ax^2 + bx + c$ will intersect x-axis. The x - coordinates of the points of intersection will be the solutions. If the vertex of the parabola lies on x-axis (i.e. the parabola meets the x-axis in only one point) then the equation $ax^2 + bx + c = 0$ has only one solution, i.e., a repeated solution. The equation $ax^2 + bx + c = 0$ will have no real solution if the parabola does not meet or intersect the x-axis. It may not be possible to read the x-coordinates of the points of intersection exactly. That is why we say that this method, in general, provides approximate values of the solutions.

Warm Up

7. Use graph to find the number of real solutions.

a) $x^2 + 6x + 9 = 0$

Example 7:

Use a graph to find the number of real solutions of the following equations.

a) $x^2 - 6x + 9 = 0$ b) $x^2 - 2x + 4 = 0$

c) $-x^2 + 3x + 5 = 0$

Solutions:

a) Solve $x^2 - 6x + 9 = 0$. Draw the graph of $y = x^2 - 6x + 9$.

Step 1 Determine coordinates of the vertex. $a = 1$, $b = -6$, $c = 9$

The x-coordinate of the vertex $= \dfrac{-b}{2a} = \dfrac{(-6)}{2(1)} = 3$.

The y-coordinate of the vertex is given by: $y = 3^2 - 6 \cdot 3 + 9 = 0$. The vertex: $(3, 0)$.

Step 2 Make a table for several x- and y- values on both sides of the vertex.

x	y	(x, y)
0	9	(0,9)
1	4	(1,4)
2	1	(2,1)
3	0	(3,0)
4	1	(4,1)
5	4	(5,4)
6	9	(6,9)

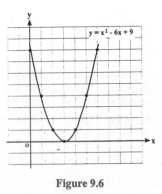

Figure 9.6

We can solve the equation graphically using calculator. See example 2 of Section 9.5 of Appendix B.

Step 3 Plot the above points and draw smooth curve through them.

Conclusion :

The vertex lies on the x-axis. In other words the parabola meets the x-axis in exactly one point, which is $(3, 0)$.

Therefore, the equation $x^2 - 6x + 9 = 0$ has only one (and therefore repeated) real solution. Therefore, the solution of the equation is $x = 3$.

b) Solve $x^2 - 2x + 4 = 0$.

Draw the graph of $x^2 - 2x + 4$ $a = 1, \ b = -2, \ c = 4$

Warm Up

b) $x^2 + 4x + 4 = 0$

Step 1   The x-coordinate of the vertex $= -\dfrac{b}{2a} = \dfrac{(-2)}{2(1)} = 1$

The y-coordinate of the vertex: $y = 1^2 - 2 \cdot 1 + 4 = 3$
The vertex: is $(1,3)$.

Step 2   Make a table for several x- and y- values on both sides of the vertex.

x	y	(x,y)
–2	12	$(-2,12)$
–1	7	$(-1,7)$
0	4	$(0,4)$
1	3	$(1,3)$
2	4	$(2,4)$
3	7	$(3,7)$
4	12	$(4,12)$

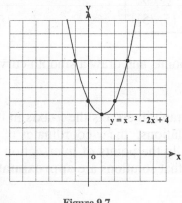

$y = x^2 - 2x + 4$

Figure 9.7

Step 3   Plot the above points and draw a smooth curve through them.

Conclusion:

Since the graph does not intersect the x-axis, the equation $x^2 - 2x + 4 = 0$ has no real solution.

c) Solve $-x^2 + 3x + 5 = 0$.

c) $2x^2 + 5x - 7 = 0$

Draw the graph of $y = -x^2 + 3x + 5$.

Step 1   Determine coordinates of the vertex $a = -1, \ b = 3, \ c = 5$

The x - coordinate of the vertex $= \dfrac{-b}{2a} = -\dfrac{3}{2(-1)} = \dfrac{3}{2}$

The y - coordinate of the vertex:

$$y = -\left(\frac{3}{2}\right)^2 + 3\left(\frac{3}{2}\right) + 5 = \frac{29}{4}$$

The vertex is $\left(\dfrac{3}{2}, \dfrac{29}{4}\right)$

Step 2   Make a table for several x - and y - values on both sides of the vertex.

$y = x^2 + 3x + 5$

Answers:

7. a) One repeated real solution
     $x = -3$

b) One repeated real solution
     $x = -2$

c) Two distinct real solutions
     $x = -\dfrac{7}{2}$ and $x = 1$

x	y	x, y
-2	-5	$(-2, -5)$
-1	1	$(-1, 1)$
0	5	$(0, 5)$
1	7	$(1, 7)$
2	7	$(2, 7)$
3	5	$(3, 5)$
4	1	$(4, 1)$
5	-5	$(5, -5)$

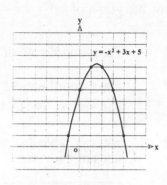

Figure 9.8

Step 3   Plot these points and draw a smooth curve through these points.

Conclusion:

Since the graph intersects the x-axis in two points, $-x^2 + 3x + 5 = 0$ has two real solutions, the x-coordinates of the points of intersection. If we read carefully the points of intersection of the graph with the x-axis, we will notice that solutions are **approximately** $x = 1$ and $x = 4$.

Observation:

The knowledge of the position of the vertex and whether the parabola opens upwards or downwards is sufficient to determine the number of real solutions.

EXERCISE   9.5

Answers:

1. _____

2. _____

3. _____

4. _____

5. _____

6. _____

7. _____

8. _____

9. _____

10. _____

In exercises 1–8, draw the graph of the equations and identify the vertex in each case.

1. $y = 4x^2$ **2.** $y = -4x^2$ **3.** $y = x^2 + 2x + 1$

4. $y = x^2 - 4x + 4$ **5.** $y = 2(x-1)^2 + 3$ **6.** $y = -2(x+2)^2 + 8$

7. $y = x^2 + 2x + 5$ **8.** $y = 3x^2 + 4x + 1$

In exercises 9–12, determine which of the parabolas open upwards or downwards.

9. $y = 2x^2 - 5x + 7$ **10.** $y = -x^2 + 4x + 2$

11. $y = 3 + 4x - 2x^2$ **12.** $y = -\left(3 + 4x - 5x^2\right)$

In exercises 13–20, find the vertex and draw appropriate graphs to determine graphically the approximate real solutions of the equations .

13. $y = 2x^2 - 8x + 8$ **14.** $y = 4x^2 - 6x + 5$

15. $y = 4 + 2x - 3x^2$ **16.** $y = -2x^2 - 5x + 1$

17. $y = x^2 - 2x + 1$ **18.** $y = x^2 - 3x - 4$

19. $y = 2x^2 - 5x + 4$ **20.** $y = -x^2 + 7x - 12$

13. _____

14. _____

15. _____

16. _____

17. _____

18. _____

19. _____

20. _____

9.6   CHAPTER SUMMARY

Examples

The Square Root Property

1.   The square Root Property of Equations: If b is a positive number then
$$a^2 = b \longrightarrow a = \sqrt{b} \text{ or } a = -\sqrt{b}.$$

2.   We can solve equations of the type $(x - a)^2 = b$ using the square root property.

2. $(3x - 2)^2 = 8$
$\rightarrow \quad 3x - 2 = \pm \sqrt{8}$
$\rightarrow \quad 3x - 2 = \pm 2\sqrt{2}$
$\rightarrow \quad 3x = 2 \pm 2\sqrt{2}$
$\rightarrow \quad x = \dfrac{2 \pm 2\sqrt{2}}{3}$

Completing The Square

3.   Completing the Square: $x^2 + bx + c$

- Add and subtract $\left(\dfrac{b}{2}\right)^2$:

- The first three terms form a perfect square:

3. $x^2 + 6x + 8$

$\left(x^2 + 6x + 9\right) - 9 + 8$

$(x + 3)^2 - 1$

Examples

4.   Solving: $x^2 + bx + c = 0$

   • Complete the square:

   • Solve the equation using square root method:

4. $x^2 + 6x + 8 = 0$

$(x+3)^2 - 1 = 0$

$(x+3)^2 = 1$

$x + 3 = \pm 1 \rightarrow x = -3 \pm 1$

$\rightarrow x = -4, -2$

5.   Solving: $ax^2 + bx + c = 0$

   • Write the equation in the standard form.

   • First divide both sides by a to change the coefficient of the x^2 term to 1.

   • We solve the new equation just like we solved $x^2 + bx + c = 0$

5. $3x^2 + 8x = 1$

$3x^2 + 8x = 1 \rightarrow 3x^2 + 8x - 1 = 0$

$\rightarrow \frac{1}{3}(3x^2 + 8x - 1) = \frac{1}{3} \cdot 0$

$\rightarrow x^2 + \frac{8}{3}x - \frac{1}{3} = 0$

$x^2 + 2\left(\frac{4}{3}\right)x - \frac{1}{3} = 0$

$\rightarrow x^2 + 2\left(\frac{4}{3}x\right) + \left(\frac{4}{3}\right)^2 - \frac{1}{3} - \left(\frac{4}{3}\right)^2 = 0$

$\rightarrow \left(x + \frac{4}{3}\right)^2 - \frac{19}{9} = 0$

$\rightarrow \left(x + \frac{4}{3}\right)^2 = \frac{19}{9}$

$\rightarrow x + \frac{4}{3} = \pm\sqrt{\frac{19}{9}}$

$\rightarrow x = -\frac{4}{3} \pm \frac{\sqrt{19}}{3}$

Complex Numbers

6. $\sqrt{-1} = i$

7. $i^2 = -1, \quad i^3 = -i, \quad i^4 = 1 \quad ....$

8.   A number of the form $a + bi$ is called a complex number. a is called the **real part** and b is called the **imaginary part.**

8.

Complex Number	Real Part	Imaginary Part
$3 + 5i$	3	5
$\sqrt{13}i$	0	$\sqrt{13}$
$1 - i$	1	-1

9.   Add complex numbers by adding the real parts and adding the imaginary parts.

9. $(4 - 7i) + (-5 + 10i)$

$= (4 + (-5)) + ((-7) + 10)i$

$= -1 + 3i$

10. Subtract two complex numbers by changing the sign of the second complex number and then performing addition.

10. $(4-7i)-(-5+10i)$

$= (4-7i)+(\mathbf{5-10i})$

$= (4+5)+(-7-10)i$

$= 9-17i$

11. Multiply two complex numbers as we multiply two binomials.

11. $(4-7i)(-5+10i)$

$= 4(-5)+4(10i)+(-7i)(-5)+(-7i)(10i)$

$= -20+40i+35i-70i^2$

$= 20+75i-70(-1)$

$= 50+75\,i$

12. If z is a complex number and $\bar{z}$ its conjugate then $z\bar{z} = (\text{real part})^2 + (\text{imaginary part})^2$.

12. Let $z = -5+10i$, then $\bar{z} = -5-10i$,

and $z\bar{z} = (-5+10i)(-5-10i)$

$= (-5)^2 + 10^2 = 125$

13. Divide complex numbers by multiplying the numerator and denominator by the conjugate of the denominator.

13. $\dfrac{4-7i}{-5+10i} = \dfrac{(4-7i)(\mathbf{-5-10i})}{(-5+10i)(\mathbf{-5-10i})}$

$= \dfrac{-20+35i-40i+70i^2}{(-5)^2+(10)^2}$

$= \dfrac{-20+35i-40i-70}{125}$

$= \dfrac{-90-5i}{125}$

$= \dfrac{-90}{125} - \dfrac{5}{125}i = -\dfrac{18}{25} - \dfrac{1}{25}i$

Quadratic Formula

14. Solutions of $ax^2+bx+c = 0$, $(a \neq 0)$ are:

$x = \dfrac{-b \pm \sqrt{b^2-4ac}}{2a}.$

14. $x^2+3x+5 = 0$

$a = 1, b = 3, c = 5$

$x = \dfrac{-3 \pm \sqrt{9-20}}{2 \cdot 1}$

$= \dfrac{-3 \pm \sqrt{-11}}{2}$

$= \dfrac{-3 \pm \sqrt{-11}}{2} = -\dfrac{3}{2} + \dfrac{i\sqrt{11}}{2}$

or $\quad -\dfrac{3}{2} - \dfrac{i\sqrt{11}}{2}$

15. b^2-4ac is called the **Discriminant** of the equation.

Examples

16. For the quadratic equation $ax^2 + bx + c = 0$, $(a \neq 0)$ solutions are:

- both real and rational if $b^2 - 4ac$ is a perfect square,

- both real and irrational if the $b^2 - 4ac$ is a positive but not a perfect square,

- both real and equal if $b^2 - 4ac = 0$, and

- both complex numbers if $b^2 - 4ac < 0$.

17. Use the following steps to solve a quadratic equation by the quadratic formula.

- Simplify the equations to: $ax^2 + bx + c$; $a \neq 0$

- Identify a, b, c

- Compute $b^2 - 4ac$, the discriminant.

- Identify the nature of the solutions

- Use the quadratic formula to find the exact solutions.

17. $2x^2 + 4x - 3 = 0$

$a = 2, b = 4, c = -4$

$b^2 - 4ac = 16 - 4(2)(-3)$

$= 16 = 24 = 40$

Solutions are irrational

$$x = \frac{-b \pm \sqrt{b^2 - 4ac}}{2a}$$
$$= \frac{-4 \pm \sqrt{40}}{4}$$
$$\frac{-2 + \sqrt{10}}{2}, \frac{-2 - \sqrt{10}}{2}$$

Solving Quadratic Equations Graphically

18. The graph of $ax^2 + bx + c$; $a \neq 0$ is a parabola, which opens upward if $a > 0$ and downwards if $a < 0$.

18. $y = 2x^2$ $(2 > 0)$

$y = -2x^2$ $(-2 < 0)$

19. To draw the graph, we need the vertex of the parabola. Perform the following steps to find the vertex.

Step 1 Complete the square for $ax^2 + bx + c$

Step 2 Equate square - term to zero and solve for x. This is x - coordinate of the vertex.

19. $y = x^2 - 2x + 5$

$y = (x-1)^2 + 4$

$(x-1)^2 = 0 \longrightarrow x = 1$

Examples

Step 3   Find the *y*-coordinate by substituting the *x*-coordinate in the equation.

$y = (1-1)^2 + 4 = 4$

Therefore, the vertex is $(1,4)$

20.   To graph $y = ax^2 + bx + c$, $(a \neq 0)$ we use the following steps.

20. $y = x^2 - 2x + 5$
Vertex is $(1,4)$

Step 1   Determine the coordinate of the vertex.

x	-2	-1	0	1	2	3	4
y	13	8	5	4	5	8	13

Step 2   Make a table of several *x*- and *y*-values (at least three) on both sides of the vertex.

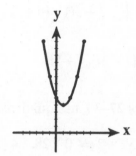

Step 3   Graph these points and draw a smooth curve through them.

21.   The solutions of the equation are given by the *x*-intercepts of $y = ax^2 + bx + c$.

21.   The equation $x^2 - 2x + 5 = 0$ has no solution since the graph of $y = x^2 - 2x + 5$ has no *x*-intercept.

22.   It is often difficult to read the exact value or the *x*-intercept from the graph. Therefore, solutions obtained graphically are usually approximate solutions.

9.7   REVIEW EXERCISE

In exercises 1–7, solve the following equations in the set of real numbers.

1. $x^2 = 9$ **2.** $x^2 = 16$ **3.** $-8p^2 = -1$ **4.** $4a^2 - 3 = 13$

5. $(3y - 1)^2 = 36$ **6.** $(1 - 2z)^2 - 13 = 36$ **7.** $(2y - 5)^2 = 27$

Complete the square in exercises 8–10.

8. $x^2 - 6x + 4$ **9.** $x^2 + 3x + 2$ **10.** $x^2 - 7x - 8$

In exercises 11–14, solve the equations using the method of completing the square.

11. $x^2 + 6x + 8 = 0$ **12.** $2y^2 + 6y = 5$ **13.** $-t^2 + 4t - 2 = 0$

14. $(2x - 1)(x + 2) = 1$

Simplify the imaginary numbers.

15. i^0 **16.** i^{37} **17.** i^{-18}

In exercises 18–19, write the complex numbers in the standard form.

18. $3 + \sqrt{-16}$ **19.** $-2 - \sqrt{-5}$

Perform the indicated operations in exercises 20–26.

20. $(3 + 7i) - [(4 + 5i) - (2 - 3i)]$ **21.** $(4 + i)(-4 + 3i)$

22. $(2 + 3i)[(-3 + 2i) + (4 + 7i)]$ **23.** $(-7 + 3i)^2$

24. $(2 + i)(1 - 2i)(4 + 5i)$ **25.** $\dfrac{3 + i}{4 - 9i}$ **26.** $\dfrac{(7 - 11i)(5 + 3i)}{1 + i}$

In exercises 27–30, use quadratic formula to solve the equations.

27. $3x^2 + 5x + 2 = 0$ **28.** $4x^2 - 4x + 1 = 0$ **29.** $y^2 - 3y + 5 = 0$ **30.** $z^3 + z^2 + z = 0$

31. The difference of the reciprocals of two consecutive even integers is $\dfrac{1}{24}$. Find the integers.

32. The perimeter of a rectangle is 80 cm. Area of the rectangle is 351 sq. cm. Find the dimensions of the rectangle.

33. A certain projectile is $d = 2t^2 - 5t + 7$ feet from the ground after being in the air for t seconds. How many seconds will it take the projectile to be 25 feet from the ground?

34. The base of a triangle is 3 inches more than the altitude drawn to it. If the area of the triangle is 35 square inches, find the base of the triangle.

35. The height h, measured in feet, reached by a model rocket t seconds after take - off is given by $h(t) = -16t^2 + 480t$. After how many seconds will the rocket be at a height of 3200 ft?

In exercises 36–38, find the vertex of each of the parabolas. Answer whether the vertex opens upwards or downwards.

36. $y = 2x^2 - 6x + 1$ **37.** $y = x^2 + 8x + 16$ **38.** $y = -2x^2 + 4x - 5$

.8   SELF TEST

1. Solve for t using square root method: $(1-5t)^2 = 49$?

Complete the Squares.

2. $x^2 + 7x - 3$ 3. $x^2 - 11x + 8$

Simplify and express the results in the standard form $a + ib$

4. i^{27} 5. $(3+i)^3$ 6. $(2+i)[(4+3i) - 2(5-2i)]$ 7. $\dfrac{-5+7i}{2-3i}$

Solve the following quadratic equations by any method.

8. $x^2 - 3x = 7$ 9. $(x-1)^2 = -1$ 10. $-2x^2 + 3x = 1$

11. $\dfrac{x^2 - 7}{3} = \dfrac{x}{2}$ 12. $2x^2 - 3x = 5 - 2x$ 13. $(2x+1)(x+2) = -3$

14. $\dfrac{1}{x-1} + \dfrac{1}{x+2} = 1$

15. The sum of a number and its reciprocal is $\dfrac{29}{10}$. Find the number.

Graph the following equations.

16. $y = x^2 + 3$ 17. $y = x^2 + 6x + 4$ 18. $y = -9 - 6x - x^2$

19. From your graphs in questions 17 through 19, determine how many real solutions the following equations have.

i) $x^2 + 3 = 0$ ii) $x^2 + 6x + 4 = 0$ iii) $9 - 6x - x^2 = 0$

Give reasons for your answers.

ANSWERS

CHAPTER 1

1.1

1. 1, 2 **2.** 1, 2, 3, 6 **3.** 1, 2, 3, 4, 6, 8, 12, 24 **4.** 1, 3, 9, 27 **5.** 23, 29, 31, 37, 41, 43, 47

6. 71, 73, 79, 83, 89 **7.** $2 \cdot 3 \cdot 3$ **8.** $2 \cdot 2 \cdot 2 \cdot 3$ **9.** $2 \cdot 2 \cdot 2 \cdot 11$ **10.** $2 \cdot 2 \cdot 5 \cdot 5$

11. $3 \cdot 3 \cdot 3 \cdot 5$ **12.** $\frac{2}{3}$ **13.** $\frac{7}{9}$ **14.** $\frac{2}{3}$ **15.** $\frac{5}{7}$

16. $\frac{3}{5}$ **17.** Equivalent **18.** Not Equivalent **19.** Equivalent **20.** Equivalent

21. $\frac{5}{18}$ **22.** $\frac{4}{15}$ **23.** $\frac{10}{11}$ **24.** $\frac{1}{10}$ **25.** $\frac{51}{112}$ **26.** $\frac{7}{6}$

27. $\frac{4}{9}$ **28.** $\frac{84}{85}$ **29.** $\frac{8}{7}$ **30.** 1 **31.** $\frac{9}{20}$ **32.** $\frac{7}{5}$

33. 4 **34.** $\frac{6}{5}$ **35.** 105 **36.** 1 8 **37.** 60 **38.** 630

39. 2 2 5 **40.** $\frac{15}{27}$ **41.** $\frac{66}{96}$ **42.** $\frac{76}{40}$ **43.** $\frac{41}{35}$ **44.** $\frac{67}{120}$

45. $\frac{14}{15}$ **46.** $\frac{58}{105}$ **47.** $\frac{2}{3}$ **48.** $\frac{1}{3}$ **49.** $\frac{4}{15}$ **50.** $\frac{5}{48}$

51. $\frac{11}{36}$ **52.** $\frac{31}{60}$ **53.** $\frac{263}{180}$ **54.** $2\frac{13}{14}$

1.2

1. 1 2 5 **2.** 49 **3.** $\frac{8}{27}$ **4.** 9 **5.** $\frac{1024}{243}$ **6.** 512

7. $20\frac{51}{64}$ **8.** Exponent, multiplication, addition and subtraction from left to right. **9.** 1 **10.** 32

11. 60 **12.** 347 **13.** 61 **14.** 23 **15.** 20 **16.** 5

17. 21 **18.** 9 **19.** 12 **20.** $\frac{7}{32}$ **21.** 34 **22.** 10

23. 3 **24.** 81 **25.** a) $<, \leq, \neq$ b) $>, \geq, \neq$ c) $\leq, \geq, =$ **26.** $11>5$

27. $8 < 13$ **28.** $6 < 8$ **29.** $7 \geq 4$ **30.** False **31.** True **32.** True

33. False **34.** True **35.** $8 + 5 > 10$ **36.** $20 \div 4 = 5$ **37.** $30 \div 5 < 9$ **38.** $5 \cdot 6 \neq 21$

39. $3 \cdot 5 + 4 = 19$ **40.** $9 - 5 \leq 4$ **41.** $17 - 2 \cdot 5 > 3$ **42.** $22 \div 2 < 3 + 12$ **43.** $9^4 \neq 4^9$ **44.** $3^5 + 7 > 200$

1.3

1. 7,21 **2.** 1,22 **3.** 1, $\frac{82}{5}$ **4.** 21,7 **5.** $\frac{3}{2}$ **6.** 2415 **7.** 31 **8.** 21

9. 26 **10.** $\frac{163}{3}$ **11.** $4 \cdot 7$ **12.** $x + 9$ **13.** $7 - 2x$ **14.** $x + 9$ **15.** $\frac{11}{x}$ **16.** $20 - \frac{7}{x}$

17. $5 + 2x$ **18.** $4 + \frac{3}{5}x$ **19.** Expression **20.** Equation **21.** Equation **22.** Expression

23. 7 **24.** 2 **25.** 10 **26.** 2 **27.** No solution in the set

28. $3x + 4 = 19; 5$ **29.** $3x - 10 = 21$; no solution in the set **30.** $\frac{16}{2x} = x - 4$; No solution in the set

31. $5x - 4 = 3x; 2$ **32.** $9 + 3x = 21; 4$ **33.** $2x = 5x; 0$ **34.** $\frac{x}{8} = \frac{2}{x}; 4$

1.4

1. **a)** 4   **b)** 0, 4, −8   **c)** 0, 4, −8, $\frac{3}{7}$, −$\frac{2}{3}$ **d)** −$\sqrt{2}$, $\sqrt{5}$

2. **a)** none **b)** −1, −2 **c)** $\frac{5}{4}$, $\frac{9}{7}$, −2, −1 **d)** $\sqrt{6}$ 3. **a)** −1, 0, 2, 4 **b)** −1, 0, 2, 4, $\frac{5}{7}$, $\frac{3}{5}$, −1$\frac{2}{3}$ **c)** $\sqrt{3}$, −$\sqrt{5}$

4. **a)** −3, 4 **b)** $\frac{2}{3}$, 1$\frac{7}{11}$, −$\frac{4}{9}$, −3, 4 **c)** $\sqrt{7}$, −$\sqrt{11}$ 5.

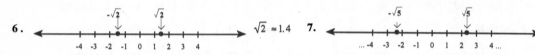

6. $\sqrt{2} \approx 1.4$ 7.

8. True   9. False   10. True   11. True   12. False   13. True   14. False   15. False

16. −6   17. 7   18. $\sqrt{2}$ 19. 0   20. $\frac{2}{3}$ 21. −2$\frac{1}{4}$ 22. 8   23. $\frac{4}{3}$

24. 2   25. 6   26. 5   27. 15   28. $\frac{1}{3}$

1.5

1. 7   2. 3   3. 2   4. −3   5. −7

6. −11   7. −9   8. −14   9. $\frac{3}{20}$ 10. $\frac{35}{6}$

11. −$\frac{5}{6}$ 12. −$\frac{11}{9}$ 13. −6   14. 11   15. −5

16. 2   17. 4 + (−6) + 7, 5   18. $[4 + (−9)] + 3$; −2   19. 4 + [(−12) + 8]; 0   20. $[3 + (−7)] + 10$; 6

21. −4 + [5 + (−2)]; −1   22. + 28,300 feet   23. 112°F

1.6

1. 2   2. −3   3. −11   4. 13   5. 12   6. 1   7. 1$\frac{2}{9}$

8. 1$\frac{3}{20}$ 9. $\frac{58}{45}$ 10. −$\frac{2}{3}$ 11. −11   12. −14   13. −18   14. −26

15. 2$\frac{7}{15}$ 16. −1$\frac{4}{9}$ 17. 4 − (−5); 9   18. −8 − 3; −11   19. 3 − (−7 + 4); 6

20. (9 + (−5)) − 15; −11   21. (−5 − 8) − 7; −20   22. 1148 feet   23. 9 yard loss   24. 2450   25. 4°F   26. 28°F

1.7

1. 8   2. $\frac{5}{2}\left(or\ 2\frac{1}{2} \right)$ 3. $\frac{4}{7}$ 4. 0   5. −35   6. −36

7. −$\frac{2}{7}$ 8. $\frac{5}{9}$ 9. −6$\frac{3}{10}$ 10. −4   11. 0   12. −1, 1, −2, 2, −13, 13, −26, 26

13. −1, 1, −2, 2, −3, 3, −6, 6, −9, 9, −18, 18   14. −1, 1   15. −138   16. 52   17. −18$\frac{5}{8}$ 18. 115

19. 47   20. 29   21. −136   22. 0   23. 300   24. −89

1.8

1. $-\frac{1}{3}$
2. $\frac{1}{4}$
3. 5
4. $-\frac{7}{3}$
5. $\frac{9}{19}$
6. 4
7. $-\frac{1}{8}$

8. $-\frac{4}{5}$
9. 0
10. $\frac{5}{6}$
11. $-1\frac{1}{3}$
12. -4
13. 40
14. 20

15. undefined
16. 1
17. 9
18. 5
19. $7\frac{1}{3}$
20. $-\frac{9}{28}$
21. $-2\frac{1}{5}$

22. $\frac{15}{7-(-3)}; \frac{3}{2}$
23. $\frac{(-8)^2}{12}; 5\frac{1}{3}$
24. $\frac{6x}{-36}; -\frac{x}{6}$
25. $5x=-35; x=-7$

26. $\frac{x}{-3}=-3; x=9$
27. $\frac{4}{x+1}=\frac{1}{2}; x=7$
28. $\frac{x^2}{3}=27; x=-9,9$
29. 13
30. 5

31. $11
32. 0
33. 9
34. 4

1.9

1. 3 Commutative property of addition
2. 4 Commutative property of addition
3. -6 Commutative property of addition
4. -3 Commutative property of multiplication
5. -6 Commutative property of multiplication
6. 6 Associative property of addition
7. -5 Associative property of addition
8. 3 Associative property of multiplication
9. -9 Associative property of multiplication
10. 2 Associative property of multiplication

11. 6, 5
12. 9, -5
13. $-9, -8, 4$
18. 1
19. 1
20. 0

21. 1
22. Additive Inverse
23. Multiplicative Inverse
24. Additive Inverse

25. Multiplicative Inverse
26. $y+3x$
27. $z+xy$
28. $yx+z$
29. $x+(4+t)$

30. $x(4t)$
31. $3x-3y+3z$
32. $8a-12p$
33. $-9(x+2y)$
34. $-p+7$

REVIEW EXERCISE SET 1.11

1. $2\cdot2\cdot3\cdot3\cdot3$
2. $2\cdot3\cdot3\cdot5$
3. Equivalent
4. not equivalent

5. $\frac{14}{55}$
6. $\frac{3}{20}$
7. $\frac{7}{30}$
8. $\frac{7}{9}$

9. 1
10. $\frac{46}{63}$
11. $\frac{29}{36}$
12. $\frac{17}{48}$

13. $\frac{5}{6}$
14. 625
15. $37\frac{1}{27}$
16. 12

17. 95
18. 11
19. $\frac{1}{3}$
20. False

21. True
22. True
23. $31-4\cdot5=11$
24. $\frac{20}{4}\le5$

25. $8\cdot3\ne\frac{8}{3}$
26. 29
27. $\frac{1}{6}$
28. 140

29. 31
30. $\frac{91}{2}$
31. $\frac{2}{7}x-7$
32. $5x+\frac{3}{x}$

33. $4+x-4x$
34. $2x+5=11; x=3$
35. $3x=4+x+6; x=5$

36. $\frac{50}{x}=2x, 5$

37. a) 1, 5; b) $-3, 0, 1, 5$; c) $\frac{4}{5}, -\frac{2}{7}$; d) $\sqrt{5}$ e) $0, -3, \frac{-2}{7}, \frac{4}{5}, \sqrt{5}$

38.

```
  ←─┼──┼─┼─┼─┼┼─┼──┼──┼──→
   -3 -5/3  0        5
```
with mark at 3/4

39. $\frac{5}{7}$
40. 10
41. 5
42. -7; Associative Property of Addition

43. 3, 2; Distributive Property
44. 7; Associative Property of Multiplication

7; Commutative Property of Multiplication

4; Associative Property of Multiplication

SELF TEST 1.12

1. $234 = 2 \cdot 3 \cdot 3 \cdot 13$
2. Equivalent
3. Not Equivalent
4. $\dfrac{9}{8}$
5. $\dfrac{10}{9}$

6. $\dfrac{1}{3}$
7. $\dfrac{14}{5}$
8. $\dfrac{13}{14}$
9. $\dfrac{53}{60}$
10. $2\dfrac{43}{105}$

11. 8
12. 0
13. $\dfrac{-16}{5}$
14. No
15. $3\left[\dfrac{5}{-3+7}\right]$

16. No
17. Yes
18. 10
19. $\dfrac{7}{10}$

20. $x + (x+1) + 7$ or $2x + 8$
21. $2[x + (x+3)] = 48$ or $4x + 6 = 48$

22. $3x + 4 = 19;\ x = 5$
23. $|3 - x| = 2;\ x = 1, 5$

24. Integers $= \{-5, -3, 0, 1, 4\}$

Rational numbers which are not natural numbers $\left\{0, -3, -5, \dfrac{5}{7}, \dfrac{3}{4}\right\}$

25. a and B;   b and C;   c and A;   d and D

CHAPTER 2

2.1

1. $9 + 3x$
2. $9x + 3$
3. $7 - 12x$
4. $-4 + 2x$
5. $3x - 16$

6. $-4x - 13$
7. $27 - 4x$
8. $3a - 11$
9. $12 - 2x$
10. $20 - x$

11. -15
12. 6
13. -7
14. 4
15. -1

16. 1
17. -1
18. $x^2,\ 2$
19. $xy,\ 2$
20. $x^2 y^2,\ 1$

21. $y^2 zx,\ -3$
22. $x^0,\ -7$
23. $x^2,\ 1$
24. $x^2 y, -2^2$
25. Unlike

26. Like
27. Like
28. Unlike
29. Like
30. Unlike

31. $-3m$
32. $11s - 18$
33. $8t^2 + 28$
34. $17 - 6x$

35. $y^2 + 3y + 13x$
36. $-17y + 2y^2 - 28$
37. $12p - 34$
38. $x + (4 - 2x);\ -x + 4$

39. $8[(x + (-4))] - 3x;\ 5x - 32$

2.2

1. Linear Equation
2. Not a Linear Equation
3. Linear Equation
4. Linear Equation

5. Linear Equation
6. Not a Linear Equation
7. $x = 5$
8. $y = 4$

9. $8x = 11$
10. $5p = -9$
11. $p = 6$
12. $x = \dfrac{5}{3}$

13. $x = -\dfrac{3}{2}$
14. $x = 3$
15. $x = 2$
16. $x = 1$
17. $x = -3$

18. $x = \dfrac{5}{4}$
19. $x = 12$
20. $x = \dfrac{8}{5}$
21. $p = -2$
22. $m = \dfrac{5}{2}$

23. $t = 5$
24. $z = \dfrac{8}{5}$
25. $r = \dfrac{7}{13}$
26. $a = -1$
27. $s = \dfrac{6}{7}$

28. $y = \dfrac{20}{3}$
29. $z = \dfrac{42}{5}$
30. $y = -\dfrac{54}{5}$
31. $x + 7 = 10;\ x = 3$

32. $-3x = 9;\ x = -3$

2.3

1. $4x = 1$ 2. $-2x = 1$ 3. $9r = 8$ 4. $7x = -3$ 5. $x = \frac{5}{3}$ 6. $x = -\frac{8}{7}$

7. $x = \frac{2}{5}$ 8. $a = -17$ 9. $y = 3$ 10. $k = -8$ 11. $z = 0$ 12. $p = -3$

13. $t = -4$ 14. $x = \frac{5}{2}$ 15. $x = \frac{1}{2}$ 16. $s = -\frac{3}{2}$ 17. $v = 10$ 18. $t = 15$

19. Contradiction 20. Conditional 21. Identity 22. Contradiction 23. 4 24. a) $t + 10$ b) $t - 7$

25. $21 - m$ 26. $\frac{28}{k}$ 27. $27n$

2.4

1. 5 2. 7 3. 8 4. 12

5. 18¢ 6. 40 7. 9 quarters, 7 dimes 8. 33 quarters, 44 nickels

9. l = 13 cm w = 4 cm 10. length = 43 yds, width = 27 yds 11. roosters = 56, hens = 94 12. 9, 19, 29 inches

13. oil = 5 ounces, gasoline = 80 ounces 14. $25°$ 15. painkillers = 42, tranquilizers = 30

16. 11, 12 13 17. 14, 15, 16 18. Kennedy: 303, Nixon: 219

19. 5m, 8m 11m 20. 16cm, 13cm, 13 cm 21. 32 yrs, 8 yrs

22. 12 years ago 23. No 24. $400 25. 9 7

2.5

1. 4 2. 4 3. 40 4. 4 5. 95 6. $4\frac{1}{3}$

7. $h = \frac{2A}{b}$ 8. $l = \frac{p - 2w}{2}$ 9. $t = \frac{A - p}{pr}$ 10. $C = \frac{5}{9}(F - 32)$ 11. $m = \frac{y - c}{x}$

12. $n = \frac{b - a}{d} + 1 \left(or \ \frac{b - a + d}{d} \right)$ 13. 20 yards 14. 197.5m 15. 21 cm 16. $49°, 49°$

17. $107°, 73°$

2.6

1. $\frac{3}{5}$ 2. $\frac{4}{3}$ 3. $\frac{2}{3}$ 4. $\frac{4}{3}$ 5. $\frac{4}{5}$ 6. $\frac{16}{1}$ 7. Not a Proportion

8. Proportion 9. Proportion 10. Not a Proportion 11. Proportion 12. Proportion 13. $a = 24$ 14. $k = 42$

15. $x = 10$ 16. $y = 100$ 17. $k = \frac{35}{8}$ 18. $m = \frac{20}{7}$ 19. 15 ounces 20. $7.80

21. 250 miles 22. 7 ft 8 inches 23. 32 ounces for $1.90 24. 32 ounces for $2.40

2.7

1. Caramels: 2 lbs, chocolate: 3 lbs 2. 40 lbs 3. 2 gallons

4. 24 liters 5. 2 quarts 6. 10 gallons

7. 440,000 8. Black and white: $3000, color: $1000

9. First: $7000, second: $8000 10. $45000 11. 9%

12. 3 hours and 45 minutes 13. 40 miles 14. 3 hours

15. 2 miles per hour 16. 8 P.M.

2.8

1. 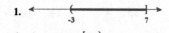 -3 7

2. 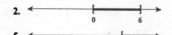 0 6

3. -5 -2

4. -2 0

5. 4

6. -3

7. 0

8. -1

9. $-12x \le 12$ (or $12x \ge -12$)

10. $8y > -1$ **11.** $r \le 4$ **12.** $r \le -\dfrac{15}{}$ **13.** $r > -7$ **14.** $r > 2$

15. $p > -2$ -2

16. $(-\infty, 3]$ 3

17. $(-\infty, -1)$ -1

18. $(-\infty, -3]$ -3

19. $(-\infty, -5]$ -5

20. $[5, \infty)$ 5

21. $(-\infty, 5)$ 5

22. $(-2, 5)$ -2 5

23. $[8, 11)$ 8 11

24. $(-4, 6]$ -4 6

25. Profit should be less than or equal to $13.
26. Greater than or equal to 88.
27. More than $5000.
29. No.

2.9

1. $x = -3, 3$ **2.** $x = 2, 6$ **3.** $x = -16, 2$ **4.** $x = -1/2, 9/2$ **5.** $x = -2/3, 4$

6. $x = 4$ **7.** $x = 7, 13$ **8.** $x = -1/2, 2$ **9.** $x = -17/3, 25/3$ **10.** No solution

13. $(-3, 3)$ -3 3

14. $(-3, 7)$ -3 7

15. $[-11, -3]$ -11 -3

16. $(-2, 3)$ -2 3

17. $(-3/2, 11/2)$ -3/2 11/2

18. $[-4/3, 4]$ -4/3 4

19. No solution

20. No solution

21. $[-2, 7/2]$ -2 7/2

22. $(-\infty, -3) \cup (3, \infty)$ -3 3

23. $(-\infty, -4) \cup (6, \infty)$ -4 6

24. $(-\infty, -11] \cup [1, \infty)$ -11 1

25. $(-\infty, -3) \cup (4, \infty)$ -3 4

26. $(-\infty, -11/3) \cup (5, \infty)$ -11/3 5

27. $(-\infty, -11/5) \cup [5, \infty)$ -11/5 5

28. All real numbers)

29. All real numbers except $x = 9/2$ 9/2

30. All real numbers

31. $(-\infty, -3] \cup [9/2, \infty)$ -3 9/2

32. $(-\infty, -1/2] \cup [3, \infty)$ -1/2 3

33. $(-\infty, -14] \cup [35/2, \infty)$ -14 35/2

34. $(-\infty, -22/5] \cup [-13/5, \infty)$ -22/5 -13/5

35. All real numbers

36. $x = 5/2$

37. $(-\infty, -2] \cup [6, \infty)$ -2 6

38. $(-\infty, -1] \cup [7/3, \infty)$ -1 7/3

39. All real numbers

REVIEW EXERCISE 2.11

1. $11x - 7$ 2. $5x - 22$ 3. $14 - 6x$ 4. $8 + 7x$ 5. $x^2 + 23x - 20$

6. $-z - 18$ 7. 2 8. -4 9. $\dfrac{4}{3}$ 10. $\dfrac{-9}{2}$

11. 7 12. -1 13. $\dfrac{6}{5}$ 14. 6 15. 18

16. 0 17. -24 18. 8 19. 75^0 20. $20,\ 50$

21. $\dfrac{v}{ab}$ 22. $y = \dfrac{4 - 2x}{-3} = \dfrac{2x - 4}{3}$ 23. $x = \dfrac{4 + 3y}{2}$ 24. $a = \dfrac{5x - 30}{2}$

25. $b = \dfrac{a}{7a - 5}$ 26. $\dfrac{4bc}{b - 3c}$ 27. $\dfrac{2}{3}$ 28. $\dfrac{5}{7}$ 29. $\dfrac{8}{1}$

30. $\dfrac{10}{1}$ 31. $\dfrac{5}{2}$ 32. $\dfrac{9}{20}$ 33. Proportion 34. Proportion

35. Not a Proportion 36. Proportion 37. 2 38. 9 39. $\dfrac{15}{4}$

40. $\dfrac{9}{4}$ 41. 3 42. 4 43. 7.5 quarts 44. 17 in, 12 in, 9 in

45. 2 46. $2600 at 6% $2400 at 7% 47. 262.50 mi 48. 70 miles per hour

49. $x \geq -12$

50. $x \leq -2$

51. $x \leq 3$

52. $x \geq -4$

53. $x < \dfrac{1}{2}$

54. $x < -4$

55. $x \geq 9$

56. $k < \dfrac{27}{10}$

57. $-4 < m \leq 3$

58. Side of the square is at most 30 ft. 59. $x = -3, 6$

60. $x = -\dfrac{3}{2}, 4$ 61. $x = -\dfrac{1}{3}, 3$ 62. $x = 3$ 63. $x = -1, 10$ 64. No solution

65. $(-3, 5)$ 66. $[-1, 6]$ 67. No Solution 68. $\left(-\dfrac{2}{5}, \dfrac{2}{3}\right)$ 69. $(-\infty, -2) \cup (6, \infty)$

70. $(-\infty, 0] \cup [3, \infty)$ 71. All real numbers 72. All real numbers 73. All real numbers

74. $\left(-\infty, -\dfrac{1}{2}\right] \cup [2, \infty)$ 75. $\left(-\infty, -\dfrac{7}{2}\right] \cup \left[\dfrac{21}{2}, \infty\right)$ 76. $\left(-\infty, -\dfrac{9}{2}\right] \cup \left[\dfrac{25}{2}, \infty\right)$

SELF TEST 2.12

1. $2x + 7y - 3$ 2. $-6x - 4y$ 3. -20 4. $\dfrac{20}{3}$ 5. -20 6. No solution

7. Identity; all real numbers are solutions 8. 14 9. $-\dfrac{8}{9}$ 10. $\dfrac{11}{3}$ 11. $W = 7cm\ \ L = 11cm$

12. 50 13. $h = \dfrac{S - 2ab}{2(a + b)}$ 14. 10 liters 15. $9000 at 7.5%; $5000 at 6.5

16. $p < -5$ $(-\infty, -5)$

17. $x \leq -12$ or $(-\infty, -12]$

18. $a \geq \dfrac{9}{5}$ $\left[\dfrac{9}{5}, \infty\right)$

19. $-4 < k \leq 3$ $(-4, 3]$

20. 93 or better 21. $x = -3, 4$ 22. $x = \dfrac{5}{2}$ 23. No solution 24. $\left[-1, \dfrac{11}{3}\right]$ 25. No solution

26. $\left[-\dfrac{5}{3}, 3\right]$ 27. $(-\infty, -2) \cup [6, \infty)$ 28. All real numbers

CHAPTER 3

3.1

1. base: 3, exponent: 6   **2.** base: 3, exponent: 6   **3.** base: -3, exponent 6   **4.** base: $-5x$, exponent: 7

5. base: $5y$, exponent: 7   **6.** base: y exponent: 7   **7.** $\dfrac{8}{9}$ **8.** 250

9. 72   **10.** $\dfrac{544}{243}$ **11.** $x^5 y^6$ **12.** $(2x)^4$ or $2^4 x^4$

13. $\dfrac{x^6}{y^4}$ **14.** $\dfrac{x^7}{y^6}$ **15.** $6y^5$ **16.** $-392a^5$

17. p^{16} **18.** $-48a^3$ **19.** false   **20.** true

21. false   **22.** false   **23.** true   **24.** false

25. true   **26.** $6x^8$ **27.** $16m^6$ **28.** $\dfrac{9\pi}{4} a^8$

3.2

1. Polynomial, yes   **2.** Polynomial, yes   **3.** Polynomial, no   **4.** Polynomial, no

5. $-3x^4 + 4x^3 + 3x^2 + 7x$; degree = 4, constant term = 0

6. $-4x^5 + 8x^3 + 7x^2 - 5$; degree = 5, constant term = -5

7. $-9x^8 + 7x^6 - 3x^5 + x^4$; degree = 8, constant term = 0

8. $7x^5 - 6x^4 - 2x^3 - 4x^2 + 1$; degree = 5, constant term = 1

9. Binomial; 2   **10.** Monomial; 3   **11.** Binomial; 3   **12.** Trinomial; 5

13. Polynomial; 10   **14.** Trinomial; 2   **15.** 3; 31   **16.** -10; 54

17. 127; 231   **18.** $4x^3 + 4x^2 - 5x + 7$ **19.** $x^4 + 16x^3 + 10x^2 + 8x$ **20.** $7p^2 - p + 2$

21. $11z^2 + 11z$ **22.** $9t^3 - 13t^2 + 12t + 3$ **23.** $2r^3 - 8r^2 + 7r + 19$ **24.** $-2x^2 - 7x + 16$

25. $8y^4 - 2y^3 - 1$ **26.** $-5t^4 + 4t^3 + 9t^2 - 8t - 8$ **27.** $-t^2 - 11$ **28.** $3n^5 - 4n^4 + 9n^3 - 8n^2 + 12$

29. $x^3 + 8x^2 - 1$ **30.** $8x^2 + 16x - 20$

3.3

1. $15x^5$ **2.** $-4x^{15}$ **3.** $8x^8$ **4.** $-21x^6$

5. $15x^5$ **6.** $8x^4 + 14x^3$ **7.** $-3x^7 + 9x^6 - 6x^5$ **8.** $30x^3 - 32x^2 - 14x$

9. $40x^{11} - 24x^9 - 15x^4 + 9x^2$ **10.** $20x^3 + 47x^2y^2 + 24xy^4$ **11.** $12q^3 - 25q^2 + 7q$ **12.** $12x^6 - 24x^5 - 8x^3 + 16$

13. $\dfrac{8}{5}x^3 - \dfrac{4}{25}x^2 - \dfrac{3}{2}x + \dfrac{3}{20}$ **14.** $12x^4 + x^3 - 32x^2 - 5x$ **15.** $5x^{12} + 5x^{11} - 3x^5 - 3x^4 + 7x^3 + 7x^2$ **16.** $9x^2 + 30x + 25$

17. $y^{12} - 7y^{10} - 10y^9 + 70y^7 + 8y^4 - 56y^2$ **18.** $9x^{10} - 30x^8 + 25x^6 + 42x^5 - 70x^3 + 49$

19. $12x^2 - 13x - 35$ **20.** $27x^4 + 15x^3 + 63x^2 + 35x$ **21.** $6s^2 - s - 12$ **22.** $12t^2 - 8t - 15$

23. $16k^2 - 25l^2$ **24.** $12m^2 - 25mn + 12n^2$ **25.** $6y^7 - 14y^6 - 9y^3 + 21y^2$

3.4

1. $x^2 - 4x + 4$ **2.** $y^2 + 8y + 16$ **3.** $4m^2 - 20m + 25$ **4.** $9t^2 + 42t + 49$ **5.** $25m^2 - 30mn + 9n^2$

6. $49r^2 + 70rs + 25s^2$ **7.** $\dfrac{9}{16}x^2 + xy + \dfrac{4}{9}y^2$ **8.** $\dfrac{25}{49}u^2 - \dfrac{8}{7}uv + \dfrac{16}{25}v^2$ **9.** $t^2 - 36$ **10.** $16t^2 - 25$

11. $49x^2 - 9y^2$ **12.** $4x^4 - 1$ **13.** $m^3 - 9m^2 + 27m - 27$ **14.** $8x^3 + 12x^2y + 6xy^2 + y^3$

15. $64x^3 - 144x^2y + 108xy^2 - 27y^3$ **16.** $x^4 - 4x^3y + 6x^2y^2 - 4xy^3 + y^4$

17. $81x^4 + 216x^3y + 216x^2y^2 + 96xy^3 + 16y^4$ **18.** $x^4 - 1$ **19.** $16 - r^4$ **20.** $9x^4 - y^2$

21. 42,436   **22.** 8,464   **23.** 1.1025   **24.** .9409   **25.** 9,919

26. 9,951

3.5

1. 4 2. $\dfrac{8}{27}$ 3. $-\dfrac{64}{125}$ 4. $\dfrac{625}{81}$ 5. $\dfrac{1}{x^{20}}$

6. $\dfrac{y^6}{x^9}$ 7. r^3s^{15} 8. $\dfrac{1}{k}$ 9. $2a^4$ 10. 1

11. $-\dfrac{27}{125x^{18}y^6}$ 12. 64 13. $27k^2l^7$ 14. $\dfrac{a^{18}}{b^{12}}$ 15. x^2

16. $\dfrac{y^9}{8x^4}$ 17. $\dfrac{8x^5}{y^5}$ 18. 72 19. $\dfrac{81}{4}$ 20. $\dfrac{27}{8}$

21. $\dfrac{x^4}{4y^4}$ 22. $-\dfrac{1}{8x^6y^3}$ 23. $\dfrac{1}{x^{14y}}$ 24. $\dfrac{1}{4^{2k+3}}$ 25. $x^{y^2+4y} \cdot y^{x^2+4x}$

26. 1 27. $\dfrac{113}{72}$ 28. $-\dfrac{1}{16}$ 29. $\dfrac{29}{675}$ 30. $\dfrac{x^2}{25}$

31. $\dfrac{y^5}{x^4}$ 32. x^8

3.6

1. $7x^2$ 2. $8x^2$ 3. $-4yz$ 4. $-3st$

5. $2m^2 - \dfrac{3}{2}m + \dfrac{5}{2m}$ 6. $2k^3 - \dfrac{1}{3}k^2 + 1 + \dfrac{3}{k} + \dfrac{10}{3k^2}$

7. $\dfrac{1}{2}x^4y^4 - \dfrac{1}{4}x^3y^9 + \dfrac{3}{4xy^2}$ 8. $\dfrac{x^4}{3y} + \dfrac{2y^3}{3x} - xy^5$ 9. $2s^k - 3s^3 - 6s$

10. $\dfrac{3a^x}{b^{y-1}} - 5b^{y+2} - \dfrac{6b^{3y}}{a^x}$

11. Divisor $= 2k-3$, dividend $= 8k^4 - 12k^3 - 2k^2 + 7k - 6$, Quotient $= 4k^3 - k + 2$, Remainder $= 0$

12. Divisor $= m^2 - 2$, Dividend $= -6m - m^2 + m^4$, Quotient $= m^2 + 1$, Remainder $= -6m + 2$

13. $x+3$ 14. $x-3$ 15. $3y+4$ 16. t^2+3t-2 17. x^2+3 18. $4x^3 - 3x^2 + 3x + 1$

19. $9a^2 - 6a + 4$ 20. $4b-3$ 21. x^2-1 22. $t^4 + 2t^3 + 4t^2 + 8t + 16$

23. $3x^2 + 7x + 3$ 24. $8x^2 - 12x + 25 - \dfrac{130}{2x+5}$ 25. $x^2 - 2 + \dfrac{-x^2+7x+4}{x^3+2x+1}$ 26. $y - \dfrac{9}{2} + \dfrac{15}{2y+4}$

27. $12x^3 - 34x^2 + 34x - 10$ 28. $-4x^5 + 23x^3 - 2x^2 - 26x + 5$

3.7

1. 4.501×10^3 2. 9.537×10 3. -8.47509×10^2 4. 4.0009×10^2 5. 3.4×10^{-2}

6. 8.09×10^{-3} 7. 5.29×10^3 8. 7.75×10^7 9. 3.7×10^{-6} 10. 6.78×10^{-7}

11. 786 12. $359,000$ 13. 49705 14. $.52349$ 15. -345.7

16. $-.003456$ 17. $.000000057095$ 18. $.0009725$

REVIEW EXERCISE 3.9

1. $\dfrac{81}{2}$ 2. -5 3. -3 4. 1000

5. $2 \cdot 3^4 x^3 y^2$ 6. $24x^4$ 7. $\dfrac{y^4}{x^6}$ 8. $\dfrac{y^2}{x^2z^2}$

9. 67 10. -1 11. $-5x^7 + 4x^3 + 3x^2 - 7x - 2$ degree: 7 12. $5x^5 + 3x^4 + 5x^2 - 7x - 5$ degree: 5

13. $4p^3 - 5p + 5$ 14. $4x^4 - 3x^3 - 8x^2 + 3x$ 15. $-4p^3 + 6p^2 - 7p + 3$ 16. $-14x^4$

17. $12x^5 - 20x^4 + 8x^3$ 18. $21x^5 - 6x^4 + 35x^3 - 3x^2 - 2x$ 19. $15y^3 - 19y^2 + 6y$ 20. $12x^3 - 11x^2 - 15x$

21. $\dfrac{16}{25}x^2 + \dfrac{24}{5}xy^2 + 9y^4$ 22. $\dfrac{9}{4}x^4 - 21x^2 + 49$ 23. $25x^2 - 9y^4$ 24. 36.6025

25. $\dfrac{1}{x^3}$ 26. $\dfrac{b^8}{a^7}$ 27. $\dfrac{12b^2}{a^4}$ 28. $\dfrac{2^3 \cdot 3 \cdot p}{q^{18}}$

29. $a^{2x^2 + 2y^2 + x^2/y^2}$ 30. $-\dfrac{8}{5}x^2$ 31. $\dfrac{2}{3}t - 1 + \dfrac{4}{3t}$ 32. Quotient $= 2a + \dfrac{1}{2}$; Remainder $= \dfrac{17}{2}$

33. Quotient $= 5x+5$; Remainder $= 14x+2$ 34. Quotient $= y^2 + 4y + 4$; Remainder $= -8y - 1$ 35. a) 1.357×10^6 b) 3.57×10^{-3} 36. a) 810 b) $.0005$

1. $\dfrac{25}{27}$ 2. -2

3. (a) 9.784×10^3
   (b) 2.35×10^{-4}

4. (a) 270,000
   (b) .0098

5. $7x^2+5x-6$; trinomial; degree = 2
6. $4x^2-1$; binomial; degree = 2

7. $15x^5$; monomial; degree = 5
8. $5x^4+4x^3+9x^2+15x+3$

9. $5x^3-10x^2-5x+3$
10. $-x^4+5x^3-2x^2+x+1$
11. $-15x^7+10x^5-15x^3$
12. $12x^5+20x^4-10x^3+33x^2-37x-7$

13. $-3x+4+\dfrac{4}{x}-\dfrac{1}{x^2}$;
14. quotient$=15x^3-15x^2-7x+30$; remainder$=-23x-21$
15. 15.9951

CHAPTER 4

4.1

1. 2   2. 15   3. 12   4. 3   5. $4mn^2$

6. $7xy^2$ 7. $36=4(9)$ 8. $5x^2=x(5x)$ 9. $3x^4y^5=3x^2\left(x^2y^5\right)$ 10. $24p^4q^5=3p^3q^2\left(8pq^3\right)$

11. No   12. No   13. Yes   14. No   15. $2x\left(2+3x^2\right)$

16. $14x^2(2+3x)$ 17. $4y^3\left(2-y^2\right)$ 18. $1\left(11y^2-12z^3\right)$ 19. $25m^3\left(m^2-2m+4\right)$ 20. $9mn\left(5mn^2-4n+7m^2\right)$

21. $(1-5b)(3a-4b)$ 22. $(r-2s)(r+s)$ 23. $(x-5)(x-y)$ 24. $(a+b)(r-1)$

25. $(x+2y)(x+3)$ 26. $(y-1)\left(x^2-3\right)$ 27. $(x-1)\left(x^3-x^2+1\right)$ 28. $(m+2)\left(m^3+2m^2+2\right)$

29. $(x-1)\left(x^2+x+1\right)$ 30. $(a-b)(a+b)$ 31. $n\left(n^2p-1\right)(2n-p+3m)$ 32. $3a(a+1)(a+2)\left(a^3+a^2-a+1\right)$

4.2

1. Yes   2. No   3. Yes   4. Yes   5. $x+5$

6. $x+7$ 7. $t+3$ 8. $3r+1$ 9. $2y(2y+1)(y-3)$ 10. $(x-11)(x+2)$

11. $(x-5)^2$ 12. $(z-6)(z+5)$ 13. $(x-3)(x+2)$ 14. $(z+3)(z-2)$ 15. $(x-3)(x-2)$

16. $(x-1)(x-4)$ 17. $(x-4)(x+1)$ 18. $(x+4)(x-1)$ 19. $(x-5)(x+1)$ 20. $(x+5)(x-1)$

21. $(x-5)(x-1)$ 22. $(x-7)(x+2)$ 23. $(x+7)(x-2)$ 24. $(x-7)(x-2)$ 25. $(x+7)(x-3)$

26. $(x-7)(x+3)$ 27. $(x-3)(x-7)$ 28. $(2x-1)(x+3)$ 29. $(2x+1)(x-3)$ 30. $(3x+1)(x-2)$

31. $(3x-1)(x+2)$ 32. $(4x+5)(x-3)$ 33. $(4x-5)(x+3)$ 34. $(3x-1)(2x+3)$ 35. $(3x+1)(2x-3)$

36. $(3x-1)(2x-3)$ 37. $(3x+1)(2x+3)$ 38. $(3x-1)(2x-1)$ 39. $(3x+1)(2x-1)$ 40. $(3x-1)(2x+1)$

41. $(3x+1)(2x+1)$ 42. $(5x-2)(2x+3)$ 43. $(5x+2)(2x-3)$ 44. $(5x+2)(2x+3)$ 45. $(5x-2)(2x-3)$

46. $(r+4)(8-r)$ 47. $-5(t+3)(t+5)$ 48. $x^3(a-7)(a-5)$ 49. $ab^4(2a-b)(6a+b)$

50. $3xy(3x+7y)(2x-5y)$ 51. $x^2(7x-8)(3x+2)$

4.3

1. $(x-3)(x+3)$ 2. $(2x-5)(2x+5)$ 3. Not factorable   4. $(9a-5b)(9a+5b)$

5. $2(a-2b)(a+2b)$ 6. $3(x-2y)(x+2y)$ 7. $2(1-2t)(1+2t)$ 8. $2(3-5a)(3+5a)$

9. $x(y-x)(y+x)$ 10. $2b(a-3b)(a+3b)$ 11. $5a(a-2b)(a+2b)$ 12. $3(t-3)(t+3)$

13. $bc(a-b)(a+b)$ 14. $(m-3)(m+3)\left(m^2+9\right)$ 15. Not factorable   16. $\left(r^2-7\right)\left(r^2+7\right)$

17. $(x-3)^2$ 18. $(x+4)^2$ 19. $(a+5)^2$ 20. $(r-7)^2$

21. $\left(y-\dfrac{7}{2}\right)^2$ 22. $\left(t+\dfrac{5}{2}\right)^2$ 23. $2(x-2)^2$ 24. $3(a+3)^2$

25. $b(a-b)^2$ 26. $(4a+3b)^2$ 27. $(7z-2t)^2$ 28. $x^2(3+8y)^2$

4.3 (contd.)

29. $a^2b^2(x-10)^2$ **30.** $(x+3)^2+4^2$ **31.** $(x-8)^2+6^2$ **32.** $(x-2)^2+3^2$

33. $(x-1)(x^2+x+1)$ **34.** $(x+3)(x^2-3x+9)$ **35.** $(3a-b)(9a^2+3ab+b^2)$

36. $(4r+5s)(16r^2-20rs+25s^2)$ **37.** $(5x+2y)(25x^2-10xy+4y^2)$ **38.** $(9p-10q)(81p^2+90pq+100q^2)$

39. $2x(x^2+3y^2)$ **40.** $8(x^2+2y^2)(x^4-2x^2y^2+4y^4)$

4.4

1. $5, -\dfrac{4}{3}$ **2.** $-\dfrac{3}{2}, -\dfrac{5}{3}$ **3.** $\dfrac{1}{3}$ **4.** $0, 2$ **5.** $-1, \dfrac{3}{2}$ **6.** $2, -2$

7. $3, -3$ **8.** $3, -3$ **9.** $0, 5, 7$ **10.** $2, 5$ **11.** $-6, -4$ **12.** $7, -1$

13. $-1, -2$ **14.** $\dfrac{8}{3}, -\dfrac{8}{3}$ **15.** $\dfrac{2}{5}, \dfrac{2}{5}$ **16.** $-2, \dfrac{5}{2}$ **17.** $0, \dfrac{7}{15}$ **18.** $11, -2$

19. $\dfrac{1}{2}, 2$ **20.** $1, -\dfrac{1}{2}$ **21.** $-\dfrac{5}{6}, 2$ **22.** $0, 0, -2$ **23.** $0, -\dfrac{5}{2}, \dfrac{5}{2}$ **24.** $0, -1, 9$

25. $0, 0, -\dfrac{5}{7}, 1$ **26.** $0, -\dfrac{1}{6}, -\dfrac{3}{2}$ **27.** $-1, -4, 1, 4$ **28.** $-3, 3$ **29.** No solution **30.** $-2, 2$

4.5

1. 12, 14; -14, -12 **2.** 17, 19; -19, -17 **3.** 7, 8, 9; -9, -8, -7 **4.** 6, 8; -8, -6 **5.** 11, 12; -12, -11

6. 9 **7.** 9 meters by 14 meters **8.** 44 yards **9.** 8 **10.** 9 feet by 12 feet

11. 3 feet, 8 feet **12.** 10 feet **13.** 4 inches **14.** 6m **15.** $77^{\mathbf{0}}, 103^{\mathbf{0}}$ **16.** $48°$

4.6

1. $-3x^2+2x+5 \geq 0$ **2.** $5x^2+3x+5 < 0$ **3.** $7x^2-2x+25 > 0$ **4.** $-x^2-x+3 \leq 0$ **5.** $\dfrac{1}{2}, 3$

6. 6, -1 **7.** $-2, \dfrac{1}{3}$ **8.** -4 **9.** None

10. $x \leq -3$ or $x \geq 7$

11. $-8 \leq z \leq -4$

12. $t < -2$ or $t > 3$

13. $-\dfrac{1}{2} < p < 5$

14. $p \leq -\dfrac{5}{4}$ or $x \geq \dfrac{7}{3}$

15. $-4 \leq x \leq -1$

16. $y \leq 4$ or $y \geq 6$

17. $-5 \leq z \leq -4$

18. $-6 \leq z \leq -5$

19. $-1 \leq x \leq 8$

20. $m < -4$ or $x > \dfrac{1}{2}$

21. $-1 \leq q \leq \dfrac{2}{5}$

22. $x < -\dfrac{3}{2}$ or $x > \dfrac{3}{2}$

23. $-3 \leq x \leq 3$

24. $x = 2$

25. No Solution

26. All Real Numbers

27. All Real Numbers Different From -1

REVIEW EXERCISE 4.8

1. 3 **2.** 1 **3.** $4p^2q$

4. 1 **5.** $9x^2(3x-4)$ **6.** $7(9y^2-2z^2)$

7. $15pq^2(2pq+3p^3-5q^2)$ **8.** $(3s-5t)(4s+5t^2)$ **9.** $(3x+4y)(4x-5)$

10. $(4x^2+y)(3x-y)$ **11.** $(r+3)(r^3+3r-2)$ **12.** $(x^2-y)(3x^3-2y^2+1)$

13. $x^2+2x-15=(x+5)(x-3)$ **14.** $4x^2+13x-14=(4x+7)(3x-2)$ **15.** $(x+8)(x-2)$

16. $(x-2)(x-4)$ **17.** $(6x-1)(6x+1)$ **18.** $(4t+1)^2$

19. $2(4y+1)(y-1)$ **20.** $(p-4)(3p+2)$ **21.** $x(2x+1)(x-3)$

22. $(x+1)(x+2)$ **23.** $(x^2+3)(x^2-2)$ **24.** $(x-2)(x+2)(2x^2+1)$

25. Prime   **26.** Prime   **27.** $(p-4)(p+4)$

28. $(2a-7)(2a+7)$ **29.** Prime   **30.** $(x^2-6)(x^2+6)$

31. $(2x+3)(2x-3)(4x^2+9)$ **32.** $(y-4)^2$ or $(y-4)(y-4)$ **33.** $2(z+3)(z+3)$ or $2(z+3)^2$

34. $\left(x-\dfrac{5}{2}\right)\left(x-\dfrac{5}{2}\right)$ **35.** $(3x+5y)(3x+5y)$ or $(3x+5y)^2$ **36.** $(3x-5y)(9x^2+15xy+25y^2)$

37. $(2rs+3t)(4r^2s^2-6rst+9t^2)$ **38.** $(6ab^2-5c^2)(36a^2b^4+30ab^2c^2+25c^4)$ **39.** $-4,\dfrac{5}{3}$

40. $-\dfrac{3}{2}$ **41.** $-10;-5$ **42.** $5,10$

43. $-5,20$ **44.** $0,-\dfrac{1}{2}$ **45.** $-\dfrac{1}{2}$

46. $-4,3$ **47.** $-\dfrac{3}{2},-1$ **48.** $-\dfrac{1}{2},\dfrac{2}{3}$

49. No solution   **50.** $-2,2,3,-3$ **51.** $-13,-11;11,13$

52. $-11,-10;10,11$ **53.** 7 **54.** $11,14$

55. 8 feet and 4 feet   **56.** 5 inch, 12 inch, 13 inch   **57.** 7 miles

58. $140°$ **59.** $-4,3$ **60.** $-2,6$

61. **None**   **62.** $-4 \le x \le 2$ **63.** $y \le -6$ or $y \ge 0$

64. $-\dfrac{2}{3} \le x \le \dfrac{3}{2}$ **65.** **Set of All Real Numbers**   **66.** **No Solution**

67. $x=2$ **68.** $x < -4$ or $x > -3$ **69.** **No Solution**

70. $-5 \le x \le 5$

SELF TEST 4.9

1. $8xy(3x^2y^3 + 5x - 8y)$ 2. $(3a - 5b)(4b - a)$ 3. $(4x - 3y)(3x + 5)$

4. $(3x - y)(4x^2 + 3y - 2)$ 5. $(4p - 3q)(2p + q - 5)$ 6. $6x^2 - 7x - 20 = (2x - 5)(3x + 4)$

7. $(5a - 1)(5a - 1)$ 8. Prime 9. $x(x - 6)(x + 3)$ 10. $(2x - 3)(4x + 5)$

11. $3(2p - 3q)(2p + 3q)$ 12. Prime 13. $(2m + n^2)(4m^2 - 2mn^2 + n^4)$

14. $6, -3$ 15. $-2, \dfrac{1}{3}$ 16. $-3, 3$ 17. $-2, 0, \dfrac{5}{6}$

18. $4, 6$ 19. 10 meters 20. 10 feet

21. Since $4x^2 - 9$ can be further factored as $(2x - 3)(2x + 3)$. 22. No solution

23. $-3 \le x \le \dfrac{4}{3}$ 24. $t \le -2$ $t \le \dfrac{4}{3}$

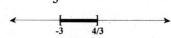

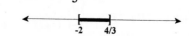

CHAPTER 5

5.1

1. None 2. 0 3. $\dfrac{2}{5}$ 4. -3 5. $-1, 1$ 6. $2, 3$ 7. None 8. $-5, -6$

9. 1 10. -13 11. $\dfrac{5}{3}$ 12. $\dfrac{7}{8}$ 13. $\dfrac{1}{5}$ 14. $\dfrac{2}{5}$ 15. $\dfrac{9}{7}$ 16. $\dfrac{17}{64}$

5.2

1. $\dfrac{2}{3}$ 2. $5x^2$ 3. $-\dfrac{2q^4}{3p}$ 4. $\dfrac{8x^5}{5}$ 5. $\dfrac{4t - 5}{2}$ 6. $\dfrac{a}{3}$ 7. $\dfrac{3p}{2}$

8. $\dfrac{3t}{4(s - t)}$ 9. $\dfrac{3}{2a - 1}$ 10. $x + y$ 11. $\dfrac{3}{x - 2}$ 12. $-\dfrac{y}{3}$ 13. $t - 1$ 14. $\dfrac{x^3 + 1}{x^3 + a}$

15. $a - b$ 16. $\dfrac{2(x - y)}{x + 2}$ 17. $\dfrac{1}{p + 3}$ 18. $\dfrac{4p + 5q}{4p - 5q}$ 19. $\dfrac{16p^2 - 25q^2}{16p^2 - 40q + 25q^2}$ 20. $\dfrac{2x + 1}{2 - x}$ 21. $\dfrac{3t - 5}{t + 2}$

5.3

1. $\dfrac{3}{5}$ 2. $\dfrac{5a^2}{6}$ 3. $\dfrac{y^2q^2}{p^3x}$ 4. $\dfrac{2x^3}{3y^4}$ 5. $\dfrac{27s}{2r^2}$ 6. $\dfrac{3}{2p}$

7. $\dfrac{50x}{27}$ 8. $a/6$ 9. $-\dfrac{p^8}{18q^6}$ 10. $\dfrac{4m^2}{5n^3}$ 11. $\dfrac{(a + 1)^2}{a - 1}$ 12. $\dfrac{18}{(x - 1)}$

13. -3 14. $(t - 6)(t + 3)$ 15. -1 16. $a - 5$ 17. $\dfrac{(t - 2)(5t + 2)}{(4t + 1)(t + 2)}$

18. $\dfrac{(x - 2)(2x + 3)}{2(x + 1)}$ 19. $\dfrac{2y}{y - 3}$ 20. $\dfrac{(z - 3)(z + 3)}{(z - 2)^2}$ 21. $\dfrac{1 - a}{3a + 2}$ 22. $\dfrac{(x - 2)(x + 2)}{x(3x - 1)}$ 23. $\dfrac{10(t + 5)}{t^2 + 15t + 30}$

24. 1 25. $\dfrac{-(p + 2)(p - 3)}{p^2(p^2 + 1)(p - 1)(p + 1)}$

5.4

1. ab **2.** x^2 **3.** $(x-1)(x-4)$ **4.** $p-4$ **5.** $(t+6)(t-2)(t-5)(t-4)$

6. $\text{LCD}=6(x-2)$; $\dfrac{4}{6(x-2)}$, $\dfrac{3}{6(x-2)}$ **7.** $\text{LCD}=8(x+2)(x-1)$; $\dfrac{x-1}{8(x+2)(x-1)}$, $\dfrac{16}{8(x+2)(x-1)}$

8. $\text{LCD}=(t-2)(t+2)$; $\dfrac{2+t}{(t-2)(t+2)}$, $\dfrac{t+2}{(t-2)(t+2)}$ **9.** $\text{LCD}=(p+1)(p-4)$; $\dfrac{2p}{(p+1)(p-4)}$, $\dfrac{p-4}{(p+1)(p-4)}$

10. $\text{LCD}=a(a-3)(a+3)$; $\dfrac{2a^2-5a-3}{a(a-3)(a+3)}$, $\dfrac{a}{a(a-3)(a+3)}$

11. $\text{LCD}=(x+3)^2(x^2-3x+9)$; $\dfrac{x^2+3x}{(x+3)^2(x^2-3x+9)}$, $\dfrac{-2x^2+6x-18}{(x+3)^2(x^2-3x+9)}$

12. $\text{LCD}=(x+2)(x-4)$; $\dfrac{3x-12}{(x+2)(x-4)}$, $\dfrac{x+2}{(x+2)(x-4)}$ **13.** $\text{LCD}=z$; $\dfrac{z^2}{z}$, $\dfrac{1}{z}$

14. $\text{LCD}=t^2(t-1)(t+1)$; $\dfrac{3t^3-3t^2}{t^2(t-1)(t+1)}$, $\dfrac{2t^2-2}{t^2(t-1)(t+1)}$, $\dfrac{t^4+t^3}{t^2(t-1)(t+1)}$

15. $\text{LCD}=m(m-5)(m+5)$; $\dfrac{m^2+3m-10}{m(m-5)(m+5)}$, $\dfrac{2m^2}{m(m-5)(m+5)}$, $\dfrac{m-5}{m(m-5)(m+5)}$

5.5

1. $\dfrac{5}{x}$ **2.** $\dfrac{-3}{x}$ **3.** $\dfrac{4x+4}{x^2}$ **4.** 2 **5.** $\dfrac{x+1}{x^2+x+1}$ **6.** $t+2$

7. $\dfrac{4}{x-3}$ **8.** 1 **9.** $\dfrac{3x+10}{24}$ **10.** $\dfrac{4x-6}{3x}$ **11.** $\dfrac{4x-7}{2x}$ **12.** $\dfrac{y+3}{y^2}$

13. $\dfrac{9}{x-2}$ **14.** $\dfrac{1}{x+y}$ **15.** $\dfrac{2b}{(3a-2b)(3a+2b)}$ **16.** $\dfrac{2(r^2+s^2)}{(r-s)^2}$ **17.** $\dfrac{1}{z+4}$ **18.** x

19. $\dfrac{t-2}{6(3t+2)}$ **20.** $\dfrac{13x-x^2}{(x-1)(x+2)(x+3)}$ **21.** $\dfrac{2m^2-2m+1}{m(m-1)}$ **22.** $\dfrac{16s+rs-6r}{r^2s^2}$ **23.** $\dfrac{2x+47}{10x}$

24. $\dfrac{7a-4}{(a-1)(a+1)}$ **25.** $\dfrac{1}{x+2}$ **26.** $\dfrac{1}{1-x^2}$

5.6

1. $\dfrac{9}{10}$ **2.** $\dfrac{1}{10}$ **3.** $\dfrac{22}{5}$ **4.** $-\dfrac{2}{3}$ **5.** $-\dfrac{5}{6}$ **6.** $\dfrac{pq}{5}$

7. $\dfrac{2(t+3)}{t(t-4)}$ **8.** $\dfrac{24x^4}{1+x}$ **9.** $-\dfrac{3}{x}$ **10.** $\dfrac{5(y+4)}{y+5}$ **11.** $-\dfrac{1}{a+b}$ **12.** $\dfrac{3t^2-3t-6}{2t^3}$

13. $\dfrac{a^3-a^2+2a}{(a-3)(a+2)}$ **14.** $4x(x+4)$ **15.** $\dfrac{2x+1}{x-2}$ **16.** $\dfrac{a^2+b}{a^2-b}$ **17.** $\dfrac{x+3}{(3x-7)(x+2)}$ **18.** $t-t^2$

19. $\dfrac{3m+1}{(m+1)^2}$ **20.** $\dfrac{10}{3}$

5.7

1. 12 **2.** 3 **3.** $\dfrac{9}{2}$ **4.** 12 **5.** 5 **6.** 5 **7.** $4,-1$

8. $1,-11$ **9.** $\dfrac{12}{7}$ **10.** $3,-\dfrac{6}{7}$ **11.** No Solution   **12.** No Solution   **13.** 1 is an extraneous solution

14. No Solution   **15.** 5; 3 extraneous   **16.** $P=\dfrac{kT}{V}$ **17.** $R=\dfrac{E-Ir}{I}$ **18.** $P=\dfrac{qr}{3q-r}$

5.8

1. 18
2. $\frac{2}{5}$
3. $\frac{3}{8}, \frac{3}{4}$
4. $\frac{1}{3}, 4$
5. 25 miles per hour
6. 3 miles per hour
7. 55 miles per hour and 40 miles per hour
8. 140 miles per hour
9. 15 hours
10. 2 hours 24 minutes
11. $\frac{84}{19} = 4\frac{8}{19}$ hours
12. $2\frac{6}{7}$ hours
13. $7\frac{1}{2}$ hours
14. $ 440
15. 1 hour 24 minutes
16. 21
17. $k = 16; \; v = \frac{1}{4}$
18. 30
19. $16t^2$
20. $x = \frac{r^2}{s^2}; \; \frac{36}{25}$

REVIEW EXERCISE 5.10

1. $\frac{2}{3}$
2. 2
3. $-\frac{1}{2}, \frac{1}{3}$
4. $\frac{-2}{5}$
5. None
6. 0
7. $\frac{1}{11}$
8. 1
9. $\frac{9}{28}$
10. $\frac{1}{2}$
11. $\frac{3}{4p^2}$
12. $\frac{2x}{3y}$
13. -1
14. $\frac{x+2}{2}$
15. $\frac{x(x+9)}{x-9}$
16. $\frac{3a-4b}{3a+4b}$
17. $\frac{4p+3q}{p+2}$
18. $\frac{6xy}{5}$
19. $\frac{15x^2+10x}{8x+4}$
20. $\frac{8x^2-14x+3}{6x^2+13x+5}$
21. $\frac{5x}{14}$
22. $\frac{3x+3}{10x+14}$
23. $\frac{3}{2}$
24. $\frac{y^2-y-2}{y-5}$
25. x^2-3x+2
26. $\frac{(x+2)^2(x+3)}{(x-4)^3}$
27. 1
28. $\frac{p^2+10p+25}{p^2-14p+49}$
29. xy
30. $x-4$
31. $(x-1)^2(2x-1)$
32. $12x^3; \; \frac{2x^2+2x}{12x^3}, \; \frac{9x-3}{12x^3}$
33. $2(x+1)^2; \; \frac{6x}{2(x+1)^2}, \; \frac{5x+5}{2(x+1)^2}$
34. $(x-2)(x-3)(x+3); \; \frac{2x^2-4x}{(x-2)(x-3)(x+3)}, \; \frac{3x^2+10x+3}{(x-2)(x-3)(x+3)}$
35. $(x-2)^2(x^2+2x+4); \; \frac{x^2-2x}{(x-2)^2(x^2+2x+4)}, \; \frac{2x^2+4x+8}{(x-2)^2(x^2+4x+8)}$
36. $8y^3+1; \; \frac{y}{8y^3+1}, \; \frac{8y^2+4y}{8y^3+1}$
37. $\frac{9}{x}$
38. $\frac{2x-5}{4x}$
39. $\frac{-a}{a-3} \left(or \; \frac{a}{3-a} \right)$
40. $\frac{3}{p-3}$
41. $\frac{y}{(x-y)^2}$
42. $-\frac{x}{x^2+x+1}$
43. $\frac{9x+2}{x(x-1)(x+2)}$
44. $\frac{11x^2-x-11}{(2x-1)(3x+2)(x+3)}$
45. $\frac{yz}{2x^2}$
46. $-\frac{x^2y^2}{(x+y)^2}$
47. $\frac{2y-3x}{3+xy}$
48. $\frac{1}{y}$
49. -1
50. -7
51. 7
52. 6
53. $\frac{xz}{z-x}$
54. $\frac{3b^2-a^2}{a+b}$
55. $\frac{32}{36}$
56. $\frac{3}{5}, \frac{6}{5}$
57. 110 miles per hour
58. 25 miles per hour
59. 12 hours
60. 10 hours
61. 1250 tons
62. 288π cubic centimeters
63. **16 times as great**

SELF TEST 5.11

1. $\frac{1}{2}, -2$ **2.** -9 **3.** a) no; b) no; c) yes   **4.** $\frac{3}{5}$ **5.** $\frac{(x-1)(x-2)}{(x+1)(x+2)}$

6. $\frac{p-1}{p-3}$ **7.** 1   **8.** $60x^3$ **9.** $(4x-5)(4x+5)^2$ **10.** $32(2x-1)$

11. $\frac{2x^3-11x^2+20x-12}{(x-2)(x-3)(x+2)}, \frac{x^2-3x}{(x-2)(x-3)(x+2)}$ **12.** $\frac{23}{12x}$ **13.** $\frac{5x^2-3x+2}{x^3}$

14. $\frac{6x+11}{(2x-3)(2x+3)}$ **15.** 0   **16.** $\frac{2x-1}{x+5}$ **17.** $\frac{(x+1)(x+3)}{x+9}$

18. -3 **19.** no solution   **20.** $-5,3$ **21.** $\frac{6}{5}, \frac{1}{2}$ **22.** 2 miles per hour

23. 3 hours   **24.** a) $y = \frac{k}{x^3}$, b) 28,672, c) 56

CHAPTER 6

6.1

1. no   **2.** yes   **3.** yes   **4.** no   **5.** no

6. yes   **7.** yes   **8.** yes   **9.** $\left(4, \frac{2}{3}\right)$ **10.** (–3,11)

11. (8,2)   **12.** (10,–4)   **13.** (0,2)   **14.** (–5,0)   **15.** (–2,2)

16.

x	0	5	4	10
y	–3	0	$-\frac{3}{5}$	3

17.

x	–1	3	7	1
y	–2	0	2	–1

18.

x	–2	0	5
y	–11	–3	17

19.

x	5	5	5
y	–3	4	7

20.

x	0	–1	4
y	–4	–4	–4

21. 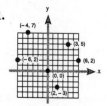   **22.** 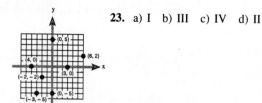   **23.** a) I b) III c) IV d) II

24. a) x-axis   b) y-axis   c) x-axis   d) none   e) y-axis   f) none

25. A: (2,3), B: (0,5), C: (–2,2), D: (5,0), E: (–2,0), F: (–4,–3), G: (–4,1), H: (0,–5)

6.2

1.

x	3	3	3
y	0	2	5
(x,y)	(3,0)	(3,2)	(3,5)

2.

x	–4	0	2
y	5	5	5
(x,y)	(–4,5)	(0,5)	(2,5)

3.

x	–2	–2	–2
y	–3	1	4
(x,y)	(–2,–3)	(–2,1)	(–2,4)

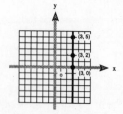

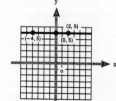

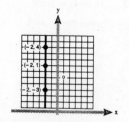

6.2 (Contd.)

4.

x	−3	1	3
y	−3	−3	−3
(x,y)	(−3,−3)	(1,−3)	(3,−3)

5.

x	−3	1	3
y	6	−2	−6
(x,y)	(−3,6)	(1,−2)	(3,−6)

6.

x	0	5	−5
y	0	3	−3
(x,y)	(0,0)	(5,3)	(−5,−3)

7.

x	−2	4	1
y	2	−2	0
(x,y)	(−2,2)	(4,−2)	(1,0)

8.

x	−1	3	−5
y	−1	2	−4
(x,y)	(−1,−1)	(3,2)	(−5,−4)

9. x − intercept: (5,0)

y − intercept: (0,3)

10. x-intercept: (−3,0)

y-intercept: (0,4)

11. x-intercept: (3,0) y-intercept: $\left(0,-\frac{3}{7}\right)$

12. x-intercept: (0,0)

y-intercept: (0,0)

13. x-intercept: $\left(-\frac{3}{2},0\right)$,

y-intercept: does not exist

14. x-intercept: does not exist,

y-intercept: $\left(0,\frac{5}{3}\right)$

15.

16.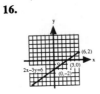

17.

18.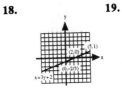

19.

20.

21.

22.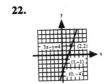

23.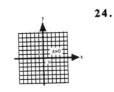

24.

25.

x	0	1	2	3	−1	−2	−3
y	0	−1	−4	−9	−1	−4	−9
(x,y)	(0,0)	(1,−1)	(2,−4)	(3,−9)	(−1,−1)	(−2,−4)	(−3,−9)

26.

x	0	1	2	−1	−2	−3	−4
y	2	5	10	1	2	5	10
(x,y)	(0,2)	(1,5)	(2,10)	(−1,1)	(−2,2)	(−3,5)	(−4,10)

6.3

1. $-\dfrac{2}{5}$ **2.** -1 **3.** undefined **4.** 0 **5.** $-\dfrac{4}{3}$ **6.** undefined

7. $-\dfrac{7}{4}$ **8.** $\dfrac{1}{2}$ **9.** 4 **10.** $-\dfrac{3}{5}$ **11.** 2 **12.** $\dfrac{1}{2}$

13. 3 **14.** -1 **15.** $\dfrac{2}{3}$ **16.** A: zero; B: positive; C: undefined; D: negative; E: negative

17. rising **18.** falling **19.** rising **20.** falling **21.** $m_A = -1 = m_B$

22. $m_A = -1$
$m_B = 1$ perpendicular

23. $m_A = -2$
$m_B = 1 / 2$ perpendicular

24. $m_A = -1$
$m_B = -1$ parallel

25. parallel **26.** neither **27.** perpendicular **28.** perpendicular **29.** parallel **30.** neither

---

6.4

1. $y = 2x + 3$ **2.** $y + 3x + 2 = 0$ **3.** $3y + 3x = 2$ **4.** $5y = 3x + 20$ **5.** $2y + 1 = 0$

6. 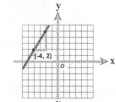 **7.** 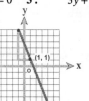 **8.**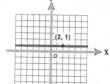

9. 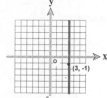 **10.** 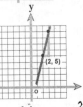 **11.**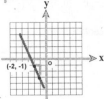

12. $y = x - 3$ **13.** $y = \dfrac{3}{5}x - \dfrac{4}{5}$ **14.** $y = -\dfrac{2}{7}x + \dfrac{9}{7}$ **15.** $y = 4x + 6$ **16.** $y + 3x = 11$

17. $4x + 5y + 4 = 0$ **18.** $7y + 3 = 0$ **19.** $2y - 5x = 0$ **20.** $8x + 12y = 13$ **21.** $7x + 9y = 28$

22. $3y = x + 7$ **23.** $5x + y = 5$ **24.** $x + y + 1 = 0$ **25.** $3y - 3x = 2$ **26.** $6y = 25x + 9$

27. $4x - 3y = 5$ **28.** $2y = x + 7$ **29.** $2x + 3y = 17$ **30.** $3x - 2y = 6$

---

1. $x + y > 3$ **2.** $2y - x \le 5$ **3.** $3x - 4y \ge 12$ **4.** $3x + y < 0$

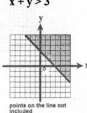
points on the line not included

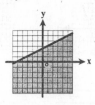

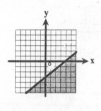

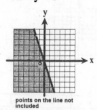
points on the line not included

5. $x > -2$ **6.** $y \le 0$ **7.** $x + 2y \le 4$ **8.** $3x - 2y > 2$

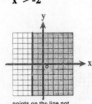
points on the line not included

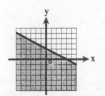

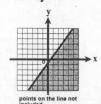
points on the line not included

6.5 (Contd.)

9. $2x - y \leq -3$

10. $x + 4y \geq 5$

11. $x < y$

points on the line not included

12. $3x \geq y$

13. $2x \geq -5$

14. $y < 5$

points on the line not included

15. $3x + 7y > 21$

points on the line not included

16. $2x + 3y < 6$

points on the line included

6.6

1. Not a function; domain = {-2,-1,-3,0} range = {2,0,5}

2. Function; domain = {3,2,-2,4} range = {1,0,-4,2}

3. Function; domain = {-1,-2,0,1,2} range = {0,1,2}

4. Function; domain = {-1,-2,0,1,2} range = { 0,1,4}

5. Not a function; domain = {4,1,0,9} range = {2,-1,0,-3,3}

6. Function

7. Not a function

8. Function

9. Function

10. Function

11. Not a function

12. Not a function

13. Not a function

14. Function

15. Function

16. Function

17. Not a function

18. Not a function

19. Function

20. Function

21. Function

22. $f(2)=12$, $f(0)=2$

23. $g(-2)=-6$, $g(0)=0$, $g(3)=-9$

24. $h(5)=25$, $h(-3)=-7$

25. $F(4)=-28$, $F(-4)=-68$

26. $P(-2)=\frac{3}{5}$, $P(0)=3$, $P(-1)=\frac{3}{2}$

27. $Q(3)=0$, $Q(-3)=-36$, $Q(0)=-9$

REVIEW EXERCISE 6.8

1. Yes

2. No

3. Yes

4. $(11,-2)$

5. $(-4,-5)$

6.

x	1	-3	7/2	3
y	-2	-10	3	2

7.

x	-2	-2	-2
y	-1	2	0

8.

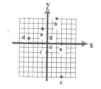

9. $A(2,2)$, $B(4,5)$, $C(-1,1)$, $D(2,5)$, $E(-4,-3)$, $F(6,-1)$, $G(4,0)$, $H(0,-3)$

10.

x	4	4	4
y	-3	1	2

11.

x	-2	0	3
y	-5	-5	-5

12.

x	-3	0	3
y	-2	0	2

13.

x	-1	3	-5
y	1	-2	4

14. x-intercept: $(2,0)$

y-intercept: $(0,3)$

15. x-intercept: $(5,0)$

y-intercept: $(0,-4)$

REVIEW EXERCISE 6.8 (Contd.)

16.

x	0	-1	-2	1	2
y	0	1	4	1	4

17.

x	0	-1	1	2	-2	3	4
y	2	5	1	2	10	5	10

18. 1 **19.** $-\dfrac{4}{3}$ **20.** $\dfrac{3}{4}; -\dfrac{1}{4}$ **21.** $-\dfrac{2}{5}; -\dfrac{3}{5}$ **22.** Neither **23.** Parallel

24. Perpendicular **25.** Perpendicular **26.** $y + 3x = 0$ **27.** $7y = 5x - 21$ **28.** $y = 5$

29. $3y = 2x + 13$ **30.** $2x + y = 9$ **31.** $3x + y = 8$ **32.** $4x + 3y + 1 = 0$

33. $3y = x + 14$ **34.** $x = 0$ **35.** $x + 3y = -11$

36.   **37.**   **38.** points on the line not included **39.** points on the line not included **40.** points on the line not included

41. Not a function;
Domain $= \{2,3,4\}$
Range $=\{-1,1,2\}$

42. Function;
Domain $= \{-2,-1,0,1,2\}$
Range $= \{0,1,3\}$

43. Function
44. Not a function
45. Not a function

SELF TEST 6.9

1. $(-1,-7)$, $\left(2,-\dfrac{5}{2}\right)$, $(5,2)$, $(3,-1)$

2. $(2,1)$, $\left(0,\dfrac{7}{3}\right)$, $(-1,3)$

3. y-intercept; $(0,0)$ **4.**   **5.** y-intercept ; not exist **6.** y-intercept; $(0,-3)$

7. $m = \dfrac{2}{5}$

8. $m = 0$; horizontal line
y-intercept $\left(0, -\dfrac{3}{2}\right)$

9. $m=$ undefined; vertical line
y-intercept does not exist

10. $m = -\dfrac{3}{2}$;
y-intercept $\left(0, \dfrac{7}{2}\right)$

11.   **12.**   **13.** 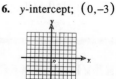 **14.**

15. points on the line not included

16. Not a function; Domain $= \{-3,-2,-1,0\}$, Range $= \{-3,-2,-1,4\}$

17. Function : Domain $= \{2,4,6,7\}$, Range $= \{-3,0,3\}$

18. Function
19. Not a function
20. Not a function
21. Not a straight line
22. Straight line

CHAPTER 7

7.1

1. Solution

2. Solution

3. Not a solution

4. Not a solution

5. Solution

6. Solution

7.

8.

9.

10.

11.

12.

13. Slopes: $\frac{3}{4}$, 1; system has unique solution

14. Slopes: $-\frac{5}{2}$, $\frac{2}{5}$; system has unique solution.

15. Slopes: $\frac{2}{3}$, $\frac{2}{3}$; lines distinct and parallel; system inconsistent.

16. Slopes: 2, 2; lines distinct and parallel; system inconsistent.

17. Slopes: $-\frac{2}{3}$, $-\frac{2}{3}$; lines identical; system dependent.

18. Slopes: $-\frac{9}{35}$, $-\frac{6}{7}$; system has unique solution.

7.2

1. (3,2)

2. (4, −1)

3. $\left(\frac{9}{2}, \frac{3}{2}\right)$

4. (−3,2)

5. (3,−7)

6. (0,2)

7. $\left(\frac{1}{7}, \frac{45}{14}\right)$

8. $\left(-1, \frac{2}{3}\right)$

9. (−2,3)

10. (2,3)

11. $\left(\frac{1}{4}, \frac{2}{3}\right)$

12. (−2, 5)

13. $\left(-\frac{1}{3}, 1\right)$

14. (7, 0)

15. (−6, 16)

16. $\left(\frac{4}{5}, \frac{3}{4}\right)$

17. inconsistent

18. dependent

19. dependent

20. inconsistent

7.3

1. (5, −2)

2. $\left(\frac{7}{2}, \frac{3}{2}\right)$

3. (−3, 1)

4. $\left(\frac{1}{2}, \frac{3}{2}\right)$

5. (1, 2)

6. $\left(\frac{1}{2}, \frac{2}{3}\right)$

7. dependent

8. (2, −5)

9. (−1, 5)

10. inconsistent

11. (8, −9)

12. $\left(\frac{1}{3}, \frac{1}{3}\right)$

13. dependent

14. inconsistent

15. (2, 4)

16. (−2, 9)

17. (−3, 2)

18. dependent

19. $\left(\frac{4}{5}, \frac{3}{4}\right)$

20. $\left(\frac{11}{19}, \frac{10}{19}\right)$

7.4

1.
points on dashed line not included

2.

3.

4.
points on the lines not included

5.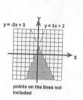
points on the lines not included

6.
points on dashed line not included

7.
points on the line not included

8.
points on the lines not included

9.
points on dashed line not included

10.
points on dashed line not included

7.5

1. −6 and 12

2. 36, 27

3. length = 20 *cm* ; width = 16 *cm*

4. 40°

5. Adult: 140 Children: 50

6. steak: $2.40 hamburger: $1.25

7. $1000

8. big: 110 small: 75

9. 20¢ 12, 10¢ : 16

10. algebra: 6,700 trigonometry: 4,800

11. 3,800 at 10%, 2,200 at 8%

12. 400 oz.

13. 30% solution: 36 liters 80% solution: 24 liters

14. 15% solution: 180 milliliters 40% solution: 120 milliliters

15. $1.50 per pound coffee: 16 lbs $2 per pound of coffee: 9 lbs

16 150 miles per hour

17. boat: $17\frac{1}{2}$ miles per hour current: $2\frac{1}{2}$ miles per hour

18. 55 miles per hour 45 miles per hour

19. 198 miles per hour

20. 100 miles per hour, 75 miles per hour

REVIEW EXERCISE 7.7

1. a) no b) no

2.   **3.**   **4.**   **5.**   **6.**

7. Inconsistent **8.** (1,1) **9.** $\left(\dfrac{8}{11}, \dfrac{26}{11}\right)$ **10.** Dependent **11.** (3,2)

12. $\left(\dfrac{10}{3}, \dfrac{14}{9}\right)$ **13.** $\left(\dfrac{-4}{5}, \dfrac{-7}{5}\right)$ **14.** Inconsistent **15.** $\left(\dfrac{8}{5}, \dfrac{-14}{5}\right)$ **16.** $\left(\dfrac{-3}{2}, \dfrac{1}{4}\right)$

17. Inconsistent **18.** Dependent

19.   **20.**   **21.**   **22.**

points on the lines not included   points on dashed line not included   points on the dashed line not included

23.   **24.**   **25.**

points on dashed line not included

No Solution

26. 69,32 **27.** 4 7 **28.** 510 miles per hour **29.** 30% acid solution = 50 liters
90% acid solution = 250 liters **30.** Stocks: $2000
bonds: $8000

SELF TEST 7.8

1.   **2.**   **3.** (4,−3) **4.** Dependent

5. $\left(\dfrac{1}{2}, 2\right)$ **6.** (−1,2)

7. $\left(\dfrac{10}{7}, \dfrac{-9}{7}\right)$ **8.** Inconsistent **9.** Dependent

10.   **11.** **12.** **13.** 48, 19
14. Coffee: 40 cups

points on dashed line not included   points on the lines not included

501

CHAPTER 8

8.1

1. 2 2. 9 3. 1/5 4. 0 5. non-real 6. 2
7. -2 8. 3 9. non-real 10. 3 11. 2/5 12. 6

13. 12 14. -4 15. 1/3 16. 2/3 17. 5 18. non-real
19. 17 20. -17 21. 17 22. -47 23. 1/47 24. $3x^2-1$
25. $\dfrac{x^2+x}{4}$ 26. rational 27. irrational 28. non-real 29. rational 30. rational
31. 5 inches 32. 6.245 inches 33. 8.062 inches 34. 75.937 feet 35. 8.66 feet

8.2

1. $\sqrt{28}$ 2. $\sqrt{40}$ 3. $\sqrt[4]{18}$ 4. $\sqrt[3]{-875}$ 5. $\sqrt[5]{63}$ 6. $\sqrt{13x^3}$

7. $\sqrt[3]{xy^2}$ 8. $\sqrt{\dfrac{7}{20}}$ 9. $\sqrt[3]{\dfrac{25}{8}}$ or $\dfrac{\sqrt[3]{25}}{2}$ 10. x 11. $\sqrt[5]{\dfrac{p^2q}{r^3}}$ 12. $4\sqrt{3}$

13. $8\sqrt{2}$ 14. $3\sqrt{6}$ 15. $2\sqrt{30}$ 16. $6\sqrt[3]{5}$ 17. $2\sqrt[4]{15}$ 18. $-2\sqrt[5]{9}$

19. $-5\sqrt[3]{25}$ 20. $5\sqrt[3]{25}$ 21. $4p^2\sqrt{2p}$ 22. $ab^2\sqrt{b}$ 23. $ab\sqrt[3]{a^2b}$ 24. $\dfrac{20\sqrt{5}}{9}$

25. $-\dfrac{6}{5}$ 26. $\dfrac{1}{2x\sqrt[4]{xy^2}}$ 27. $\sqrt[3]{5x^2y}$ 28. $2xy\sqrt[3]{9xy^2}$ 29. $-\dfrac{ab^3\sqrt[3]{a^2}}{2}$ 30. $\dfrac{5}{3}xy$

8.3

1. $-\sqrt{2}$ 2. $3\sqrt{7}$ 3. $3\sqrt[3]{4}$ 4. $-4\sqrt[4]{2}$ 5. $6\sqrt[5]{3}$ 6. $4\sqrt[3]{5}$
7. $\dfrac{3}{40}\sqrt{15}$ 8. $\dfrac{23}{18}\sqrt[4]{11}$ 9. 0 10. $-10\sqrt[3]{3}$ 11. $72-40\sqrt{6}$ 12. 7
13. $9x+25y+30\sqrt{xy}$ 14. $4p-6q^2+(12q-2)\sqrt{pq}$ 15. $x-8y-6\sqrt[3]{x^2y}+12\sqrt[3]{xy^2}$ 16. $(4x-7xy)\sqrt{x}$
17. $4x-9y$ 18. $p^2-2q^2-2pq\sqrt[3]{pq}+\sqrt[3]{p^2q^2}$ 19. $3x-2y$ 20. $(48r+50)\sqrt{3}-120\sqrt{2r}$

8.4

1. $\dfrac{3\sqrt{2}}{2}$ 2. $\dfrac{4\sqrt{5}}{5}$ 3. $\dfrac{2\sqrt{6}}{3}$ 4. $\dfrac{\sqrt{2}}{4}$ 5. $\dfrac{2\sqrt[3]{100}}{5}$ 6. $\dfrac{5\sqrt[4]{4^3}}{8}$ or $\dfrac{5\sqrt[4]{4}}{4}$
7. $\dfrac{\sqrt[4]{12}}{4}$ 8. $\dfrac{3\sqrt{10}}{10}$ 9. $\dfrac{4\sqrt{7}}{7}$ 10. $\dfrac{2\sqrt{30}}{3}$ 11. $\dfrac{\sqrt{3}}{5}$ 12. $\dfrac{\sqrt{30}}{10}$ 13. $\dfrac{\sqrt{6}}{3}$
14. $\dfrac{2\sqrt{x}}{x}$ 15. $\dfrac{x\sqrt{6xy}}{2y}$ 16. $\dfrac{p\sqrt[3]{5pq^2}}{q}$ 17. $\dfrac{2r\sqrt{3s}}{3}$ 18. $\dfrac{a}{b}\sqrt[3]{11b^2}$ 19. $2(\sqrt{3}+\sqrt{2})$ 20. $\dfrac{3(\sqrt{5}-1)}{4}$
21. $\dfrac{1}{5}(9-2\sqrt{14})$ 22. $2-\sqrt{3}$ 23. $\dfrac{x+2\sqrt{xy}+y}{x-y}$ 24. $\sqrt{3x}(\sqrt{2}+1)$ 25. $\dfrac{x^2\sqrt{5x}(\sqrt{11}+\sqrt{2})}{5}$

8.5

1. $\sqrt{16}$, 4 2. $\sqrt{36}$, 6 3. $\sqrt[3]{8}$, 2 4. $-\sqrt[3]{8}$, -2 5. $\sqrt[3]{-8}$, -2
6. $\sqrt{4^5}$, 32 7. $\dfrac{1}{\sqrt[3]{27^2}}$, $\dfrac{1}{9}$ 8. $\sqrt{121^3}$, 1331 9. $-\sqrt[4]{81}$, -3 10. $\sqrt[5]{243^2}$, 9

11. $2x^{1/3}$ 12. $\dfrac{y^{1/3}}{2x^{2/3}}$ 13. $\dfrac{3x^{1/3}}{y}$ 14. $\dfrac{2p}{3}$ 15. $\dfrac{8\sqrt{2}\,y^{21/2}}{x^{14}}$

16. $x^{1/2}y^{1/2}$ 17. $\dfrac{p^{1/3}}{q^{3/8}}$ 18. $\dfrac{1}{2}y^{5/4}$ 19. $x^{1/9}y^{2/9}z^{2/3}$ 20. $4x^{1/2}y$

21. $\dfrac{\sqrt[3]{18}}{3}$ 22. $\dfrac{5\sqrt[3]{7}}{7}$ 23. $\dfrac{\sqrt{5y}}{y}$ 24. $\dfrac{\sqrt[3]{3y^2}}{y}$

8.6

1. 9	**2.** 16	**3.** 5	**4.** No solution	**5.** 16
6. 81	**7.** No solution	**8.** 1,3	**9.** 4,3	**10.** 2
11. −3 (Extraneous) or no solution	**12.** 2	**13.** 6 (Extraneous) or no Solution	**14.** 1	**15.** 2, 10
16. 5	**17.** 0,4	**18** 6	**19.** − 4 (Extraneous) or no solution	**20.** 2

REVIEW EXERCISE 8.8

1. 5. **2.** not a real number **3.** 9 **4.** $-\dfrac{3}{5}$ **5.** $\dfrac{t^2 + 2t - 1}{2t - 1}$

6. Irrational **7.** Non - real **8.** Rational **9.** a) 12, −12 b) $\dfrac{9}{4}, -\dfrac{9}{4}$

10. a) $\dfrac{5}{4}$ b) $-\dfrac{2}{7}$ **11.** $\sqrt{40}$ cm **12.** 6.71 feet **13.** $\sqrt{30}$

14. − 4 **15.** xy **16.** $3rs\sqrt[3]{r^2 s^2}$ **17.** $-6p\sqrt[5]{p^2 q^3}$ **18.** −2

19. $\dfrac{1}{2xy^2}$ **20.** $3a\sqrt{2b}$ **21.** $\dfrac{|b|}{2}$ **22.** $4xy^2$ **23.** $-\dfrac{2a^2 b}{3}$

24. $5\sqrt{3} - 9\sqrt{2}$ **25.** $11\sqrt{5} - \sqrt[3]{5}$ **26.** $\left(9x^2 - 4x\right)\sqrt{x} - 3x\sqrt[3]{x}$ **27.** 5 **28.** $x^2 - 2\sqrt{2}\,xy + 2y^2$

29. $x + 4\sqrt{xy} + 4y$ **30.** $2x + \left(\sqrt{7} - 2\sqrt{3}\right)\sqrt{x} - \sqrt{21}$ **31.** $y - \sqrt[3]{y^2} + \sqrt[3]{y} - 1$ **32.** 1 **33.** $\dfrac{7\sqrt{6}}{6}$

34. $\dfrac{3\sqrt{x}}{4}$ **35.** $\dfrac{5\sqrt[3]{2}}{2}$ **36.** $\dfrac{15 - 5\sqrt{5}}{4}$ **37.** $\dfrac{8 + 2\sqrt{3} + 4\sqrt{5} + \sqrt{15}}{13}$

38. $4 - \sqrt{15}$ **39.** $\dfrac{2a + b + 3\sqrt{ab}}{a - b}$ **40.** $\dfrac{p\sqrt{5pq}}{2q^3}$ **41.** $\dfrac{a\sqrt{3} - 3\sqrt{a}}{a - 3}$ **42.** $\dfrac{2p + 5q - 2\sqrt{10pq}}{5q - 2p}$

43. $\dfrac{\sqrt{x^2 + 2x} - 2\sqrt{x + 2}}{x + 2}$ **44.** $\dfrac{\sqrt{y^2 + 3y} + 2\sqrt{y + 3}}{y + 3}$ **45.** 5 **46.** −3 **47.** 125

48. $8x^4$ **49.** $2x^{2/3}$ **50.** $\dfrac{a^3}{8b^{3/2}}$ **51.** $\dfrac{-2p^{\frac{8}{3}} \cdot q}{3}$ **52.** $\dfrac{8y^{3/2}}{x^3}$

53. 6 **54.** 6 **55.** 3 **56.** $\dfrac{1}{4}$ (extraneous) ; no solution

57. 3, 8 **58.** 28.278 sq. in.

SELF TEST 8.9

1. 13 **2.** − 7 **3.** $3x\sqrt{3}$ **4.** $\dfrac{5}{9}$ **5.** $-2\sqrt[5]{4}$

6. $8x^2 y^3 \sqrt{3x^3 y}$ **7.** $-2x^6 y$ **8.** $2\sqrt{3}$ **9.** $\sqrt{3p} + 25\sqrt{3}$ **10.** −7

11. $\sqrt{6}\,y - 7\sqrt{2y} + 7\sqrt{3y} - 49$ **12.** $\dfrac{3\sqrt{2} + \sqrt{10}}{4}$ **13.** $\dfrac{21 + 11\sqrt{6}}{-19}$ **14.** $4\sqrt[3]{x^2} + \dfrac{\sqrt[3]{3x^2}}{x}$ **15.** $\dfrac{25x + 9y + 30\sqrt{xy}}{25x - 9y}$

16. $2^{\frac{1}{4}}$ **17.** $8xy$ **18.** 4 [Extraneous] or no solution **19.** 25, 1 **20.** $\dfrac{1}{4}$ [Extraneous] or no solution

CHAPTER 9

9.1

1. ± 5 **2.** ± 9 **3.** $\pm 7\sqrt{2}$ **4.** $\pm 2\sqrt{11}$ **5.** ± 3

6. $\pm\sqrt{5}$ **7.** ± 2 **8.** $\pm 3\sqrt{3}$ **9.** $\pm\sqrt{5}$ **10.** $\pm\sqrt{3}$

11. $1, -\dfrac{1}{3}$ **12.** $\dfrac{-5 \pm 2\sqrt{2}}{2}$ **13.** $\dfrac{3 \pm 3\sqrt{2}}{5}$ **14.** No real solution **15.** $-\dfrac{1}{3}$

16. $\dfrac{1 \pm 2\sqrt{2}}{2}$ **17.** $\dfrac{3}{4}, -\dfrac{1}{4}$ **18.** $\dfrac{-7 \pm 2\sqrt{3}}{2}$ **19.** $\dfrac{7 \pm 2\sqrt{3}}{2}$ **20.** No real solution

9.2

1. 4 **2.** $\dfrac{49}{4}$ **3.** 9 **4.** $\dfrac{1}{4}$ **5.** $(x+4)^2 - 7$

6. $\left(x-\dfrac{7}{2}\right)^2 - \dfrac{29}{4}$ **7.** $\left(y+\dfrac{1}{2}\right)^2 - \dfrac{41}{4}$ **8.** $\left(z-\dfrac{3}{2}\right)^2 + \dfrac{19}{4}$ **9.** $-2 \pm \sqrt{2}$ **10.** $-\dfrac{1}{2} \pm \dfrac{\sqrt{41}}{2}$

11. $\dfrac{3}{2} \pm \dfrac{3\sqrt{5}}{2}$ **12.** $-\dfrac{7}{2} \pm \dfrac{\sqrt{77}}{2}$ **13.** $-2, -4$ **14.** $\dfrac{5}{2} \pm \dfrac{\sqrt{37}}{2}$ **15.** $\dfrac{7}{4} \pm \dfrac{\sqrt{57}}{4}$

16. $1, -\dfrac{1}{3}$ **17.** $\dfrac{2}{5} \pm \dfrac{\sqrt{19}}{5}$ **18.** $\dfrac{3}{8} \pm \dfrac{\sqrt{41}}{8}$ **19.** $\dfrac{3}{2} \pm \dfrac{\sqrt{65}}{2}$ **20.** $-\dfrac{19}{6} \pm \dfrac{\sqrt{85}}{6}$

9.3

1. i **2.** $-i$ **3.** i **4.** 1 **5.** -1

6. $2i$ **7.** $\sqrt{15}i$ **8.** $\sqrt{45}i$ or $3\sqrt{5}\,i$ **9.** $2 + 2i$; real parts = 2, imaginary part = 2

10. $2 + \dfrac{1}{2}i$; real part = 2, imaginary part = $\dfrac{1}{2}$ **11.** $25 + 4\sqrt{3}\,i$; real part = 25, imaginary part = $4\sqrt{3}$

12. $7 + 4i$ **13.** $-2 - 3i$ **14.** $2 + 3i$ **15.** $-2 + \left(\sqrt{3} - 1\right)i$ **16.** $19 + i$

17. $5 - 11i$ **18.** $-2 - 7i$ **19.** $67 - 13i$ **20.** $-39 + 4i$ **21.** 97

22. $95 + 45i$ **23.** $-32 - i$ **24.** $-6 + 18i$ **25.** $14 + 42i$ **26.** $2 + 5i$

27. $-2 - 9i$ **28.** $-\sqrt{2}i$ **29.** $\dfrac{2}{29} + \dfrac{5}{29}i$ **30.** $\dfrac{-9}{25} + \dfrac{12}{25}i$ **31.** $\dfrac{9}{2} - \dfrac{5}{2}i$

32. $-\dfrac{12}{13} + \dfrac{8}{13}i$

9.4

1. $1, 2$ **2.** $1, \dfrac{1}{2}$ **3.** $-1, -5$ **4.** $-1, -\dfrac{1}{5}$ **5.** 1

6. $-\dfrac{2}{3}$ **7.** $-\dfrac{5}{2} \pm \dfrac{\sqrt{41}}{2}$ **8.** $\dfrac{7}{2} \pm \dfrac{\sqrt{41}}{2}$ **9.** $\dfrac{-5}{2} \pm \dfrac{\sqrt{129}}{6}$ **10.** $-\dfrac{7}{10} \pm \dfrac{\sqrt{89}}{10}$

11. $\dfrac{7}{4} \pm \dfrac{\sqrt{7}}{4}i$ **12.** $\dfrac{3}{10} \pm \dfrac{\sqrt{31}}{10}i$ **13.** $\dfrac{3}{2} \pm \dfrac{\sqrt{7}}{2}i$ **14.** $x = 0, -\dfrac{5}{2} - \dfrac{\sqrt{7}}{2}i, -\dfrac{5}{2} + \dfrac{\sqrt{7}}{2}i$ **15.** $\pm 2, \pm\sqrt{2}i$

16. $14, 16$ **17.** $3, 5,$ **18.** 6 **19.** (i) 50 ft (ii) 2.5 seconds   **20.** 120

21. 15 **22.** length = 8 inches, width = 6 inches

9.5

1. Vertex is (0, 0)   **2.** Vertex is (0, 0)   **3.** Vertex is (-1, 0)   **4.** Vertex is (2, 0)

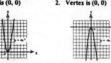

5. Vertex is (1, 3)   **6.** Vertex is (-2, 8)   **7.** Vertex is (-1, 4)   **8.** Vertex is (-2/3, -1/3)

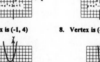

9. Upward   **10.** Downward   **11.** Downward   **12.** Upward

13. (2, 0); x = 2   **14.** (3/4, 11/4); No solution   **15.** (1/3, 13/3); x ~ 1.5 or -1   **16.** (-5/4, 33/8); x ~ -2.5, 0.2

17. (1, 0); x = 1   **18.** (3/2, -25/4); ~ 4, -1   **19.** (5/4, 7/8); No solution   **20.** (7/2, 1/4); x ~ 3, 4

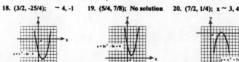

REVIEW EXERCISE 9.7

1. ± 3 2. ± 4 3. $\dfrac{\pm\sqrt{2}}{4}$ 4. ± 2 5. $\dfrac{-5}{3}, \dfrac{7}{3}$ 6. $-3, 4$

7. $\dfrac{5 \pm 3\sqrt{3}}{2}$ 8. $(x-3)^2 - 5$ 9. $\left(x + \dfrac{3}{2}\right)^2 - \dfrac{1}{4}$ 10. $\left(x + \dfrac{7}{2}\right)^2 - \dfrac{81}{4}$ 11. $-4, -2$ 12. $\dfrac{-3 \pm \sqrt{19}}{2}$

13. $2 \pm \sqrt{2}$ 14. $\dfrac{-3 \pm \sqrt{33}}{4}$ 15. 1 16. i 17. -1 18. $3 + 4i$

19. $-2 - \sqrt{5}\,i$ 20. $1 - i$ 21. $-19 + 8i$ 22. $-25 + 21i$ 23. $40 - 42i$ 24. $31 + 8i$

25. $\dfrac{3}{97} + \dfrac{31}{97}i$ 26. $17 - 51i$ 27. $-1, \dfrac{-2}{3}$ 28. $\dfrac{1}{2}$ 29. $\dfrac{3}{2} \pm \dfrac{\sqrt{11}}{2}i$

30. $0, -\dfrac{1}{2} \pm \dfrac{\sqrt{3}}{2}i$ 31. $6, 8$ or $-6, -8$ 32. length = 27 cm, width = 13 cm   33. 4.5 seconds

34. 10 inches   35. 20 sec. and 10 sec.   36. $\left(\dfrac{3}{2}, -\dfrac{7}{2}\right)$; upwards   37. $(-4, 0)$; upwards   38. $(1, -3)$; downwards

---

SELF TEST 9.8

1. $t = -\dfrac{6}{5}$ or $\dfrac{8}{5}$;   2. $\left(x + \dfrac{7}{2}\right)^2 - \dfrac{61}{4}$ 3. $\left(x - \dfrac{11}{2}\right)^2 - \dfrac{89}{4}$ 4. $-i$
Square Root Property

5. $18 + 26i$ 6. $-19 + 8i$ 7. $-\dfrac{31}{13} - \dfrac{1}{13}i$ 8. $\dfrac{3 \pm \sqrt{37}}{2}$ 9. $1 \pm i$

10. $\dfrac{1}{2}, 1$ 11. $-2, \dfrac{7}{2}$ 12. $\dfrac{1 \pm \sqrt{41}}{4}$ 13. $\dfrac{-5 \pm \sqrt{15}\,i}{4}$ 14. $\dfrac{1 \pm \sqrt{13}}{2}$

15. $\dfrac{2}{5}$ or $\dfrac{5}{2}$ 16.   17.   18.

19. i)   No real solution; parabola does not intersect x - axis.

   ii)   Two real solutions; parabola intersects x - axis in two points.

   iii)   Only one real solutions parabola meets x - axis in just one point.

Appendix B

USE OF CALCULATOR (TI-82)

Some General Remarks

1. Press **MODE**

    a. On the first line: **Normal Sci Eng**
        determine whether the calculations are desired in normal form, scientific notation, or engineering notation.

    b. Second line: **Float**   **0 1 2 3 4 5 6 7 8 9**
        determine the number of places of decimals to which the calculations are desired to be rounded.

    c. On fourth line: Always select **Func**; unless told to do otherwise.

2. If the display is too light or too dark, adjust to the contrast by pressing $\boxed{2\text{nd}}$ and $\boxed{\Delta}$ or $\boxed{\nabla}$.

3. Expressions are entered from left to right horizontally in the same way as you will write them.

Examples:

*   To enter the expression $4^3\left(5+\left(7^2-\sqrt{2}\right)\right)$

    Use the following key strokes:

    $\boxed{4}\ \boxed{\wedge}\ \boxed{3}\ \boxed{(}\ \boxed{5}\ \boxed{+}\ \boxed{(}\ \boxed{7}\ \boxed{x^2}\ \boxed{-}\ \boxed{2\text{nd}}\ \boxed{\sqrt{}}\ \boxed{2}\ \boxed{)}\ \boxed{)}$

*   To enter the expression $\dfrac{3^2+7^5\cdot 6^4}{-3+5.4}$
    press the following sequence of keys:

    $\boxed{(}\ \boxed{3}\ \boxed{\wedge}\ \boxed{2}\ \boxed{+}\ \boxed{7}\ \boxed{\wedge}\ \boxed{5}\ \boxed{\times}\ \boxed{6}\ \boxed{\wedge}\ \boxed{4}\ \boxed{)}\ \boxed{\div}$
    $\boxed{(}\ \boxed{(-)}\ \boxed{3}\ \boxed{+}\ \boxed{5}\ \boxed{.}\ \boxed{4}\ \boxed{)}$

Note: Sometimes an expression inside brackets will be used to show what the screen looks like.

CHAPTER 1   Real Number System

Section 1.1   Fractions

Set Mode to **Float.**

Example 1:   Check if 3 and 5 are factors of 20?

A number is a factor of 20 if the quotient of 20 and the number is a positive integer.

- To check if 3 is a factor of 20, press

     $\boxed{2}$ $\boxed{0}$ $\boxed{\div}$ $\boxed{3}$ $\boxed{\text{ENTER}}$ Answer = **6.666666667**

     which is not a positive integer. Therefore, 3 is not a factor of 20.

- To check if 5 is a factor of 20, press

     $\boxed{2}$ $\boxed{0}$ $\boxed{\div}$ $\boxed{5}$ $\boxed{\text{ENTER}}$ Answer = **4**

     which is a positive integer. This shows that 5 is a factor of 20.

Example 2:   Check if 13 and 21 are prime numbers?

(i)   **13:**   Use the method in Example 1 above, to see that 1 and 13 are the only factors of 13.

         Check that $\dfrac{13}{2}, \dfrac{13}{3}, \dfrac{13}{4}, \dfrac{13}{5}, \dfrac{13}{6}, \dfrac{13}{7}$ are not positive integers

         Hence 13 is prime.

(ii)   **21:**   Check if 21 has a factor different from 1 and 21. For this, press:

         $\boxed{2}$ $\boxed{1}$ $\boxed{\div}$ $\boxed{2}$ $\boxed{\text{ENTER}}$ Answer = **10.5**

         Thus 2 is not a factor of 21. Now try 3 for a factor.

         $\boxed{2}$ $\boxed{1}$ $\boxed{\div}$ $\boxed{3}$ $\boxed{\text{ENTER}}$ Answer = **7**

         This shows that 3 and 7 are factors of 21. Therefore, 21 is not prime.

Following examples should be used to check the answers only.

Example 3: Write the fraction $\dfrac{14}{21}$ in lowest terms.

- Enter $\dfrac{14}{21}$.

  $\boxed{1}\ \boxed{4}\ \boxed{\div}\ \boxed{2}\ \boxed{1}$

- Press $\boxed{\text{MATH}}\ \boxed{1}$.   for converting the answer to a fraction if possible

- Press $\boxed{\text{ENTER}}$.   Answer $= \dfrac{2}{3}$

Example 4: Perform the following operations:

     (i) $\dfrac{4}{5} \cdot \dfrac{7}{8}$ **(ii)** $\dfrac{5}{6} \div \dfrac{7}{9}$

     (iii) $\dfrac{4}{8} + \dfrac{7}{8}$ **(iv)** $\dfrac{5}{6} - \dfrac{7}{9}$

(i)
- Enter $\dfrac{4}{5} \cdot \dfrac{7}{8}$.

  $\boxed{4}\ \boxed{\div}\ \boxed{5}\ \boxed{\times}\ \boxed{7}\ \boxed{\div}\ \boxed{8}$

- Press $\boxed{\text{MATH}}\ \boxed{1}$.   [for ▷ Frac]

- Press $\boxed{\text{ENTER}}$.   Answer $= \dfrac{7}{10}$

Other parts can be done similarly.

Section 1.2   Order of Operations

Example 1: Evaluate $(3 + 5 \cdot 6) \div \left[12 - \dfrac{6 - 2 \cdot 2}{3^2 - 7} \right]$.

- Enter the expression. Keystrokes:

  $\boxed{(}\ \boxed{3}\ \boxed{+}\ \boxed{5}\ \boxed{\times}\ \boxed{6}\ \boxed{)}\ \boxed{\div}\ \boxed{(}\ \boxed{1}\ \boxed{2}\ \boxed{-}\ \boxed{(}\ \boxed{6}\ \boxed{-}$
  $\boxed{2}\ \boxed{\times}\ \boxed{2}\ \boxed{)}\ \boxed{\div}\ \boxed{(}\ \boxed{3}\ \boxed{x^2}\ \boxed{-}\ \boxed{7}\ \boxed{)}\ \boxed{)}$

- Press $\boxed{\text{ENTER}}$ Answer $= 3$

Note: Observe that we entered *parentheses* even where brackets are shown in the expression. While using the calculator, parentheses are used for groupings.

Example 2:   Which of the following are true:

(i) $12 \div 2 > 5$ (ii) $8 + 5 \cdot 2 \le 15$

(i)   Enter the keystrokes:

- $\boxed{1}\ \boxed{2}\ \boxed{\div}\ \boxed{2}\ \boxed{\text{2nd}}\ \boxed{\text{MATH}}\ \boxed{3}\ \boxed{5}$

- Press $\boxed{\text{ENTER}}$.   Answer = **1: True**

(ii)   Enter the keystrokes:

- $\boxed{8}\ \boxed{+}\ \boxed{5}\ \boxed{\times}\ \boxed{2}\ \boxed{\text{2nd}}\ \boxed{\text{MATH}}\ \boxed{6}\ \boxed{1}\ \boxed{5}$

- Press $\boxed{\text{ENTER}}$.   Answer = **0: False**

In verification of *statements* **1** → **True** and **0** → **False.**

Section 1.3   Expressions and Equations

To enter x press $\boxed{X, T, \theta}$ [Remember that you are in **Func** mode.]

To enter any alphabet, press $\boxed{\text{ALPHA}}$ and the key over which the desired alphabet sits in white color.

Example 1:   Enter the expressions:

(i) $(4x + 7) \left\{ 5x^2 + 6x + \dfrac{4}{x} \right\}$ (ii) $\dfrac{4A^2 + 7B^2}{3A - 4B}$

(i)   Enter the keystrokes:

$\boxed{(}\ \boxed{4}\ \boxed{X,T,\theta}\ \boxed{+}\ \boxed{7}\ \boxed{)}\ \boxed{(}\ \boxed{5}\ \boxed{X,T,\theta}\ \boxed{x^2}\ \boxed{+}\ \boxed{6}\ \boxed{X,T,\theta}$
$\boxed{+}\ \boxed{4}\ \boxed{\div}\ \boxed{X,T,\theta}\ \boxed{)}$

(ii)   Enter the keystrokes:

$\boxed{(}\ \boxed{4}\ \boxed{\text{ALPHA}}\ \boxed{A}\ \boxed{x^2}\ \boxed{+}\ \boxed{7}\ \boxed{\text{ALPHA}}\ \boxed{B}\ \boxed{x^2}\ \boxed{)}\ \boxed{\div}$
$\boxed{(}\ \boxed{3}\ \boxed{\text{ALPHA}}\ \boxed{A}\ \boxed{-}\ \boxed{4}\ \boxed{\text{ALPHA}}\ \boxed{B}\ \boxed{)}$

Example 2:   Evaluate the following:

(i) $(4x + 7) \left\{ 5x^2 + 6x + \dfrac{4}{x} \right\}$, at $x = 4$ and $x = -6$

(ii) $\dfrac{4A^2 + 7B^2}{3A - 4B}$, at $A = 5$ and $B = 3$.

(i) Method #1

Enter the following

- $\boxed{4}\ \boxed{\text{STO}\,\triangleright}\ \boxed{X, T, \theta}$

- Enter the expression $(4x+7)\left\{5x^2+6x+\dfrac{4}{x}\right\}$.
  [Refer to the preceding example]

- Press $\boxed{\text{ENTER}}$.   Answer = **2415**

- Press $\boxed{(-)}\ \boxed{6}\ \boxed{\text{STO}\,\triangleright}\ \boxed{X, T, \theta}$.

- Press $\boxed{\text{ENTER}}$.

- Press $\boxed{\text{2nd}}\ \boxed{\text{ENTRY}}$ repeatedly until the expression $(4x+7)\left\{5x^2+6x+\dfrac{4}{x}\right\}$
  shows up on the screen.

- Press $\boxed{\text{ENTER}}$.   Answer = $\mathbf{-2436.666667}$

Notes: (1)   Pressing $\boxed{\text{2nd}}\ \boxed{\text{ENTRY}}$ repeatedly recalls upto last ten commands entered in the calculator.

(2)   To see whether the second answer is a fraction or not, press $\boxed{\text{MATH}}\ \boxed{1}$ for $\triangleright$ **Frac** press $\boxed{\text{ENTER}}$
Answer = -7310/3 shows that the answer is indeed a fraction.

Method # 2

- Press $\boxed{Y=}$.

There are ten function slots $Y_1, Y_2, \ldots Y_9, Y_0$

- Enter the expression $(4x+7)\left\{5x^2+6x+\dfrac{4}{x}\right\}$ against $Y_1 = $, say

- Press $\boxed{\text{2nd}}\ \boxed{\text{QUIT}}$ to leave Function screen.

- Press $\boxed{\text{2nd}}\ \boxed{\text{Y - VARS}}\ \boxed{1}$ (for function) $\boxed{1}$ (for Y_1).
  Y_1 is printed on the Home Screen.

- Continue to type (4) next to Y_1. [Screen looks like $Y_1(4)$]

- Press $\boxed{\text{ENTER}}$.   Answer = **2415**

- Edit 4 to -6. [Screen looks like $Y_1(-6)$.]

- Press $\boxed{\text{ENTER}}$.   Answer = $\mathbf{-\,2436.666667}$

Press $\boxed{\text{MATH}}\ \boxed{1}\ \boxed{\triangleright}$.   Answer = $-\,7310\,/\,3$ [See Note above]

(ii)
- Store 5 in A: `5` `STO ▷` `ALPHA` `A`.

- Press `ENTER`.

- Store 3 in B.

- Press `ENTER`.

- Enter the expression $\dfrac{4A^2 + 7B^2}{3A - 4B}$.

- Press `ENTER`.   Answer = **54.33333333**

- Use ▷ **Frac**.   Answer = **163/3**

Section 1.4   Real Numbers

Example 1:   Which of the numbers $\dfrac{\sqrt{16} - 1}{5}$ and $\sqrt{2}$ are rational?

$\dfrac{\sqrt{16} - 1}{5}$:

- Enter $\dfrac{\sqrt{16} - 1}{5}$.

  KEYSTROKES: `(` `2nd` `√` `1` `6` `−` `1` `)` `÷` `5`

- Press `ENTER`.   Answer = **.6**

- Use ▷ **Frac**.   Answer = **3/5**

  This shows that $\dfrac{\sqrt{16} - 1}{5}$ is a rational number.

$\sqrt{2}$:

- Enter $\sqrt{2}$.

- Press `ENTER`.   Answer = **1.414213562**

- Use ▷ **Frac**.   Answer = **1.414213562**

This does not convert the answer into a fraction. Therefore, $\sqrt{2}$ is not a rational number.

Example 2:   Find $\left| \dfrac{2^2 - 13}{4 \cdot 5 + 7} \right|$.

- Press $\boxed{\text{2nd}}$ $\boxed{\text{ABS}}$ (for absolute value).

- Enter $\left(\dfrac{2^2 - 13}{4 \cdot 5 + 7} \right)$.

$$\left[\text{ABS}\left(\left(2^2 - 13\right) / \left(4 \cdot 5 + 7\right)\right) \right]$$

- Press $\boxed{\text{ENTER}}$.   Answer = .3333333333

- Use ▷ **Frac**.   Answer = $\dfrac{1}{3}$

Note: Above techniques are applicable to Sections 1.5 - 1.9.

Example 3:   Round 4.720562 to;

   (i)   5 places of decimal
   (ii)   4 places of decimal.

- Press $\boxed{\text{MATH}}$ $\boxed{\triangleright}$ $\boxed{1}$ [for **round** ( )].

(i)   Enter 4.720562, 5
[**round** (4.720562, 5) means round 4.720562 to five places of decimal]

- Press $\boxed{\text{ENTER}}$.   Answer = **4.72056**

(ii)   Press $\boxed{\text{2nd}}$ $\boxed{\text{ENTRY}}$.

- Edit number of places to 4. $\left[\text{round} \left(4.720562, 4\right) \right]$

- Press $\boxed{\text{ENTER}}$.   Answer = **4.7206**

CHAPTER 2   Linear Equations and Inequalities in One Variable

Sections 2.2 - 2.3   Solving Equations

Example 1:   Solve the equation

$$3(6x - 2) + 4(3 - 4x) = 2(1 - x)$$

and check your answer using the calculator.

513

Solution of the above equation is -1. [Refer to Section 2.2, Example 6]

- Store -1 in x.

  KEYSTROKES: $\boxed{(-)}$ $\boxed{1}$ $\boxed{\text{STO}}$ $\boxed{X,T,\theta}$

- Enter the equation $3(6x-2)+4(3-4x)=2(1-x)$.

- Press $\boxed{\text{ENTER}}$.　　Answer = **1:**　　　**True**

  Note:　Recall that: Answer 1 means **true**, 0 means **false**.

Example 2:　　Solve the following equation and check your solution

$$\frac{2}{3}x+2=x-\frac{x-1}{2}+\frac{5}{3}$$

- Solve the equation using the methods of Sections 2.2 and 2.3. Solution is $x=1$.

- Store 1 in x:　　　$\boxed{1}$ $\boxed{\text{STO}}$ $\boxed{X,T,\theta}$.

- Enter the equation $\dfrac{2}{3}x+2=x-\dfrac{x-1}{2}+\dfrac{5}{3}$.

- Press $\boxed{\text{ENTER}}$.　　Answer = **1:**　　　**True**

Example 3:　　Solve the equation

$$\frac{2}{3}x+2=x-\frac{x-1}{2}+\frac{5}{3}$$

using calculator and check your solution too.

- Convert $\dfrac{2}{3}x+2=x-\dfrac{x-1}{2}+\dfrac{5}{3}$ into $\dfrac{2}{3}x+2-\left(x-\dfrac{x-1}{2}+\dfrac{5}{3}\right)=0$.

  [Transfer everything to one side.]

- Press $\boxed{Y=}$.

- Enter $\dfrac{2}{3}x+2-\left(x-\dfrac{x-1}{2}+\dfrac{5}{3}\right)$ in one of the function slots, say Y_1.

- Press $\boxed{\text{2nd}}$　$\boxed{\text{QUIT}}$ to go to the HOME screen.

- Press $\boxed{\text{CLEAR}}$ or move the cursor to a new line.

- Press $\boxed{\text{MATH}}$ $\boxed{0}$ [for **Solve(**].

- Next to **solve** (; type: $y_1, x, 0$)

  $\left[\text{Recall } \mathbf{Y_1} \text{ is entered by } \boxed{2\text{nd}} \; \boxed{Y - VARS} \; \boxed{1}\,\boxed{1}\right]$

- Press $\boxed{\text{ENTER}}$.   Answer **= 1**

Check:
- On a new line enter Y_1
- Type (1) next to Y_1 [Screen: $Y_1(1)$]
- Press $\boxed{\text{ENTER}}$ Answer **= 0**

Notes: 1. Remember $Y_1(1)$ is the value of Y_1 at $x = 1$.. Therefore, $Y_1(1) = 0$ means 1 is a solution of the equation $Y_1 = 0$.

2. Notice the difference in checking by using the *equation* in terms of true or false in Examples 1 and 2 above. In example 3 above we *did not* use the equation $\frac{2}{3}x + 2 = x - \frac{x-1}{2} + \frac{5}{3}$. In fact, we used the *expression* $\frac{2}{3}x + 2 - \left(x - \frac{x-1}{2} + \frac{5}{3}\right)$, which defines the equation when equated to 0.

Section 2.8   Solutions of Linear Inequalities

Example 1:   Which of the following satisfy the inequality $\frac{3}{4}x - 4 < \frac{4}{5}x + 1$?

$x: \quad 0, \; -2, \; -100, \; -150, \; 25$

- Enter $\frac{3}{4}x - 4 < \frac{4}{5}x + 1$ $\left[< \text{ is entered by } \boxed{2\text{nd}} \; \boxed{MATH} \; \boxed{5}\right]$.

- Store 0 in x.

- Use $\boxed{2\text{nd}}$ $\boxed{\text{ENTRY}}$ repeatedly to get back the inequality on the next line.

- Press $\boxed{\text{ENTER}}$.   Answer **= 1:   True**

  Thus $x = 0$ satisfies the inequality.

- Store -100 in x.

- Use $\boxed{2\text{nd}}$ $\boxed{\text{ENTRY}}$ repeatedly to get the inequality on the next line.

- Press $\boxed{\text{ENTER}}$.   Answer **= 0:   False**

  Thus $x = -100$ does not satisfy the inequality.

  Similarly, check $x = -2$, -150 and 25.

Example 2:   Solve the inequality

$$\frac{3}{4}x - 4 < \frac{4}{5}x + 1 \text{ using the calculator.}$$

*   Solve the equation:

$$\frac{3}{4}x - 4 = \frac{4}{5}x + 1$$

    [Use the method of Sections 2.2 - 2.3, Example 2.]

    Answer = **−100**

*   Enter the inequality:

$$\frac{3}{4}x - 4 < \frac{4}{5}x + 1$$

*   Select a number and store in x. Suppose you store 0 in x.

*   Use $\boxed{2\text{nd}}$ $\boxed{\text{ENTRY}}$ repeatedly until the inequality shows up on the next line.

*   Press $\boxed{\text{ENTER}}$.   Answer = **1 True**

Thus $x = 0$ satisfies the inequality. This means that between $x < -100$ and $x > -100$ the solution of the inequality is that which *contains 0*. Therefore, $x > -100$ is the solution.

Note: Answer is 0 when we store -200 in x. Answer 0 means false. Thus between $x > -100$ and $x < -100$, the solution of the given inequality is that which *does not contain* -200. Hence $x > -100$ is the solution. Recall you can use any *test point*.

CHAPTER 3   Exponents and Polynomials

Section 3.7   Scientific Notation

Example 1:   Write 95.37 and .000000678 in scientific notation

*   Press **Mode**.

*   Select **Sci** on the top line.

*   Press $\boxed{2\text{nd}}$ $\boxed{\text{QUIT}}$.

*   Enter 95.37

*   Press $\boxed{\text{ENTER}}$.   Answer = **9.537E1** $\rightarrow$ **9.537 $\times$ 10^1**

*   Enter .000000678

*   Press $\boxed{\text{ENTER}}$.   Answer = **6.78E1** $\rightarrow$ **6.78 $\times$ 10^{-7}**

CHAPTER 5   Rational Expressions

Rational expressions can be entered in the normal way by making adequate use of parentheses. For example,

- $t + \dfrac{t}{1 - \dfrac{t+1}{t}}$ will be entered as $t + \left(t \div \left(1 - (t+1) \div t\right)\right)$

- $\dfrac{4x}{x^2 + 2x - 3} - \dfrac{5x}{x^2 + 5x + 6}$ is entered as $(4x) \div \left(x^2 + 2x - 3\right) - (5x) \div \left(x^2 + 5x + 6\right)$

Rational expressions are evaluated as in Section 1.3, Example 2.

PREPARATION FOR GRAPHING

For graphing we should have a suitable screen to graph. This is done by setting the window. Press $\boxed{\text{WINDOW}}$.

Format: You will always need to set the **Window Format** as **RectGC.** Other choices are optional. Unless stated otherwise, we shall select, **CoordOn, GridOff, AxesOn and LabelOff.**

WINDOW: Xmin defines the *left end* of the screen; Xmax defines the *right end* of the screen; Ymin defines the *lower end* of the screen; and Ymax defines the *upper end* of the screen. Together they form the viewing rectangle or viewing screen. Xscl and Yscl should be set appropriately to see the hash marks on the two axes.

Built in Window Setting

- Press $\boxed{\text{ZOOM}}$.

In this menu ZDecimal and Zstandard are built-in Window Settings. You may like to select these and view their defining parameters.

Zsquare

Setting Xmin = Ymin = Xmax = Ymax should be supposed to define a square view screen, but actually it does not do that. Thus, for example, when you select ZStandard [Xmin = Ymin = -10, Xmax = Ymax = 10], and if you draw a circle, it will not look like a circle. ZDecimal is an example of a Square screen. Sometimes, it may be desireable to have a square screen bigger than Zdecimal for viewing actual shape. For this select Xmin and Xmax with desired scales and press $\boxed{\text{ZOOM}}$ $\boxed{\text{Zsquare}}$. Ymin and Ymax will be automatically set, so that the resulting view screen is square.

We shall use the following window setting:

(i)   Xmin = −9.4 ,   Xmax = 9.4,   Xscl = 1
      Ymin = −12.4, Ymax = 12.4,   Yscl = 1

This window will be referred as **Friendly Window I**

(ii) Xmin = −9.4 ,   Xmax = 9.4,   Xscl = 1
      Ymin = −6.2,   Ymax = 6.2,   Yscl = 1

This window will be referred as **Friendly Window II**

(iii) Xmin = −4.7 ,   Xmax = 4.7,   Xscl = 1
      Ymin = −6.2,   Ymax = 6.2,   Yscl = 1

This window will be referred as **Friendly Window III.**

Set any of these windows or the **ZDecimal** Window, and press ⎡GRAPH⎤. You are in Graph-Screen. Now if you press various arrow keys, you will notice a cursor moving on the screen. Coordinates of its position are shown at the bottom of the screen. As the cursor moves, you will notice that the coordinates jump by a convenient unit fraction. Compare this to **ZStandard** Window.

A Note About Clearing Graphs

⎡CLEAR⎤ *does not* clear graphs. It clears text on the Home Screen only. TI-82 constructs graphs using essentially three menus.

1. **STAT-PLOT:**   This menu helps construct statistical plots Option 4 on the menu turns off all *Stat Plots*. Since we shall not discuss Stat Plots you are advised to select PlotsOff on this menu.

   KEYSTROKES : ⎡2nd⎤ ⎡STAT PLOT⎤ ⎡4⎤ ⎡ENTER⎤

2. **Graph using Y=**   This menu constructs graphs using the functions stored in **Y=.** Graphs of only active functions are plotted. A function is active or not according as ' = ' sign next to Y, where the function is stored, is highlighted or not. To activate or deactivate a function, move the cursor on '=' and press ⎡ENTER⎤.

3. **Draw:**   This menu also constructs graphs. All graphs drawn using this menu can be cleared by using **ClrDraw** in **DRAW** menu.

   KEYSTROKES: ⎡2nd⎤ ⎡DRAW⎤ ⎡1⎤ ⎡ENTER⎤

CHAPTER 6   Linear Equations/Inequalities In Two Variables

Section 6.1   Linear Equations In Two Variables

Example 1:   Which of $(1, -3)$ and $(2, 4)$ are solutions of $2P - Q = 5$?

Use the method of Sections 2.2-2.3, Example 1.

- Store 1 in P.
  KEYSTROKES : $\boxed{1}$ $\boxed{\text{STO} \triangleright}$ $\boxed{\text{ALPHA}}$ $\boxed{P}$

- Store -3 in Q.

- Enter the equation $2P - Q = 5$.
  $\boxed{2}$ $\boxed{\text{ALPHA}}$ $\boxed{P}$ $\boxed{-}$ $\boxed{\text{ALPHA}}$ $\boxed{Q}$ $\boxed{\text{2nd}}$ $\boxed{\text{MATH}}$ $\boxed{1}$ $\boxed{5}$

- Press $\boxed{\text{ENTER}}$.   Answer $= \mathbf{1}$

This means **True.** Therefore $(1, -3)$ is a solution of $2P - Q = 5$.

Next

- Store 2 in P.

- Store 4 in Q.

- Use $\boxed{\text{2nd}}$ $\boxed{\text{ENTRY}}$ repeadly to bring $2P - Q = 5$ on the next line.

- Press $\boxed{\text{ENTER}}$.   Answer $= \mathbf{0}$

This means **False.** Therefore, $(2, 4)$ is not a solution of $2P - Q = 5$.

Example 2:   Plot the point $(-2, 5)$.

- Set **Window** to **ZStandard.**
  KEYSTROKES: $\boxed{\text{ZOOM}}$ $\boxed{6}$

- Press $\boxed{\text{2nd}}$ $\boxed{\text{QUIT}}$.

- Press $\boxed{\text{CLEAR}}$.

- Press $\boxed{\text{2nd}}$ $\boxed{\text{DRAW}}$.

- Select **POINTS** menu using $\boxed{\triangleright}$.

- Press $\boxed{1}$ [for **Pt - On** (].

- Type the point so that your screen looks **Pt - On** $(-2, 5)$.

- Press $\boxed{\text{ENTER}}$.

You see $(-2, 5)$ plotted on the screen.

In the last example, the calculator plotted the point $(-2, 5)$ for us. How about if we want to plot this point ourselves directly on the Graph Screen.

Example 3:   Plot the point $(-2, 5)$ on a coordinate plane.

- Clear Graph Screen.

- Set Friendly Window II.

- Press ⎡GRAPH⎤.

- Press ⎡2nd⎤ ⎡DRAW⎤ ⎡▷⎤ ⎡1⎤.   [for **Pt-On** ( ]
  [You are brought back to Graph Screen, with $x = 0$ and $y = 0$ at the bottom line, and a cursor blinking at the origin.]

- Use ⎡◁⎤ until $x = -2$ appears in the bottom line.

- Use ⎡△⎤ until $y = 5$ appears in the bottom line. Now cursor is at $(-2, 5)$.

- Press ⎡ENTER⎤ , $(-2, 5)$ is plotted.

To plot additional points, move the cursor at the desired location and press ⎡ENTER⎤

Section 6.2   Graphing Linear Equations

Example 1:   Graph the equation $x = 4$.

- Clear Graph Screen.

- Set ZDecimal Window.

- Press ⎡GRAPH⎤.

- Press ⎡2nd⎤ ⎡DRAW⎤ ⎡4⎤ [for **Vertical**; notice $x = 4$ is a vertical line.]
  [Graph screen appears with $x = 0$, $y = 0$ in the bottom line, and a blinking cursor at the origin.]

- Use ⎡▷⎤ until $x = 4$ in the bottom line.

- Press ⎡ENTER⎤

The moving vertical line is now located at $x = 4$.

Alternatively, you may press ⎡2nd⎤ ⎡DRAW⎤ ⎡4⎤ after setting window. **Vertical** appears on the Home Screen. Type 4, and press ⎡ENTER⎤ to see the line $x = 4$ graphed on the Graph Screen.

Horizontal line may be graphed either by selecting **Horizontal** from **DRAW** menu as above or alternatively, use the method described below:

Example 2:   Graph the equation $2x + 3y = 6$.

- Rewrite the equation as $y = \dfrac{1}{3}(6 - 2x)$ by solving for y.

- Set ZStandard Window.

- Press $\boxed{Y=}$.

- Enter $\dfrac{1}{3}(6 - 2x)$ in one of the slots [This function becomes active.]

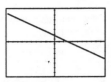

Pic 1

- Press $\boxed{\text{GRAPH}}$. The line appears.

Example 3:   Graph the equation $2x + 3y = 6$, and find its x-intercept and y-intercept.

You have drawn the graph in Example 2 above.

- Press $\boxed{\text{TRACE}}$. [Coordinates appear at the bottom, and a cursor blinks on the line at that position.]

- Use $\boxed{\triangleleft}$ and $\boxed{\triangleright}$ only to move the cursor along the line and explore the coordinates of various points on the line.

As you move along the curve, you find that x-intercept is not found exactly as the cursor never sits on x-axis. *Try with Friendly Window III.* This will bring out the necessity of setting a suitable window.

Any equation of the form $y = f(x)$ can be graphed using DRAW menu $\left[\boxed{\text{2nd}} \ \boxed{\text{DRAW}} \ \boxed{6}\right.$ (for **DrawF**)]. But graphs drawn in this manner cannot be explored.

Section 6.4   Line Joining Two Points

Example 1:   Draw the line joining $(-2, 5)$ and $(3, 4)$.

If you are interested in the extended line, the best method is to find its equation and graph as explained above [Section 6.2]. In case you are interested only in the line segment joining $(-2, 5)$ and $(3, 4)$, proceed as follows:

- Set a suitable Window.

- Clear Graph Screen.

- Clear Home Screen.

- Press $\boxed{2nd}$ $\boxed{DRAW}$ $\boxed{2}$ [for **Line** ( ].

- Type $(-2, 5, 3, 4)$.
  [Screen looks like : **Line** $(-2, 5, 3, 4)$].

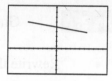

Pic 2

- Press $\boxed{ENTER}$. (There appears the desired line segment.)

Note: You can also draw line segment using **Line** (from Graph Screen). Recall how points were plotted in two different ways.

Section 6.5   Graphing Linear Inequalities

Example 1:   Graph the linear inequality $2x - y > 3$.

- Clear Graph Screen.

- Set ZStandard Window.

- Rewrite $2x - y > 3$ as $y < 2x - 3$.

- Press $\boxed{2nd}$ $\boxed{DRAW}$ $\boxed{7}$ [For **Shade** ( ]

- Type $-20, 2x - 3, 1)$.
  [Screen looks like **Shade** $(-20, 2x - 3, 1)$].

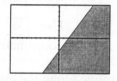

Pic 3

- Press $\boxed{ENTER}$.

Shaded portion is the graphical solution of the inequality.

Note: A syntax for **Shade** is Shade $(f_1(x), f_2(x),$ resolution) where $f_1(x)$ is the lower function $f_2(x)$ is the upper function, and resolution number is between 1 and 9. In the above example, since $y < 2x - 3$, $2x - 3$ was selected as an upper function. Lower function should be selected as $y = k$ where $k < Y_{min}$. You may like to change the resolution numbers, and observe the difference.

Example 2:   Graph the inequality $x + 4y \geq 5$.

- Rewrite $x + 4y \geq 5$ as $y \geq \dfrac{5 - x}{4}$.

- Clear Graph Screen.

- Set ZStandard Window.

- Press $\boxed{2nd}$ $\boxed{DRAW}$ $\boxed{7}$ [For **Shade** ( ].

- Type $\dfrac{5-x}{4}$, 20, 1).

[Screen looks like **Shade** $\left(\dfrac{5-x}{4}, 20, 1\right)$.

- Press ENTER.

Shaded area is the solution of the inequality.

Note: Observe that $-20 < Y_{min}$ and $20 > Y_{max}$.

Section 6.6   Functions

Example 1:   For the function $f(x) = 3x^2 + 4x - 1$ find $f(-3)$.

- Use any of the methods explained in Section 1.3, Example 2(i).

Example 2:   Find the domain and range of $f(x) = \dfrac{2}{2-x}$.

Method #1   We know that the rational expression $\dfrac{2}{2-x}$ is not defined when the denominator is $2 - x = 0$. Solve $2 - x = 0$ and determine domain. Use the domain to determine the range. [Use of calculator will be justified if there was a complicated expression in place of $2 - x$.]

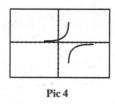

Pic 4

Method #2
- Clear Graph Screen.

- Set to ZStandard Window.

- Press MODE and select **DOT.**

- Press Y= and enter the expression $\dfrac{2}{2-x}$ in one of the function slots, say Y_1.

- Press GRAPH.

Observe that the *graph appears in dots and not connected lines.* Also observe that the graph exists on the left of $x = 2$ and on the right of $x = 2$, and the two pieces are not connected at $x = 2$.

- Press TRACE.

- Continously press ▷ or ◁ to explore the graph on the right or left of outside the viewing window.

523

It is found that the graph exists at all points x except $x = 2$. Therefore, domain of $f(x) = \dfrac{2}{2-x}$ is $\{x \mid x \neq 2\}$, i.e., all real numbers except 2.

Again the graph never touches or crosses x-axis. Range of $f(x)$ is $\{x \mid x \neq 0\}$, i.e., all nonzero real numbers.

CHAPTER 7   Linear Equations and Inequalities

Section 7.1   Solving Systems of Linear Equations

Example 1:   Show graphically that the system of linear equations: $2x + 3y = 6$ is inconsistent.
$4x + 6y = 24$

- Write $2x + 3y = 6$ as $y = \dfrac{6 - 2x}{3}$. [Solve for y]

- Write $4x + 6y = 24$ as $y = \dfrac{24 - 4x}{6}$.

- Set ZStandard Window.

- Clear the Graph Screen.

- Press $\boxed{Y=}$.

- Enter $\dfrac{6 - 2x}{3}$ for Y_1.

- Enter $\dfrac{24 - 4x}{6}$ for Y_2.

- Enter $\boxed{\text{GRAPH}}$.

Graph of two linear equations is a pair of parallel lines. Therefore, the given system of linear equations is inconsistent.

Example 2:   Show graphically that the system of linear equations: $2x + y = 1$ is independent
$x - 2y = 7$

- Use the steps in Example 1 above.
Graph of the two linear equations
of this system is a pair of intersecting
lines. Therefore, the system is linearly
independent.

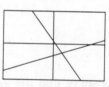

Pic 5

Example 3:   Show graphically that the system of linear equations: $3x - 2y = 5$
is dependent
$6x = 4y + 10$

- Use the steps in Example 1 above.
Graph is a single line. Therefore, the system is linearly dependent.

In example 2 above, we saw that the system $2x + y = 1$, $x - 2y = 7$ of linear equations is independent. In the following example we demonstrate how to solve this system.

Example 4:   Solve the system of linear equations: $2x + y = 1$, $x - 2y = 7$.

Method #1

- Clear Graph Screen

- Rewrite $2x + y = 1$ as $y = 1 - 2x$ and $x - 2y = 7$ as $y = \dfrac{x - 7}{2}$.

- Set to ZDecimal Window.

- Enter $Y_1 = 1 - 2x$ and $Y_2 = \dfrac{x - 7}{2}$ in the $Y =$ menu.

- Press Graph.

   Two intersecting lines appear.

- Press ⎡TRACE⎤ use ⎡▷⎤ and ⎡◁⎤ to move the cursor to the point of intersection.

Coordinates of this point appear as $x = 1.8$ and $y = -2.6$. This is the solution. You may like to verify this solution.

Note: Sometimes the cursor may not sit on the point of intersection since cursor jumps and does not move continuously. In that case ZBox ⎡⎡ZOOM⎤ ⎡1⎤⎤ can be used to get a better approximation.

Method #2   Follow all the steps of the above example starting from clearing the Graph Screen to entering the expressions in Y_1 and Y_2.

- Press ⎡2nd⎤ ⎡CALC⎤ ⎡5⎤ [for **intersect**].

- Cursor is on the first line. Prompt is *First Curve?*
   Select it by pressing ⎡ENTER⎤.

- Cursor is on the second line. Prompt is *Second Curve?*
   Select it by pressing ⎡ENTER⎤.

- Press ⎡ENTER⎤ for *Guess?*
   Cursor moves to the point of intersection with coordinates of the point displayed at the bottom as $x = 1.8$ and $y = -2.6$.
   Therefore solution of the system is $x = 1.8$, $y = -2.6$.

Notes: 1. In this method even when you select ZStandard, you set the answer as x = 1.8 and y = -26. This not so if you use ZStandard Window with Method #1.

2. Do the above example using ZStandard Window and Method #1. Observe the difference.

Section 7.4   Solving Systems of Linear Inequalities

Shade ([KEYSTROKES: [2nd] [DRAW] [7]]) can be used for solving systems of linear inequalities graphically. [Refer to Section 6.5, Examples 1&2]. There are four syntaxes for using **Shade** (and can be picked up according to the situation).

Syntax 1:   **Shade (lowerfunc, upperfunc)**

Syntax 2:   **Shade (lowerfunc, upperfunc, resolution)**

Syntax 3:   **Shade (lowerfunc, upperfunc, resolution, xleft)**

Syntax 4:   **Shade (lowerfunc, upperfunc, resolution, xleft, xright)**

Note: Resolution number is between 1 and 9. 1 produces the most devise and dark shade. We shall always use 1 for resolution number. In Syntax 1, default resolution number is 1.

Remark: **Shade** (cannot be used if there is not a lower function [[$form\ y > f(x)$ or $y \geq f(x)$] and an upper function $[y < f(x)$ or $y \leq f(x)]$. Recall how we created artificially a lower function in Section 6.5, Example 1.

Example 1:   Graph the solution of the linear system: $x + y \leq 2$
                                                                        $2x - y > 3$

- Rewrite $x + y \leq 2$ as $y \leq 2 - x$
  and $2x - y > 3$ as $y < 2x - 3$
  Observe both are lower functions.
  Shade (*cannot be used.*

- Set to ZDecimal Window.

- Graph $y = 2 - x$.

- Graph $y = 2x - 3$.

- Use a test point, say $x = 0$, and select the suitable region for solution.

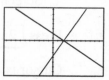

Pic 6

Example 2:   Graph the solution of the linear system:

$$x + y \leq 2$$
$$2x - y < 3$$

- Rewrite $x + y \leq 2$ as $y \leq 2 - x$ and $2x - y < 3$ as $y > 2x - 3$.

- lowerfunc is $2x - 3$ and upperfunc is $2 - x$.

- Clean Graph Screen .

- Set Window to ZDecimal.

- Press $\boxed{2\text{nd}}$ $\boxed{\text{DRAW}}$ $\boxed{7}$ [for **Shade** ( ].

- Enter $2x-3$ for lowerfunc.

- Enter $2-x$ for upperfunc [Syntax 1]
  [Screen Shade $(2x-3,\ 2-x$; or you may enter
  Y_1 as $2x-3$ and Y_2 as $2-x$ and use the command
  Shade $(Y_1,Y_2]$.

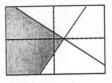

Pic 7

- Press $\boxed{\text{ENTER}}$.

Shaded region is the solution. You may like to use Shade (lowerfunc, upperfunc, resolution) with varying resolution numbers, and observe the difference.

Note: You may simply graph the lines $y=2-x$ and $y=2x-3$, and explore the region in which $y=2-x$ lies above $y=2x-3$.

Example 3:   Graph the solution of the system: $x\geq 1,\ y\geq x,\ 3x+4y<12$.

Rewrite $3x+4y<12$ as $y<\dfrac{12-3x}{4}$. Here $y\geq x$ will be used for

lowerfunc, $y<\dfrac{12-3x}{4}$ for upperfunc, and $x\geq 1$ for Xleft.

- Set window to ZDecimal.

- Press $\boxed{2\text{nd}}$ $\boxed{\text{DRAW}}$ $\boxed{7}$ [for **Shade** (].

- Enter the command.
  Shade $\left(x,\ \dfrac{12-3x}{4},\ 1,\ 1\right)$.

- Press $\boxed{\text{ENTER}}$.

Shaded region is the solution of the system.

CHAPTER 8   Roots and Radicals

Section 8.1   Finding Roots

TI - 82 does not find the square root of a negative number. If you calculate $\sqrt{-2}$ for example, it will show error. It is possible to write programs to work with complex numbers.

527

- Enter $\sqrt[5]{2}$

  Keystrokes: [5] [MATH] [2]

- Enter $\left(-\sqrt[3]{-9}\right)^3$.

  Keystrokes: [(] [(−)] [MATH] [4] [(−)] [9] [)] [^] [3]
  ([^] [3] at the end can also be replaced by [MATH] [3])

- Enter $\left(\sqrt{8x^2+5}\right)^2$.

  Keystrokes: [(] [2nd] [√] [(] [8] [X,T,θ] [x^2] [+] [5] [)] [x^2]

- Enter $\left(\sqrt{\dfrac{4}{27}}\right)$

  Keystrokes: [2nd] [√] [(] [4] [÷] [2] [7] [)]

Example 1: Find the value of

(i) $\sqrt[3]{-64}$ 　　　 (ii) $\sqrt[5]{\dfrac{32}{243}}$

(i) Enter the keystrokes:

[MATH] [4] [(−)] [6] [4] [ENTER]

Answer: **−4**

(ii) Enter the keystrokes:

[5] [MATH] [5] [(] [3] [2] [÷] [2] [4] [3] [)]

[ENTER]

Answer = **.6666666667**

[MATH] [1] 　　　 [For ▷ Frac]

Answer = $\dfrac{2}{3}$

528

Example 2:   Show that $\sqrt{\dfrac{4}{49}}$ is a rational number.

- $\boxed{\text{2nd}}$ $\boxed{\sqrt{}}$ $\boxed{(}$ $\boxed{4}$ $\boxed{\div}$ $\boxed{4}$ $\boxed{9}$ $\boxed{)}$ $\boxed{\text{ENTER}}$

   Answer = **.2857142857**

- $\boxed{\text{MATH}}$ $\boxed{1}$ [For ▷ Frac]

- $\boxed{\text{ENTER}}$ Answer = $\dfrac{2}{7}$

   This shows that $\sqrt{\dfrac{4}{49}}$ is rational.

Example 3:   Show that $\sqrt{18}$ is an irrational number.

- $\boxed{\text{2nd}}$ $\boxed{\sqrt{}}$ $\boxed{1}$ $\boxed{8}$ $\boxed{\text{ENTER}}$

   Answer = **4.242640687**

- $\boxed{\text{MATH}}$ $\boxed{1}$ $\boxed{\text{ENTER}}$

   Answer = **4.242640687**

Answer does not convert into a fraction. Therefore, $\sqrt{18}$ is an irrational number.

Example 4:   Show that $\sqrt{-25}$ is non-real.

- $\boxed{\text{2nd}}$ $\boxed{\text{MATH}}$ $\boxed{(-)}$ $\boxed{2}$ $\boxed{5}$ $\boxed{\text{ENTER}}$

Error is displayed. Therefore, $\sqrt{-25}$ is not real.

Section 8.2   Radicals

Show that $\sqrt{x^2} = |x|$

- Enter $\sqrt{x^2}$ in Y_1.

- Enter $|x|$ in Y_2.

- Press $\boxed{\text{2nd}}$ $\boxed{\text{TblSet}}$
  Enter TblMin = any number, say -10
  ΔTbl = 1(say).
  Indpnt = Auto, **Depend** = Auto

- Press $\boxed{\text{2nd}}$ $\boxed{\text{TABLE}}$

X	Y1	Y2
-10	10	0
-9	9	9
-8	8	8
-7	7	7
-6	6	6
-5	5	5
-4	4	4
X = -10		

Pic. 8

529

Three columns appear on the screen, one with values of x differing by 1, second with value of $Y_1 = \sqrt{x^2}$ for the corresponding values of x, and third with values of $Y_2 = |x|$.

- Move the cursor in the x-column. Browse through this column using $\boxed{\Delta}$ and $\boxed{\nabla}$, and observe the values in the $Y_1 = \sqrt{x^2}$ and $Y_2 = |x|$ columns. You find that $\sqrt{x^2} = |x|$ for all values of x.

Section 8.6   Equations With Radicals

Equations with radicals can be solved graphically, by using **root** or by using **Solve(**.

Extraneous roots *cannot* be determined with the calculator.

Example 1:   Solve the equation $x - \sqrt{x - 2} = 4$.

Method #1

- Clear Graph Screen.
- Enter $x - \sqrt{x - 2} - 4$ in Y_1..
- Set Friendly Window II.
- Use **Solve** $(y_1, x, 4)$.   Answer = **6**

Notes: 1.   You may like to view the graph to find approximately where the curve meets x-axis.

2.   If you use **Solve** $(Y_1, x, 1)$, you get **error**. (why?).

3.   You may try to **Solve** $(Y_1, x, 3)$, still the answer is $x = 6$. $x = 3$ is an extraneous root of this equation, but the calculator does not show this. {Refer to Section 8.6, Example 5] .

Method #2

With the same settings as above:

- Press $\boxed{\text{2nd}}$ $\boxed{\text{CALC}}$ $\boxed{2}$.   [for **root**]
  [Graph pops up with some prompts.]

- Select *lower bound* by pressing $\boxed{\text{ENTER}}$ on the left of the point of intersection of the curve with x-axis.

- Move the cursor to the right of the point of intersection of the curve with the x-axis, and select *upper bound* by pressing $\boxed{\text{ENTER}}$.

- With the cursor either at the upperbound or anywhere between the lower and upper bounds press ⎡ENTER⎤ to accept a *guess*.   Answer = **6**

Note: Value of x is obtained correctly, no matter what the window setting is. Correspondingly, the value of the y-coordinate of the point of intersection is approximated by a certain process, and depends upon the choice of the two bounds.

Method #3

- Clear Graph Screen.

- Set a suitable window, say ZStandard.

- Enter $Y_1 = x - \sqrt{x-2}$.

- Enter $Y_2 = 4$.

- Press ⎡2nd⎤ ⎡CALC⎤ ⎡5⎤   [for **intersect**]
  [Graphs pop up with some prompts]

- Press ⎡ENTER⎤ to accept *first curve*.

- Press ⎡ENTER⎤ to accept *second curve*.

- Press ⎡ENTER⎤ to accept *third curve*.   Answer: $x = 6$, $y = 4$

- Therefore, solution is $x = 6$.

Pic 9

CHAPTER 9   Quadratic Equations

Section 9.4   Quadratic Formual

To solve a quadratic equation $Ax^2 + Bx + C = 0$ by quadratic formula, we make the following preparation.

- Enter $B^2 - 4AC$ in Y_8.

- Enter $\dfrac{-B - \sqrt{Y_8}}{2A}$ in Y_9.

  Keystrokes: ⎡(⎤ ⎡(−)⎤ ⎡ALPHA⎤ ⎡B⎤ ⎡−⎤ ⎡2nd⎤ ⎡√⎤ ⎡2nd⎤
  ⎡Y − VARS⎤ ⎡1⎤ ⎡8⎤ ⎡)⎤ ⎡÷⎤ ⎡2⎤ ⎡ALPHA⎤ ⎡A⎤

- Enter $\dfrac{-B + \sqrt{Y_8}}{2A}$ in Y_0.

Deactivate these functions.

Example 1:   Find the nature of the roots of the equations:

(i) $2x^2 + 3x - 7 = 0$
(ii) $x^2 + 3x + 5 = 0$
(iii) $2x^2 + 12x + 18 = 0$

(i)   Here $A = 2$, $B = 3$ and $C = -7$.

- Store 2 in A.

- Store 3 in B.

- Store -7 in C.

- Press $\boxed{\text{2nd}}$ $\boxed{\text{Y} - \text{VARS}}$ $\boxed{1}$ $\boxed{8}$.
(to bring Y_8 on the next line).

- Press $\boxed{\text{ENTER}}$.   Answer = **65**
Since $Y_8 = B^2 - 4AC = 65 > 0$, the roots are real and distinct.

(ii)   - Store 1 in A, 3 in B, and 5 in C.

- Press $\boxed{\text{2nd}}$ $\boxed{\text{Y} - \text{VARS}}$ $\boxed{1}$ $\boxed{8}$ $\boxed{\text{ENTER}}$.

Answer = **−11**
Since $B^2 - 4AC = -11 < 0$, the roots are complex numbers.

(iii)   - Store 2 in A, 12 in B, and 18 in C.

- Press $\boxed{\text{2nd}}$ $\boxed{\text{Y} - \text{VARS}}$ $\boxed{1}$ $\boxed{8}$ $\boxed{\text{ENTER}}$.

Answer = **0**

Since $B^2 - 4AC = 0$, the roots are real and equal.

Example 2:   Solve $5x - 2x^2 = 2$ (with Quadratic Formula)

Method #1

- Rewrite $5x - 2x^2 = 2$ as $2x^2 - 5x + 2 = 0$.

- Store 2 in A, -5 in B, and 2 in C.

- Press $\boxed{\text{2nd}}$ $\boxed{\text{Y} - \text{VARS}}$ $\boxed{1}$ $\boxed{9}$ $\boxed{\text{ENTER}}$.

Answer $= .5 = \dfrac{1}{2}$

- Press $\boxed{\text{2nd}}$ $\boxed{\text{Y} - \text{VARS}}$ $\boxed{1}$ $\boxed{0}$ $\boxed{\text{ENTER}}$.

Answer = **2**

Solutions are $x = \dfrac{1}{2}$ and $x = 2$**.**

Notes: 1. To verify the solutions, evaluate $2x^2 - 5x + 2$ at $x = \dfrac{1}{2}$ and $x = 2$ by the methods explained in Section 1.3, Example (2(ii)).

2. You may like to find the value of $B^2 - 4AC$ by evaluating Y_8 to first see if the solutions are real. If the solutions are complex numbers, evaluation of Y_9 and Y_0 with show error. (why?)

Method #2   (without Quadratic Formula)

- Rewrite $5x - 2x^2 = 2$ as $2x^2 - 5x + 2 = 0$.

- Clear Graph Screen.

- Set a suitable window, say ZStandard.

- Use **Trace** to explore approximate values of the x-coordinates of the points of intersection of the graph and the x-axis.
  x is approximately .2 and 3.

- Press $\boxed{\text{2nd}}$ $\boxed{\text{QUIT}}$ to go to Home Screen.

- Press $\boxed{\text{CLEAR}}$.

- Use **Solve** $(y_1,\ x,\ .2)$.   Answer = **.5**

- Use **Solve** $(y_1,\ x,\ 3)$.   Answer = **2**

Section 9.5   Solving Quadratic Equations Graphically

Example 1:   Determine graphically if the equation $x^2 + 3x + 5 = 0$ has real roots.

- Clear Graph Screen.

- Set window to ZStandard.

- Enter $x^2 + 3x + 5$ in Y_1.

- Press $\boxed{\text{GRAPH}}$.

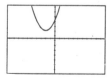

Pic 10

Points of intersection of the graph of $y = x^2 + 3x + 5$ with x-axis correspond to real solutions of the equation. There are no such points in this case.
Hence $x^2 + 3x + 5 = 0$ has no real solutions.

Example 2:   Solve $5x - 2x^2 = 2$ graphically.

Method #1

- Rewrite the equation as $2x^2 - 5x + 2$.

- Clear Graph Screen.

- Set window to ZStandard.

- Enter $2x^2 - 5x + 2$ in y_1.

- Press 2nd CALC 2   [for **root**].

- Press ENTER.

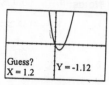

Pic 11

There are two points of intersection of the graph with x-axis. To determine a solution:

- Move the cursor to the left of the point of intersection and accept it as a lower bound by pressing ENTER.

- Move the cursor to the right of the point of intersection, and accept it as an upper bound by pressing ENTER.

- Press ENTER [for **guess**].   Answer : root = **.5**
                                                    root = **2**

Method #2

- Clear Graph Screen.

- Set ZStandard Window.

- Enter $5x - 2x^2$ in Y_1.

- Enter 2 in Y_2.

- Press 2nd CALC 5 for [**intersect**].

  [Graph screen pops up.]

There are two points of intersection of $y = 5x - 2x^2$ and $y = 2$

- Press ENTER to accept *first curve*.

- Press ENTER to accept *second curve*.

- Move the cursor near the point corresponding to which the solution is to be determined and press ENTER for *guess*.

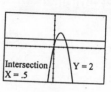

Pic 12

(Suppose you wanted to find a smaller of the two roots.)

                                Answer : $x = .5$, $y = 2$

Therefore a root is $x = .5$.

Repeat Steps #5 onward for the other root.

                                Answer : $x = 2$, $y = 2$

Another root is $x = 2$.

INDEX